PYRAZOLONES, PYRAZOLIDONES, AND DERIVATIVES

Richard H. Wiley
University of Louisville, Louisville, Kentucky

Paul Wiley
Upjohn Laboratories, Kalamazoo, Michigan

1964
INTERSCIENCE PUBLISHERS
a division of
JOHN WILEY & SONS • NEW YORK • LONDON • SYDNEY

First published by John Wiley & Sons, 1964

Library of Congress Catalog Card Number 63–20237

MADE AND PRINTED IN GREAT BRITAIN BY
WILLIAM CLOWES AND SONS, LIMITED, LONDON AND BECCLES

The Chemistry of Heterocyclic Compounds

The Chemistry of heterocyclic compounds is one of the most complex branches of organic chemistry. It is equally interesting for its theoretical implications, for the diversity of its synthetic procedures, and for the physiological and industrial significance of heterocyclic compounds.

A field of such importance and intrinsic difficulty should be made as readily accessible as possible, and the lack of a modern detailed and comprehensive presentation of heterocyclic chemistry is therefore keenly felt. It is the intention of the present series to fill this gap by expert presentations of the various branches of heterocyclic chemistry. The subdivisions have been designed to cover the field in its entirety by monographs which reflect the importance and the interrelations of the various compounds and accommodate the specific interests of the authors.

ARNOLD WEISSBERGER

Research Laboratories
Eastman Kodak Company
Rochester, New York

The Chemistry of Heterocyclic Compounds

The chemistry of heterocyclic compounds is one of the most complex branches of organic chemistry. It is equally interesting for its theoretical implications, for the diversity of its synthetic procedures, and for the physiological and industrial significance of heterocyclic compounds.

A field of such importance and intrinsic difficulty should be made as readily accessible as possible, and the lack of a modern detailed and comprehensive presentation of heterocyclic chemistry is therefore keenly felt. It is the intention of the present series to fill this gap by expert presentations of the various branches of heterocyclic chemistry. The subdivisions have been designed to cover the field in its entirety by monographs which reflect the importance and the interrelations of the various compounds, and accommodate the specific interests of the authors.

ARNOLD WEISSBERGER

Research Laboratories
Eastman Kodak Company
Rochester, New York

Preface

Perhaps one of the most unusual facets of pyrazole chemistry is the extensive literature on the pyrazolin-5-ones. Although this will probably come as no surprise to those who have had any interest in this class of compounds, the basic chemical reasons underlying this extensive literature, and the man-hours of chemical research which have gone into producing it, deserve careful consideration. There are very real practical and theoretical bases for the situation.

Historically, dyes and pharmaceuticals derived from pyrazolin-5-ones were among the first successful commercial synthetic organic chemicals in which interest has continued actively until the present. Ludwig Knorr's discovery in 1883 of antipyrine (2,3-dimethyl-1-phenyl-3-pyrazolin-5-one) and Ziegler's discovery in 1884 of the yellow dyestuff tartrazine: 4-(4-sulfophenylazo)-1-(4-sulfophenyl)-5-oxo-2-pyrazolin-3-carboxylic acid gave useful compounds before their structures were known. The value of these materials was immediately recognized and both are still in use. Much of the voluminous literature has resulted from studies directed toward modification of these structures to enhance their useful characteristics. A group of widely used pharmaceuticals including aminopyrine (4-dimethylamino-2,3-dimethyl-1-phenyl-3-pyrazolin-5-one); dipyrone (2,3-dimethyl-1-phenyl-5-oxo-2-pyrazolin-4-methylaminomethanesulfonic acid sodium salt); and sulfamipyrine (a dipyrone analog) were developed. This research has recently culminated in the discovery of the useful anti-inflammatory properties of phenylbutazone (4-butyl-1,2-diphenyl-3,5-pyrazolidinedione). In spite of the problems encountered in the undesirable side-reactions, principally agranulocytosis, produced by these drugs, interest in them has never abated and one feels confident in predicting the discovery of additional useful and improved drugs in this structural classification.

The development of new and improved dyes based on pyrazolinone structures has likewise led to modern developments of no inconsiderable magnitude. The use of tartrazine as an approved color for foodstuffs is of significance. The development of pyrazolinone dyes for use as magenta couplers and sensitizers in color photography and in metal chelate dye structures has established a renewed, modern interest in these dyes. The chelating characteristics, which will be of continuing theoretical structure interest in coordination chemistry, have been used in developing picrolonates (salts of 3-methyl-4-nitro-1-*p*-nitrophenyl-2-pyrazolin-5-one) of possible utility in analytical procedures.

The overwhelming deluge of chemical research arising from these utilitarian values has probably obscured the possibilities for fundamental research with these compounds. For the most part the structural problems that have been encountered are not complex. This is probably due in part to the fact that modern organic reaction techniques, such as radiation-induced transformations, modern structural concepts, such as molecular orbital theory and conformational analysis, and modern physical instrumentation, such as n.m.r., have not as yet been applied to the possibilities inherent in the chemistry of these compounds. It is also perhaps unusual that no pyrazolinone has been found to occur in nature. With the discovery in 1959 of β-(1-pyrazolyl)alanine in the seeds of *Citrullus vulgaris*, it would now appear probable that a pyrazolinone may likewise be found in some living tissue. This would certainly provide a new type of fundamental interest in the bio-organic chemistry of these materials. It might lead ultimately to a clue as to the mode of action of the pharmaceuticals—a problem about which there appears to be little or no current available information.

With the hope that the availability of the information on pyrazolinones presented in this volume might be of value in the furtherance of both fundamental and applied studies, the publishers and authors have considered it best to present this material as promptly as possible in the present volume rather than as part of the pyrazole volume for which it was originally intended. The authors are appreciative of this cooperation on the part of the publishers and it is hoped that users of this book will be aware that the immensity and sheer bulk of the literature has posed an unusual, but altogether interesting, challenge to all concerned in the preparation of this volume. The authors also wish especially to thank Miss Ollidene Weaver who did much of the typing of the manuscript in her spare time.

Richard H. Wiley
Paul Wiley

Contents

Systematic Tables of Pyrazolones and their Derivatives

PART I

CHEMISTRY

CHAPTER I

General

1. Introduction

Pyrazolinones and pyrazolidinones are oxo derivatives of pyrazolines and pyrazolidines, respectively, and are so named in *Chemical Abstracts* at present. However, the usual method of naming in the earlier literature is the pyrazolone–pyrazolidone system. Although a large number of tautomeric structures are possible for pyrazolinones, the usual assignment of ring structures is as shown in (I), (II) and (III). The *Chemical Abstracts* names for these are: (I) 2-pyrazolin-5-one, (II)

```
HC———CH2        HC═══CH         HC———C=O
‖3    4|        |3    4‖        ‖3    4|
N2 1 5C=O       HN2 1 5C=O      N2 1 5CH2
  \N/             \N/             \N/
   H               H               H
  (I)             (II)            (III)
```

3-pyrazolin-5-one and (III) 2-pyrazolin-4-one. The names most frequently used in the literature for (I) and (II) are 5-pyrazolone and 3-pyrazolone, respectively. In many cases there has been no certain identification of a compound as a 2-pyrazolin-5-one or a 3-pyrazolin-5-one. Because of this it will be assumed that all pyrazolin-5-ones having no substituent at N–2 are 2-pyrazolin-5-ones unless this has been definitely shown to be incorrect. The basic ring structures for pyrazolidinones are (IV) and (V) but no compounds of type (V) have been

```
H2C———CH2       H2C———C=O
|5    4|        |5    4|
HN1  3C=O       HN1  3CH2
  \2N/            \2N/
    H               H
  (IV)             (V)
```

reported. Compounds of type (IV) are usually called pyrazolidones in the literature.

The nomenclature used in this discussion will generally be in accordance with *Chemical Abstracts*, although some trivial names will be used since these are very common among pyrazolinones and are frequently well known. Examples of such names are antipyrine, pyrazole blue and aminopyrine. The numbering is as shown in formulas (I)–(V).

As an aid to classification all compounds in which the tautomerism

$$>CH{-}\overset{|}{C}{=}X \rightleftharpoons >C{=}\overset{|}{C}{-}XH$$

can theoretically exist will be considered as $>CH{-}\overset{|}{C}{=}X$ compounds (X = O, S, Se, Te, NH, NR or NCOR). It is recognized that this will frequently be in disagreement with the actual structure which, if known, will be indicated in the discussion.

This review will cover all pyrazolinones and pyrazolidinones reported up to and including the 1956 *Chemical Abstracts* and will cover the more important publications which have appeared since. However, a number of publications dealing with applications, biological activities and analysis were omitted as they were regarded as being of insufficient significance for coverage. A rather extensive list of the compounds of these types which have been reported is included, although here again there are many omissions. A number of dyes were not included as their structure was uncertain. Some very complex dyes which would require considerable space for inclusion are omitted and a reference to them is given. In general, the large number of salts reported were not included and in particular all picrolonates were omitted. However, many of the complexes which pyrazolin-5-ones form so readily are discussed, although in some cases these may be of a salt-like nature. Compounds in which the oxo substituents are replaced by such groups as imino, thiono and seleno are considered in this review. The early literature, which is available from standard sources (Beilstein, Meyer-Jacobson) has not been exhaustively compiled.

2. Historical

The well-known German chemist, Ludwig Knorr, reported the preparation of the first pyrazolinone in 1883.[805] This compound was 3-methyl-1-phenyl-2-pyrazolin-5-one prepared by the reaction of ethyl acetoacetate with phenylhydrazine. In the first publication no structure was proposed, but in a later publication[806] structure (VI) was suggested.

In this same article synthesis of the widely used analgesic and antipyretic, antipyrine, was reported. This was one of the first synthetic

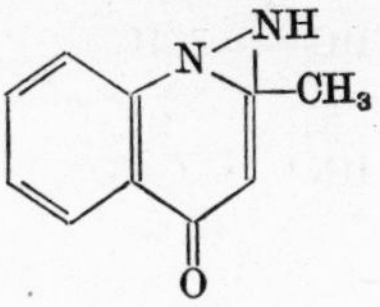

(VI)

organic drugs. It was marketed and used before the correct structure for pyrazolinones was suggested by Knorr[809] in 1887 and the name by Ruhemann.[1230]

3. Structure

A short time after the discovery of pyrazolin-5-ones Knorr[809] proposed the 2-pyrazolin-5-one and the 3-pyrazolin-5-one structures on the basis of analyses, methods of preparation and reactions. These structures in the main approximate the correct ones and in some cases are correct. However, a large number of structures are theoretically possible for most pyrazolin-5-ones and in many cases no one structure can be said to fit completely. The tautomeric isomers (VII)–(XIII) are possible for unsubstituted pyrazolin-5-ones:

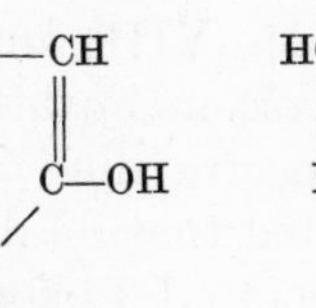

(VII) 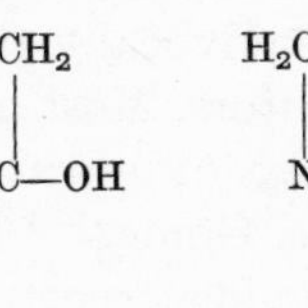 (VIII) 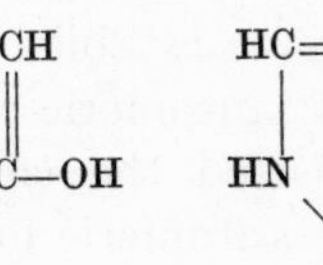 (IX)

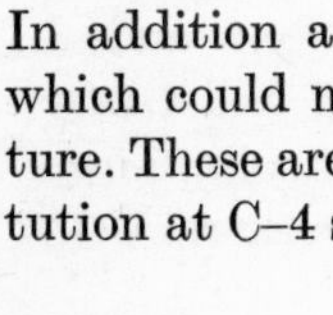

(X) 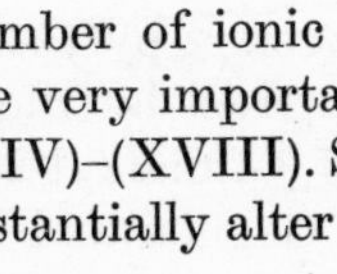 (XI) 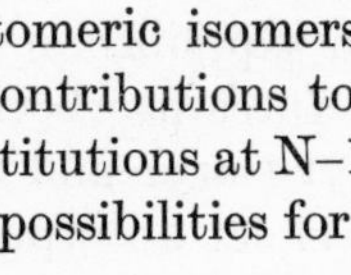 (XII) 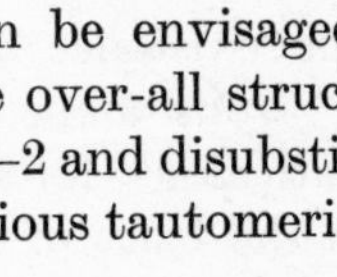 (XIII)

In addition a number of ionic tautomeric isomers can be envisaged which could make very important contributions to the over-all structure. These are (XIV)–(XVIII). Substitutions at N–1, N–2 and disubstitution at C–4 substantially alter the possibilities for various tautomeric and resonance forms. Of the possible tautomeric forms shown, only (VII), (VIII) and (X) appear to exist to any extent although Valyashko

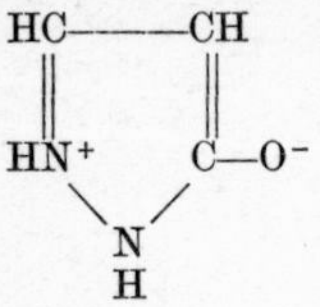

(XIV) 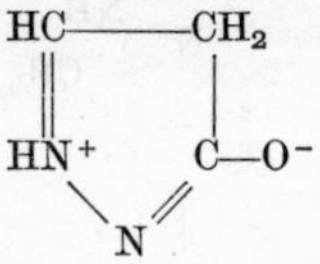 (XV) 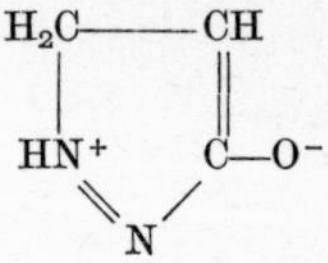 (XVI)

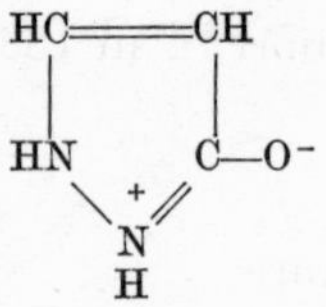

(XVII) 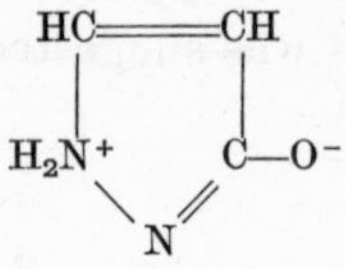 (XVIII)

and Bliznykov[1510] report diazo structures as present on the basis of rather complex ultraviolet absorption spectra. There is extensive evidence, both chemical and physical for these three structures. The presence of enolic forms is shown by the fact that one of the most common tests for 2-pyrazolin-5-ones is the use of ferric chloride to form a colored complex[809,1551] and by the ready formation of 5-alkoxy-pyrazoles from pyrazolinones.[655,811] Dmowska and St. Weil[376] have claimed the isolation of the keto and enol forms of 4,4′-(3-nitrobenzylidene)bis(3-methyl-1-phenyl-2-pyrazolin-5-one) and keto and enol forms of similar compounds have been isolated.[1134,1135] Existence of the form (VIII) is shown by alkylation of 3-phenyl-2-pyrazolin-5-one to give 2-methyl-3-phenyl-3-pyrazolin-5-one.[54]

The structures of pyrazolin-5-ones have been very extensively studied using ultraviolet and infrared absorption spectra and such techniques have established unequivocally that (VII), (VIII) and (X) are the chief tautomeric contributors. Most of the workers in this field have emphasized the complexity of ultraviolet spectra due to the existence of tautomeric mixtures. Gomez[584] has stated that no deduction can be drawn from the ultraviolet spectra of 1-methyl-3-phenyl-2-pyrazolin-5-one, 2,3-dimethyl-1-phenyl-3-pyrazolin-5-one and its 4-dimethylamino analog because of the tautomeric equilibria present. The existence of an equilibrium between 2-pyrazolin-5-one and 3-pyrazolin-5-one structures has been proposed by Biquard and Grammaticakis[95] for 3-alkyl-1-aryl- and 1-aryl-3,4-dialkyl-2-pyrazolin-5-ones on the basis of ultraviolet absorptions. Gagnon and co-workers[503,505] have been most active in this field and have drawn several conclusions from ultraviolet studies, some of which were in disagreement with infrared absorption spectra interpretations. These workers have found that pyrazolin-5-ones absorb ultraviolet light either in the neighborhood of 240–260 mμ with a log ϵ value of 4.0–4.4 or at 295–325 mμ with a log ϵ value of 3.3–4.0, or in both regions. The shorter wave length absorption is believed to be due to >C═C< absorption while the longer is due to >C═N—. Thus type (VII) would show the longer wave length absorption, type (VIII) the shorter, and type (X) both, or a mixture of any two would show absorption at both wave lengths. 4-Alkyl-3-aryl-2-pyrazolin-5-ones absorb at the lower wave length only, indicating that they possess only structure (VIII). However, this conclusion was in disagreement with the finding that these compounds exhibited absorption in the infrared at 1600 cm.$^{-1}$ due to >C═N— and at 3300 cm.$^{-1}$ [505] and showed no absorption attributable to carbonyl. Thus they must actually be of type (X). From the ultraviolet spectra 4-alkyl-1,3-diaryl-2-pyrazolin-5-ones were concluded to be a mixture of types, but the infrared spectra very clearly showed them to be type (VII) as there was only carbonyl and >C═N— absorption. It would appear that the 1-arylpyrazolin-5-ones with no N–2 substituent are usually of type (VII), since Glauert and Mann[578] found no imino or hydroxyl absorption in the infrared spectra of 1,4-diaryl-2-pyrazolin-5-ones. Recently[366a] the infrared spectra of 3-methyl-, 3-trifluoromethyl-, 1,3-dimethyl-, 1-methyl-3-trifluoromethyl- and 1-phenyl-3-trifluoromethyl-2-pyrazolin-5-one have been studied. The presence of absorption bands at 2400–2700 cm.$^{-1}$ believed due to zwitterionic forms indicated that these compounds exist largely as form (XIV).

The effect of substitution on the structure of pyrazolinones is a very important one, because certain of the tautomeric forms then become impossible. For example, substitution at N–1 allows only structures (VII), (VIII) and (X). Substitution at N–2 would make (VIII) and (XIII) the only possible tautomers. A combination of N–1 and N–2 substitution leaves (VIII) as the only possibility. If there is substitution at N–1 and disubstitution at C–4, then only isomer (VII) is possible. There has been little investigation of the possibilities for tautomeric structures of N–2 substituted pyrazolinones. However, Kitamura[788] has suggested that such compounds exist as a mixture of forms (VIII) and (XIII).

There has been considerable discussion of the situation in regard to the ionic structures. About fifty years ago Michaelis[978,983,984,1002,1003] proposed (XIX) as the structure for 1,2-disubstituted pyrazolinones. In modern terminology this could correspond to structure (XIV).

Komada[844-846] recently has used this structure to explain the structure of the tetrabromides of this type of pyrazolinones. Kitamura[788]

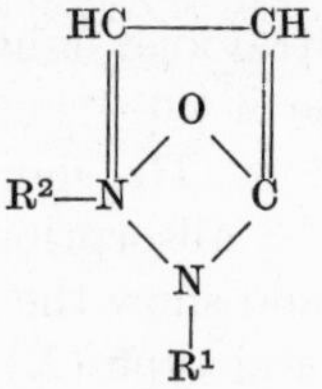

(XIX)

has used rather inconclusive chemical evidence in support of the exis tence of 3-pyrazolin-5-ones in form (XVII). Somewhat better evidence for the structural contributions of these resonance forms has been given in the form of dipole moments, ultraviolet data and bond lengths. Jensen and Friedinger[715] and Brown *et al.*[245] have found abnormally high dipole moments for 2,3-dimethyl-1-phenyl-3-pyrazolin-5-one and its thiono analog. This was considered to be due to contributions by forms (XIV) and (XVII) to the extent of about 35 per cent. A structure analogous to (XVII) has been proposed for 2-pyrazolin-5-thiones also on the basis of dipole moments.[934] Valyashko and Bliznykov[1509] have found that 4-amino-2,3-dimethyl-1-phenyl-3-pyrazolin-5-ones have ultraviolet spectra very similar to that of 5-chloro-3-methyl-1-phenylpyrazole methochloride, indicating a considerable contribution by form (XIV). Krohs[860] has demonstrated a considerable contribution from the carbonyl form, as shown by infrared absorption in the carbonyl region. This has been confirmed by other infrared studies, and it has been proposed on the basis of this that form (VIII) is the predominating one in some cases.[366a] Romain[1208] has studied the bond lengths in 4-bromo-2,3-dimethyl-1-phenyl-3-pyrazolin-5-one. These bond lengths indicate a resonance hybrid structure composed of forms (VIII) and (XIV) with some contribution from (XVII).

Chattaway and co-workers[287-290, 294] have synthesized a number of 1-aryl-2-pyrazolin-4-ones which, as a rule, have been considered to have the 4-hydroxypyrazole structures. However, some of these must have the 2-pyrazolin-4-one structure due to disubstitution at C–5. Emerson and Beegle[425] have synthesized some 2-pyrazolin-4-ones unsubstituted at N–1 permitting more possibilities for isomerism. These will be discussed later.

The pyrazolidinones (IV) present a number of possibilities for structural isomerism, but very little study of their structure has been made. It is generally assumed that they have the classical form (IV).

Certainly they would not be expected to have the tendency of 2-pyrazolin-5-ones to enolize, since they could not achieve an aromatic-like structure.

4. Synthesis

Only a few of the principal synthetic methods for pyrazolinones and pyrazolidinones will be discussed at this point. Other methods will be mentioned in connection with various classes of compounds. The procedures mentioned here will be discussed in greater detail at the appropriate places.

By far the most widely used synthesis for 2-pyrazolin-5-ones is the condensation of a β-ketoester with a hydrazine (eq. 1).[6,11,64,269,303,805]

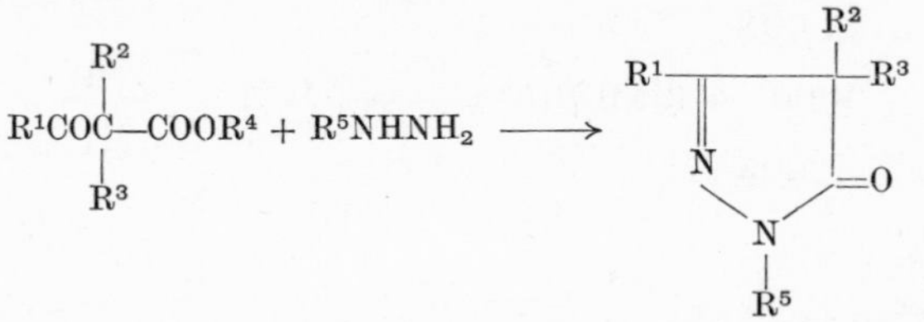

$$R^1COC(R^2)(R^3)—COOR^4 + R^5NHNH_2 \longrightarrow \text{(2-pyrazolin-5-one: } R^1 \text{ at C-3, } R^2, R^3 \text{ at C-4, =O at C-5, } R^5 \text{ at N-1)} \quad (1)$$

The R groups in this reaction can be almost anything, H, alkyl, aralkyl, aryl, heterocyclic and many others. Modifications of this procedure have employed β-thionoesters,[1006,1008] β-oximinoesters[1555] and β-ketoamides.[99,197,1276]

Perhaps the most common procedure for preparing 3-pyrazolin-5-ones is alkylation of a 2-pyrazolin-5-one at N–2 as shown for the synthesis of antipyrine (eq. 2).[806] Other alkylating agents such as dimethyl

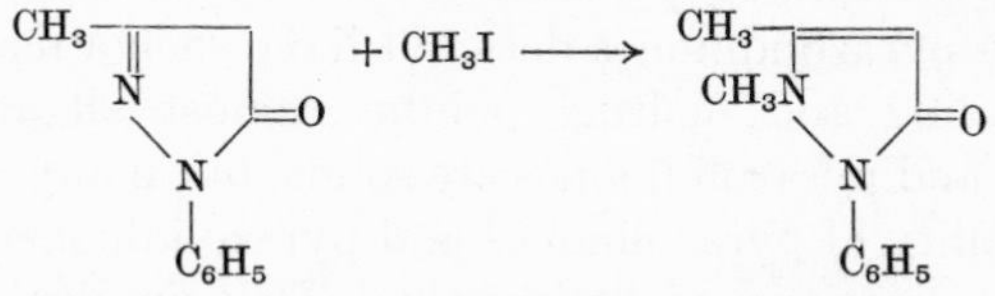

$$\text{(3-methyl-1-phenyl-2-pyrazolin-5-one: } CH_3, N, N—C_6H_5, =O) + CH_3I \longrightarrow \text{(antipyrine: } CH_3, CH_3N, N—C_6H_5, =O) \quad (2)$$

sulfate[781] can be used, and almost any 2-pyrazolin-5-one can be alkylated, although frequently *O*-alkylation occurs and also alkylation at N–1 if it has no substituent. Another useful synthesis of 3-pyrazolin-5-ones is the condensation of a β-ketoester with acetylphenylhydrazine (eq. 3). The acetyl group is lost and the phenyl group appears at

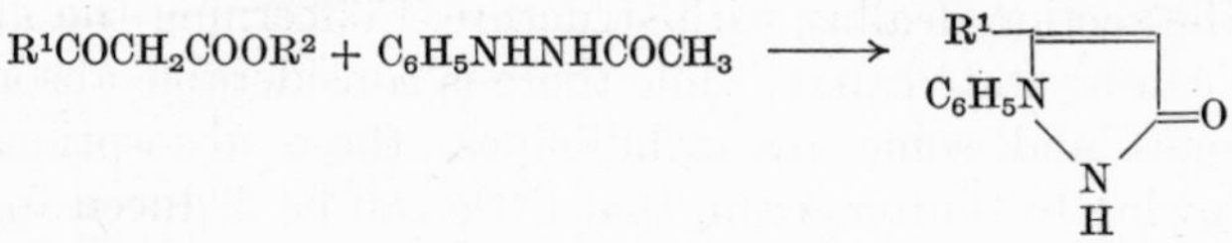

$$R^1COCH_2COOR^2 + C_6H_5NHNHCOCH_3 \longrightarrow \text{(3-pyrazolin-5-one: } R^1, C_6H_5N, NH, =O) \quad (3)$$

N–2.[984,988,993] A modification of this consists of using a symmetrically substituted hydrazine to give 1,2-disubstituted-3-pyrazolin-5-ones.[54]

The synthesis of pyrazolidinones is readily achieved by condensation of an α,β-unsaturated acid,[1550] ester[1209,1569] or amide[758] with a hydrazine. In eq. 4 is shown the reaction for an amide.

$$R^1R^2C{=}C(R^3)CONHR^4 + R^5NHNH_2 \longrightarrow \text{(pyrazolidinone: } R^1, R^2 \text{ at C-4, } R^3 \text{ at C-3... } R^5N, =O, NH) \quad (4)$$

The reaction of a malonic ester or chloride with hydrazines gives 3,5-pyrazolidinediones (eq. 5).[188,222,248,252,1234]

$$R^1CH(COX)_2 + R^2NHNHR^3 \longrightarrow \text{(3,5-pyrazolidinedione: } R^1 \text{ at C-4, } R^3\text{–N, } N\text{–}R^2, \text{ two } =O) \quad (5)$$

5. Physical Properties

Most pyrazolinones and pyrazolidinones are solids, although many, some very complex, can be distilled as high-boiling liquids. 2-Pyrazolin-5-one is a liquid boiling at 163°. Reduction of the >C=N— lowers this to 132°. Substitution on N–1 and N–2 gives a low-melting solid. However, substitution at C–3 or C–4 has a more pronounced effect, as for example in 3-methyl-2-pyrazolin-5-one, which melts at 215°. Alkyl substitution in pyrazolidinones does not have such a marked effect but does raise boiling and melting points. Almost all aryl substituted pyrazolinones and pyrazolidinones are solids, but many can be distilled.

The solubility of pyrazolinones and pyrazolidinones is so varied as to make generalizations of little value. The simpler ones, of lower molecular weight, are soluble in hot water and a few are even soluble in cold water. Almost all are soluble in polar organic solvents and many are soluble in ether and benzene. However, most are insoluble in petroleum ether.

Ultraviolet and infrared spectra have been considered in some detail in the section dealing with structure. Concerning the ultraviolet spectra it can be stated that, while there is considerable absorption by pryazolinones and some pyrazolidinones, these absorptions are so complex, owing to tautomerism, that little can be deduced from them.

The infrared spectra are as would be expected. In some cases there are clear bands due to carbonyl and >C=N— and in others the carbonyl band is missing but hydroxyl bands are present. Raman spectra of antipyrine and aminopyrine have been investigated.[273,1167]

Dipole moments have already been discussed in the section dealing with structure. They have been found to be quite high for the few 3-pyrazolin-5-ones studied. The only value reported for a 2-pyrazolin-5-one is considerably lower, being 2.54 for 3-methyl-2-pyrazolin-5-one.

A number of miscellaneous physical properties of antipyrine and a few of its derivatives have been studied. These are listed with references in Table I.

TABLE I. Physical Properties of Antipyrine Investigated

Physical Property	Reference
Crystal Form	844
Dielectric Constant	367
Dielectric Coefficient	367
Heat Capacity	1466
Latent Heat	668
Phase Diagram	669
Surface Activity	561

6. Chemical Properties

Only a few of the more important chemical properties of pyrazolinones and pyrazolidinones will be discussed in this section, since these will be covered more thoroughly in connection with the different classes.

The pyrazolinones are in general weak acids[805] and many can be titrated with strong bases. The 2-pyrazolin-5-ones are stronger acids than the 3-pyrazolin-5-ones[1523] which are very weak. Most pyrazolinones are readily soluble in bases. The pyrazolidinones are not acidic, unless some special feature makes them so. The most extensive data on basicity have been provided by Veibel and co-workers[1521,1522,1525] who have titrated a number of pyrazolinones with perchloric acid in acetic acid. The pK_b values range from 10.3 to 12.3, except for 4,4-disubstituted and 4-halogen substituted 2-pyrazolin-5-ones. The 4,4-disubstituted 2-pyrazolin-5-ones are so weak that they are essentially neutral, while the halogenated compounds have pK_b values of about 13.2.

Both 2-pyrazolin-5-ones and 3-pyrazolin-5-ones undergo substitution at C–4 in an aromatic fashion. Halogenation, nitration and coupling with diazonium salts occur readily. In 2-pyrazolin-5-ones such reactions as condensation with aldehydes and ketones and alkylations occur readily at C–4. The pyrazolinone and pyrazolidinone rings do not have aromatic stability, although in many cases they can assume an aromatic-like structure. The ring is readily destroyed by acid or base hydrolysis and by oxidation. Pyrazolidinones react very much as do aliphatic hydrazides.

CHAPTER II

Pyrazolin-5-ones

1. Introduction

The pyrazolin-5-ones are classified and discussed according to their functional groups. Compounds having more than one pyrazolinone ring will be classified similarly to the monocyclic ones and discussed in the same section. All compounds which can theoretically assume the 2-pyrazolin-5-one structure, except those classified as 3,5-pyrazolidinedione derivatives will be considered to be such. Only those for which this is impossible, i.e. 2-substituted pyrazolin-5-ones, will be considered 3-pyrazolin-5-ones. A number of compounds having no functional group on the pyrazolinone ring, which have been synthesized for study as coloring agents are listed in connection with the discussion of pyrazolinones used in photography. A number of very complex compounds of similar type are not included in this review, but references to them are given in the dye section. All compounds having no functional group attached to the pyrazolinone ring will be considered in the section dealing with alkyl, alicyclic, aralkyl, aryl and heterocyclic substituted pyrazolin-5-ones. All oximes are classified as nitroso compounds unless it is manifestly impossible to do so as in a case having the substituent =NOR. This would be listed in the section concerning amino-2-pyrazolin-5-ones. The 5-iminopyrazolines and the aminopyrazoles which in this discussion are classified as 5-iminopyrazolines are considered with the 2-pyrazolin-5-ones appropriate to their substitution, as are the 2-pyrazolin-5-thiones.

2. Unsubstituted Alkyl, Alicyclic, Aralkyl, Aryl and Heterocyclic Substituted Derivatives

A. 2-Pyrazolin-5-ones

(1) *Syntheses*

Syntheses of the 2-pyrazolin-5-one ring will be discussed in this section. Those syntheses of this class which depend upon introduction of a substituent into the already formed ring will be discussed under reactions. Compounds of this type are listed in Table II (see Appendix).

Methods for synthesis of 2-pyrazolin-5-ones are extremely numerous but the one most frequently used is that shown in eq. 1, the condensation of a β-aldehydo- or β-keto-ester with a hydrazine. The substituents on the ester and the hydrazine have been greatly varied. All types of alkyl, alicyclic, aralkyl, aryl and heterocyclic substituted esters have been used. In general the yields are the better the smaller the substituents R^2, R^3 and R^4. In the case in which R^2 and R^3 are benzyl, pyrazolinone formation does not occur when R^4 is phenyl.[849] Also, if R^2 and R^3 are aryl, pyrazolinone formation fails. When R^3 is larger than methyl, formation of pyrazolinones is more difficult, although many more complex esters having one α-substituent or none have been used.[629] Ethyl α,α-diethylacetoacetate does not form a pyrazolinone with hydrazine hydrate, but the corresponding methyl ester does.[61] R^1 may be hydrogen, in which case the ester would be a β-aldehydo-ester,[303,813,1636] or it may be alkyl,[42,53,61,97,135,572,805,1582] aryl,[54,469,505] heterocyclic,[10,307,682] alicyclic,[274] or of other types.[124] It has been reported that cyclization of benzoylacetic esters to pyrazolinones is easier than is that of acetoacetic esters.[777] Almost any monosubstituted hydrazine can be used to prepare a pyrazolinone. The simpler the substituent the better the yield usually is,[505] though alkyl,[250,788] alicyclic,[101] aralkyl,[250] aryl[25,136,229,1251] and heterocyclic[74,91,413,833] hydrazines have been successfully employed. The conditions used in condensing β-ketoesters and hydrazines to form pyrazolinones are quite varied. The most widely used method is simply heating the ester and the hydrazine together without added catalysts. The temperatures used are most frequently 100–200°.[250,505,805] Quite frequently the hydrazine is condensed with the ketoester to form a hydrazone under milder conditions than are used in the final cyclization step.[505] A modification of this is to use an already prepared hydrazone.[1100,1490] Acidic[25,1372] and basic conditions are frequently used, particularly in the cyclization step. Under favorable circumstances the yields are very good. Gagnon and co-workers[505] have prepared a series of 4-alkyl-3-phenyl-2-pyrazolin-5-ones in yields of 83–96 per cent, although yields of corresponding 1-phenyl compounds were much lower, varying from 50 to 81 per cent.

In summarizing this method of synthesis it can be said that it is so extremely general that almost any non-substituted or monosubstituted β-ketoester will react with almost any monosubstituted hydrazine to form a 2-pyrazolin-5-one.

A number of modifications of the β-ketoester–hydrazine synthesis of pyrazolinones has been used. One of these modifications is the use of acid hydrazides (eq. 6).[6,96,360] Under mild conditions the pyrazolinone

$$CH_3COCH_2COOC_2H_5 + RCONHNH_2 \xrightarrow{\Delta} \text{3-methyl-2-pyrazolin-5-one } (CH_3\text{ on C-3; N-1–H; C-5=O}) \qquad (6)$$

obtained has the acyl substituent on N–1, but at temperatures of 25° to 100° this substituent is lost. In addition to β-ketoesters, the corresponding amides and anilides have been employed in a number of cases[197,378,872,1030,1276] under very similar conditions. The amides may or may not be substituted on the nitrogen atom. Mitra[1006,1007] has reported the use of β-thionoacetoacetates instead of acetoacetic esters to form pyrazolinones. The use of β-ketoesters in which R^1 or R^2 of eq. 1 is CH_3CO or C_2H_5OOC[165,358] gives pyrazolinones with elimination of the acyl substituent. A further modification of this synthesis is shown in eq. 7.

$$\underset{\displaystyle \|\atop NNHCOCH_3}{CH_3CCH_2COOC_2H_5} \xrightarrow{Na-Hg} \text{3-methyl-2-pyrazolin-5-one } (CH_3\text{ on C-3; N-1–H; C-5=O}) \qquad (7)$$

A number of syntheses of 2-pyrazolin-5-ones depend on the reaction of compounds, other than β-ketoesters, substituted in the β-position or of α,β-unsaturated acids, esters and amides. The most frequently used unsaturated compounds are those having a triple bond in the α,β-position.[1023,1024,1075,1548,1680] R^2 can be HO,[1552] RO[1023,1024,1686] or H_2N (eq. 8).[1023,1024] A similar reaction is the condensation of ethyl

$$R^1C{\equiv}C{-}CO{-}R^2 + H_2NNH_2 \longrightarrow \text{3-}R^1\text{-2-pyrazolin-5-one } (R^1\text{ on C-3; N-1–H; C-5=O}) \qquad (8)$$

α-chlorocinnamate with hydrazine to give 3-phenyl-2-pyrazolin-5-one.[610] This probably goes through an acetylenic intermediate. The condensation of methyl crotonate, isocrotonic esters and methyl methacrylate with hydrazines gives as a side-product small yields of 2-pyrazolin-5-ones, the main products being pyrazolidinones.[479,1569] The pyrazolidinones are probably dehydrogenated to a slight extent to give the pyrazolinones. The reaction of β-alkoxy-α,β-unsaturated esters[1023,1024] and β-alkylthio- and β-acylthio-α, β-unsaturated esters[1007] with hydrazines to give pyrazolinones (eq. 9) proceeds quite readily. The reaction of ketene with arylhydrazines forms 2-pyrazolin-5-ones.[723,885]

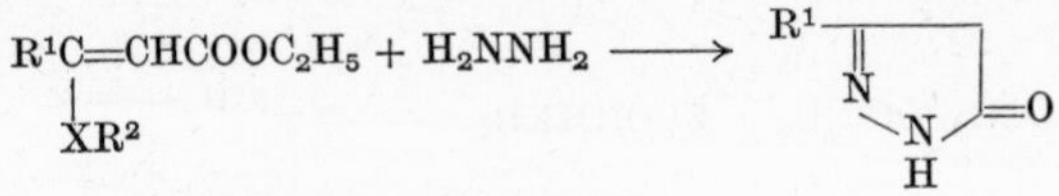

$$R^1C{=}CHCOOC_2H_5 + H_2NNH_2 \longrightarrow \text{3-}R^1\text{-2-pyrazolin-5-one (N-H)} \quad (9)$$
(with XR^2 on the R^1C carbon)

$X{=}O$ or S; $R^2{=}$alkyl or acyl

The first product formed is the hydrazone of the corresponding acetoacethydrazide (XX). This then cyclizes to the desired product at ele-

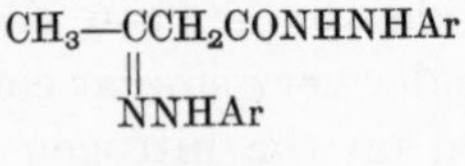

$$CH_3{-}C(=NNHAr)CH_2CONHNHAr$$

(XX)

vated temperatures. The reaction of phenylhydrazine with β-halogenated acids to give pyrazolinones as shown in eqs. 10 and 11 has been reported.[446,858] These reactions probably occur by removal of water

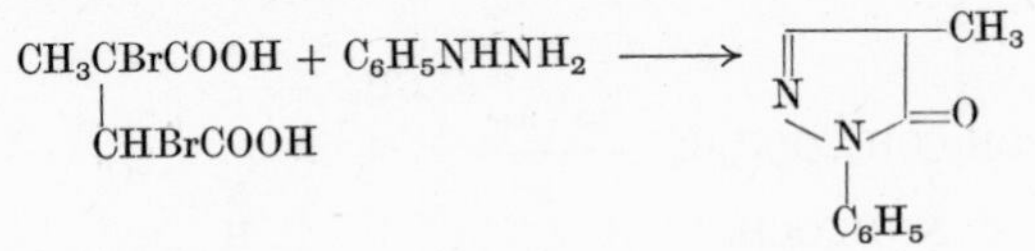

$$CH_3CBr(COOH)CHBrCOOH + C_6H_5NHNH_2 \longrightarrow \text{4-}CH_3\text{-1-}C_6H_5\text{-pyrazolin-5-one} \quad (10)$$

$$ClCH_2CH(OH)COOH + C_6H_5NHNH_2 \longrightarrow \text{1-}C_6H_5\text{-pyrazolin-5-one} \quad (11)$$

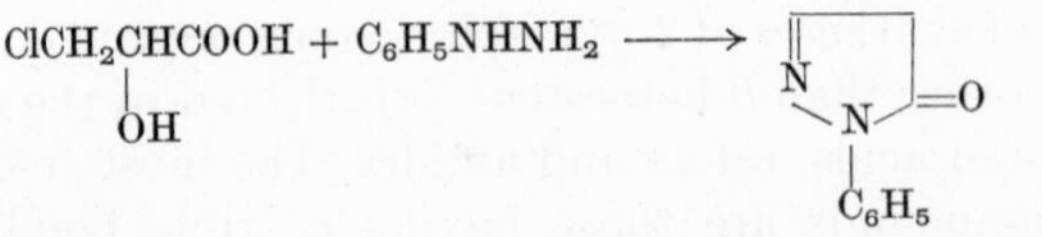

or hydrogen bromide to give an unsaturated intermediate. It has been shown that such an intermediate, methyl β-chloroisocrotonate, reacts with hydrazine hydrate to give 3-methyl-2-pyrazolin-5-one.[479]

A number of heterocyclic systems react with hydrazine to give pyrazolinones. These are shown in eqs. 12–17 and are of little synthetic utility.

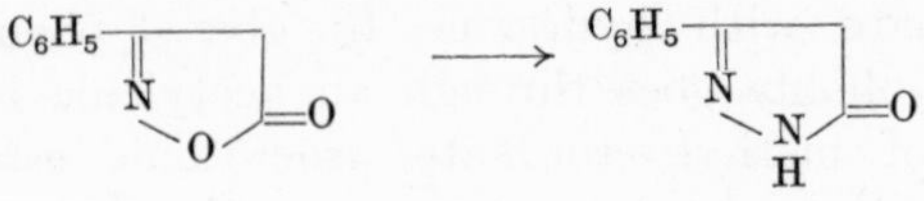

$$\text{3-}C_6H_5\text{-isoxazolin-5-one} \longrightarrow \text{3-}C_6H_5\text{-2-pyrazolin-5-one (N-H)} \quad (12)^{1549}$$

$$\text{6-R-3-COR-pyran-2,4-dione} \longrightarrow \text{3-R-2-pyrazolin-5-one (N-H)} \quad (13)^{1347,1553}$$

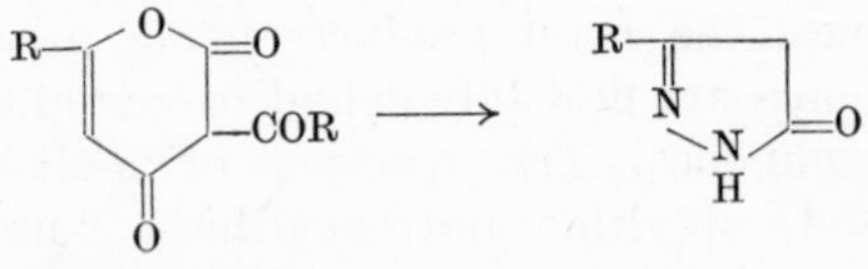

$R{=}CH_3$ or C_6H_5

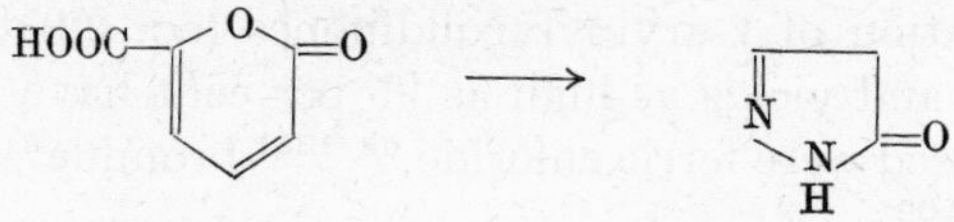

(14)[1553]

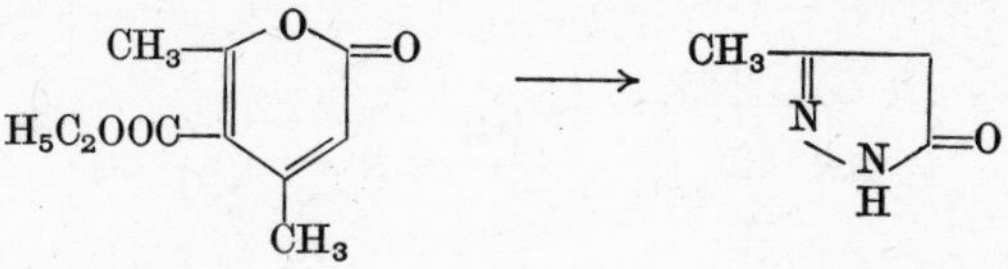

(15)[1622]

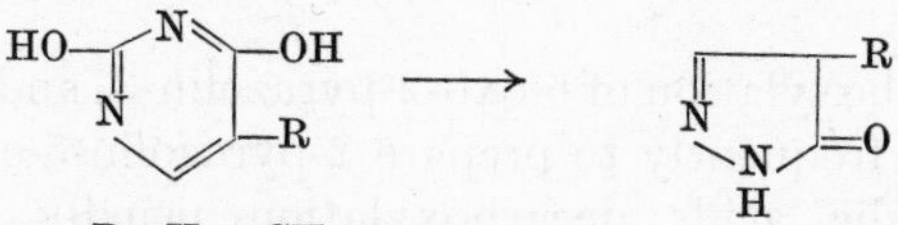

(16)[457]

R=H or CH_3

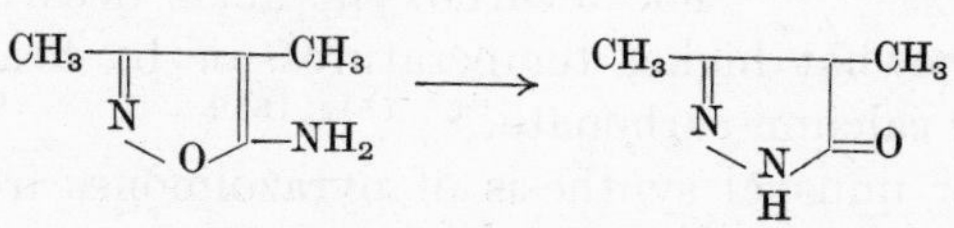

(17)[729]

Various pyrazole systems having appropriate substituents in the 5-position can be converted into pyrazolinones. The most frequently used synthesis of this type is hydrolysis of 5-alkoxypyrazoles which is shown with others in eqs. 18–21.

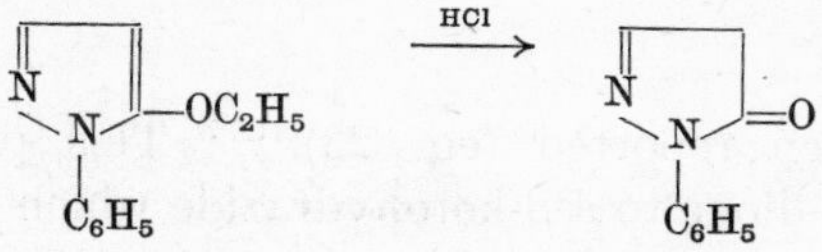

(18)[1350]

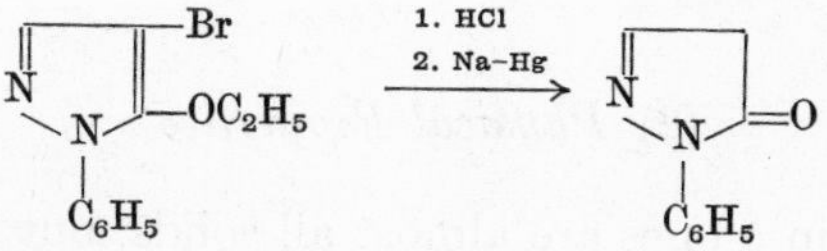

(19)[450]

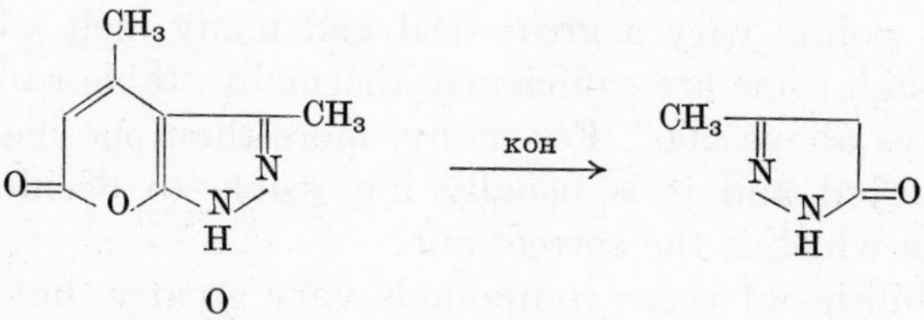

(20)[1047]

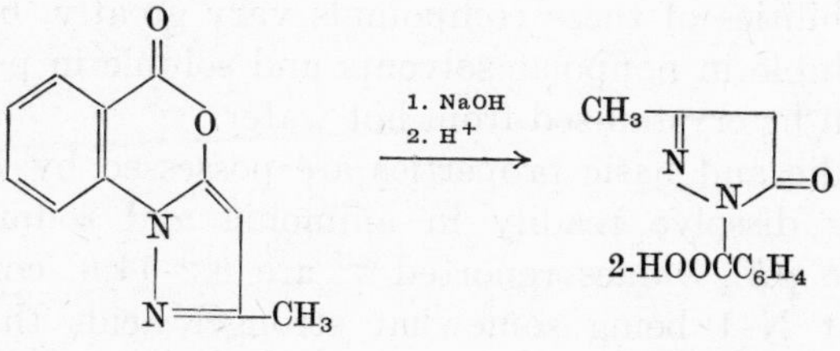

(21)[1004]

The oxidation of 2-arylpyrazolidinones (eq. 22) to pyrazolinones occurs readily and yields as high as 95 per cent have been reported.[68] The reagents used were ferric chloride,[68,1351] bromine[816,1569] or calcium hypochlorite.[1569]

HN, N, Ar, =O $\xrightarrow{[O]}$ N, N, Ar, =O (22)

The decarboxylation of 5-oxo-2-pyrazolin-3- and 4-carboxylic acids has been used frequently to prepare 2-pyrazolin-5-ones. In the case of the 4-carboxylic acids decarboxylation usually occurs in boiling water.[306,532,1228,1230] The 3-carboxylic acids decarboxylate by pyrolysis, at somewhat higher temperatures, or by heating with sodium carbonate or calcium carbonate.[506,1544,1546]

A rather unusual synthesis of pyrazolinones from a cyclobutane

CH_3, O=, $COOCH_3$, CH_3—, =O $+ H_2NNH_2 \longrightarrow$ $H_2NHNCOCH$, CH_3, H_3C, N, N, H, =O (23)

derivative has been reported (eq. 23).[1277] This probably involves cleavage of the 1,3-dione to a β-ketohydrazide which cyclizes.

(2) *Physical Properties*

The 2-pyrazolin-5-ones are almost all solids, but a few are liquids. Their melting points vary a great deal and many melt with decomposition although some are sufficiently thermally stable to be distilled at temperatures above 200°. For many, more than one melting point has been reported and it is usually impossible to decide from the published data which is the correct one.

The solubilities of these compounds vary greatly, but in general they are insoluble in nonpolar solvents and soluble in polar ones and frequently can be crystallized from hot water.

Both acidic and basic properties are possessed by 2-pyrazolin-5-ones.[807] They dissolve readily in ammonia and sodium carbonate solutions. The pK_a values reported[505] are 6.2–11.0, compounds unsubstituted at N-1 being somewhat stronger acids than are those substituted at N–1. Veibel and co-workers[1522,1524] have reported that 2-pyrazolin-5-ones have pK_b values of 10–13, indicating very weak basicity. Only those compounds which can assume the betaine form shown in (XIV) (p. 6) can be titrated with acid. No basic properties are shown by those compounds in which disubstitution at C–4 precludes the existence of this form.

A number of studies of ultraviolet and infrared absorption spectra of 2-pyrazolin-5-ones have been made.[95,505,506,578] The ultraviolet spectra show maxima in the neighborhood of 250 mμ with log ϵ values of 4.10–4.40 and at about 310 mμ with log ϵ values of 3.90, or in both of these regions of the spectrum. The shorter wave length absorption is attributed to the presence of >C=N— and the longer wave length absorption to >C=C<. Infrared absorption occurs at 1600 cm.$^{-1}$ in all cases owing to the >C=N— absorption and either at 3300 cm.$^{-1}$ for compounds existing in the enol form, or at 1700–1710 cm.$^{-1}$ for compounds having the carbonyl form. From the spectral data it has been concluded that 2-pyrazolin-5-ones having aryl substitution at N–1 generally exist in the oxo forms (VII) and (VIII) (p. 5) unless substitution prevents formation of the (VIII) type. If N–1 is unsubstituted, the form (X) predominates. However, recently de Stevens and co-workers[366a] have reported somewhat different findings for infrared spectra of 2-pyrazolin-5-ones having H, alkyl and aryl at N–1 and alkyl groups at C–3. Their results led them to suggest the form (XIV) as the principal one for these compounds.

A study of the absorption of 2-pyrazolin-5-ones by silver bromide has been made by Stolyarova and Chel'tsov.[1348] These workers found that there was absorption of a unimolecular layer of pyrazolinones with the heterocyclic rings parallel to the absorbent surface.

(3) *Chemical Properties*

The most outstanding chemical property of 2-pyrazolin-5-ones is the activity of the hydrogen atoms at C–4. This position is very reactive, undergoing the characteristic condensations and substitutions of the active methylene group. Aldehydes and ketones react readily at this position, giving in the simpler cases a mixture of products as shown in eq. 24.[22,34,110,296,311,333,633,702,809,980,1123,1241,1250,1263,1288,1351] This type of reaction is generally true of aldehydes, but in the case of ketones where one R is aryl only the monopyrazolinone product is obtained.[1128] Some more active aldehydes such as formaldehyde[24] and chloral[107,895] do not eliminate water but form, as one of the products, a hydroxyalkyl compound, as shown for formaldehyde in eq. 25. This type of reaction is used for synthesis of the 4-(α-hydroxyalkyl)-2-pyrazolin-5-ones listed

R^2, N, N, =O, R^1 + R^3COR^4 ⟶ R^2, $=CR^3R^4$, N, N, =O, R^1 + bis: R^2, $C(R^3)(R^4)$, R^2, N, N, =O, O=, N, N, R^1, R^1 (24)

in Table II, Section F. The formation of the bispyrazolinone can be suppressed by use of acetic acid as the condensing agent.[1036,1123] Other condensing agents, such as potassium hydroxide,[22] piperidine[311] and

CH_3, N, N, =O, C_6H_5 + CH_2O ⟶ CH_3, CH_2OH, N, N, =O, C_6H_5 (25)

hydrochloric acid[22] have been used, although these are not necessary. This type of reaction has been used extensively to form 4-alkyl- and 4-benzyl-2-pyrazolin-5-ones. The unsaturated product first formed is reduced catalytically to the desired product (eq. 26). Condensation of

R^2, $=CHR^3$, N, N, =O, R^1 $\xrightarrow{H_2}$ R^2, CH_2R^3, N, N, =O, R^1 (26)

an aldehyde or ketone with pyrazolinones is the most common method of synthesis for bispyrazolinones of the type shown as a product in eq. 24. A modification of this synthesis which gives 4-benzylpyrazolinones is condensation of a pyrazolinone with formaldehyde in the presence of an activated aromatic compound such as guaiacol.[24] In the presence of piperidine, 3-methyl-1-phenyl-2-pyrazolin-5-one undergoes an intermolecular aldol condensation (eq. 27). The carbonyl compounds

2 CH_3, N, N, =O, C_6H_5 ⟶ CH_3, N, N, =O, C_6H_5, CH_3, N, N, C_6H_5 (27)

which have been most frequently condensed with 2-pyrazolin-5-ones have been aromatic ones and a very large number of these have been used.

Ridi and Checchi[1188,1189] have studied the condensation of formamides with 2-pyrazolin-5-ones. This condensation occurs at a temperature of 160–200° and appears to be an aldol condensation followed by dehydration (eq. 28). R^1 may be hydrogen, alkyl or aryl, while R^2

$$\text{2-pyrazolin-5-one }(3\text{-}R^2,\ 1\text{-}R^1) + HCONHR^3 \longrightarrow 4\text{-}(=CHNHR^3)\text{-}3\text{-}R^2\text{-}1\text{-}R^1\text{-2-pyrazolin-5-one} \quad (28)$$

has been only alkyl and aryl. R^3 has been either hydrogen or aryl. Acetamide and other amides also react in this way with 2-pyrazolin-5-ones.[1188,1192,1193] The compounds synthesized in this manner are shown in Table II, Section G. It is not completely certain that the 4-substituent is as shown in eq. 28. It may be the isomeric form, $R^3N{=}CH$. One of the products frequently obtained in this reaction is a 4,4′-methylidynebispyrazolinone, formed by the reaction of the first product with the starting material with elimination of ammonia or an amine.

A reaction analogous to the condensation of amides with 2-pyrazolin-5-ones is the reaction of amidines first reported by Dains (eq. 29).[348,349] This has been extended by Ogata, Tauno and Nishida[1070] to vinylogs of amidines of the type $C_6H_5NH(CH{=}CH)_2CH{=}NC_6H_5$.

$$\text{2-pyrazolin-5-one }(3\text{-}R^2,\ 1\text{-}R^1) + R^3NHCH{=}NR^3 \longrightarrow 4\text{-}(=CHNHR^3)\text{-}3\text{-}R^2\text{-}1\text{-}R^1\text{-2-pyrazolin-5-one} \quad (29)$$

If α,β-unsaturated ketones are condensed with 2-pyrazolin-5-ones the reaction is a Michael addition (eq. 30)[686,721] resulting in alkylation.

$$3\text{-}CH_3\text{-}1\text{-}C_6H_5\text{-2-pyrazolin-5-one} + (CH_3)_2C{=}CHCOCH_3 \longrightarrow 4\text{-}[C(CH_3)_2CH_2COCH_3]\text{-}3\text{-}CH_3\text{-}1\text{-}C_6H_5\text{-2-pyrazolin-5-one} \quad (30)$$

The alkylation of 2-pyrazolin-5-ones at C–4 occurs readily (eq. 31)[113,1321] with compounds having reactive halogen atoms. An example

$+ RX \longrightarrow$ or (31)

of this is the alkylation of 3-methyl-1-phenyl-2-pyrazolin-5-one with methyl iodide and sodium methoxide to give the corresponding 4,4-dimethyl compound.[809] However, this reaction may give alkylation at N–2 or *O*-alkylation and as a rule it is easier to alkylate at these positions than it is at C–4 when aliphatic halides are used. Indeed, in the case of 3-methyl-1-phenyl-2-pyrazolin-5-one the N–2 alkylation occurs to a much greater extent than does exclusive alkylation at C–4, the products being 2,3-dimethyl-1-phenyl-3-pyrazolin-5-one and 1-phenyl-2,3,4-trimethyl-3-pyrazolin-5-one. Various triaryl carbinols and ethers of such carbinols alkylate 2-pyrazolin-5-ones in the presence of acids to give 4-triarylmethyl-2-pyrazolin-5-ones.[567,570] A somewhat similar reaction is that of orthoesters (eq. 32).[764] 2-Methyl-4-chloroquinoline also alkylates 2-pyrazolin-5-ones at C–4.[971]

$+ R^3C(OR^4)_3 \longrightarrow$ (32)

A very important reaction in the synthesis of merocyanine dyes is the alkylation of 2-pyrazolin-5-ones with various heterocyclic rings as illustrated in eqs. 33–35.[166,238,239] 2-Pyrazolin-5-ones other than the

(33)

one shown here can be used, and a large variety of heterocyclic compounds such as quinolines, benzoxazoles and numerous others have been employed. The anion may be halogen or *p*-tosyl.

The hydrazones of 5-formylbarbituric acid react with 2-pyrazolin-5-ones in a fashion rather similar to that of aldehydes and ketones

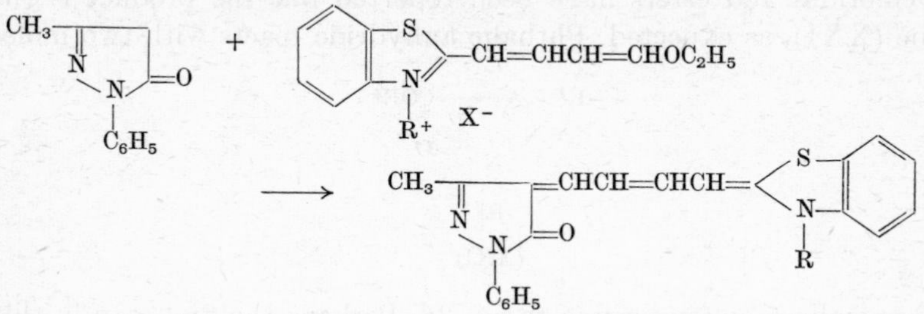

(34)

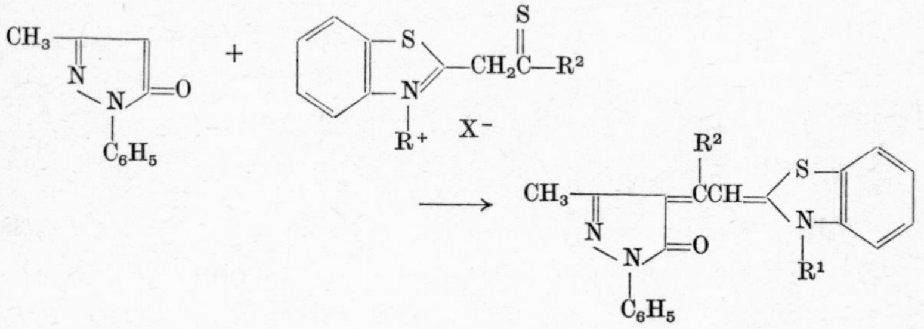

(35)

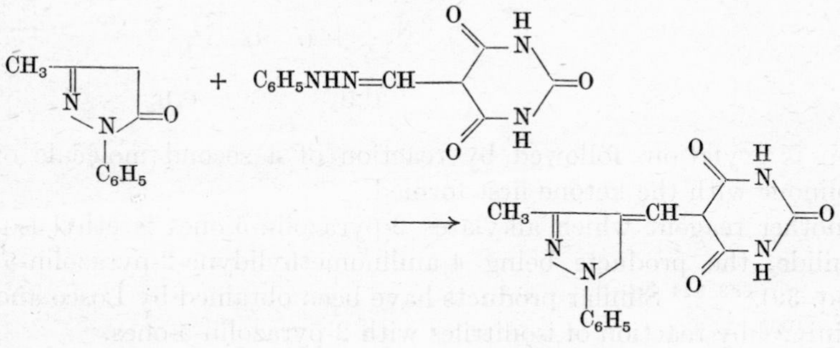

(36)

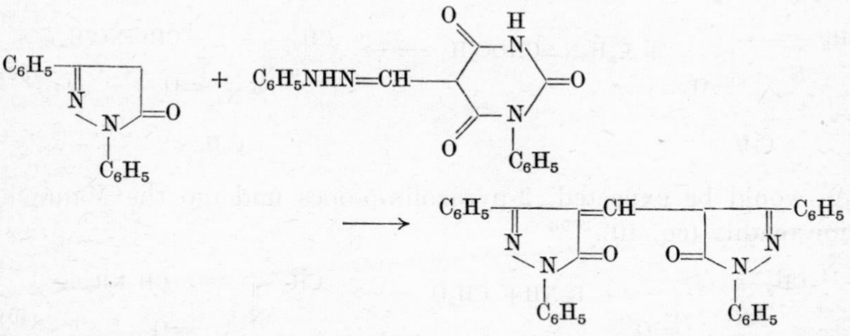

(37)

(eqs. 36 and 37).[1188] Apparently it cannot be predicted which of these two types of reaction will occur.

2-Pyrazolin-5-ones can be readily acylated at C–4 with acid chlorides,[110] esters[1641] and anhydrides.[1279] Very few reactions with acid chlorides and esters have been reported but the product is the ketone (XXI), as expected. Phthalic anhydride reacts with two moles

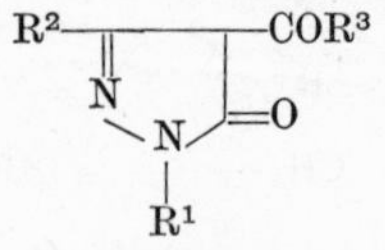

(XXI)

of 2-pyrazolin-5-one according to eq. 38. Perhaps the first step in this

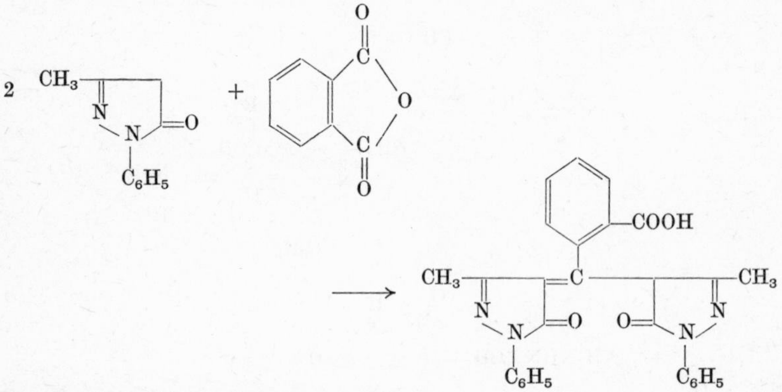

(38)

reaction is acylation, followed by reaction of a second molecule of pyrazolinone with the ketone first formed.

Another reagent which alkylates 2-pyrazolin-5-ones is ethyl isoformanilide, the products being 4-anilinomethylidyne-2-pyrazolin-5-ones (eq. 39).[823,824] Similar products have been obtained by Losco and Passerini[1089] by reaction of isonitriles with 2-pyrazolin-5-ones.

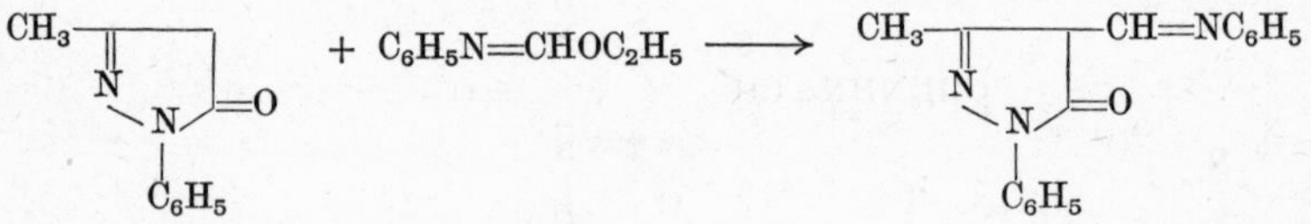

$+ C_6H_5N{=}CHOC_2H_5 \longrightarrow$ (39)

As would be expected, 2-pyrazolin-5-ones undergo the Mannich reaction readily (eq. 40).[1098]

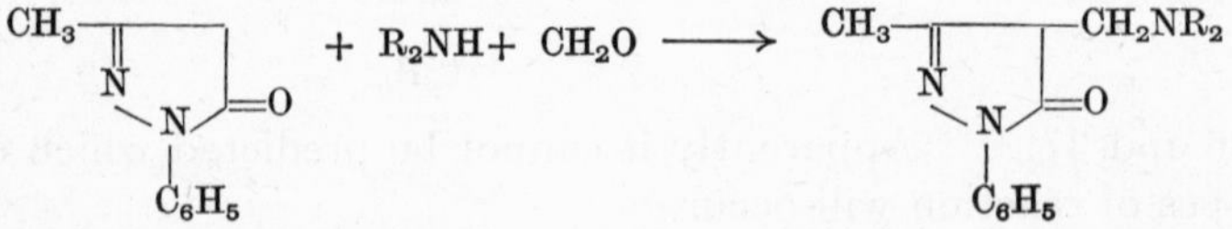

$+ R_2NH + CH_2O \longrightarrow$ (40)

A variety of functional groups can be introduced directly into the 4-position of 2-pyrazolin-5-ones. Perhaps the most important of these is the arylazo group which is introduced by reaction with diazonium salts (eq. 41).[333,809,813] This reaction has been used to prepare a vast

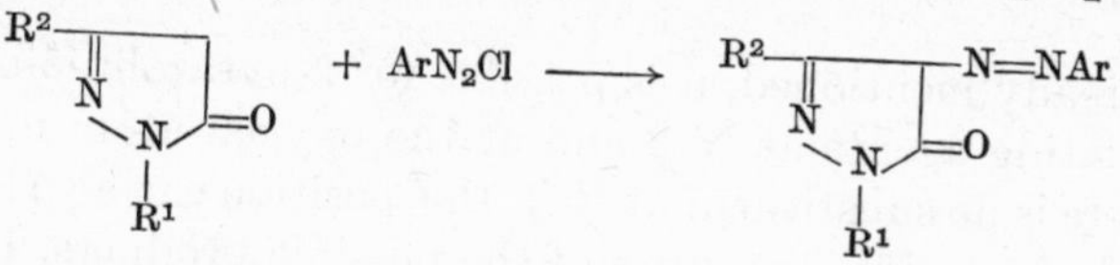

$$\text{R}^2\text{-pyrazolin-5-one (N}-\text{R}^1\text{, C=O)} + \text{ArN}_2\text{Cl} \longrightarrow \text{R}^2\text{-pyrazolin-5-one (4-N=NAr, N}-\text{R}^1\text{, C=O)} \qquad (41)$$

number of azo dyes, many of which have been of considerable commercial importance. It will be discussed in more detail in connection with pyrazolinone dyes and preparation of azo derivatives. Another reaction of commercial importance is that of 2-pyrazolin-5-ones with aromatic amines in the presence of oxidizing agents to form color couplers which are 4-arylimino-2-pyrazolin-5-ones (eq. 172).[244,1538] The same kind of product is obtained by the reaction of 4-arylidene-2-pyrazolin-5-ones with aromatic amines. The net result is replacement of the arylidene group with the arylimino group.[1255] Halogenation at the 4-position also occurs readily with phosphorus pentachloride,[333,809] phosphorus tribromide[333] or bromine.[333,809,816] The phosphorus halides form 4,4-dihalogenated derivatives. Direct bromination with an equivalent of bromine gives 4-bromo-2-pyrazolin-5-ones, but excess of bromine gives the 4,4-dibromo and even some tribromo compound. 2-Pyrazolin-5-ones react with nitrous acid to give nitroso derivatives which exist usually as the corresponding oximes (XXII).[333,809,816] Nitration with

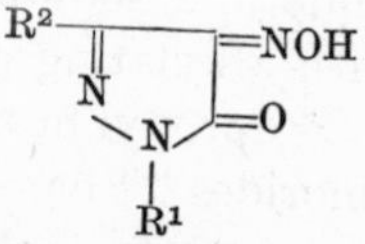

$$\text{R}^2\text{-pyrazolin-5-one (4=NOH, N}-\text{R}^1\text{, C=O)}$$

(XXII)

dilute nitric acid forms 4-nitro-2-pyrazolin-5-ones.[61,333,806] A 4-formyl group can be introduced by using the Reimer-Tiemann reaction. Sulfonation of 3-methyl-1-phenyl-2-pyrazolin-5-one with 20 per cent oleum at 10–15° results in formation of the corresponding 4-sulfonic acid.[684] Higher temperatures cause not only sulfonation of the heterocyclic ring, but sulfonation of the phenyl group. A cyano group can be introduced into the 4-position of 2-pyrazolin-5-ones by reaction with cyanogen bromide in the presence of aluminum chloride.[24] These substitutions are much more difficult if an alkyl substituent is present in the 4-position, although in some cases such a group is eliminated. 4-Triarylmethyl-2-pyrazolin-5-ones react with diazonium salts with replacement of the triarylmethyl substituent by the arylazo group.[567] Of course, 4,4-dialkyl-2-pyrazolin-5-ones do not react with these substituting reagents. These reactions are discussed further in sections devoted to preparation of the various types of compounds arising from such reactions.

As already mentioned, it is possible for 2-pyrazolin-5-ones to react with alkylating agents at N–2 and at the oxygen atom in addition to C–4. If there is no substituent at N–1, this position can also be alkylated. Most alkylations give a mixture of the possible products. However, by alkylation at temperatures of 100–130°, with or without basic catalysts, 2-pyrazolin-5-ones can be converted to 2-alkyl-3-pyrazolin-5-ones in excellent yields (eq. 42). This reaction has been extensively studied

$$R^2\text{-}(\text{2-pyrazolin-5-one, N-}R^1\text{, =O}) + R^3X \longrightarrow R^2\text{-}(\text{3-pyrazolin-5-one, }R^3N\text{, N-}R^1\text{, =O}) \qquad (42)$$

because, in the case of 3-methyl-1-phenyl-2-pyrazolin-5-one and methyl iodide, the product is the commercially important analgesic and antipyretic, antipyrine. The most widely used procedure for carrying out this reaction is the use of methyl iodide and methanol at 100°.[806] Methylation has also been accomplished by use of methyl sulfate and sodium hydroxide,[110] methyl *p*-toluenesulfonate and sodium methoxide,[54] dimethyl sulfate,[94,985] methyl iodide at 130°,[1475] diazomethane,[94] and methyl iodide and sodium methoxide.[1205] Alkylation under similar conditions with alkylating agents having longer carbon chains, such as ethyl iodide,[1205] propyl bromide,[1321] benzyl chloride[1321] and 2-dialkylaminoethyl chlorides[249] has been successful. Nef[1056] has reported that alkylation of 3-methyl-1-phenyl-2-pyrazolin-5-one with methyl iodide and sodium methoxide occurs at C–4 with no N–2 alkylation, at N–2 with no C–4 alkylation, and at both positions. In 2-pyrazolin-5-ones lacking a 1-substituent alkylation occurs to give 1-substituted 2-pyrazolin-5-ones,[54,1205] usually with little or no *O*-alkylation, and alkylation with alkylchloroformates leads to substitution only at N–1.[61] Somewhat more drastic conditions form 5-alkoxypyrazoles.[811,1321]

Acylation of 2-pyrazolin-5-ones having no substituent at N–1 occurs readily with such agents as acetyl chloride,[1499,1598] acetic anhydride,[1499,1598] benzoyl chloride[1056,1598] and aryl sulfonyl chlorides.[1199] The usual product is a 1-acyl-2-pyrazolin-5-one, but acylation may also occur on oxygen, or both on oxygen and at N–2.[1598]

The reaction of 2-pyrazolin-5-ones with phosphorus oxychloride to give 5-chloropyrazoles (eq. 43) is a very general one.[51,307,985,992,1003,1205]

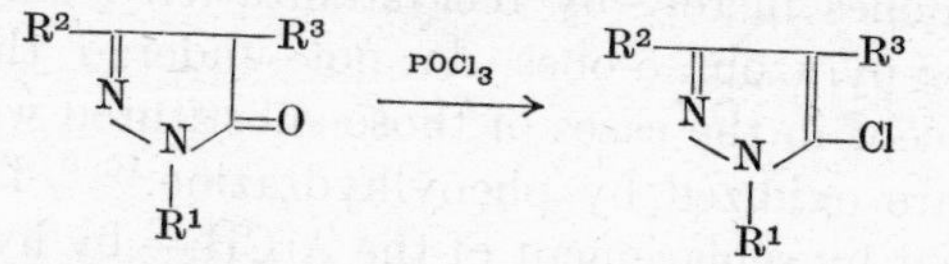

$$\text{(1-R}^1\text{-3-R}^2\text{-4-R}^3\text{-2-pyrazolin-5-one)} \xrightarrow{POCl_3} \text{(1-R}^1\text{-3-R}^2\text{-4-R}^3\text{-5-chloropyrazole)} \tag{43}$$

The reaction requires temperatures of 100–150° and all pyrazolinones of this type undergo it. The oxygen of 2-pyrazolin-5-ones can also be replaced by sulfur if phosphorus pentasulfide at about 130–150° is used (eq. 44).[759,1343] This reaction is widely used for preparation of 2-pyrazolin-5-thiones.

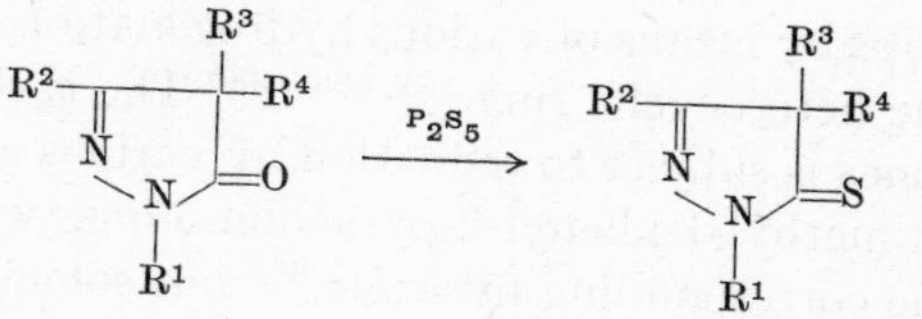

$$\text{(1-R}^1\text{-3-R}^2\text{-4-R}^3\text{-4-R}^4\text{-2-pyrazolin-5-one)} \xrightarrow{P_2S_5} \text{(1-R}^1\text{-3-R}^2\text{-4-R}^3\text{-4-R}^4\text{-2-pyrazolin-5-thione)} \tag{44}$$

The hydrogen atoms on C-4 of 2-pyrazolin-5-ones are readily attacked by mild oxidizing agents. The products of this reaction are bispyrazolinones (eq. 45) when such oxidizing agents as phenyl

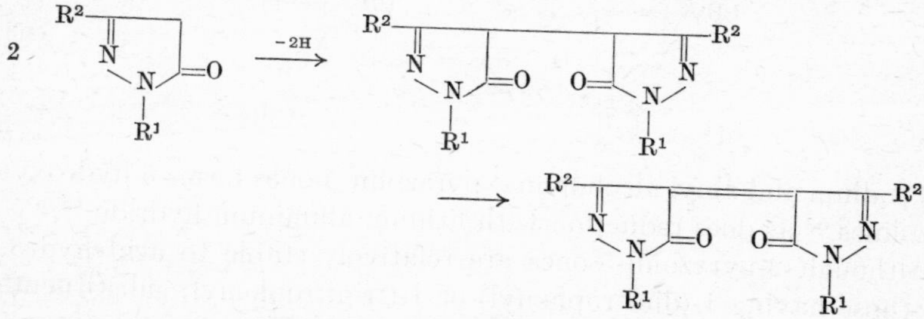

$$2\ \text{(1-R}^1\text{-3-R}^2\text{-2-pyrazolin-5-one)} \xrightarrow{-2H} \text{(4,4'-bi(1-R}^1\text{-3-R}^2\text{-2-pyrazolin-5-one))} \longrightarrow \text{(}\Delta^{4,4'}\text{-bi(1-R}^1\text{-3-R}^2\text{-2-pyrazolin-5-one))} \tag{45}$$

hydrazine[333,636,809,818,991] or nitrous acid are used.[809] The use of ferric chloride in limited amounts gives the bispyrazolinones in which the two rings are connected by a single bond,[1582] but larger amounts of ferric chloride give further oxidation and in the product the two pyrazolinone rings are attached to each other by double bonds[809] as shown in eq. 45. Oxidation of 2-pyrazolin-5-ones having a 1-aryl substituent with *t*-butylhydroperoxide[1526] or oxygen in neutral solution[1528] leads to bispyrazolinones, as shown in the first step of eq. 45. In contrast to this, the use of *t*-butylhydroperoxide in the presence of sodium alkoxides[1526] or of oxygen in acid media[1528] converts the 2-pyrazolin-5-one to the corresponding hydroxy compound. These are excellent preparative methods for 4-hydroxy-2-pyrazolin-5-ones. Shirai and Yashiro[1299] have found that some 2-pyrazolin-5-ones can be converted to bispyrazolinones merely by recrystallization from hot water. 4,4-Disubstituted-2-pyrazolin-5-ones do not undergo the oxidative dimerization, except in the cases of those substituted with a 4-arylidene group which are oxidized by phenylhydrazine.[1090] These compounds apparently react by replacement of the ArCH= by hydrogen from the phenylhydrazine and the unsubstituted pyrazolinone thus arising is oxidized. Strong oxidizing agents, such as potassium permanganate, completely destroy the 2-pyrazolin-5-one ring, forming pyruvic acid, water, nitrogen and carbon dioxide.[1549]

The heterocyclic ring of 2-pyrazolin-5-ones is quite stable to catalytic reduction. Aromatic substituents present can be reduced to cyclohexyl groups by means of various hydrogenation catalysts without reduction of the heterocyclic ring.[161,859,1280] The carbonyl function of 2-pyrazolin-5-ones is subject to reduction by various chemical reagents. Treatment of 3-methyl-1-phenyl-2-pyrazolin-5-ones with zinc results in reduction to the corresponding pyrazole,[809] but somewhat more drastic conditions cause complete decomposition of the heterocyclic ring, giving aniline and acetonitrile.[809] Reduction of the same compound with sodium and alcohol forms the corresponding pyrazoline (eq. 46).[809] The

$$\text{3-}CH_3\text{-1-}C_6H_5\text{-2-pyrazolin-5-one} \xrightarrow[C_2H_5OH]{Na} \text{3-}CH_3\text{-1-}C_6H_5\text{-2-pyrazoline} \qquad (46)$$

use of sodium and amyl alcohol on 2-pyrazolin-5-ones forms 5-hydroxypyrazolines,[53] as does reduction with lithium aluminum hydride.[1505]

Although 2-pyrazolin-5-ones are relatively stable to acid hydrolysis, those having 1-(dinitrophenyl) or 1-(trinitrophenyl) substituents are decomposed, forming arylhydrazones (eq. 47).[777]

$$\text{3-}R^2\text{-1-}R^1\text{-2-pyrazolin-5-one} \xrightarrow[\Delta]{HCl} (R^2)(CH_3)C{=}NNHR^1 + CO_2 \qquad (47)$$

Hydrolysis of 2-pyrazolin-5-ones with 33 per cent sodium hydroxide solution also destroys the ring.[1286] The hydrolysis products were not identified with certainty, but it was thought that acetic and propionic acids were among them.

2-Pyrazolin-5-ones form a variety of complexes with various metals and metal salts.[393,394,482] 3-Methyl-1-phenyl-2-pyrazolin-5-one has been reported to form complexes with iron, cobalt, silver, cupric oxide, cupric iodide, silver iodide, ferric iodide, cobalt iodide and beryllium chloride. These complexes actually are salts of the enolic form of the pyrazolinone in many cases, although in others the only bonds may be those formed by donation of the electrons by the C═N—N< group.[394] In some cases both types of linkages are present. The compounds formed usually have the number of molecules of 2-pyrazolin-5-one corresponding to the valence of the metal atom present.

(4) *Hydroxyalkyl Types*

Most of the syntheses of α-hydroxyalkyl and α-alkoxyalkyl-2-pyrazolin-5-ones have been discussed in connection with the reactions of 2-pyrazolin-5-ones. However, there is one synthesis by which compounds of this type are obtained directly. This is by reaction of the appropriate alkoxy- or phenoxymethylacetoacetic esters with hydrazines (eq. 48).[532,1314,1315,1316,1562] The reactions of these compounds

$$R^1OCH_2COCH(R^2)COOC_2H_5 + R^3NHNH_2 \longrightarrow \text{1-}R^3\text{-3-}(R^1OCH_2)\text{-4-}R^2\text{-2-pyrazolin-5-one} \xrightarrow{HCl} \text{1-}R^3\text{-3-}(HOCH_2)\text{-4-}R^2\text{-2-pyrazolin-5-one} \quad (48)$$

are the general ones for 2-pyrazolin-5-ones and for hydroxy and alkoxy functions except for the condensation of 4-hydroxymethyl-2-pyrazolin-5-ones with another pyrazolinone to give bis(2-pyrazolin-5-ones) (eq. 49).[24]

$$\text{3-}CH_3\text{-4-}CH_2OH\text{-1-}C_6H_5\text{-2-pyrazolin-5-one} + \text{3-}CH_3\text{-1-}C_6H_5\text{-2-pyrazolin-5-one} \longrightarrow \text{4,4'-}CH_2\text{-bis(3-}CH_3\text{-1-}C_6H_5\text{-2-pyrazolin-5-one)} \quad (49)$$

(XXII–A)

The α-hydroxyalkyl and α-alkoxyalkyl-2-pyrazolin-5-ones are listed in Table II, Section F.

(5) *Aminoalkyl Types*

A number of syntheses of compounds having nitrogen on a carbon attached to 2-pyrazolin-5-one rings have already been mentioned, but several others are known. The most important of these is the reaction of 4-formyl- or 4-acyl-2-pyrazolin-5-ones with hydroxylamine, hydrazines, semicarbazide and similar chemicals.[559,1641] These compounds can also be obtained by direct synthesis from an appropriate β-ketoester or derivative and a hydrazine (eq. 50).[138,512,1100] An interesting synthesis of this type of compound is that shown in eq. 51.[1179] Presumably condensation of one molecule of semicarbazide with the ketone carbonyl

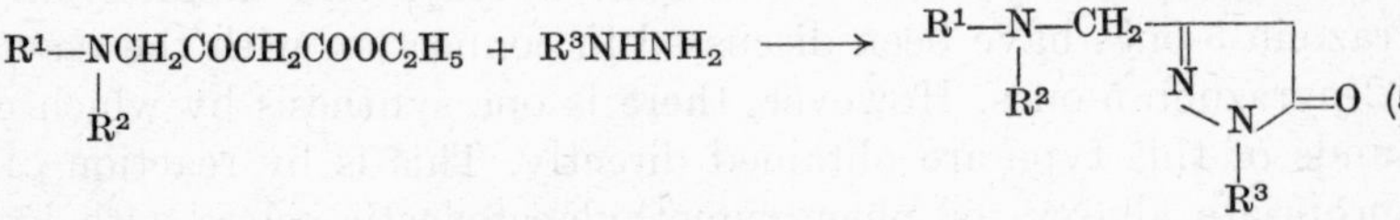

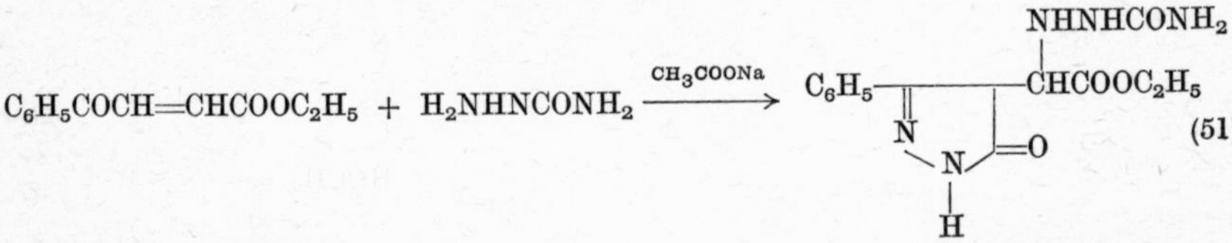

$$R^1\text{—N(}R^2\text{)CH}_2COCH_2COOC_2H_5 + R^3NHNH_2 \longrightarrow \text{3-(}R^1N(R^2)CH_2\text{)-1-}R^3\text{-2-pyrazolin-5-one} \quad (50)$$

$$C_6H_5COCH{=}CHCOOC_2H_5 + H_2NNHCONH_2 \xrightarrow{CH_3COONa} \text{3-}C_6H_5\text{-4-[CH(NHNHCONH}_2\text{)COOC}_2H_5\text{]-2-pyrazolin-5-one (1-H)} \quad (51)$$

is followed by cyclization to the C–3 of the ester with elimination of ammonia after addition of a second molecule of semicarbazide. Two other syntheses of these compounds are shown in eqs. 52 and 53.[925,1206]

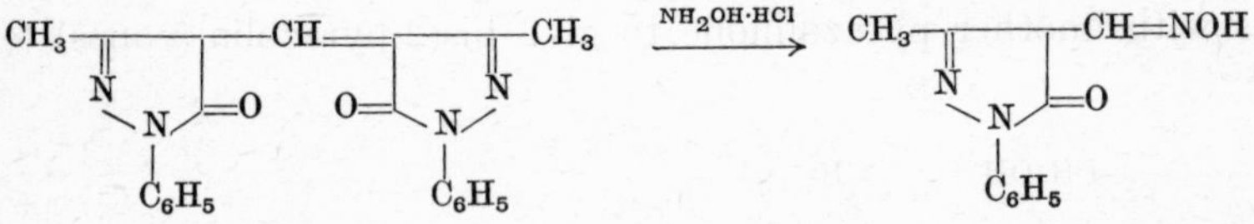

$$\text{(XXII-B)} \xrightarrow{NH_2OH\cdot HCl} \text{3-}CH_3\text{-4-(CH=NOH)-1-}C_6H_5\text{-2-pyrazolin-5-one} \quad (52)$$

(XXII-B): 4,4'-methylidyne bis(3-methyl-1-phenyl-2-pyrazolin-5-one), CH_3—C—CH=C—CH_3 rings with N, =O, C_6H_5

$$\text{3-}CH_3\text{-4-CHO-5-Cl-1-}C_6H_5\text{-pyrazole} + H_2NNH_2\cdot H_2O \longrightarrow \text{3-}CH_3\text{-4-(CH=NNH}_2\text{)-1-}C_6H_5\text{-2-pyrazolin-5-one} \quad (53)$$

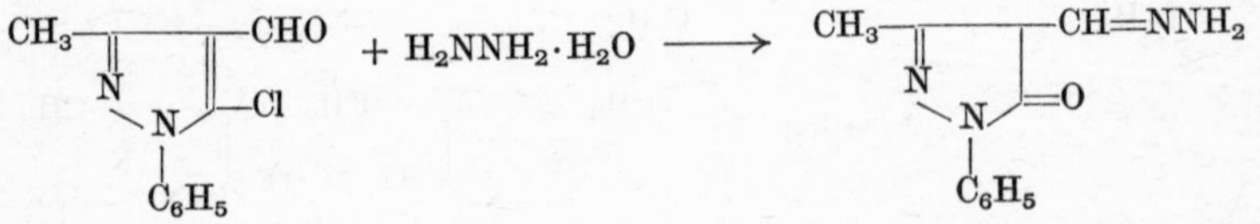

The reactions of these derivatives are typical of the functional groups present.

Compounds having nitrogen on a carbon atom which is attached to a 2-pyrazolin-5-one ring are listed in Table II, Section G.

(6) *Bis(2-pyrazolin-5-ones)*

A large number of 2-pyrazolin-5-ones exist in which two or more such rings are combined. These are almost all combined symmetrically, that is the same positions in the two rings are linked, and the vast majority are combined in the 4,4′-positions, although many are connected at the 3,3′-positions and some by way of the 1,1′-positions. Those 4,4′-bispyrazolinones in which the two rings are directly connected are listed in Tables III and IV. Those having atoms between the rings are listed in Tables V–VII. The 3,3′-bispyrazolinones are listed in Table VIII and the 1,1′-bispyrazolinones in Table IX.

The most widely used synthesis of 4,4′-bis(2-pyrazolin-5-ones) is mild oxidation of monocyclic 2-pyrazolin-5-ones, which has already been discussed in the section devoted to reactions of 2-pyrazolin-5-ones (eq. 45). These compounds can also be synthesized by reaction of α,α'-diacylsuccinic esters with hydrazines (eq. 54).[357,807,815] A number

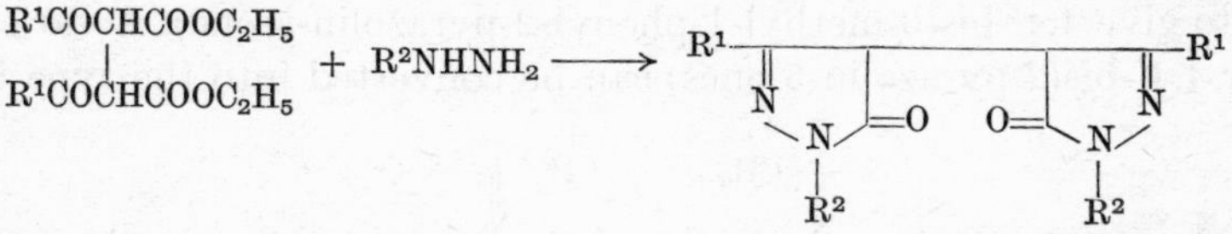

$$\begin{matrix} R^1COCHCOOC_2H_5 \\ | \\ R^1COCHCOOC_2H_5 \end{matrix} + R^2NHNH_2 \longrightarrow \text{4,4'-bis(3-}R^1\text{-1-}R^2\text{-2-pyrazolin-5-one)} \qquad (54)$$

of miscellaneous dimerizations of 2-pyrazolin-5-ones and 3-pyrazolin-5-ones have been reported to give 4,4′-bis(2-pyrazolin-5-ones). 3-Methyl-1-phenyl-2-pyrazolin-5-one reacts with various acylanilides[1192] and with sodium ethoxide[1645] to give dimers. Ethyl groups are introduced at the 4,4′-positions by the use of sodium ethoxide. Heating a 4-oximino-2-pyrazolin-5-one has been reported to give a dimer in which the 4-substituent has been eliminated (eq. 55).[925] According to van

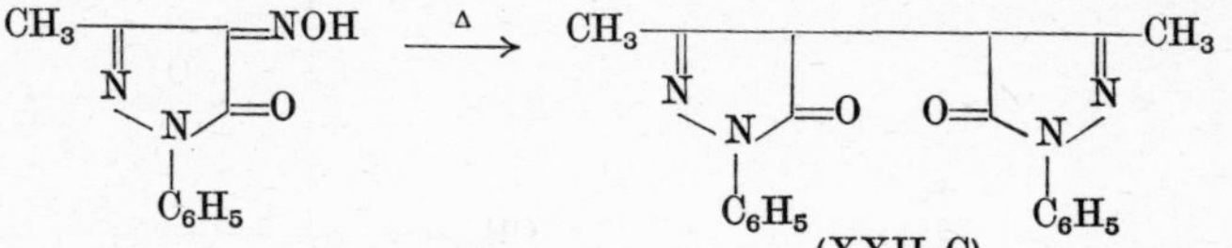

$$\text{3-}CH_3\text{-4-(=NOH)-1-}C_6H_5\text{-2-pyrazolin-5-one} \xrightarrow{\Delta} \text{4,4'-bis(3-}CH_3\text{-1-}C_6H_5\text{-2-pyrazolin-5-one)}\ \text{(XXII–C)} \qquad (55)$$

Alphen[1513] it is also obtained by the reductive cyclization of a crotonic ester (eq. 56). The replacement of a 4-imino function in a 2-pyrazolin-5-one by a 2-pyrazolin-5-one lacking a 4-substituent also leads to a

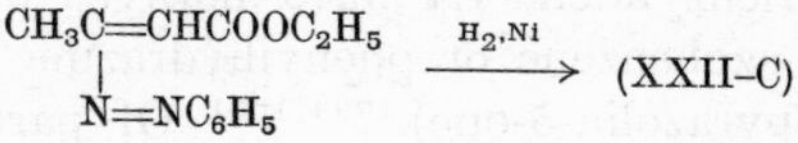

$$\begin{matrix} CH_3C{=}CHCOOC_2H_5 \\ | \\ N{=}NC_6H_5 \end{matrix} \xrightarrow{H_2,Ni} \text{(XXII–C)} \qquad (56)$$

dimer.[1538] Hydrazines react with various heterocyclic compounds to give 4,4′-bis(2-pyrazolin-5-ones). These reactions are shown in eqs. 57–59.[129,725,729] Ridi and co-workers[1194] have treated various pyrazolo-

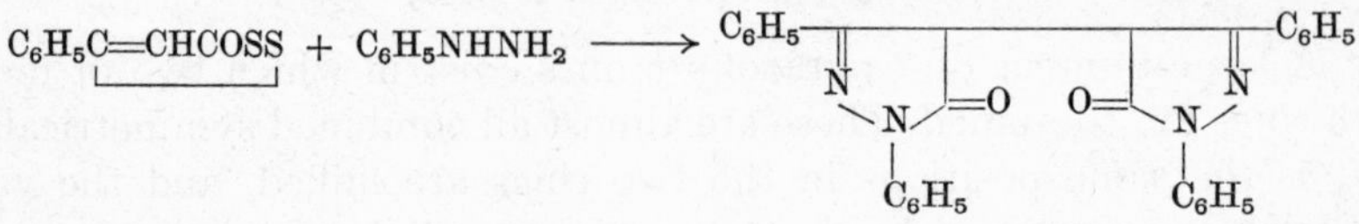

$C_6H_5C{=}CHCOSS + C_6H_5NHNH_2 \longrightarrow$ (57)

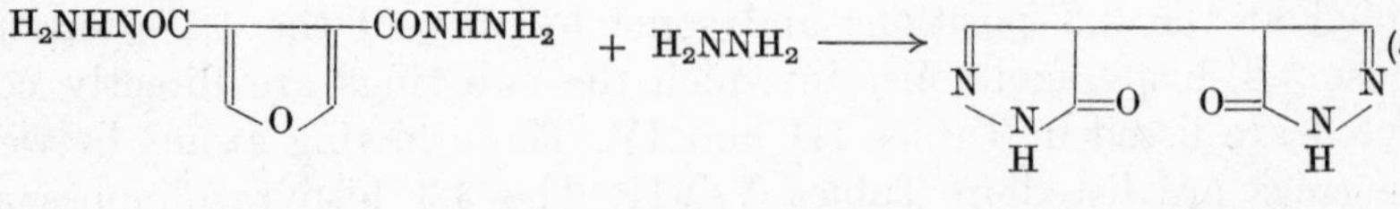

H_2NHNOC–(furan)–$CONHNH_2 + H_2NNH_2 \longrightarrow$ (58)

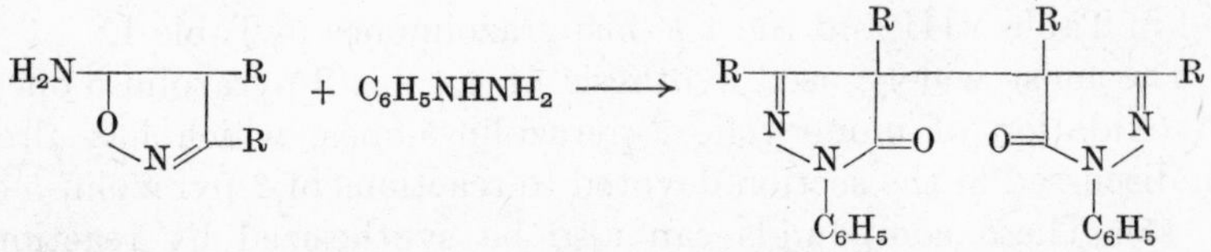

H_2N–(isoxazole, R, R)$ + C_6H_5NHNH_2 \longrightarrow$ (59)

2-pyrones and phenylmethyltartonylurea and imide with phenylhydrazine to give 4,4′-bis(3-methyl-1-phenyl-2-pyrazolin-5-one). A variety of other 4,4′-bis(2-pyrazolin-5-ones) can be converted into the type being

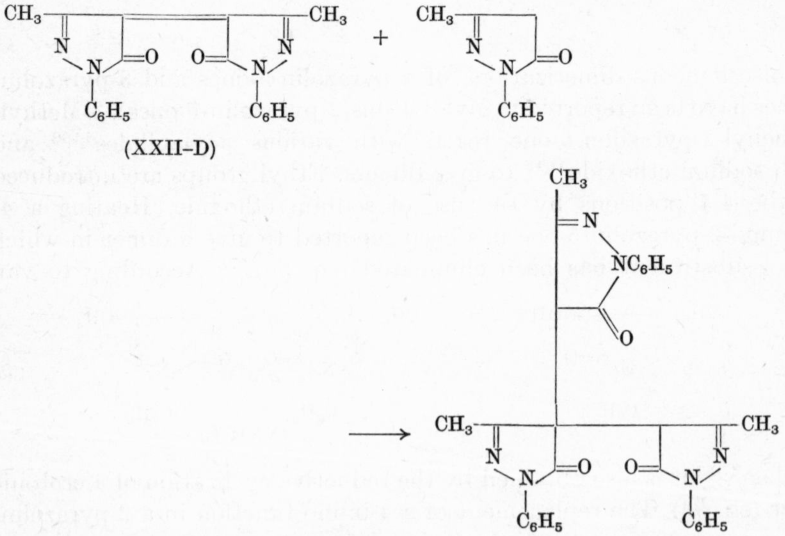

(XXII–D) + (60)

discussed here. 4-Benzylidene-4,4′-bis(3-methyl-1-phenyl-2-pyrazolin-5-one) reacts with azobenzene or phenylhydrazine to give 4,4′-bis(3-methyl-1-phenyl-2-pyrazolin-5-one).[1090,1091] Of particular interest is the addition of various compounds having active methylene to the 4,4′-bis(2-pyrazolin-5-ones) connected by a double bond since this leads in some cases to trimers.[1607,1609,1613,1614] This reaction is shown in eq. 60.

Only a very few 4,4′-bis(2-pyrazolin-5-ones) linked by a double bond have been prepared. The parent compound of this series, 4-(3-methyl-1-phenyl-5-oxo-2-pyrazolin-4-ylidene)-3-methyl-1-phenyl-2-pyrazolin-5-one (XXII–D), is known as pyrazole blue.[323,807,809,816,1090,1091] It was so named by Knorr because of its great resemblance to indigo blue. All these compounds are strongly colored. The usual synthesis is by ferric chloride oxidation of monomeric 2-pyrazolin-5-ones (eq. 61)[296,809] or by oxidation of the corresponding bis compounds

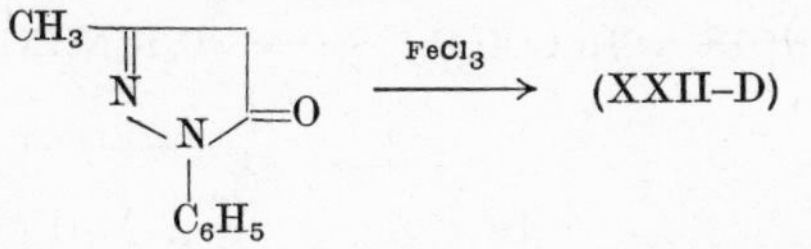

CH_3, N, N, =O, C_6H_5 $\xrightarrow{FeCl_3}$ (XXII–D) (61)

linked by a single bond with ferric chloride, nitrous acid, nitric acid or various nitriles.[296,333,1090] The product in eq. 61 is pyrazole blue. Other methods of synthesis are treatment of 4-(3-methyl-1-phenyl-2-pyrazolin-5-ylidene)-3-methyl-1-phenyl-2-pyrazolin-5-one with bromine in alkali,[323] heating of 4-bromo-3-methyl-1-phenyl-2-pyrazolin-5-one

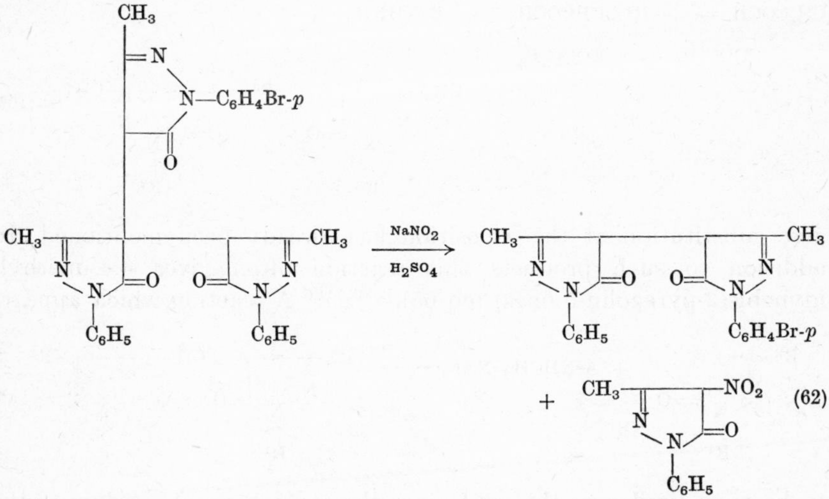

CH_3, =N, N—C_6H_4Br-*p*, O; CH_3, N, N, =O, C_6H_5; O=, N, N, CH_3, C_6H_5 $\xrightarrow[H_2SO_4]{NaNO_2}$ CH_3, N, N, =O, C_6H_5; O=, N, N, CH_3, C_6H_4Br-*p* + CH_3, NO_2, N, N, =O, C_6H_5 (62)

with alcohol[809] and degradation of trimers.[1607,1608] The trimer degradation procedure gives unsymmetrical compounds of the pyrazole blue type (eq. 62). The double bond connecting the rings in these compounds reacts as do normal olefins and in addition undergoes additions with compounds having active hydrogen[1607,1608] or with such compounds as hydrogen cyanide.[1612]

4,4′-bis(2-pyrazolin-5-ones) linked by carbon chains have been prepared in a multitude of ways, several of which have been mentioned in the discussion concerning reactions of 2-pyrazolin-5-ones. The only method of any importance is the condensation of 2-pyrazolin-5-ones with aldehydes and ketones (eq. 24, p. 20) and this has already been discussed. An interesting modification of this is the use of an anil as a substitute for the aldehyde.[1094] The anil functions similarly to the aldehyde. A second modification in which the aldehyde is generated in the course of the reaction has also been used (eq. 63).[1351] Another

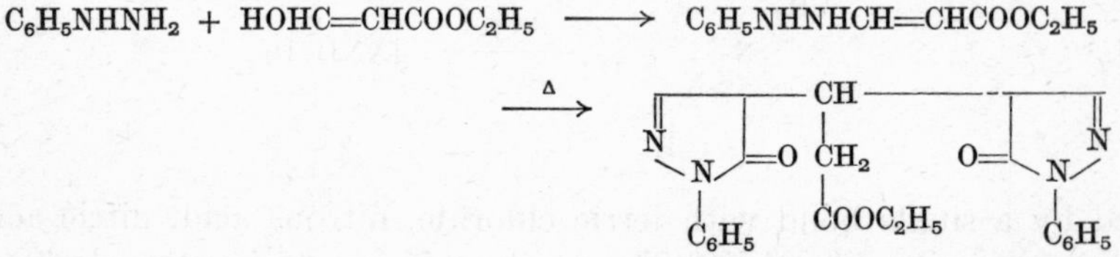

$$C_6H_5NHNH_2 + HOHC{=}CHCOOC_2H_5 \longrightarrow C_6H_5NHNHCH{=}CHCOOC_2H_5$$

$$\xrightarrow{\Delta} \text{bis(1-}C_6H_5\text{-2-pyrazolin-5-one-4-yl)}CH\text{—}CH_2COOC_2H_5 \quad (63)$$

method used to some extent for the synthesis of 4,4′-bis(2-pyrazolin-5-ones) is the reaction of bis-β-ketoesters with hydrazines (eq. 64).[451,513,514,1154] The reaction of 2-pyrazolin-5-ones with amidines to

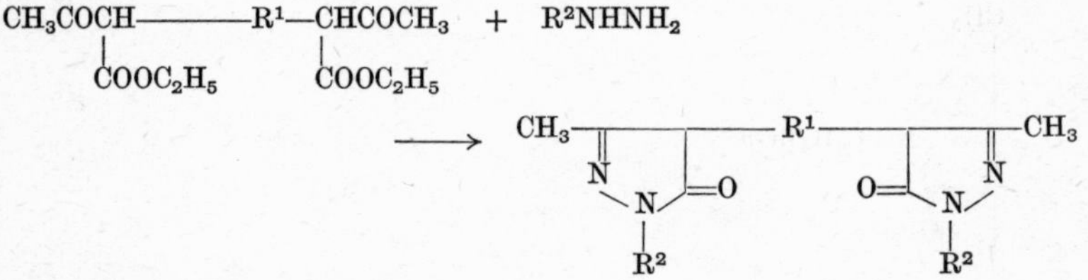

$$CH_3COCH(COOC_2H_5)\text{—}R^1\text{—}CH(COOC_2H_5)COCH_3 + R^2NHNH_2$$

$$\longrightarrow \text{3-}CH_3\text{-1-}R^2\text{-2-pyrazolin-5-one-4-yl—}R^1\text{—3-}CH_3\text{-1-}R^2\text{-2-pyrazolin-5-one-4-yl} \quad (64)$$

give substitution at the 4-position has already been mentioned. In addition to such products this reaction often gives 4,4′-methylidynebis(2-pyrazolin-5-ones) (eq 65).[1070,1186] A reaction which appears

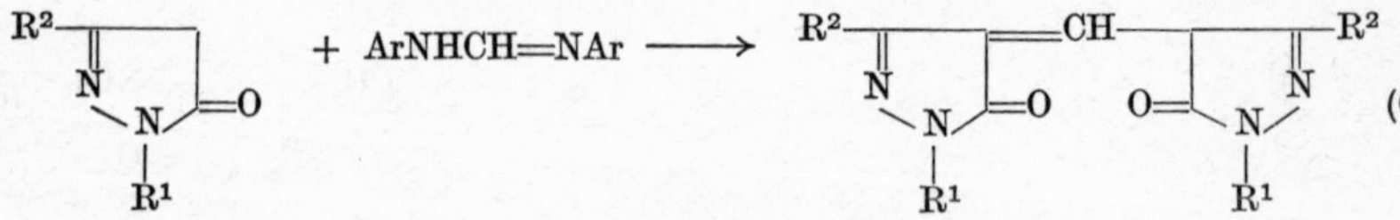

$$\text{3-}R^2\text{-1-}R^1\text{-2-pyrazolin-5-one} + ArNHCH{=}NAr \longrightarrow \text{(3-}R^2\text{-1-}R^1\text{-2-pyrazolin-5-on-4-ylidene)}{=}CH\text{—(3-}R^2\text{-1-}R^1\text{-2-pyrazolin-5-one-4-yl)} \quad (65)$$

to be very similar to this and gives the same type of product is the condensation of 2-pyrazolin-5-ones with 1-phenyl-1,2-dihydro-4,6-diamino-1,3,5-triazines.[300] The synthesis of 4,4′-methylidynebis(2-pyrazolin-5-ones) has usually been achieved by condensation of

2-pyrazolin-5-ones with ethyl orthoformate[611,1188,1669] (eq. 66) or by the condensation of 5-oxo-2-pyrazolin-4-carboxaldehydes with

R^2, N, N, =O, R^1 + $HC(OC_2H_5)_3$ ⟶ R^2, CH, R^2, N, N, =O, O=, N, N, R^1, R^1 (66)

2-pyrazolin-5-ones (eq. 67).[926,1093,1185] The latter condensation can be modified by boiling the aldehyde alone in water which causes partial

R^2, CHO, N, N, =O, R^1 + R^2, N, N, =O, R^1 ⟶ R^2, CH, R^2, N, N, =O, O=, N, N, R^1, R^1 (67)

hydrolysis of the formyl group. The reactants shown in eq. 67 are then present and can react to form the bis compound. A variety of miscellaneous methods of preparing such compounds is given in eqs. 68–81.

CH_3, =CH–C_6H_4–NO_2, N, N, O, C_6H_5 + CH_3, N, N, O, C_6H_5

(68)[110]

⟶ NO_2, CH_3, CH, CH_3, N, N, O, C_6H_5, O, N, N, C_6H_5

$CH_3C(=NNHC_6H_5)$–$CH(COOC_2H_5)$–CH_2SCH_3 $\xrightarrow{CH_3CO_2H}$ (XXII–A) (69)[117]

CH_3, N, N, O, C_6H_5 + $ClCH_2SCH_3$ $\xrightarrow{C_2H_5ONa}$ (XXII–A) (70)[117]

$$\text{(XXII–B)} + \text{3-methyl-1-phenyl-5-pyrazolone} \xrightarrow{\text{KOH}} \text{bis(pyrazolone) product bearing } N{=}CCH_3,\ C_6H_5N,\ C{=}CH \quad (71)^{187}$$

$$\text{1-(4-}SO_3NH_4\text{-phenyl)-3-methyl-5-pyrazolone} + \text{2-(CHONa)cyclohexanone} \longrightarrow \text{bis-product with } CH_3,\ CH{=},\ SO_3NH_4 \quad (72)^{187,1224}$$

$$\text{3-methyl-1-phenyl-5-pyrazolone} + CH_3COOCH(OC_2H_5)_2 \xrightarrow{(C_2H_5)_3N} \text{(XXII–B)} \quad (73)^{365,687}$$

$$\text{3-methyl-1-phenyl-5-pyrazolone} + (CH_2)_6N_4 \longrightarrow \text{(XXII–B)} \quad (74)^{365,687}$$

$$\text{3-methyl-1-phenyl-5-pyrazolone} + \text{pyrido-fused compound (N, O, C, HO)} \longrightarrow \text{(XXII–B)} \quad (75)^{825,1088}$$

$$\text{3-methyl-1-phenyl-5-pyrazolone} + C_6H_5NC \longrightarrow \text{(XXII–B)} \quad (76)^{923}$$

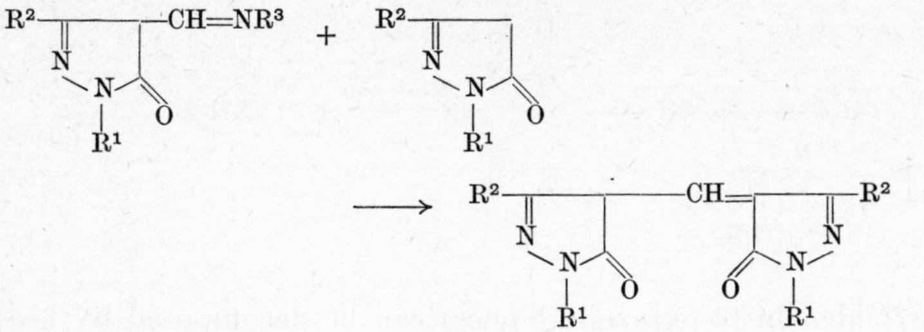

(77)[923, 1189]

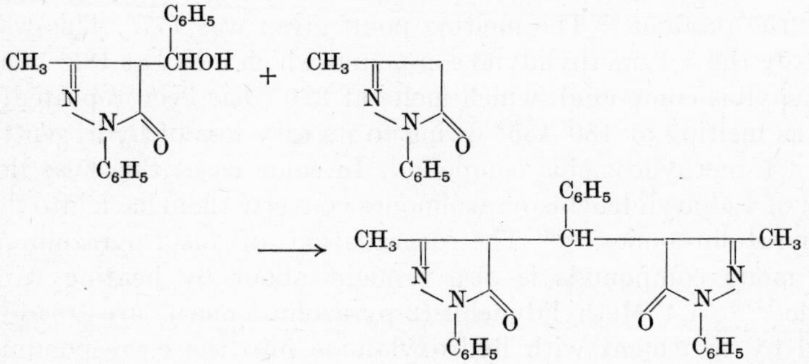

(78)[977]

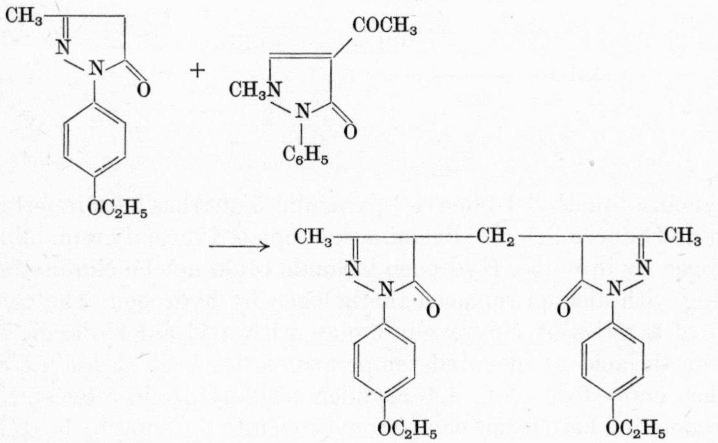

(79)[1097]

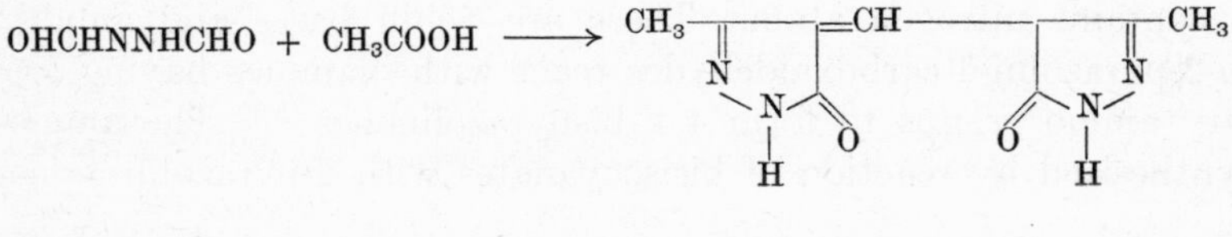

$OHCHNNHCHO + CH_3COOH \longrightarrow$ (80)[1185]

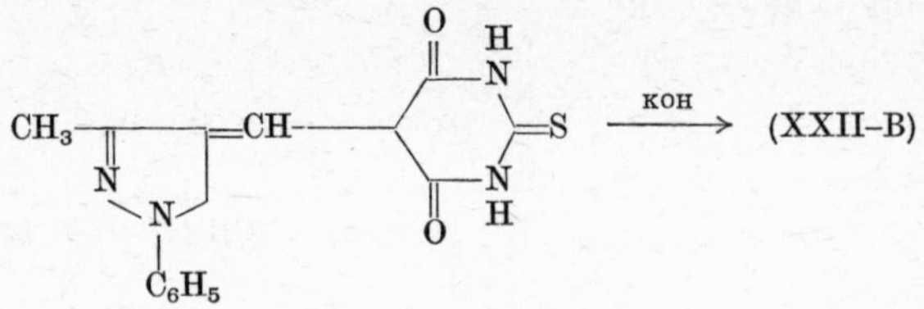

$$\text{(pyrazolinylidene-thiobarbituric acid)} \xrightarrow{\text{KOH}} \text{(XXII–B)} \qquad (81)^{1187}$$

4,4′-Arylidenebis(2-pyrazolin-5-ones) can be decomposed by heat or acid to give 4,4′-methylidynebis(2-pyrazolin-5-ones).[93,1036] In one case 4,4′-methenylbis(3-methyl-1-phenyl-2-pyrazolin-5-one) was reported as the product.[22] The melting point given was 177°. This was undoubtedly the 4,4′-methylidyne compound which melts at 185°. The 4,4′-methenylbis compound, which melts at 220°, has been repeatedly reported as melting at 180–185° owing to its easy loss of hydrogen to give the 4,4′-methylidynebis compound. In some cases this heat degradation of 4,4′-arylidenebispyrazolinones converts them back into the mono-2-pyrazolin-5-ones.[1036] The degradation of bis(2-pyrazolin-5-ones) to mono compounds is also brought about by heating with formamide.[1189] 4,4′-Methylidynebis-(2-pyrazolin-5-ones) are readily converted by treatment with hydroxylamine into the corresponding 5-oxo-2-pyrazolin-4-carboxaldehyde oxime[925] or by hydrolysis with base to the 4-carboxaldehyde (eq. 82).[926] The bromination of 4,4′-

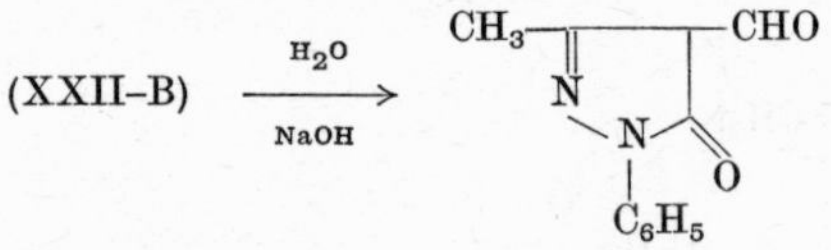

$$\text{(XXII–B)} \xrightarrow[\text{NaOH}]{H_2O} \text{3-methyl-1-phenyl-5-oxo-2-pyrazolin-4-carboxaldehyde } (CH_3, CHO, C_6H_5) \qquad (82)$$

methylidynebis(3-methyl-1-phenyl-2-pyrazolin-5-one) has been reported by Ziegler and Sauermilch.[1682] Bromination replaced the only remaining C–4 hydrogen by bromine. Hydrogen bromide could not be eliminated, but heating with alcohol replaced the halogen by hydrogen. The condensation of a series of 2-pyrazolin-5-ones with aryl aldehydes in 70 per cent acetic acid at elevated temperatures has been described as giving the enol form of 4,4′-arylidenebis(2-pyrazolin-5-ones).[1135] The corresponding keto forms can be converted into the enols by heating in alcohol.

A few 4,4′-bis(2-pyrazolin-5-ones) are known in which the linking chain contains nitrogen atoms. These are Schiff bases and amides. 5-Oxo-2-pyrazolin-4-carboxaldehydes react with diamines having two primary amino groups to form 4,4′-bispyrazolinones.[1190] The amides are synthesized by reaction of bisisocyanates with 2-pyrazolin-5-ones (eq. 83).[1111] This reaction is of particular interest because it illustrates the great activity of the hydrogen atoms at C–4.

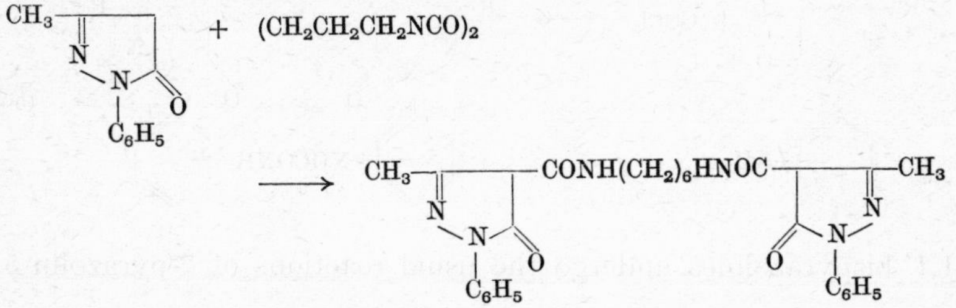

CH_3 N N O C_6H_5 + $(CH_2CH_2CH_2NCO)_2$ ⟶ CH_3—CONH$(CH_2)_6$HNOC—CH_3 (N N O C_6H_5 rings) (83)

The 3,3′-bis(2-pyrazolin-5-ones) in which the rings are connected by carbon chains (Table VIII) are usually prepared by condensation of a hydrazine with an appropriate β,β'-dioxodiester (eq. 84).[419,462,1222,1225] Such bispyrazolinones linked by a carbonyl group have been prepared by pyrolysis of the calcium salt of 5-oxo-2-pyrazolin-5-one.[1549]

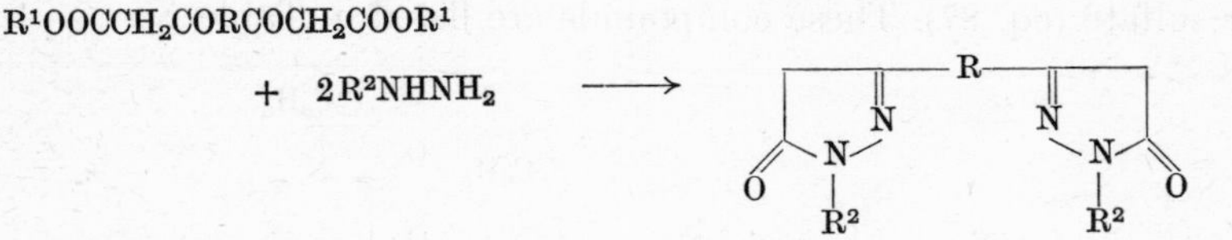

$R^1OOCCH_2CORCOCH_2COOR^1$ + $2R^2NHNH_2$ ⟶ (rings linked by R; N N O R^2) (84)

The 1,1′-bis(2-pyrazolin-5-ones) (Table IX) have been prepared by three methods. Two of these are variants on the familiar β-ketoester condensation with hydrazines but in these cases compounds having two hydrazine moieties are used.[116,212,255,459,1037] These two methods are illustrated in eq. 85. The R in the hydrazines used in the direct con-

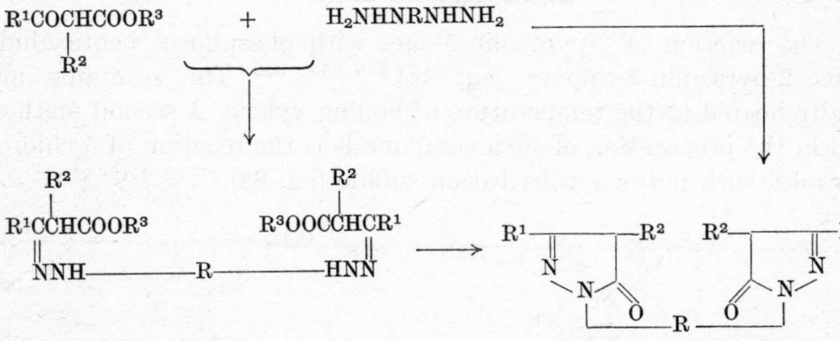

$R^1COCHCOOR^3$ (R^2) + $H_2NHNRNHNH_2$ ⟶ $R^1CCHCOOR^3$ (R^2) $R^3OOCCHCR^1$ (R^2) NNH—R—HNN ⟶ R^1—R^2 R^2—R^1 (N N O, rings linked by R) (85)

densation is usually aryl. The commonly used hydrazine when going through the bishydrazone has been carbazide[1632] or a similar compound.[255] The reaction of phosgene with 1-(X-amino-phenyl)-2-pyrazolin-5-ones also forms 1,1′-bis(2-pyrazolin-5-ones) (eq. 86).[152,511]

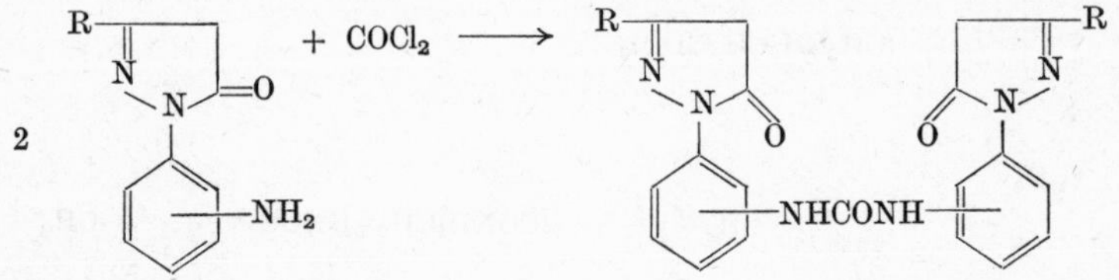

(86)

The 1,1′-bispyrazolines undergo the usual reactions of 2-pyrazolin-5-ones.

Westoö has reported the synthesis of complex bispyrazolinones which he has called furlones.[1608,1610,1611] These have two 2-pyrazolin-5-one rings connected through a dihydrofuran ring which in turn is fused with a pyrazole ring. These were prepared by condensation of 4-halogenated-2-pyrazolin-5-ones, together, with 1-aryl-2-pyrazolin-5-ones, or with pyrazole blue (XXII–D) in the presence of a base and copper sulfate (eq. 87). These compounds are listed in Table X.

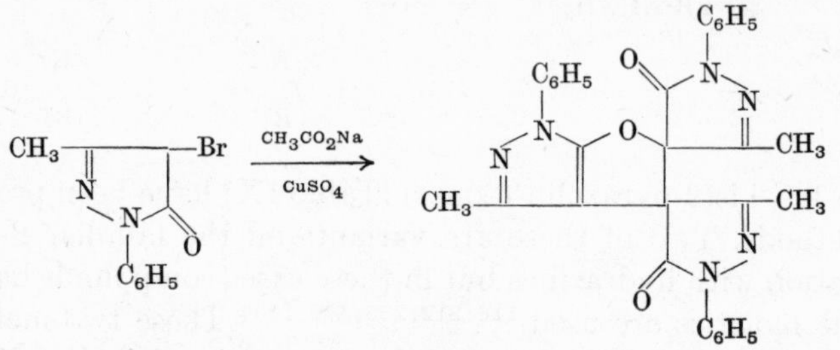

(87)

B. 2-Pyrazolin-5-thiones

The reaction of 2-pyrazolin-5-ones with phosphorus pentasulfide forms 2-pyrazolin-5-thiones (eq. 44).[759,990,1343] The reactants are usually heated at the temperature of boiling xylene. A second method used in the preparation of such compounds is the reaction of 5-chloropyrazoles with potassium hydrogen sulfide (eq. 88).[977,990,1003]

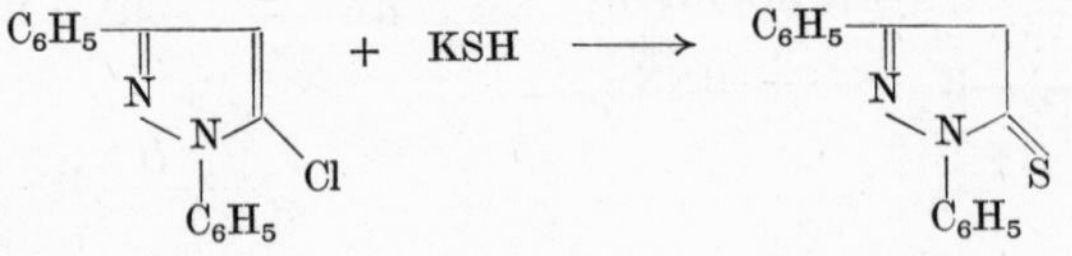

(88)

The properties of these compounds are very similar to those of the 5-oxo analogs. They are usually colorless but are yellow if substituted in the 4-position. Acidic and basic properties are both present. Kendall and Ruffin[759] claim that 3,4,4-trialkyl-2-pyrazolin-5-thiones exist as mercapto pyrazoles having the structure (XXIII).

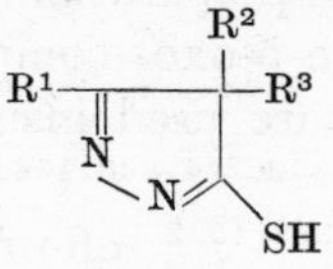

R^2 R^1 R^3 N N SH

(XXIII)

Reactions of 2-pyrazolin-5-thiones at the 4-position are quite similar to those of the 5-oxo analogs. Condensation of one mole of the pyrazolinthione with one mole of ketone or aldehyde to form 4-alkylidene- or arylidene-2-pyrazolin-5-thiones occurs.[990] Coupling with diazonium salts forms 4-azo compounds[990] and nitrosation occurs.[990] Alkylation or acylation ordinarily attacks the sulfur atom to give 5-mercaptopyrazoles.[977,990] Oxidation with mild oxidizing agents such as iodine or nitrous acid forms a disulfide,[990] but the use of hydrogen peroxide gives a sulfonic acid, according to Michaelis,[990] or replacement of the sulfur by oxygen, according to Kitamura.[785] Mercaptides are formed with mercuric oxide or mercuric salts.[990] The 4,4′-bis(2-pyrazolin-5-thiones) cyclize very readily to form a tricyclic compound with elimination of hydrogen sulfide (eq. 89).[990] The 2-pyrazolin-5-thiones are listed in Table XI.

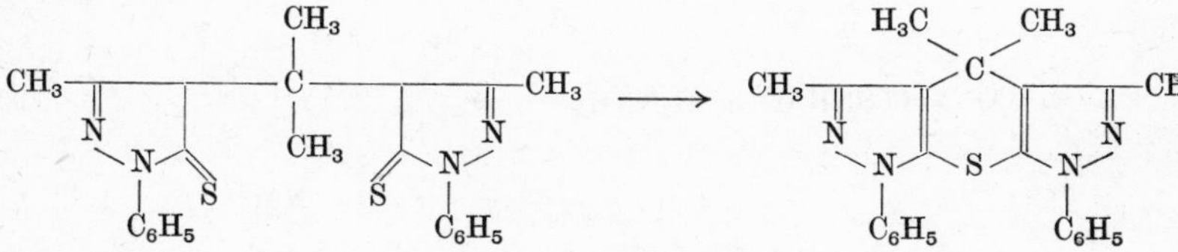

CH_3 CH_3 C CH_3 CH_3 N N S C_6H_5 S N N C_6H_5 $\longrightarrow$ H_3C CH_3 CH_3 C CH_3 N N S N N C_6H_5 C_6H_5 (89)

C. 5-Imino-2-pyrazolines

It is probable that most of the 5-imino-2-pyrazolines exist as the corresponding aminopyrazoles (XXIV). Gagnon, Boivin and Tremblay[506] have studied the ultraviolet absorption spectra of these com-

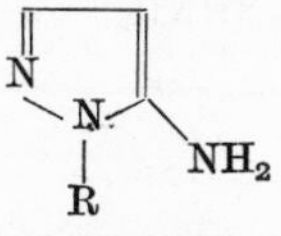

N N NH_2 R

(XXIV)

pounds and concluded that the usual structure is the aminopyrazole one, although frequently more than one isomer is present. The chemical literature usually refers to what are here called 5-imino-2-pyrazolines as 5-aminopyrazoles.

The principal methods of preparation of these compounds are very similar to those used for the 5-oxo- compounds, except that nitriles, and in some cases amides, are used instead of esters, acids or acid derivatives. β-Ketonitriles,[342,344,838,1562] β-aldehydonitriles,[127] β-iminonitriles,[90,324,996,1010,1285,1542] α,β-unsaturated trithiones[129] and α,β-acetylenic nitriles[1025] are condensed with hydrazines. In many cases the intermediate hydrazones have been isolated and cyclized.[86,132,310,996,1011,1285,1287] These reactions are shown in eqs. 90 and 91. Worrall and co-workers[1655,1656] have reported the condensation of aromatic acetylenic amides with hydrazines to give 5-imino-2-pyrazolines (eq. 92). Presumably the amides react like the iminothioacids, hydrogen

$$R^1CXCH_2CN + R^2NHNH_2 \longrightarrow \text{(3-}R^1\text{-1-}R^2\text{-5-imino-2-pyrazoline)} \qquad (90)$$

X=O or NH

$$R^1C{\equiv}CCN + R^2NHNH_2 \longrightarrow \text{(3-}R^1\text{-1-}R^2\text{-5-imino-2-pyrazoline)} \qquad (91)$$

$$Ar^1C{\equiv}CCSNHAr^2 + H_2NNH_2 \longrightarrow \text{(3-}Ar^1\text{-5-}NAr^2\text{-2-pyrazoline, N-H)} \qquad (92)$$

sulfide being eliminated. Bottcher and Bauer[129] have condensed α,β-unsaturated trithiones with hydrazines to form 5-imino-2-pyrazolines (eq. 93).

$$C_6H_5C{=}CHCSSS + C_6H_5NHNH_2 \longrightarrow \text{(3-}C_6H_5\text{-1-}C_6H_5\text{-5-imino-2-pyrazoline)} \qquad (93)$$

Several methods for the synthesis of 5-imino-2-pyrazolines depend upon the amination of a pyrazole ring. 5-Chloropyrazoles react with aniline to give the corresponding 5-amino compound.[826,1002] The chloropyrazoles can be prepared and amination accomplished in one step by treatment of 2-pyrazolin-5-one with phosphorus oxychloride and aryl amines at the same time.[827,828] Also reduction of a 5-nitropyrazole has been used.[1086] Ethyl 3-phenylpyrazole-5-carboxylate has been converted into a hydrazide, then to an azide, and finally, by a Curtius rearrangement, to the amino compound (eq. 94).[1086] Also amides can be rearranged to give iminopyrazolines.[1046]

C_6H_5, N, N, H, $COOC_2H_5$ + H_2NNH_2 ⟶ C_6H_5, N, N, H, $CONHNH_2$

$\xrightarrow[2.\ NaOH]{1.\ NaNO_2-HCl}$ C_6H_5, N, N, H, NH (94)

Cusmano[340,341,345] has converted 5-alkyl- and 5-arylisoxazole-3-carboxylic acids into 5-imino-2-pyrazolines by treatment with phenyl hydrazine. Musante has also used this procedure.[1043-1045] This reaction goes by way of β-ketonitrile intermediates and gives very poor yields.[86]

The decarboxylation of 1,3-diphenyl-5-imino-2-pyrazolin-3-carboxylic acid gives 1,3-diphenyl-5-imino-2-pyrazoline.[506] Druey and Schmidt[391] have taken advantage of the selective replacement of an oxo group by chlorine over that of an imino group to prepare 5-imino-2-pyrazolines (eq. 95).

HN=, C_2H_5, C_2H_5, HN, N, H, O + $POCl_3$ ⟶ Cl, C_2H_5, C_2H_5, N, N, H, NH $\xrightarrow{H_2}$ C_2H_5, C_2H_5, N, N, H, NH (95)

The reactions of 5-imino-2-pyrazolines are very similar to those of the 5-oxo analogs, except for reactions specifically involving the 5-imino group as its amino tautomer. For example, condensations with aromatic aldehydes occur to form 4,4′-arylidenebis(5-imino-2-pyrazolines). Michaelis[996] has prepared compounds of this type from 3-methyl-1-phenyl-5-imino-2-pyrazoline in which the arylidene groups and melting points are respectively: C_6H_5CH, 66°; $2\text{-}NO_2C_6H_4CH$, 89°; X-HOC_6H_4CH, 120°; $4\text{-}CH_3C_6H_4CH$, 219°. However, reaction with aldehydes or ketones can also occur at the amino group to give Schiff bases or alkylation.[1011] Ketones such as acetoacetic ester used in vigorous conditions give pyrazolopyrimidines.[329] Halogenation,[996,1656] nitration,[1656] nitrosation,[340,1002,1010] and coupling with diazonium salts[996] occur at C–4 as expected. The nitrosation products are usually oximes. The condensation of phenyl isocyanate with the 5-imino-2-pyrazolines occurs to give the 4-carboxyanilides (eq. 96).[826] These com-

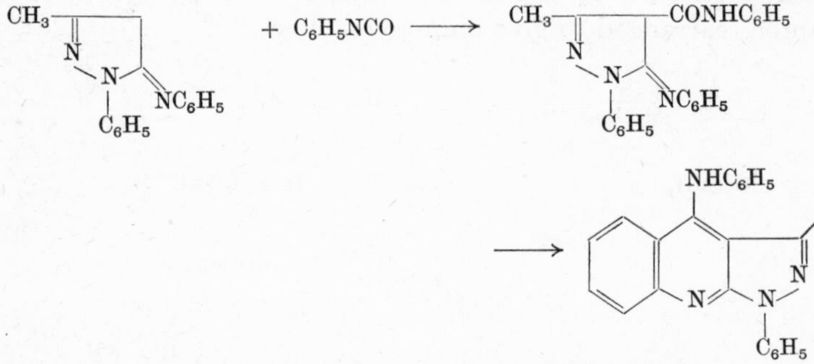

$$\text{3-methyl-1-phenyl-5-(phenylimino)-2-pyrazoline} + C_6H_5NCO \longrightarrow \text{4-}CONHC_6H_5\text{ derivative} \longrightarrow \text{4-}NHC_6H_5\text{-3-}CH_3\text{-1-}C_6H_5\text{-pyrazolo[3,4-b]quinoline} \quad (96)$$

pounds then readily cyclize to quinoline derivatives. Phenyl isothiocyanate, N,N′-diphenylurea and N,N′-diphenylthiourea also react in this way. *p*-Nitrophenylsulfenyl chloride reacts with 3-methyl-1-phenyl 5-imino-2-pyrazoline to give 3-methyl-4-(4-nitrophenylmercapto)-1 phenyl-5-imino-2-pyrazoline.[325]

Druey and Schmidt[391] have reported that alkylation of N–1 unsubstituted 4,4-dialkyl-5-imino-2-pyrazolines with dimethyl sulfate occurs at the N–1 position.

As illustrated in eq. 97, the acylation of 5-imino-2-pyrazolines

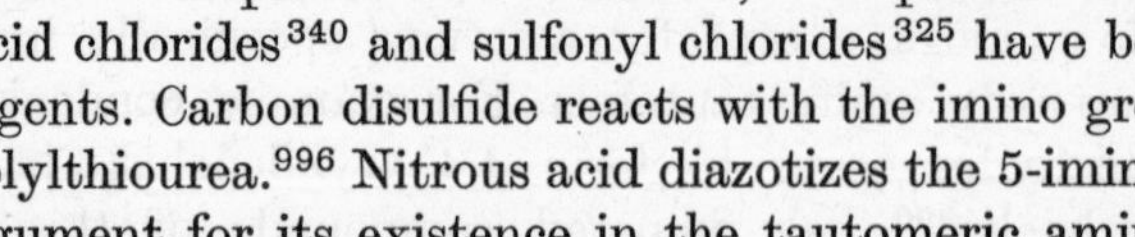

$$\text{3-}R^2\text{-1-}R^1\text{-5-}(NH)\text{-2-pyrazoline} + R^3COCl \longrightarrow \text{3-}R^2\text{-1-}R^1\text{-5-}(NCOR^3)\text{-2-pyrazoline} \quad (97)$$

occurs on the 5-imino group rather than at C–4 as in the 5-oxo analogs. However, the use of diethylmalonyl chloride gives acylation at both positions.[322] Aliphatic acid chlorides,[391] aliphatic anhydrides,[325] aromatic acid chlorides[340] and sulfonyl chlorides[325] have been used as acylating agents. Carbon disulfide reacts with the imino group to give a bispyrazolylthiourea.[996] Nitrous acid diazotizes the 5-imino group,[996] another argument for its existence in the tautomeric amino form. If insufficient nitrous acid to diazotize all of the 5-imino-2-pyrazolines is used, the resulting diazonium salt couples with undiazotized material, giving an iminoazo compound (XXV). The diazonium salt also couples with phenols.

Moureu and Lazennec[1025] were unable to hydrolyze 3-alkyl-5-imino-2-pyrazolines to the 5-oxo analogs, but Cusmano[340] claims to have hydrolyzed the imino group of 4-nitroso-1,3-diphenyl-5-imino-2-pyrazoline to an oxo group using acid conditions.

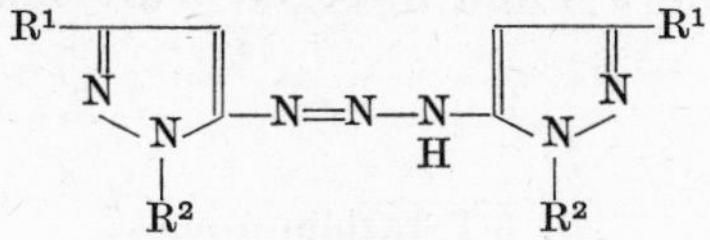

(XXV)

Michaelis[996] has reported that oxidation of various 5-imino-2 pyrazolines with hydrogen peroxide or nitrous acid gives what were called azipyrazoles of type (XXVI). It seems highly unlikely that these

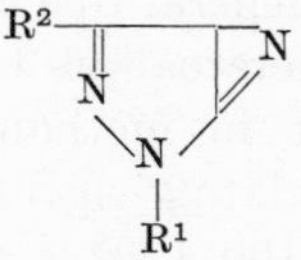

(XXVI)

products actually had the structure proposed. It may be that the compounds formed were 5,5′-bis(5-imino-2-pyrazolines), as indicated in eq. 98, although the evidence is not completely consistent with this interpretation. 5-Imino-2-pyrazolines are listed in Table XII.

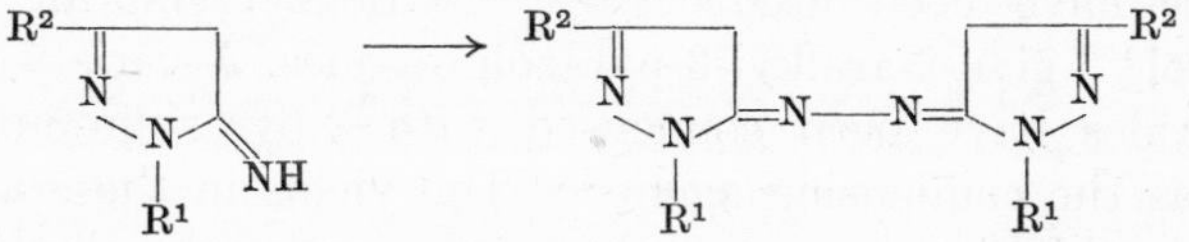

(98)

A few bis(2-pyrazolin-5-ones) having one or both 5-oxo groups replaced by imino groups have been prepared. The preparation of those having one imino group is shown in eqs. 99 and 100. Those linked

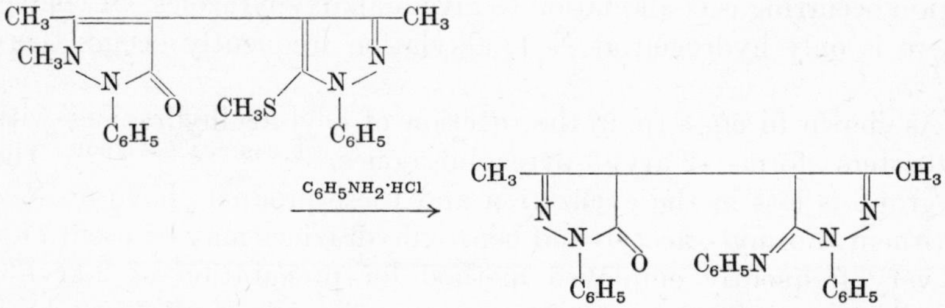

$\xrightarrow{C_6H_5NH_2\cdot HCl}$ (99)

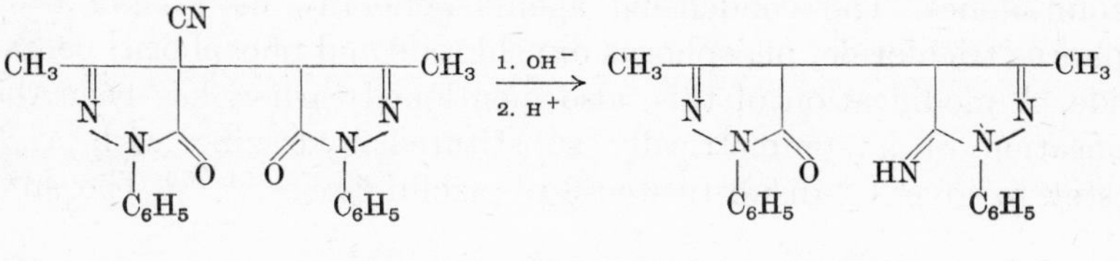

$\xrightarrow[2.\ H^+]{1.\ OH^-}$ (100)

through the nitrogen atoms of the 5-imino group are listed in Table XIII. The usual preparation is reaction of a 5-imino-2-pyrazoline having no substituent on the 5-imino nitrogen with oxalic acid[322] or phosgene.[301]

D. 3-Pyrazolin-5-ones

(1) *Syntheses*

As has been mentioned previously (eq. 42, p. 26) the method most frequently used to synthesize 3-pyrazolin-5-ones is alkylation of 2-pyrazolin-5-ones at N–2. In general this can be used only for synthesis of 2-alkyl-, 2-aralkyl- and 2-heteroalkyl-3-pyrazolin-5-ones. The earliest workers used methyl iodide in methanol at temperatures of 100–130°.[806,818,992] Other methylating agents used have been dimethyl sulfate at temperatures of 100–130°,[113,362,781,1173] dimethyl sulfate with base,[110] diazomethane,[94] methyl iodide,[141,1475] methyl iodide in the presence of sodium methoxide,[1205] methanol and dry hydrogen chloride at 140°[1508] and methyl *p*-toluenesulfonate in the presence of base.[102,1198,1205] A number of other short-chain alkyl halides, such as ethyl iodide, allyl chloride and isopropyl chloride with and without added base have been used.[250,1205,1447] Benzyl chloride[54,250] and xanthhydrol[457] give 2-aralkyl-3-pyrazolin-5-ones. A variety of heteroalkyl chlorides have been condensed with 2-pyrazolin-5-ones using sodamide as the condensing agent.[249] The yields in these alkylations vary considerably, but in general the more complex the alkyl or aralkyl halide used the lower the yields. Methylation has been reported in yields of 85 per cent,[781] but benzylation occurs only to the extent of 15 per cent.[250] The usual yields appear to be 40–65 per cent. The chief side reaction occurring is *O*-alkylation to give 5-alkoxypyrazoles. Of course, if there is only hydrogen at N–1, alkylation frequently occurs there also.[54]

As shown in eq. 3 (p. 9) the reaction of acyl arylhydrazines with β-ketoesters forms 2-aryl-3-pyrazolin-5-ones.[679,849,984,988,1001] The acyl group is lost in the cyclization and these products have no N–1 substituent. Formyl-, acetyl- and benzoylhydrazines may be used. This is a very frequently employed method for preparation of 2-aryl-3-pyrazolin-5-ones. The condensing agents generally used have been phosphorus trichloride, phosphorus oxychloride and phosphorus pentachloride. A modification of this, also mentioned earlier, has been the condensation of a symmetrically substituted hydrazine with a β-ketoester to give 1,2-disubstituted-3-pyrazolin-5-ones.[54,370] The substituents on N–1 and N–2 may be both alkyl or both aryl, although very few 1,2-diaryl-3-pyrazolin-5-ones are known.

A large number of other syntheses of 3-pyrazolin-5-ones have been reported, although most are not of importance as practical methods of preparation. These are illustrated in eqs. 101–113.

[pyrazolium salt: CH_3, CH_3N, N–R, Cl]$^+$ I^- $\xrightarrow{Ag_2O \text{ or } NaOH}$ [pyrazolinone: CH_3, CH_3N, N–R, O] (101)[54,978,985]

$R^1CH{=}CHCOOR^2 + C_6H_5NHNH_2 \longrightarrow$ [pyrazolinone: R^1, C_6H_5N, N–H, O] (102)[808,1569]

$R^2 = H$ or CH_3

$C_6H_5NHNHCOCH_3 + CH_3OK \xrightarrow[300°]{MgO}$ [pyrazolinone: CH_3, C_6H_5N, N–H, O] (103)[247]

$ClCH_2CH(OH)COOH + C_6H_5NHNH_2 \longrightarrow$ [pyrazolinone: C_6H_5N, N–H, O] (104)[858]

$HOOC{-}C(CH_3)(Br){-}CH(Br)COOH + ArNHNH_2 \longrightarrow$ [pyrazolinone: CH_3, C_6H_5N, N–H, O] (105)[446]

$CH_3C({=}NNHAr)CH_2CONHNHAr \xrightarrow[\Delta]{HCl}$ [pyrazolinone: CH_3, ArN, N–H, O] (106)[885]

Lecher, Parker and Conn[885] report that the cyclization of the hydrazone hydrazide, as in eq. 106, is the preferred synthesis for 2-aryl-3-methyl-3-pyrazolin-5-ones.

A number of 4-heterocyclic-3-pyrazolin-5-ones have been prepared using the appropriate 4-substituted pyrazolinone in the usual reactions to form the particular heterocyclic ring. For example, 4-amino-2,3-dimethyl-1-phenyl-3-pyrazolin-5-one has been condensed with 1,4-diketones to form pyrazolinones substituted by pyrroles.[452] Isatin has

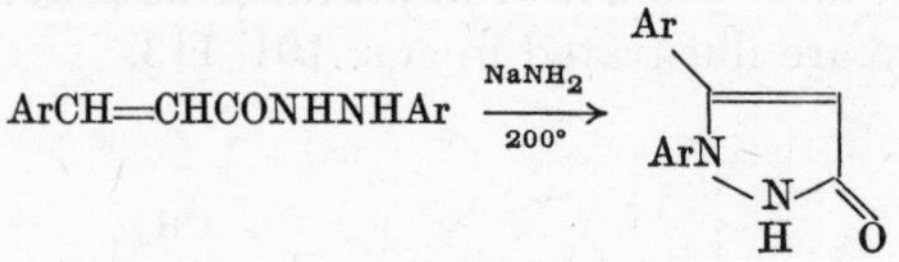

ArCH=CHCONHNHAr $\xrightarrow[200°]{NaNH_2}$ 5-aryl-1-aryl-pyrazolinone (107)[1333]

$C_6H_5N(NH_2)CH_2CH_2CN$ $\xrightarrow[2.\ H^+]{1.\ KOH,\ H_2O}$ C_6H_5-pyrazolinone (108)[1122]

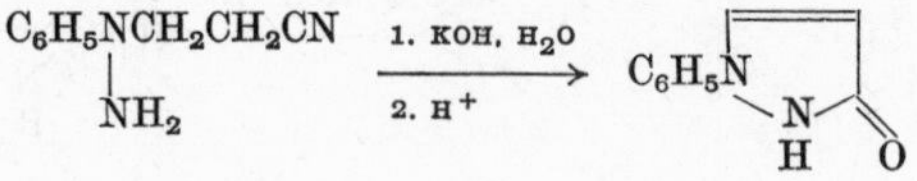

$RC(OC_2H_5)$=$CHCOOC_2H_5$ + $C_6H_5NHNH_2$ ⟶ (109)[1023,1024]

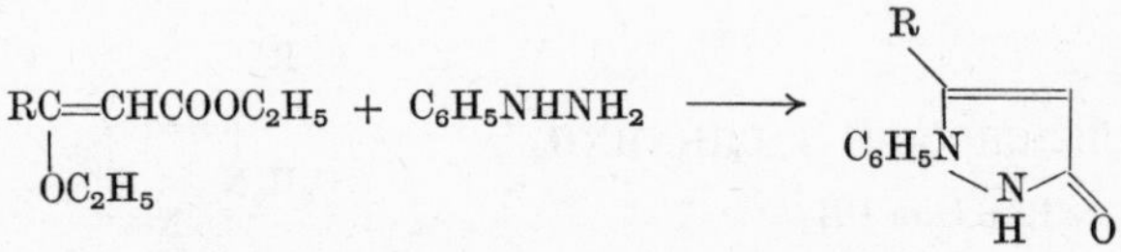

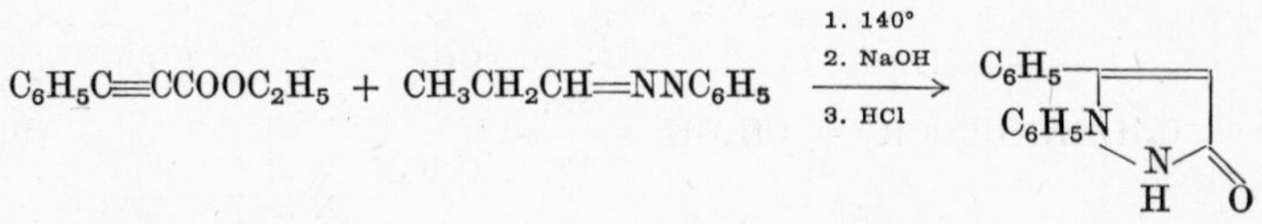

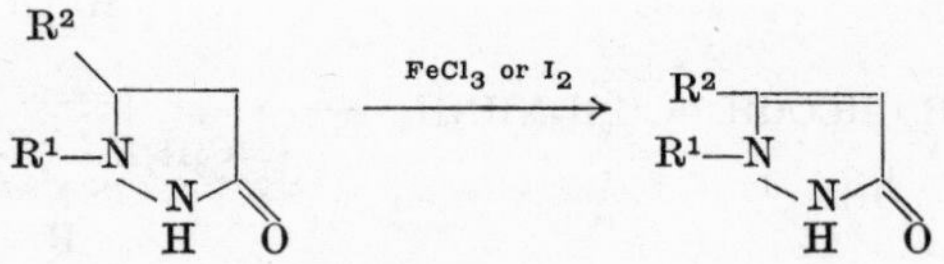

$C_6H_5C{\equiv}CCOOC_2H_5$ + $CH_3CH_2CH{=}NNC_6H_5$ $\xrightarrow{1.\ 140°;\ 2.\ NaOH;\ 3.\ HCl}$ (110)[1042]

$\xrightarrow{FeCl_3\ or\ I_2}$ (111)[56,888]

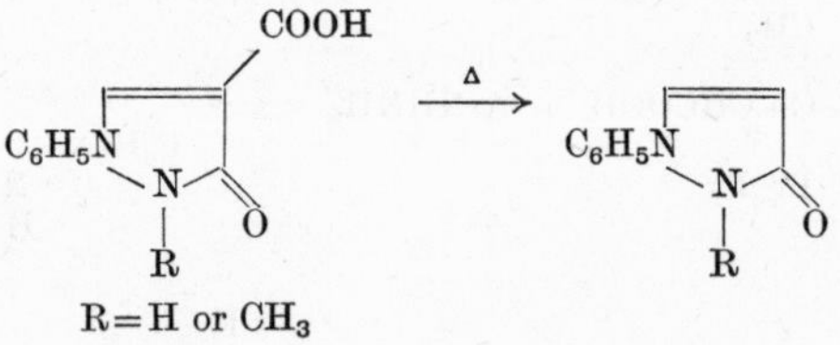

$\xrightarrow{\Delta}$ (112)[108,993]

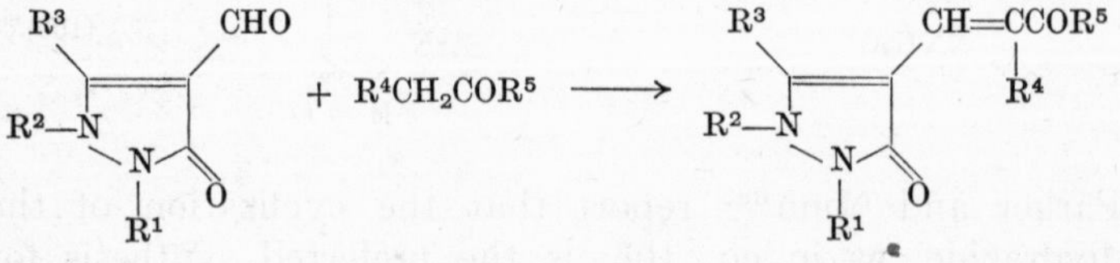

R=H or CH_3

+ $R^4CH_2COR^5$ ⟶ (113)[316,890]

been used in the Pfitzinger reaction with 4-acetyl-2,3-dimethyl-1-phenyl-3-pyrazolin-5-one to give pyrazolinones substituted by quinolines.[903]

(2) *Properties*

Like the 2-pyrazolin-5-ones, most of the 3-pyrazolin-5-ones are solids with a wide range of melting points. Among the 3-pyrazolin-5-ones having only alkyl, heterocyclicalkyl and aryl substituents a number having four substituents are very high boiling liquids. Those having fewer substituents are all solids, as are those substituted by aralkyl and heterocyclic groups. Solubility varies greatly and no generalizations can be made.

In contrast to the 2-pyrazolin-5-ones, the 3-pyrazolin-5-ones are basic, but usually are not acidic[807] or only very weakly so.[1524] It does appear that 3-pyrazolin-5-ones having no N–1 substituent are more acid than those substituted at N–1,[885] presumably because they can tautomerize to the lactim structure (XIII). The basic nature of 3-pyrazolin-5-ones is demonstrated by their ability to form stable hydrochlorides, picrates, methiodides and other salts.[801,818,984] The infrared and ultraviolet absorption of 3-pyrazolin-5-ones has been discussed previously in connection with the structures of these compounds.

The vast majority of reactions undergone by 3-pyrazolin-5-ones occur at the 4-position. These pyrazolinones react by direct substitution, very much as do activated benzene rings. Such reactions as halogenation, nitrosation, sulfonation, acylation, the Mannich reaction and many others give 4-substituted-3-pyrazolin-5-ones.

3-Pyrazolin-5-ones react with formaldehyde to give 4-hydroxymethyl-3-pyrazolin-5-ones (eq. 114).[17] In the presence of phenols

$$\text{(3-}CH_3\text{, 2-}CH_3N\text{, 1-}C_6H_5\text{-3-pyrazolin-5-one)} + CH_2O \longrightarrow \text{(3-}CH_3\text{, 2-}CH_3N\text{, 1-}C_6H_5\text{, 4-}CH_2OH\text{-3-pyrazolin-5-one)} \qquad (114)$$

further condensation occurs, forming 4-benzyl-3-pyrazolin-5-ones (eq. 115).[20,21] The phenol condenses in the para position. A similar reaction occurs with dialkylanilines.[1483] The Mannich reaction is also a reaction

$$\text{(3-}CH_3\text{, 2-}CH_3N\text{, 1-}C_6H_5\text{-3-pyrazolin-5-one)} + C_6H_5OH + CH_2O \longrightarrow \text{(3-}CH_3\text{, 2-}CH_3N\text{, 1-}C_6H_5\text{, 4-}CH_2\text{-}C_6H_4\text{-}OH\text{-3-pyrazolin-5-one)} \qquad (115)$$

with formaldehyde, but in the presence of amines and is readily undergone by 3-pyrazolin-5-ones. With aliphatic amines the products are 4-dialkylaminomethyl-3-pyrazolin-5-ones,[110,637,945] but aniline gives a

4-arylaminomethyl derivative.[1483] When methylaniline is used a bispyrazolinone is also obtained by reaction at the amino group and at the 4-position of the aromatic ring.[1483] Hydroxylamines react analogously to dialkylamines with 3-pyrazolin-5-ones and formaldehyde.[1482] Reactions of 3-pyrazolin-5-ones with chloral[902,1190] are entirely analogous to their reactions with formaldehyde. This is illustrated in eq. 116. The reaction of aromatic aldehydes with 3-pyrazolin-5-ones is

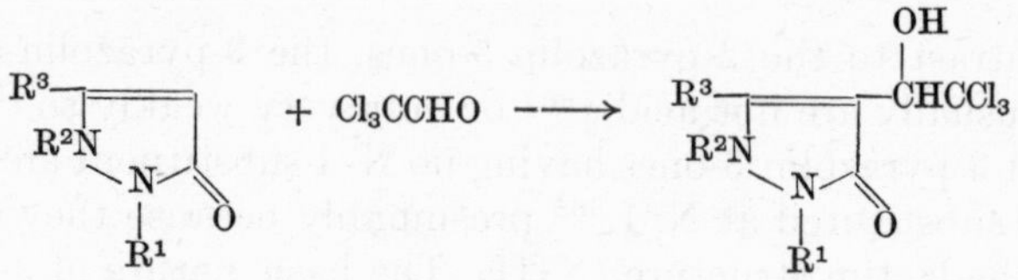

$$\text{3-pyrazolin-5-one} + Cl_3CCHO \longrightarrow \text{4-CH(OH)CCl}_3\text{ derivative} \quad (116)$$

analogous to the reaction of such aldehydes with 2-pyrazolin-5-ones, except that the products are always bispyrazolinones,[21,809,988,992] as shown in eq. 117.

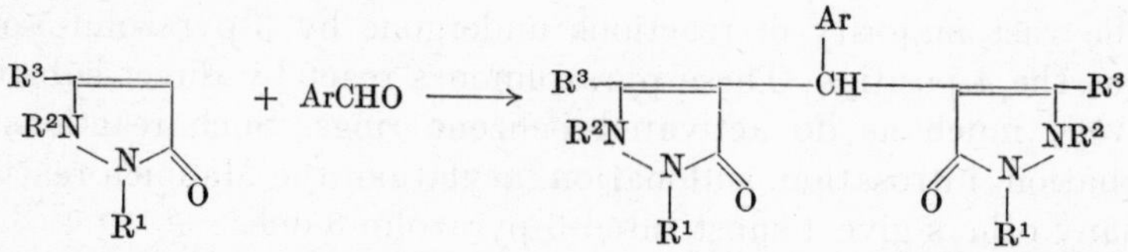

$$\text{3-pyrazolin-5-one} + ArCHO \longrightarrow \text{4,4'-(ArCH)-bis(3-pyrazolin-5-one)} \quad (117)$$

Nitrosation of 3-pyrazolin-5-ones is quite easy, commonly occurring in the 4-position (eq. 118). The usual reagent is nitrous acid,[145,781,809,860,984,992,1174] prepared *in situ* by the use of sodium

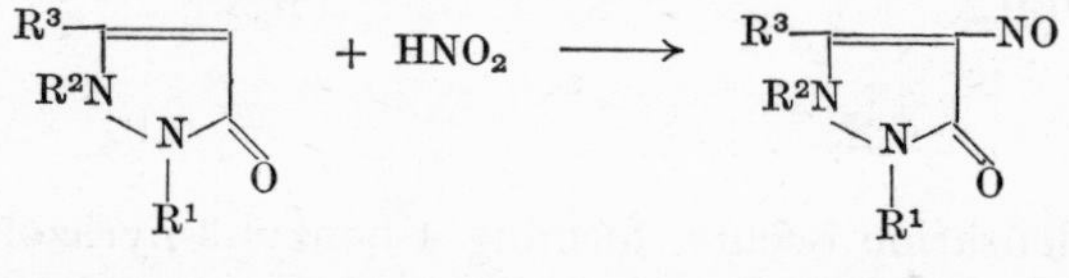

$$\text{3-pyrazolin-5-one} + HNO_2 \longrightarrow \text{4-NO derivative} \quad (118)$$

nitrite and acid. However, nitrogen trioxide has also been used successfully.[1001] If a substituent is present in the 4-position and the 3-position is vacant, nitrosation occurs to give a 3-nitroso-3-pyrazolin-5-one.[972]

Halogenation of 3-pyrazolin-5-ones with elemental chlorine, bromine, and iodine occurs readily to form the corresponding halogenated compounds.[540,809,988,1001,1056] In the case of bromine, addition frequently occurs to give the 3,4-dibromo derivatives (eq. 119) which lose hydrogen bromide very readily and the usual product is the 4-bromo-3-pyrazolin-5-one.[809,818,1024,1320] Various other agents also react with 3-pyrazolin-5-ones to introduce halogen at C–4. Chlorination occurs with sodium hypochlorite[795] and phosphorus pentachloride.[1001]

N-Bromosuccinimide brominates 3-pyrazolin-5-ones but an excess brominates alkyl groups in the 3-position.[362,899] Iodination occurs by treatment of 3-pyrazolin-5-ones with mercuric chloride followed by iodine.[1001]

$$\text{3-pyrazolin-5-one }(R^1,R^2,R^3) \xrightarrow{Br_2} \text{4,4-dibromo adduct} \longrightarrow \text{4-Br-3-pyrazolin-5-one} \qquad (119)$$

3-Pyrazolin-5-ones react with concentrated nitric acid[809,860,888,992,1001] or an excess of nitrous acid[984,992,1001] to form 4-nitro-3-pyrazolin-5-ones. Presumably the excess of nitrous acid first nitrosates and this product is oxidized to the nitro compound.

A variety of miscellaneous reactions which occur by substitution at C–4 are illustrated in the following equations. None of these reactions

$$\text{(CH}_3\text{, CH}_3\text{N, C}_6\text{H}_5\text{)} + ClSO_3H \xrightarrow{NH_3} \text{4-}SO_2NH_2 \text{ derivative} \qquad (120)^{316}$$

$$\text{(CH}_3\text{, CH}_3\text{N, C}_6\text{H}_5\text{)} + CH_2{=}CHCH_2Br \xrightarrow{120°} \text{4,4-bis(}CH_2CH{=}CH_2\text{)-3-}CH_3\text{-2-pyrazolin-5-one, N-}C_6H_5 \qquad (121)^{1321}$$

$$\text{(CH}_3\text{, CH}_3\text{N, C}_6\text{H}_5\text{)} + HCONR^1R^2 \xrightarrow{POCl_3} \text{4-CHO derivative} \qquad (122)^{696}$$

$$\text{(CH}_3\text{, CH}_3\text{N, C}_6\text{H}_5\text{)} + CH_3COCl \longrightarrow \text{4-}COCH_3 \text{ derivative} \qquad (123)^{799}$$

has been used, or investigated, extensively. Benzyl chloride has also been used in reaction (121) and only one benzyl moiety is introduced. Reaction (125) may also give 3-substitution if the 4-position is blocked.[972]

Those 3-pyrazolin-5-ones which have no N–1 substituent can be alkylated at this position by use of methyl iodide in methanol[888,988] or dimethyl sulfate (eq. 126).[1001] *O*-Methylation occurs as a side-

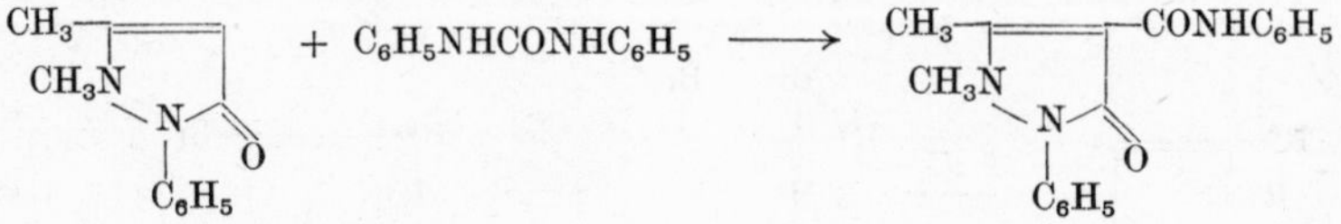

$$\text{(1-phenyl-2,3-dimethyl-3-pyrazolin-5-one)} + C_6H_5NHCONHC_6H_5 \longrightarrow \text{4-}CONHC_6H_5\text{ derivative} \quad (124)^{826}$$

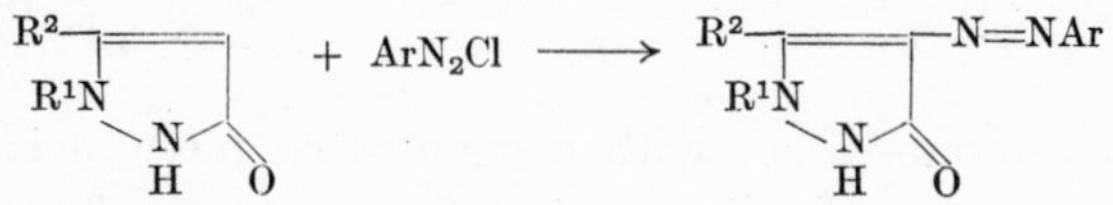

$$\text{(}R^2, R^1N\text{-3-pyrazolin-5-one, N-H)} + ArN_2Cl \longrightarrow \text{4-}N{=}NAr\text{ derivative} \quad (125)^{885,1001}$$

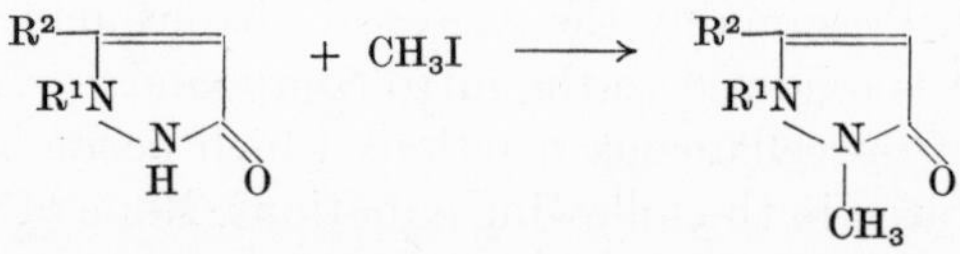

$$\text{(}R^2, R^1N\text{-3-pyrazolin-5-one, N-H)} + CH_3I \longrightarrow \text{N-}CH_3\text{ derivative} \quad (126)$$

reaction. Krohs[860] has reported that halogenated pyridines, pyrimidines and thiazoles in the presence of sodamide react with the oxygen rather than the nitrogen (eq. 127). An analogous reaction occurs between such

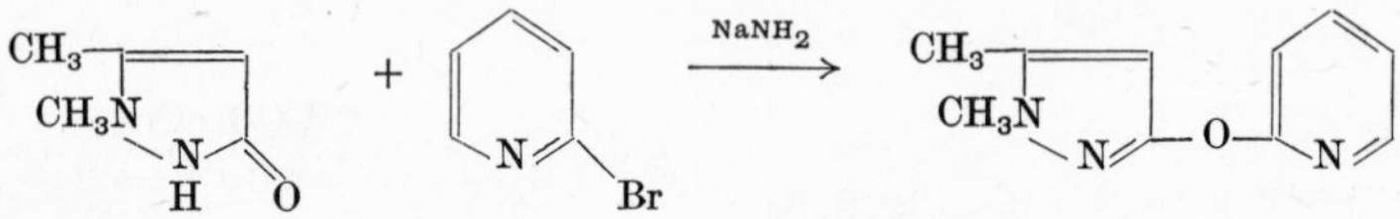

$$\text{(2,3-dimethyl-3-pyrazolin-5-one, N-H)} + \text{2-bromopyridine} \xrightarrow{NaNH_2} \text{5-(2-pyridyloxy)pyrazole} \quad (127)$$

3-pyrazolin-5-ones and benzenesulfonyl chloride and acyl chlorides to give *O*-acylpyrazoles.[988,1001]

The reaction of phosphorus oxychloride with 3-pyrazolin-5-ones is rather similar to the reaction with 2-pyrazolin-5-ones in that oxygen is replaced by halogen. In those cases in which there is no substitution at N–1 and aryl substitution occurs at N–2, chloropyrazoles are formed,

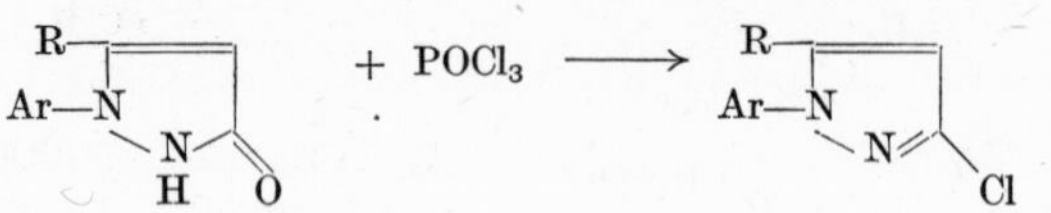

$$\text{(R, Ar—N-3-pyrazolin-5-one, N-H)} + POCl_3 \longrightarrow \text{(R, Ar—N, 5-Cl pyrazole)} \quad (128)$$

$$\text{(}R^2, R^1N\text{-3-pyrazolin-5-one, N-H)} + POCl_3 \longrightarrow \text{(}R^2\text{, 5-Cl pyrazole, N-H)} + R^1Cl \quad (129)$$

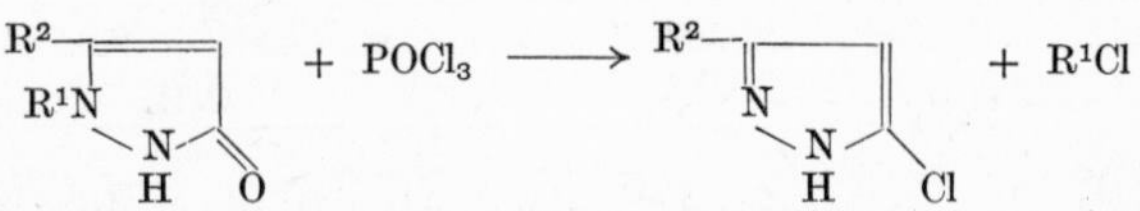

as shown in eq. 128.[984,988,1001] This reaction takes a different course when the N–2 substituent is alkyl or aralkyl.[700,795] In these cases the N–2 substituent is eliminated (eq. 129). In cases in which both nitrogen atoms are substituted, the 3-pyrazolin-5-one is converted to a quaternary salt of a 5-chloropyrazole (eq. 130).[789]

The 3-pyrazolin-5-one ring is stable to mild catalytic reductions, such as reduction with low pressure hydrogen in the presence of platinum or palladium catalyst.[532,860] However, under extremely drastic conditions, hydrogen at a pressure of 1000 atmospheres and a temperature of 180° and nickel catalyst, ring cleavage occurs[859] with elimination of one nitrogen atom and formation of anilides (eq. 131).

$$R^3, R^2N, N\text{-}R^1, O \text{ (3-pyrazolin-5-one)} + POCl_3 \longrightarrow \left[R^3, R^2N, N\text{-}R^1, Cl \right]^+ Cl^- \qquad (130)$$

$$R^3, R^4, R^2N, N\text{-}R^1, O \text{ (3-pyrazolin-5-one)} \longrightarrow R^3CH_2CH(R^4)CONHR^1 \qquad (131)$$

Hot acid destroys the ring system of 3-pyrazolin-5-ones.[700,807] Various products have been reported from this reaction, depending upon substituents in the pyrazolinone ring and conditions. Destruction of the 3-pyrazolin-5-one ring system with base[700] leads to a β-ketoanilide.

The reaction of zinc with 2,3-dimethyl-1-phenyl-3-pyrazolin-5-one has been reported by Knorr[807] to give benzene, aniline and unidentified products. Heymons and Rohland[647] treated 1,2-diphenyl-3-methyl-3-pyrazolin-5-one with metallic sodium, obtaining addition of sodium at the 1,4-position of the conjugated system present (eq. 132).

$$CH_3, C_6H_5N, N\text{-}C_6H_5, O \text{ (3-pyrazolin-5-one)} \xrightarrow{Na} CH_3, Na, C_6H_5N, N\text{-}C_6H_5, ONa \qquad (132)$$

The compounds discussed in the previous sections are listed in Sections A, B, C, and D of Table XIV.

3-Pyrazolin-5-ones having 3- and 4-α-hydroxyalkyl substituents are prepared in a number of ways. Two of these, alkylation of the corresponding 2-pyrazolin-5-one at N–2 and reaction of 3-pyrazolin-5-ones with aliphatic aldehydes, have already been mentioned. The reduction of 4-acyl substituents will be discussed in the section dealing with such 3-pyrazolin-5-ones. A fourth method used has been the hydrolysis of 3-bromomethyl-3-pyrazolin-5-ones at elevated temperatures (eq. 133).[532,697] The reactions of these compounds are those of

$BrCH_2$, C_2H_5, CH_3N, N, O, $4\text{-}NO_2C_6H_4$ $\xrightarrow[H_2O]{120°}$ $HOCH_2$, C_2H_5, CH_3N, N, O, $4\text{-}NO_2C_6H_4$ (133)

alcohols and esters and of 3-pyrazolin-5-ones, except for a few special ones. 4-Hydroxymethyl-3-pyrazolin-5-ones in mild acid solution form 4,4′-bis(3-pyrazolin-5-ones) (eq. 134).[970] The alcohols obtained by con-

CH_3, CH_2OH, CH_3N, N, O, C_6H_5 $\longrightarrow$ CH_3, CH_2, CH_3, CH_3N, NCH_3, N, O, O, N, C_6H_5, C_6H_5 (134)

densing chloral with 3-pyrazolin-5-ones decompose in the presence of potassium carbonate to give the corresponding 4-carboxaldehydes (eq. 135).[107,196,889] This is the principal method used for preparation

R^3, $CHCCl_3$, R^2N, OH, N, O, R^1 $\xrightarrow[H_2O]{K_2CO_3}$ R^2, CHO, R^2N, N, O, R^1 (135)

of such aldehydes. These compounds are listed in Table XIV, Section E.

Bodendorf and Ziegler[113] have reported the conversion of a 4-(1-hydroxy-2-methylaminopropyl)-3-pyrazolin-5-one into a 4-(2-oxopropyl)-3-pyrazolin-5-one in the presence of acid (eq. 136).

CH_3, OH, $CHCHCH_3$, CH_3N, $NHCH_3$, N, O, C_6H_5 $\cdot HCl$ $\xrightarrow{HCl}$ CH_3, CH_2COCH_3, CH_3N, N, O, C_6H_5 (136)

Only a few α-alkylthiomethyl-3-pyrazolin-5-ones are known.[1127] These have been prepared by reaction of mercaptans with 4-dimethylaminomethyl-2,3-dimethyl-1-phenyl-3-pyrazolin-5-one (eq. 137). These compounds are listed in Table XIV, Section E.

The most frequently used method of preparation of compounds having nitrogen attached to a carbon atom which is substituted on the 3-pyrazolin-5-one ring is reaction of hydroxylamine, amines, hydrazines, hydrazides, etc., with 5-oxo-3-pyrazolin-4-carboxaldehydes.

CH_3, $CH_2N(CH_3)_2$, CH_3N, N, O, C_6H_5 + RSH ⟶ CH_3, CH_2SR, CH_3N, N, O, C_6H_5 (137)

This will be discussed in more detail in the section devoted to the reactions of the 4-carboxaldehydes. A frequently used method for preparing 4-dialkylaminomethyl-3-pyrazolin-5-ones is the Hoffmann method for preparing amines (eq. 138).[697,1318,1319] A rather interesting

$BrCH_2$, R^3, R^2N, N, O, R^1 + R_2NH ⟶ R_2NCH_2, R^3, R^2N, N, O, R^1 (138)

synthesis of 4-benzamidomethyl-3-pyrazolin-5-ones has been published by Monti.[1014] *N*-Methylolbenzamide was condensed with 2,3-dimethyl-1-phenyl-3-pyrazolin-5-one (eq. 139).

CH_3, CH_3N, N, O, C_6H_5 + $C_6H_5CONHCH_2OH$ ⟶ CH_3, $CH_2NHCOC_6H_5$, CH_3N, N, O, C_6H_5 (139)

The reactions of these compounds are for the most part normal for such functional groups. The only unusual one reported is the rearrangement shown in eq. 140.[110,1483] Hellmann and Schumacher[638] have

CH_3, $CH_2NHC_6H_5$, CH_3N, N, O, C_6H_5 —1.0 N HCl⟶ CH_3, CH_2–C_6H_4–NH_2, CH_3N, N, O, C_6H_5 (140)

reported that 4-dimethylaminomethyl-3-pyrazolin-5-ones can react as alkylating agents. Nitro- and formamidomalonic esters react with these pyrazolinones by elimination of dimethylamine and introduction of the 5-oxo-3-pyrazolin-4-methyl system into the malonic ester (eq. 141).

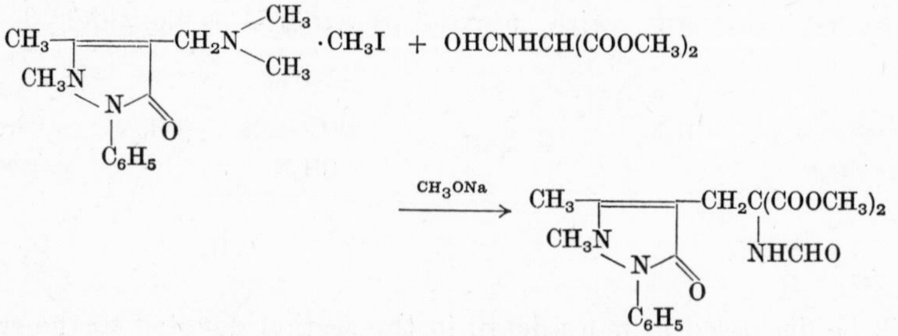

$$CH_3 \quad CH_2N(CH_3)_2 \cdot CH_3I + OHCNHCH(COOCH_3)_2 \quad CH_3N \quad N \quad O \quad C_6H_5$$

$$\xrightarrow{CH_3ONa} CH_3 \quad CH_2C(COOCH_3)_2 \quad CH_3N \quad NHCHO \quad N \quad O \quad C_6H_5 \qquad (141)$$

This reaction is quite analogous to such alkylations with gramine. These compounds are listed in Table XIV, Section F.

(3) *Bis*(3-*pyrazolin*-5-*ones*)

Only a very few 4,4′-bis(3-pyrazolin-5-ones) are known in which the rings are linked directly. These are prepared by methylation of 4,4′-bis(2-pyrazolin-5-ones)[807,809] or by treatment of the methiodides of 4-(5-chloropyrazol-4-yl)-3-pyrazolin-5-ones with alkali.[991] These compounds are listed in Table XV.

Bis(3-pyrazolin-5-ones) in which the linking chain is not attached to the pyrazolinone nucleus by functional groups are listed in Tables XVI and XVII. Most of these compounds have as the linking chain an arylidene group and are prepared by the reaction of 3-pyrazolin-5-ones with aryl aldehydes,[566,568,569,807,1001,1133] as shown in eq. 117 (p. 50). Some aliphatic aldehydes have also been used in this reaction.[409] 3-Pyrazolin-5-ones react with formaldehyde or formamide to form the corresponding bis compounds (eq. 142).[910,1192] Under basic conditions

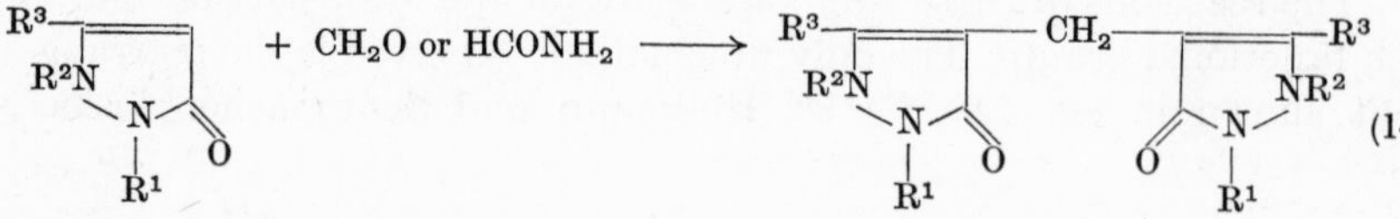

$$R^3 \quad R^2N \quad N \quad O \quad R^1 + CH_2O \text{ or } HCONH_2 \longrightarrow R^3 \quad CH_2 \quad R^3 \quad R^2N \quad NR^2 \quad N \quad O \quad O \quad N \quad R^1 \quad R^1 \qquad (142)$$

4-hydroxymethyl-3-pyrazolin-5-ones condense to form bispyrazolinones (eq. 134),[107,481,896] apparently by partial elimination of the 4-hydroxymethyl group and the condensation of this product with unchanged starting material. Bis(2-pyrazolin-5-ones) can be converted into the corresponding 3-pyrazolin-5-ones by alkylation at N–2,[116] as is done so frequently in the mononuclear series. 4,4′-Methylenebis(3-pyrazolin-5-ones) have been prepared by reduction of the corresponding ketone with zinc and acid.[740] A variety of 3-pyrazolin-5-ones having a 4-acyl substituent react with various reagents to form bis(3-pyrazolin-5-ones).[316,799,902] These preparations are illustrated in eqs. 143–145. The

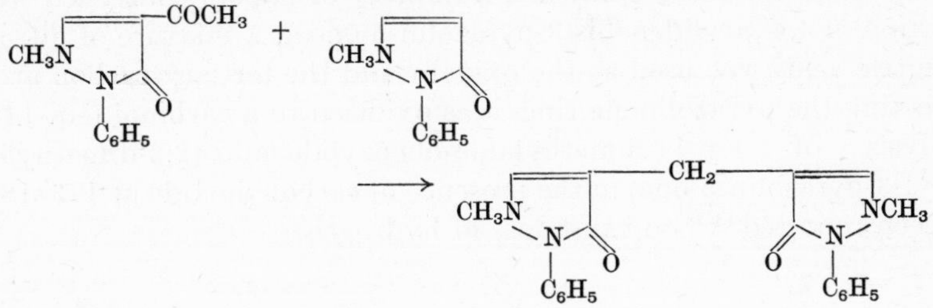

$$\text{1-phenyl-2-methyl-4-}COCH_3\text{-3-pyrazolin-5-one} + \text{1-phenyl-2-methyl-3-pyrazolin-5-one} \longrightarrow \text{bis(1-}C_6H_5\text{-2-}CH_3\text{-3-pyrazolin-5-on-4-yl)}CH_2 \quad (143)$$

$$\text{1-}C_6H_5\text{-2,3-di}CH_3\text{-4-}CHO\text{-3-pyrazolin-5-one} + CH_3COCH_3 \xrightarrow{OH^-} \text{pyrazolinone-}CH{=}CHCOCH{=}CH\text{-pyrazolinone} \quad (144)$$

$$\text{1-}R^1\text{-2-}R^2\text{-3-}R^3\text{-4-}(R^4C{=}O)\text{-3-pyrazolin-5-one} + NH_2NH_2 \longrightarrow \text{pyrazolinone-}C(R^4){=}NN{=}C(R^4)\text{-pyrazolinone} \quad (145)$$

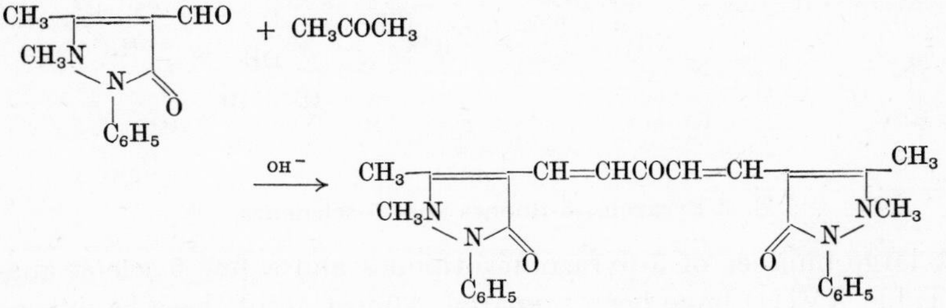

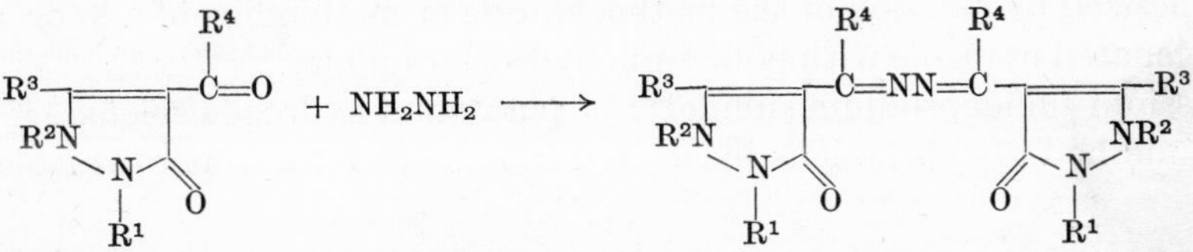

Mannich reaction using primary amines, when applied to 3-pyrazolin-5-ones, forms bispyrazolinones.[945] Two more preparations of such compounds are shown in eqs. 146 and 147.

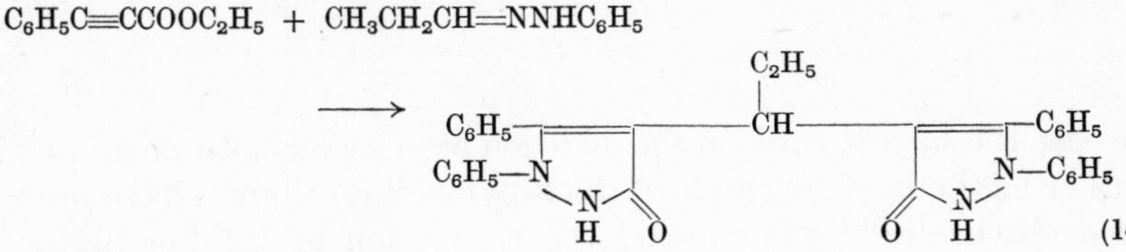

$$C_6H_5C{\equiv}CCOOC_2H_5 + CH_3CH_2CH{=}NNHC_6H_5 \longrightarrow \text{bis(2,3-di}C_6H_5\text{-1-H-3-pyrazolin-5-on-4-yl)}CH(C_2H_5) \quad (146)^{1042}$$

$$\text{1-}C_6H_5\text{-2,3-di}CH_3\text{-4-}CH(C_6H_5)NHC_6H_5\text{-3-pyrazolin-5-one} \xrightarrow[\Delta]{HCl} \text{bis(1-}C_6H_5\text{-2,3-di}CH_3\text{-3-pyrazolin-5-on-4-yl)}CH(C_6H_5) \quad (147)^{1094}$$

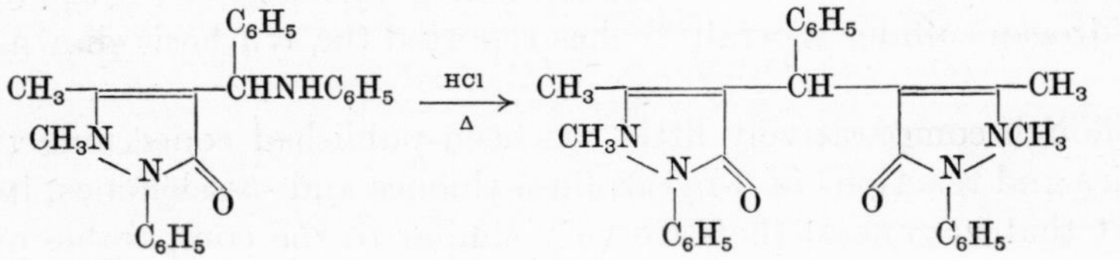

Very little investigation of the reactions of bis(3-pyrazolin-5-ones) has been done, but presumably the typical reactions occurring at C–4 in the mononuclear compounds would not occur. Ginzburg and coworkers[566,568,569] have published a number of papers concerned with oxidation of 4,4′-arylidenebis(3-pyrazolin-5-ones). A mixture of nitrous and nitric acids was used as the oxidant and the tertiary carbon atom connecting the pyrazolinone rings was oxidized to a carbinol (eq. 148). Pyrolysis of 4,4′-(4-dimethylaminobenzylidene)bis(2,3-dimethyl-1-phenyl-3-pyrazolin-5-one) in the presence of carbon dioxide at 175–180° has been reported[1133] to cause loss of hydrogen.

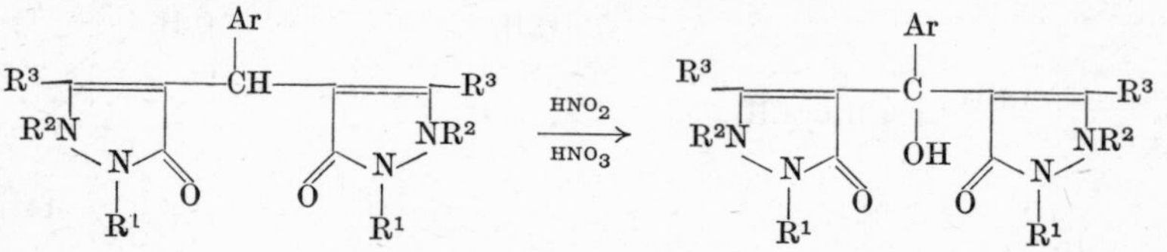

$$\text{Ar–CH(pyrazolinone: }R^3, R^2N, N–R^1, C{=}O)_2 \xrightarrow[HNO_3]{HNO_2} \text{Ar–C(OH)(pyrazolinone: }R^3, R^2N, N–R^1, C{=}O)_2 \qquad (148)$$

E. 3-Pyrazolin-5-thiones and -5-selenones

A large number of 3-pyrazolin-5-thiones and a few 5-seleno analogs (Table XVIII) have been prepared. Almost all of these have been synthesized by reaction of the methochloride or methiodide of a 3- or 5-halogenated pyrazole with potassium hydrogen sulfide,[844,984,986,988,992] potassium sulfide, sodium sulfide[981] or potassium hydrogen selenide.[986] This method of synthesis is illustrated in eq. 149 for a 5-halopyrazole.

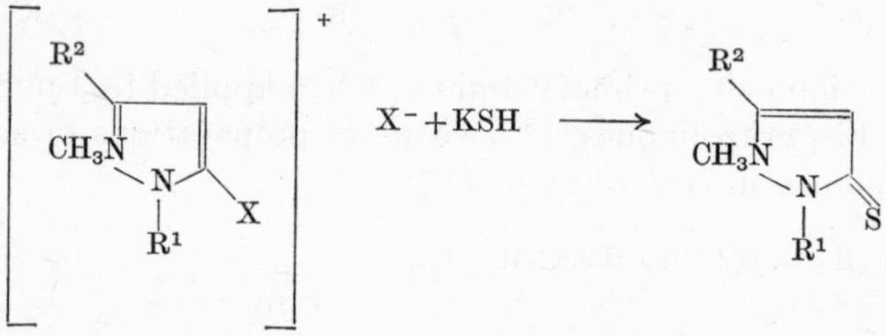

$$\left[\text{pyrazolium: }R^2, CH_3N, N–R^1, X\right]^+ X^- + KSH \longrightarrow \text{pyrazolinethione: }R^2, CH_3N, N–R^1, C{=}S \qquad (149)$$

In one case the substituents on the nitrogen atoms were both phenyl.[789] Two other methods of synthesis of the 3-pyrazolin-5-thiones have been reported. Michaelis[992] has claimed the conversion of 1,2-dimethyl-3-phenyl-3-pyrazolin-5-one to the thione analog by reaction with potassium hydrogen sulfide. Worrall[1653] has reported the synthesis shown in eq. 150.

Although comparatively little has been published concerning the properties and reactions of 3-pyrazolin-5-thiones and -5-selenones, it is apparent that in general they are very similar to the comparable oxo compounds. These compounds are basic, forming stable salts with mineral acids.[978,984,988] They undergo nitration at C–4 and presumably would react similarly in other electrophilic substitutions. Reaction with

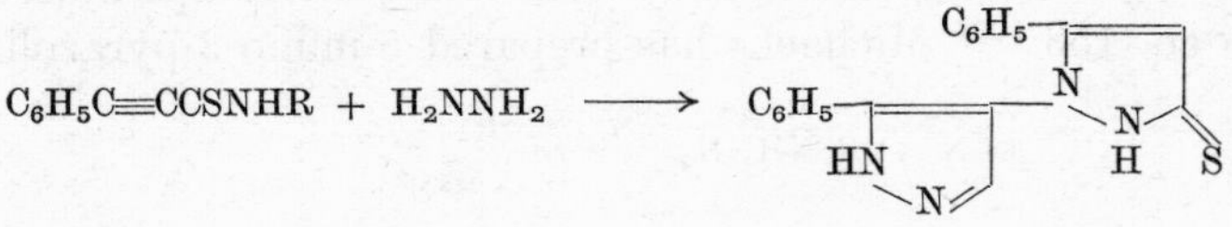

$$C_6H_5C{\equiv}CCSNHR + H_2NNH_2 \longrightarrow \quad (150)$$

halogens gives a perhalide having four atoms of halogen per molecule of pyrazolinone.[988,992] These then lose halogen readily to leave a dihalo derivative, which is probably the corresponding 4,5-dihalo-3-pyrazolidinethione or -3-pyrazolidineselenone. Alkylation of the sulfur or selenium atom occurs by heating the methiodide (eq. 151)[984,988,992] or other

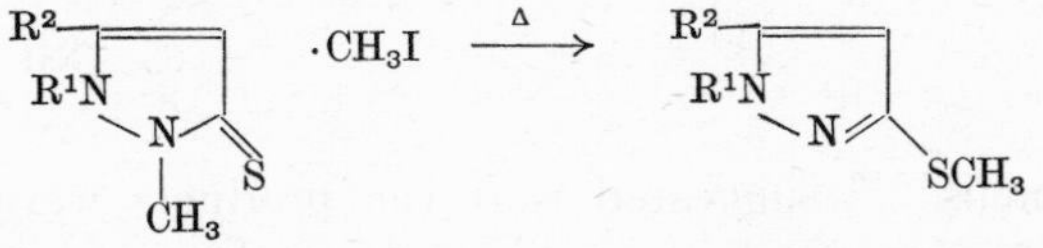

$$\cdot CH_3I \xrightarrow{\Delta} \quad (151)$$

alkyl iodides. The 3-pyrazolin-5-thiones are capable of oxidation at the sulfur atom and several such oxidation products have been reported. Kitamura[785,789] has found that oxidation of 2,3-dimethyl-1-phenyl-3-pyrazolin-5-thione with hydrogen peroxide gives 2,3-dimethyl-1-phenyl-3-pyrazolin-5-one. Komada[845] has oxidized the same compound with chlorine, hydrogen peroxide, sodium hypochloride and perbenzoic acid to give what was called a dioxide, the structure of which was not reported. The oxidation of various 3-pyrazolin-5-thiones with peroxide[785,789] or with chlorine[978,985,988,1001] gives what was called a trioxide. It is possible that this is a zwitterion as shown in eq. 152. A

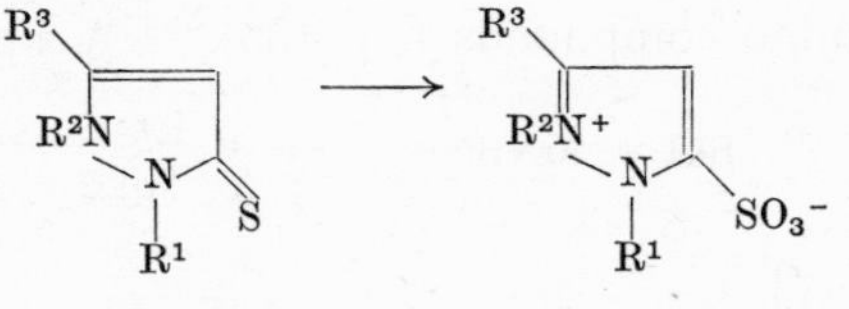

$$\longrightarrow \quad (152)$$

few 5-oxo-5′-thiono-, 5,5′-thiono- and 5,5′-selenobis(3-pyrazolines) have been prepared by methods used for the mono compounds and they are listed in Table XV.[785,986,991]

F. 5-Imino-3-pyrazolines

A number of 5-imino-3-pyrazolines are known and are listed in Table XIX. Those which have no substituent at N–1 can exist as aminopyrazoles and probably are in this tautomeric form. Most preparative methods for these compounds depend upon conversion of chloropyrazoles or 3-pyrazolin-5-ones to 5-imino-3-pyrazolines, although they can be formed directly from noncyclic compounds. This is shown in eq. 153.[1025] Michaelis has prepared 5-imino-3-pyrazolines by

$$R^1C{\equiv}CCN + R^2NHNH_2 \longrightarrow \text{(ring: } R^1\text{, } R^2N\text{, } \underset{H}{N}\text{, =NH)} \qquad (153)$$

reaction of the methochlorides of chloropyrazoles with ammonia or amines (eq. 154).[985,996,1352] From an analogous reaction with aryl-

$$\text{(ring: } R^2\text{, N, } \underset{R^1}{N}\text{, Cl)}\cdot CH_3Cl \xrightarrow{NH_3} \text{(ring: } R^2\text{, } CH_3N\text{, } \underset{R^1}{N}\text{, =NH)} \qquad (154)$$

amines Michaelis[1002] suggested that the products were of the type (XXVII). It seems much more likely that these were 5-arylimino-3

$$\text{(bicyclic: } R^2\text{, } R^1N\text{, N–Ar, N–Ar)}$$

(XXVII)

pyrazolines. 5-Imino-3-pyrazolines can also be prepared by treatment of 5-imino-2-pyrazoline methiodides with sodium hydroxide.[996]

3-Pyrazolin-5-one hydrochlorides react with hydrazines at about 100° to form 5-imino compounds (eq. 155).[983] A similar reaction has

$$\text{(ring: } R^3\text{, } R^2N\text{, } \underset{R^1}{N}\text{, =O)}\cdot HCl + ArNHNH_2 \longrightarrow \text{(ring: } R^3\text{, } R^2N\text{, } \underset{R^1}{N}\text{, =NNHAr)} \qquad (155)$$

been reported for 3-pyrazolin-5-thiones.[1653] Other syntheses are shown in equations 156[826] and 157.[402] Very little has been published concerning reactions and properties of these compounds.

$$\text{(ring: } CH_3\text{, } C_6H_5N\text{, } \underset{H}{N}\text{, =O)} + C_6H_5NH_2\cdot HCl + POCl_3 \longrightarrow \text{(ring: } CH_3\text{, } C_6H_5N\text{, } \underset{H}{N}\text{, =NC}_6H_5) \qquad (156)$$

A few 5-imino- and 5,5′-iminobis(3-pyrazolines) are listed in Table XV. These are prepared by reaction of the appropriate chloropyrazole methiodide with ammonia.[991]

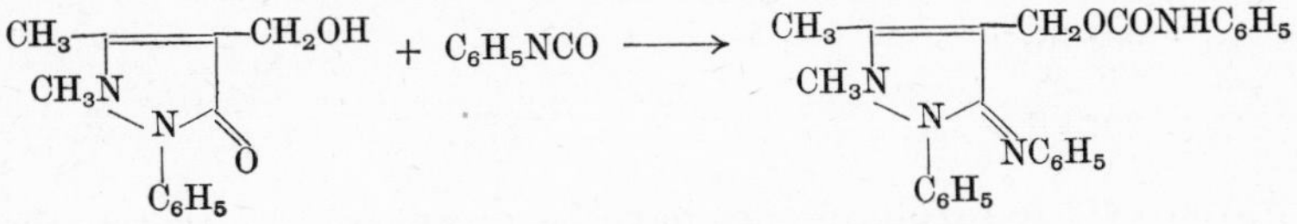

CH_3, CH_2OH, CH_3N, N, O, C_6H_5 + C_6H_5NCO ⟶ CH_3, $CH_2OCONHC_6H_5$, CH_3N, N, NC_6H_5, C_6H_5 (157)

3. Hydroxy and Mercapto Derivatives

A. 2-Pyrazolin-5-ones

Both 3-hydroxy- and 4-hydroxy-2-pyrazolin-5-ones can exist theoretically and quite a number of 4-hydroxy compounds are known. The 3-hydroxy-2-pyrazolin-5-ones are tautomeric with 3,5-pyrazolidinediones which probably exist principally as the 3-hydroxy isomers. However, for the purposes of this discussion these compounds will be considered as diones.

The most widely used and certainly most general procedure for preparation of 4-hydroxy-2-pyrazolin-5-ones is that developed by Veibel, Linholt and Westoo.[1525–1528] Usually oxidations of 2-pyrazolin-5-ones lead to formation of bispyrazolinones. These workers found that oxidation of 1-substituted-2-pyrazolin-5-ones in alkaline solutions gave very good yields of the 4-hydroxy analogs (eq. 158). Oxidizing agents

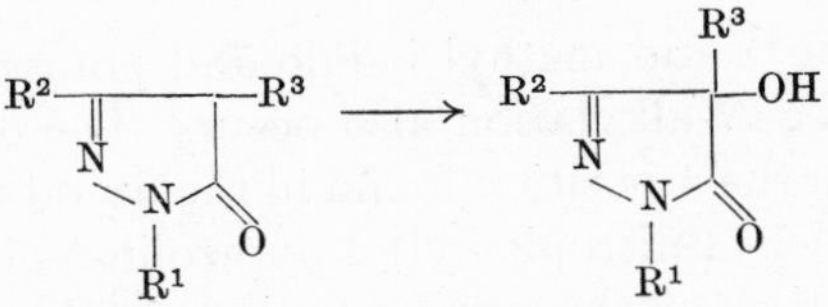

R^2, R^3, N, N, O, R^1 ⟶ R^3, R^2, OH, N, N, O, R^1 (158)

used were hydroperoxides and oxygen. Acid media were also found to suppress the formation of bis(2-pyrazolin-5-ones). Various other methods have been used for preparation of 4-hydroxy-2-pyrazolin-5-ones but none extensively. Thoms and Schmupp[1491] have used catalytic reduction of 2-pyrazolin-4,5-diones. The 4-oxo group is reduced to hydroxyl in preference to other unsaturated centers. Bülow and Haas,[262] in reducing 4-phenylazo- and 4-nitro-2-pyrazolin-5-ones with zinc and acetic acid, obtained as side-products 4-hydroxy-2-pyrazolin-5-ones. The oxidation of 4,4′-bis[3-methyl-1-(4-nitrophenyl)-2-pyrazolin-5-one] with ferric chloride forms the corresponding mononuclear 4,4′-dihydroxy compound.[690] The condensation of α-acyloxy-β-ketoesters with an equivalent of phenylhydrazine gives rise to a 4-acyloxypyrazolinone, but excess phenylhydrazine forms the 4-hydroxy analog (eq. 159).[372]

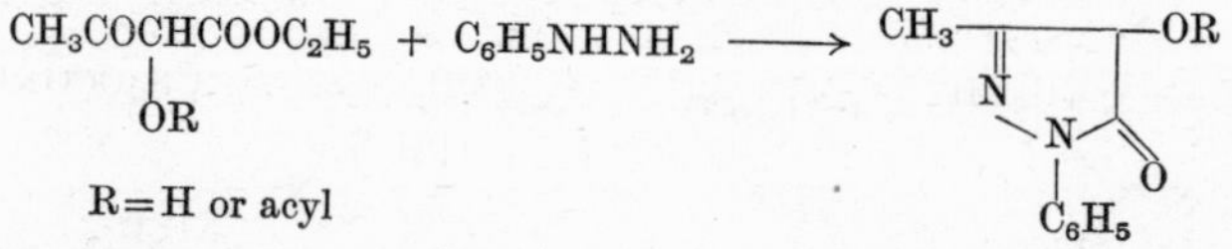

$$CH_3COCH(OR)COOC_2H_5 + C_6H_5NHNH_2 \longrightarrow \text{3-}CH_3\text{-4-}OR\text{-1-}C_6H_5\text{-2-pyrazolin-5-one} \qquad (159)$$

R=H or acyl

3-Alkoxy-2-pyrazolin-5-ones have been prepared by two methods. In one of these a hydrazine is condensed with a β-substituted ester (eq. 160).[598,1143] The second is *O*-alkylation of a 4,4-disubstituted-1-substituted-3,5-pyrazolidinedione (eq. 161). The reagents used have

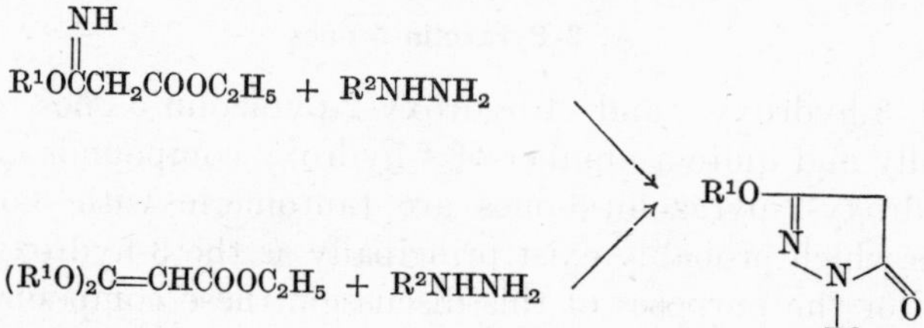

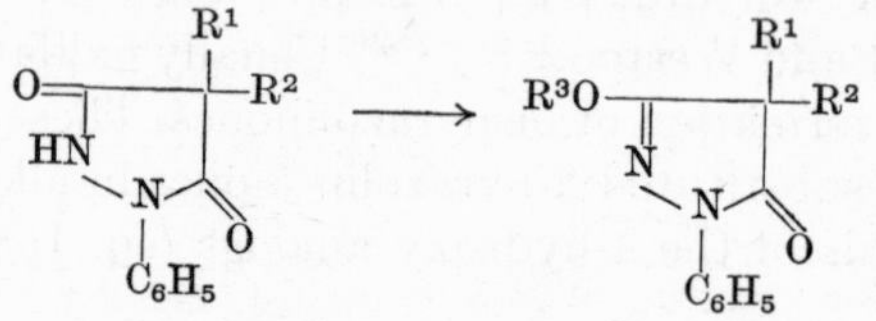

$$R^1OC(=NH)CH_2COOC_2H_5 + R^2NHNH_2 \text{ or } (R^1O)_2C{=}CHCOOC_2H_5 + R^2NHNH_2 \longrightarrow \text{3-}R^1O\text{-1-}R^2\text{-2-pyrazolin-5-one} \qquad (160)$$

$$\text{4-}R^1\text{-4-}R^2\text{-1-}C_6H_5\text{-3,5-pyrazolidinedione} \longrightarrow \text{3-}R^3O\text{-4-}R^1\text{-4-}R^2\text{-1-}C_6H_5\text{-2-pyrazolin-5-one} \qquad (161)$$

been diazomethane[41] and methyl iodide and potassium hydroxide.[994] With diazomethane *N*-alkylation also occurs. The only example with an alkoxy group in the 4-position found in the literature is 4-hydroxy-4-methoxy-3-methyl-1-(4-nitrophenyl)-2-pyrazolin-5-one, obtained by repeated crystallization of the corresponding 4,4-dihydroxy compound from methanol.[690]

One method of preparing acyloxy-2-pyrazolin-5-ones has already been mentioned (eq. 159). The second method is acylation of 3,5-pyrazolidinediones having no N-2 substituent (eq. 162). The acylations

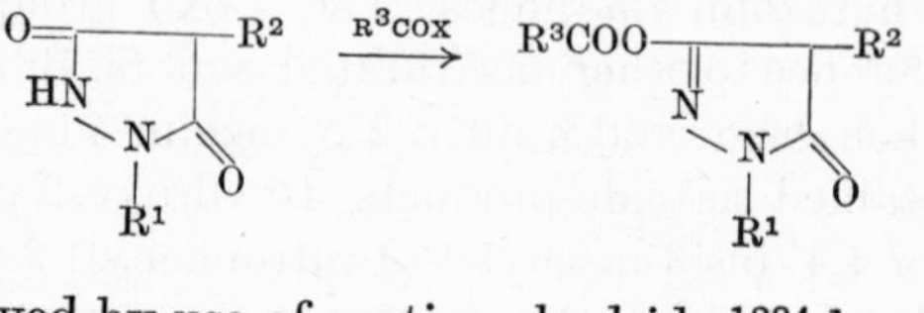

$$\text{4-}R^2\text{-1-}R^1\text{-3,5-pyrazolidinedione} \xrightarrow{R^3COX} \text{3-}R^3COO\text{-4-}R^2\text{-1-}R^1\text{-2-pyrazolin-5-one} \qquad (162)$$

have been achieved by use of acetic anhydride,[1234] benzoyl chloride[998] and by trans-esterification.[200]

A number of 4-arylmercapto-2-pyrazolin-5-ones have been prepared by reaction of a 2-pyrazolin-5-one with aryl mercaptans (eq. 163).[27,28] It was concluded that the first reaction was oxidation of the

$$\text{3-}CH_3\text{-1-}C_6H_5\text{-2-pyrazolin-5-one} + ArSH \longrightarrow \text{3-}CH_3\text{-4-}SAr\text{-1-}C_6H_5\text{-2-pyrazolin-5-one} \quad (163)$$

mercaptan to a disulfide which then reacted with the pyrazolin-5-one. In support of this theory it was found that disulfides give the same reaction. The same types of compounds were also prepared by reaction of 4-bromo-3-methyl-1-phenyl-2-pyrazolin-5-one with the sodium salts of various mercaptans.[27,28] Takahashi and Yoshii[1474] have treated 6-ethoxy-5-methyl-6-carbethoxypyrido-[2,3:2′,3′]-*p*-thiazine with hydrazine and obtained a 4-arylmercapto-2-pyrazolin-5-one. This is scarcely a practical synthetic method. α-Arylmercapto- and α-acylmercaptoacetoacetic esters react with hydrazines to give sulfur-containing substituents at C–4.[27]

This group of compounds is listed in Table XX.

A few bis(2-pyrazolin-5-ones) having alkoxy substituents are known and are listed in Table III. These are prepared by addition of alcohols to the double bond connecting the pyrazolinone rings in pyrazole blue.

A few 4,4′-bis(2-pyrazolin-5-ones) in which the rings are linked by sulfur atoms are known. The linking group is almost always disulfide and is prepared by oxidation of 2-pyrazolin-5-ones substituted in the 4-position with mercaptoaryl groups.[578] These compounds are listed in Table VII.

The few 3-acyloxy-5-imino-2-pyrazolines known are prepared by acylation of 5-imino-3-pyrazolidinones.[391,594,1599] Crippa and Gaumeri[32] have treated 3-methyl-1-phenyl-5-imino-2-pyrazoline with *p*-nitrophenylsulfenyl chloride to obtain a 4-arylmercapto compound. These compounds are listed in Table XII.

B. 3-Pyrazolin-5-ones

The two possible hydroxy-3-pyrazolin-5-ones (3-hydroxy and 4-hydroxy) are isomeric with pyrazolidinediones, the former with 3,5-pyrazolidinediones and the latter with 3,4-pyrazolidinediones. In conformity with the usage of this discussion the hydroxy-3-pyrazolin-5-ones will be considered as the isomeric diones. However, the derivatives of the hydroxyl groups will be considered in this section. Konek and Szasz[783] have methylated 4-acyloxy-3-methyl-1-phenyl-2-pyrazolin-5-ones at N–2 with methyl iodide to give the 4-acyloxy-3-pyrazolin-5-ones. Treatment of 3,5-pyrazolidinediones having no substituent at the 4-position with diazomethane has been used by Arndt and coworkers[41] to give 3-methoxy-3-pyrazolin-5-ones. It is necessary to have a 2-substituent. 3-Acyloxy-3-pyrazolin-5-ones have been prepared in a similar fashion by acylation of 3,5-pyrazolidinediones.[200,1048] A number of 4-acyloxy-3-pyrazolin-5-ones have been synthesized by the reaction of 2,3-dimethyl-1-phenyl-3,4-pyrazolidinedione with various chlorinated aromatic compounds (eq. 164). The halogen in the aromatic halide was

CH_3, CH_3N, N, C_6H_5, =O, O + ArCl ⟶ CH_3, –OAr, CH_3N, N, C_6H_5, O (164)

usually quite active, for example picryl chloride. The preparation of sulfur analogs of these compounds according to eq. 165 has been

CH_3, CH_3N, N, C_6H_5, O + $CH_2SC_6H_5$, OH (naphthalene) ⟶ CH_3, –SCH_2–, OH (naphthalene), CH_3N, N, C_6H_5, O (165)

reported by Poppelsdorf and Holt.[1127] These compounds are listed in Table XXI. The only bis(3-pyrazolin-5-one) having alkoxy or aryloxy substituents has been prepared as shown in eq. 164, except that a disubstituted aromatic compound was used.[744] This compound is included in Table XVI.

Bis(3-pyrazolin-5-ones) having the 4,4′-positions connected by a disulfide bridge have been prepared by the action of sulfur dichloride on 2,3-dimethyl-1-phenyl-3-pyrazolin-5-one (eq. 166).[8,848] The same

CH_3, CH_3N, N, C_6H_5, O + S_2Cl_2 ⟶ CH_3, CH_3N, N, C_6H_5 –S—S– CH_3, NCH_3, N, O, C_6H_5 (166)

type of compound is formed as a by-product in the reaction of 4-bromo-2,3-dimethyl-1-phenyl-3-pyrazolin-5-one with potassium thiocyanate to form the 4-thiocyano compound[742] and also by treatment of the 4-thiocyano compound with acid, base or heat.[742] The disulfides shown as products in eq. 166 have been reported by Konek[848] to react with mercury to give products of the type (XXVIII). A few bis(3-pyrazolin-

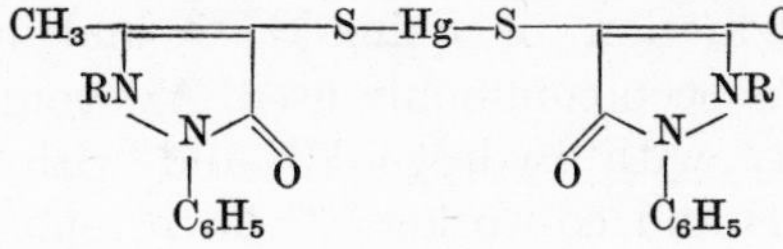

(XXVIII)

5-ones) in which the pyrazolinone rings are linked by selenium in the 4,4′-positions are known. Preparation of these is by the reaction of mono-3-pyrazolin-5-ones with selenium,[545] selenium dioxide,[545] selenium dichloride[850] or selenium tetrachloride.[850] In the first two cases the bridge is one selenium atom; in the third there is a mixture of selenide and a two-atom bridge of the type —Se— ↓ Se. In the last case the bridge is a dichloroselenide function. These last two types of bridge systems

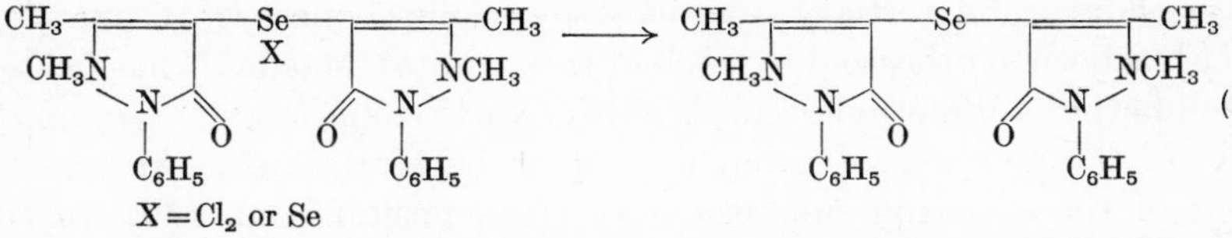

(167)

$X = Cl_2$ or Se

can be converted into monoselenides by base, acid or heat treatment (eq. 167). These bispyrazolinones are listed in Table XVI.

4. Amino, Imino, Hydrazino, Azo and Related Derivatives

A. 2-Pyrazolin-5-ones

All functional groups having nitrogen attached to the pyrazolinone nucleus are considered in this section except nitroso, nitro and some oximes. Only those oximes which cannot be considered as tautomeric with the nitroso group are discussed here. Hydrazones are in this section. These compounds are listed in Tables XXII and XXIII.

All of these derivatives of 2-pyrazolin-5-ones have a nitrogen atom substituted at the 4-position as the 3-nitrogen-substituted-2-pyrazolin-5-ones are tautomeric with the 5-imino-3-pyrazolidinones and are considered as such in this discussion. The 4-nitrogen-substituted-2-pyrazolin-5-ones are not usually prepared by cyclization directly to the desired pyrazolinone ring but rather by modification of already formed pyrazolinones. The methods used are usually those employed in preparing such derivatives in aliphatic or aromatic compounds. For example, 4-amino-2-pyrazolin-5-ones in which the amine is primary are prepared by reduction of 4-oximino-, 4-nitro- or 4-azo-2-pyrazolin-5-ones. For the reduction of oxime[52,992] and nitro-groups[478,480] stannous chloride has been commonly used. Azo compounds have been reduced catalytically with hydrogen[670] and with a zinc and acid mixture.[397] Michaelis and co-workers[996] have reported the oxidation of 4-phenylazo-3-methyl-1-phenyl-5-imino-2-pyrazoline to a fused pyrazolinone-azirane system as shown in eq. 168 and subsequent

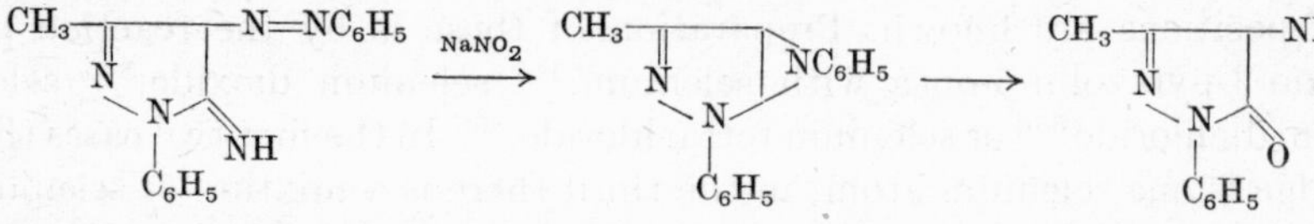

CH3—N=NC6H5 (NH, N—N—C6H5) —NaNO2→ CH3 (NC6H5, N—N—C6H5) ⟶ CH3—NH2 (N—N, O, C6H5) (168)

reduction of this to the 4-amino-2-pyrazolin-5-one which was isolated only as its oxidation product, rubazonic acid. The structure proposed for the intermediate seems most unlikely. Four methods have been reported for the direct preparation (i.e., with no amino intermediate) of secondary and tertiary 4-amino-2-pyrazolin-5-ones. Only one product has been synthesized by each of these routes. Maeda[938] has heated 2,3-dimethyl-4-dimethylamino-1-phenyl-3-pyrazolin-5-one (aminopyrine) in the presence of salicylic acid or barbital causing rearrangement of the 2-methyl substituent to the 4-position (eq. 169). In the

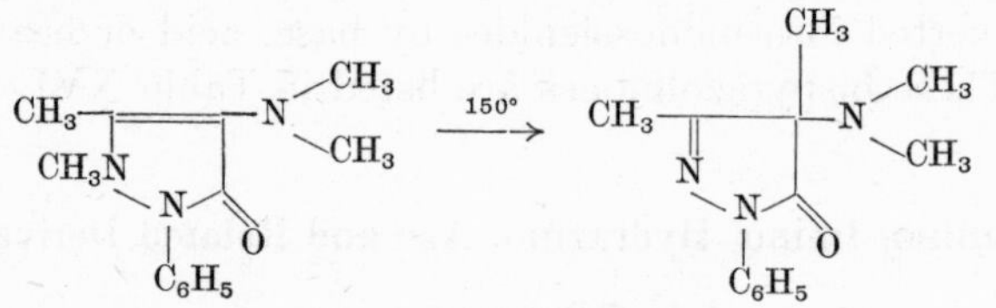

CH3—N(CH3)2 (CH3N, N, O, C6H5) —150°→ CH3, CH3—N(CH3)2 (N, N, O, C6H5) (169)

oxidation of 3-methyl-1-phenyl-2-pyrazolin-5-one with nitrobenzene Perroncito[1107] has found that the principal product is the expected bispyrazolinone, but 4-anilino-3-methyl-1-phenyl-2-pyrazolin-5-one is also formed. This may occur through reaction of nitrobenzene reduction products formed by oxidation of some of the 3-pyrazolin-5-one. The cyclization of a tertiary amino β-aldehydoester to a pyrazolinone has been reported (eq. 170).[1537] Itano[695] has used a method for preparation

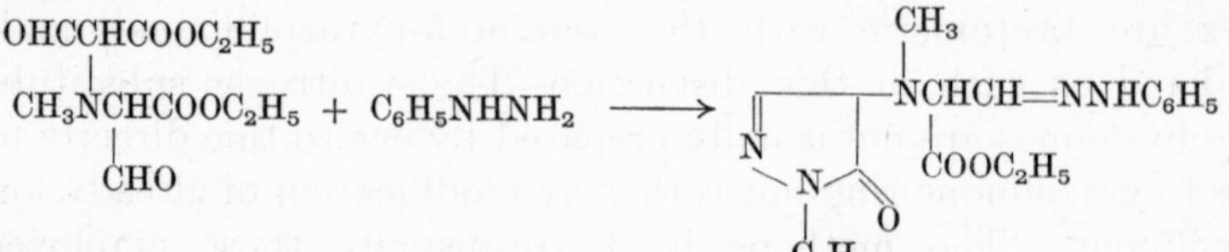

$OHCCHCOOC_2H_5$ / $CH_3NCHCOOC_2H_5$ / CHO + $C_6H_5NHNH_2$ ⟶ CH_3 / —$NCHCH{=}NNHC_6H_5$ / $COOC_2H_5$ (N, N, O, C_6H_5) (170)

of such compounds that may be fundamentally the same as that of Perroncito, the reaction of an amine with a 2-pyrazolin-5-one in the presence of an oxidant (eq. 171).

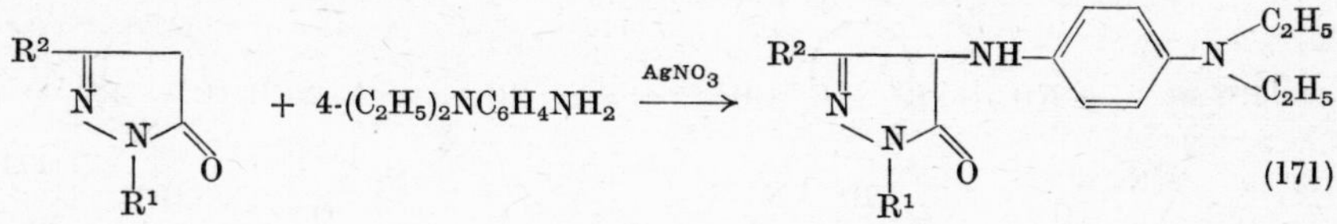

R² N N R¹ O + $4\text{-}(C_2H_5)_2NC_6H_4NH_2$ $\xrightarrow{AgNO_3}$ R² NH– C_6H_4 –N$(C_2H_5)_2$ N N R¹ O (171)

4-Imino-2-pyrazolin-5-ones of the type (XXIX) have become very important in the field of color photography and will be discussed in

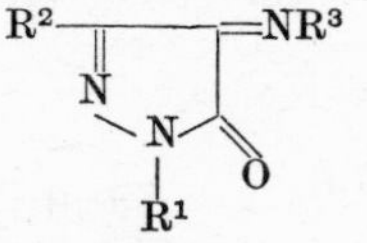

R² =NR³ N N R¹ O

(XXIX)

more detail in respect to this use. They have been particularly investigated at Eastman Kodak by Weissberger and Vittum who oxidized an alkaline solution of a 2-pyrazolin-5-one and 2-amino-5-diethylaminotoluene with silver nitrate or silver chloride (eq. 172) to obtain the

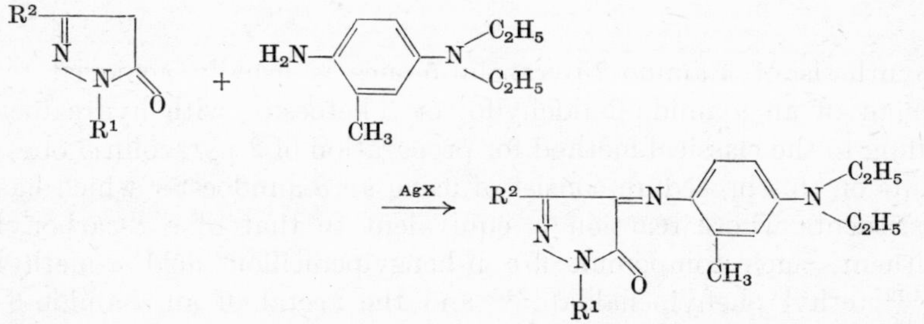

R² N N R¹ O + H_2N– $C_6H_3(CH_3)$ –N$(C_2H_5)_2$ $\xrightarrow{AgX}$ R² =N– $C_6H_3(CH_3)$ –N$(C_2H_5)_2$ N N R¹ O (172)

desired 4-iminopyrazolinones. Gerbeaux[519] has used the same procedure and in addition has used potassium ferricyanide and sodium hypochlorite as oxidizing agents. Mann and Haworth[943] and Gerbeaux[519] have taken advantage of the active hydrogen atoms in the 4-position of 2-pyrazolin-5-ones for the preparation of the imino derivatives. Various aromatic nitroso compounds were condensed with 2-pyrazolin-5-ones (eq. 173). Brooker and White[240] have prepared this same type

R² N N R¹ O + R^3NO $\longrightarrow$ R² =NR³ N N R¹ O (173)

of compound by reaction of 4-nitroso (or oximino)-2-pyrazolin-5-ones with quaternary salts of heterocyclic compounds having active hydrogen on a methyl substituent (eq. 174). Similar products are obtained by

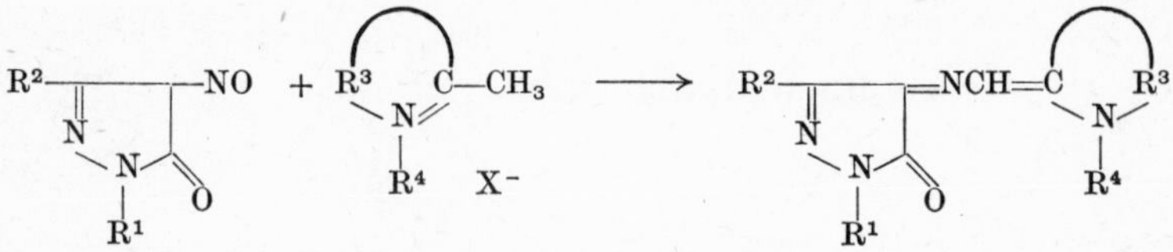

(174)

the reaction of 4-benzylidene-2-pyrazolin-5-ones with aromatic amines.[1255] The benzylidene group is replaced by an arylimino group (eq. 175).

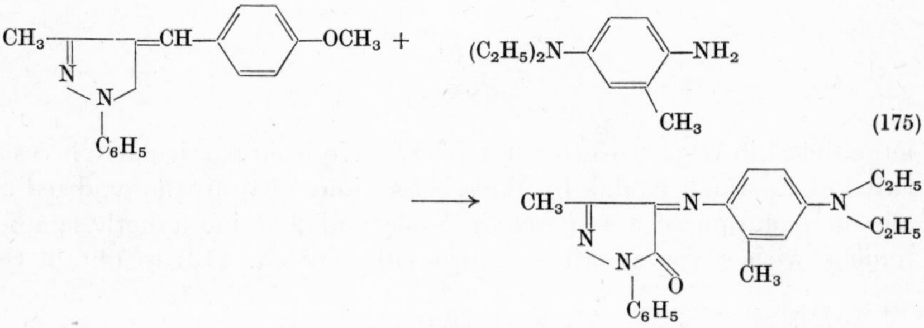

(175)

Synthesis of 4-amino-2-pyrazolin-5-ones is usually achieved by treatment of an α-amido-β-aldehydo- or β-ketoester with hydrazines according to the classical method for preparation of 2-pyrazolin-5-ones. Variants on this procedure consist of using an α-amidoester which has β-substituents whose reaction is equivalent to that of a β-carbonyl substituent. Such compounds are D-benzylpenicilloic acid α-methyl ester,[1027] ethyl phenylpenaldate[243] and the acetal of an α-amido-β-formyl ester.[59,243] Cornforth has isomerized 2-phenyl-4-hydrazinomethylidyneoxazolidone to 4-benzamido-2-pyrazolin-5-one. The same compound was obtained by treatment of 1-ethoxyvinyl-2-phenyloxazolidone with phenylhydrazine.[319]

The synthesis of 4-azo-3-methyl-1-phenyl-2-pyrazolin-5-one is shown in eq. 176.[1144] The 4-hydrazones of 2-pyrazolin-4,5-diones have

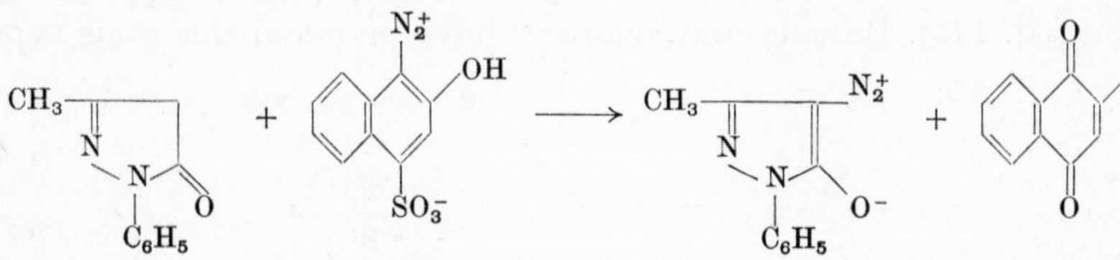

(176)

been prepared by Auwers and co-workers[52] who used the reaction of a hydrazine with the 4,5-dione (eq. 177). This same compound was

$$\text{3-CH}_3\text{-1-C}_6\text{H}_5\text{-2-pyrazoline-4,5-dione} + C_6H_5N(CH_3)NH_2 \longrightarrow \text{3-CH}_3\text{-4-}(=NN(CH_3)C_6H_5)\text{-1-C}_6\text{H}_5\text{-2-pyrazolin-5-one} \quad (177)$$

synthesized by methylation of 3-methyl-4-phenylazo-1-phenyl-2-pyrazolin-5-one and by cyclization of the bis(phenylmethylhydrazone) of ethyl α,β-diketobutyrate. These compounds are listed in Table XXI.

The 4-amino-2-pyrazolin-5-ones react as do other amines. They can be alkylated with alkyl halides[992] and react with aldehydes to form Schiff bases.[633,992] Oxidation of these amino compounds with ferric chloride leads to the rubazonic acids (eq. 178) in which two 2-pyrazolin-

$$\text{3-R}^2\text{-4-NH}_2\text{-1-R}^1\text{-2-pyrazolin-5-one} \xrightarrow{FeCl_3} \text{(3-R}^2\text{-1-R}^1\text{-5-oxo-2-pyrazolin-4-ylidene)}=N-\text{(3-R}^2\text{-1-R}^1\text{-2-pyrazolin-5-on-4-yl)} \quad (178)$$

5-one rings are connected at the 4,4′-position by nitrogen having no hydrogen.

Rubazonic acid itself is 4-(3-methyl-1-phenyl-5-oxo-2-pyrazolin-4-ylideneamino)-3-methyl-1-phenyl-2-pyrazolin-5-one. 4-Arylimino-2-pyrazolin-5-ones are readily reduced to the corresponding 4-arylamino-2-pyrazolin-5-ones.[1538] 2-Pyrazolin-5-ones react with 4-arylimino-2-pyrazolin-5-ones to give bispyrazolinones (eq. 179).[1538]

$$\text{3-CH}_3\text{-1-C}_6\text{H}_5\text{-2-pyrazolin-5-one} + \text{3-CH}_3\text{-4-(=NAr)-1-C}_6\text{H}_5\text{-2-pyrazolin-5-one} \longrightarrow \text{4,4'-bis(3-CH}_3\text{-1-C}_6\text{H}_5\text{-2-pyrazolin-5-one)} \quad (179)$$

4-Arylazo-2-pyrazolin-5-ones are strongly colored and have good dyeing properties. These compounds have been prepared in vast numbers for use in dyeing all types of fabrics and are of great importance in the dye industry. They will be discussed fully from this viewpoint in the section dealing with pyrazolinone dyes. The 4-arylazo-2-pyrazolin-5-ones are listed in Table XXIII.

Of the many methods which have been used for preparing 4-arylazo-2-pyrazolin-5-ones by far the most important is the direct coupling of a diazonium salt with a 2-pyrazolin-5-one (eq. 41).[77,809,813,818,980,1251] This reaction goes extremely readily with practically all 2-pyrazolin-4-ones having no 4-substituent. Coupling occurs with any aromatic amine capable of forming a diazonium salt and under a wide variety of conditions. Even 4-substituted-2-pyrazolin-5-ones have been reported to react with diazonium salts by replacement of the 4-substituent to form a 4-arylazo-2-pyrazolin-5-one. Substituents replaced have been triarylmethyl,[567] acyl[591] and halogen.[1514] 4,4′-Arylidenebis(2-pyrazolin-5-ones) react with diazonium salts to form 4-arylazo compounds (eq. 180).[1255,1351] A variation of this procedure is

Ar^1 | R^2—CH—R^2 (N, N—R^1, O; O, N—R^1, N) + Ar^2N_2X ⟶ R^2—N=NAr^2 (N, N—R^1, O) (180)

reaction of a 5-acyloxypyrazole with a diazonium salt.[591] This reaction hydrolyzes the ester linkage and, if an acyl substituent is present at the 4-position, replaces it to form 4-arylazo-2-pyrazolin-5-ones (eq. 181).

R^2—R^3 (N, N—R^1, $OCOR^4$) + ArN_2X ⟶ R^2—N=NAr (N, N—R^1, O) (181)

R^3 = H or R^4CO

A method frequently used and capable of a large number of variations is the cyclization of α-substituted-β-ketoesters, amides or hydrazides with hydrazines to 4-arylazo-2-pyrazolin-5-ones. One variant of this is the treatment of an α,β-diketoester with hydrazine (eq. 182).[627,1573,1574,1576] Instead of the ester, hydrazides of α,β-diketoacids

$RCOCOCOOC_2H_5$ + $2ArNHNH_2$ ⟶ R—N=NAr (N, N—Ar, O) (182)

have been used.[99] A very similar synthesis is the use of an α-oximino-β-ketoester and a hydrazine.[99] Also quite similar is the cyclization of an α-hydrazone of an α,β-diketoester[255,259,262,314,732] or α,β-diketoamide[261] with a hydrazine. The bishydrazones of α,β-diketoesters also react with hydrazines to form 4-arylazo-2-pyrazolin-5-ones.[255,257] It is not necessary that the α-substituent be unsaturated. α-Amino-β-ketoesters,[1535] α-chloro-β-ketoesters[1513,1514] and α-acyloxyesters[372] have also been used (eq. 183). Apparently an oxidation of a hydrazino to an azo function occurs in the course of the reaction.

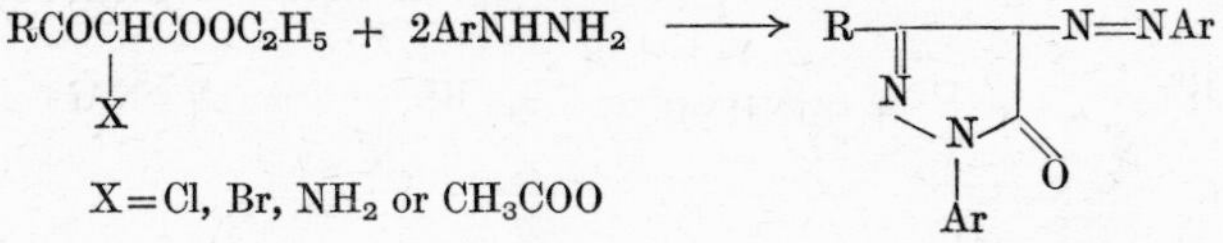

$$\underset{\substack{|\\ X}}{RCOCHCOOC_2H_5} + 2ArNHNH_2 \longrightarrow \text{4-(N=NAr)-3-R-1-Ar-2-pyrazolin-5-one} \quad (183)$$

$X=Cl, Br, NH_2$ or CH_3COO

Cyclization of a variety of bishydrazones of α,β-diketoacids,[52,285] α,β-diketoesters[52,264,397,732,782] and α,β-diketoamides,[352] using either acid, base or heat, to 4-arylazo-2-pyrazolin-5-ones has been reported (eq. 184). In this reaction the aryl groups have usually been the same

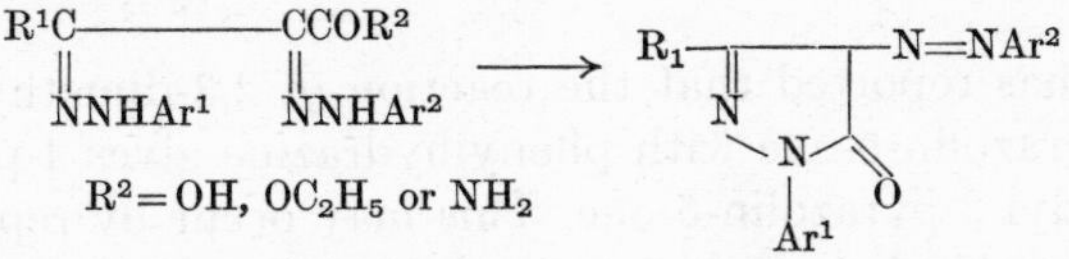

$$\underset{\substack{\|\\ NNHAr^1}}{R^1C}-\underset{\substack{\|\\ NNHAr^2}}{CCOR^2} \longrightarrow \text{4-(N=NAr}^2\text{)-3-R}_1\text{-1-Ar}^1\text{-2-pyrazolin-5-one} \quad (184)$$

$R^2=OH, OC_2H_5$ or NH_2

although Kleene[782] has used different aryl groups. Another modification of this reaction is due to Chargaff and Magasanik,[283] who report that oxidation of the 1,2-bisphenylhydrazone of mesoxaldehyde gave rise to 4-phenylazo-1-phenyl-2-pyrazolin-5-one.

Fichter[446] has reported an arylazopyrazolinone as one of the products from the reaction of α,α'-dibromo-α-methylsuccinic acid with p-bromophenylhydrazine (eq. 185).

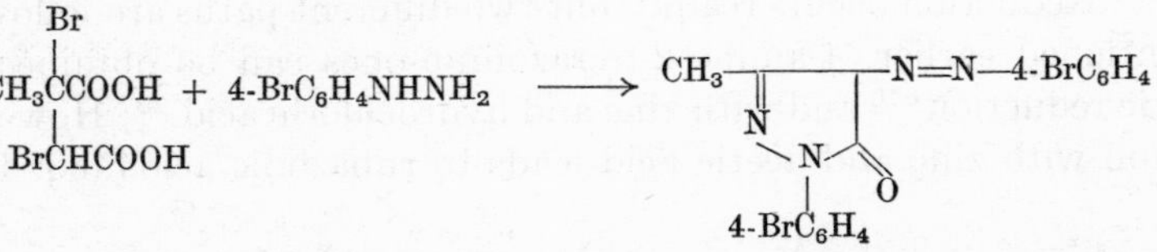

$$\begin{array}{c}Br\\ |\\ CH_3CCOOH\\ |\\ BrCHCOOH\end{array} + 4\text{-}BrC_6H_4NHNH_2 \longrightarrow \text{3-CH}_3\text{-4-(N=N-4-BrC}_6\text{H}_4\text{)-1-(4-BrC}_6\text{H}_4\text{)-2-pyrazolin-5-one} \quad (185)$$

Huebner and Link[670] have prepared 4-arylazo-2-pyrazolin-5-ones by the reaction of hydrazines with 4-hydroxycoumarin, 3,3′-methylene-bis(4-hydroxycoumarin) and with 2,3,4-triketochroman derivatives. In the case of the 4-hydroxycoumarins oxidation by phenylhydrazine occurs to give the bisphenylhydrazone of an α,β-ketoester. The reaction then proceeds as previously discussed for such compounds.

Bülow and Hecking[263] have treated 4-arylazoisoxazolidones with hydrazines to form 4-arylazo-2-pyrazolin-5-ones (eq. 186) and other heterocycles undergo similar transformations.[118]

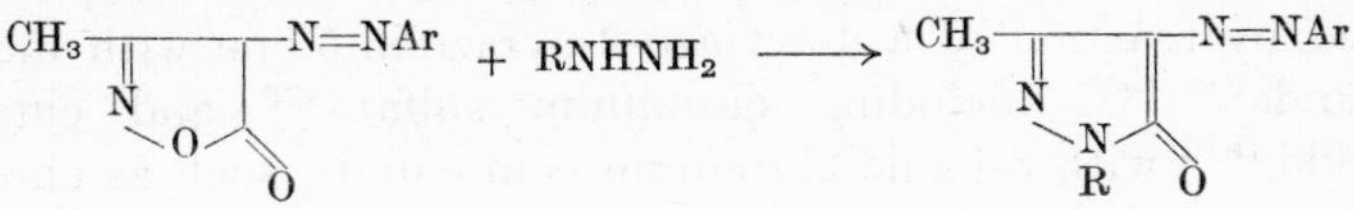

$$\text{3-CH}_3\text{-4-(N=NAr)-isoxazol-5-one} + RNHNH_2 \longrightarrow \text{3-CH}_3\text{-4-(N=NAr)-1-R-2-pyrazolin-5-one} \quad (186)$$

A number of 2-pyrazolin-5-ones having substituents at C–4 react with arylhydrazines by replacement of the substituent to give 4-arylazo derivatives. These syntheses are illustrated in eqs. 187 and 188.

R² =O N N R¹ O + ArNHNH₂ ⟶ R² N=NAr N N R¹ O (187)[125,690]

CH_3 Cl N N C_6H_5 O + $C_6H_5NHNH_2$ ⟶ CH_3 $N{=}NC_6H_5$ N N C_6H_5 O (188)[1514]

Ridi[1185] has reported that the reaction of 2,3-dimethyl-1-phenyl-4-nitroso-3-pyrazolin-5-one with phenylhydrazine gives 4-phenylazo-3-methyl-1-phenyl-2-pyrazolin-5-one. This may occur by replacement of the methylphenylhydrazine moiety in the 3-pyrazolin-5-one by phenylhydrazine. The 4-oximino-2-pyrazolin-4-one could then react with phenylhydrazine to give the reported product.

Although in this discussion the 4-arylazo-2-pyrazolin-5-ones have been written as 5-oxo compounds, it is likely that they exist largely in the tautomeric enol form.[262]

The methylation of 4-arylazo-2-pyrazolin-5-ones has already been mentioned.[52] Nitration occurs with replacement of the 4-arylazo group.[262] Reduction occurs readily but two different paths are followed. As mentioned earlier, 4-amino-2-pyrazolin-5-ones can be obtained by catalytic reduction[670] and with zinc and hydrochloric acid.[397] However, reduction with zinc and acetic acid leads to rubazonic acids (eq. 189).

R² N=NAr N N R¹ O ⟶ R² N= R² N N N N R¹ O O R¹ (189)

The conditions which determine the course of this reduction are not known.

The most important reactions of 4-arylazo-2-pyrazolin-5-ones are those with various salts to form metal complexes. These products are of great importance in the dye industry and will be discussed more completely in the section devoted to dyes. Chromium complexes are prepared by reaction of a 4-arylazo-2-pyrazolin-5-one with inorganic compounds[213,1457] including chromium sulfate[475] and chromium trifluoride,[1616] with organic chromium compounds, such as chromium formate[865] and chromium complexes with salicylic acid.[207] Copper,[213] nickel,[213] lead,[213] zinc[1616] and cobalt[1680] have also been used. The aromatic moiety of the arylazo group usually has a hydroxyl or carboxyl group *ortho* to the azo linkage. The complexes thus obtained with chromium contain either one or two molecules of the dye per atom of

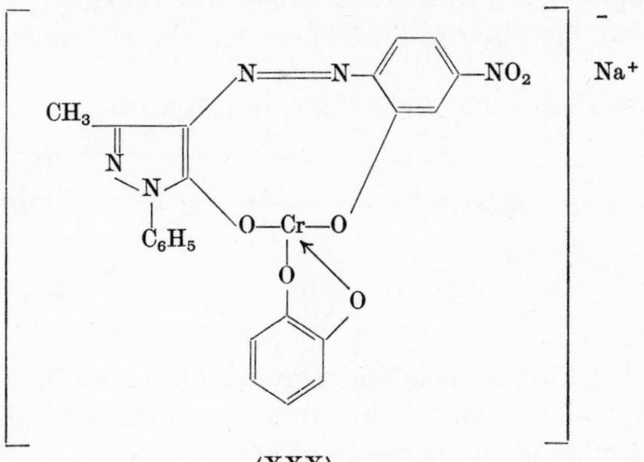

(XXX)

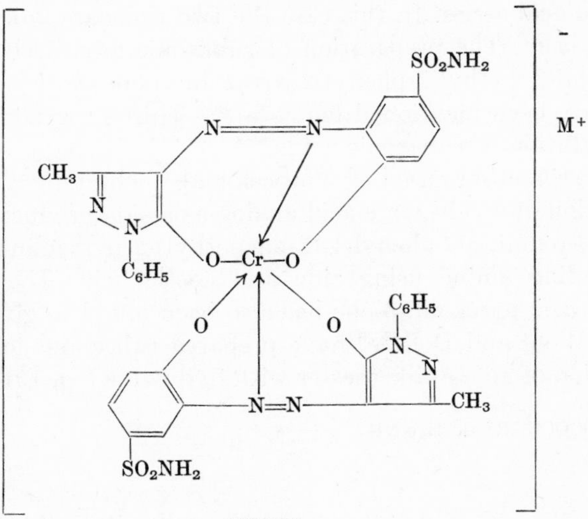

(XXXI)

metal. The metal atoms react with the C–5 oxygen of the pyrazolinone ring in its enol form and with the hydroxyl group of the aromatic ring to form more or less covalent bonds. There is also electron donation by other oxygen atoms and by the azo nitrogen atoms to the metal atom. The structure (XXX) has been proposed for 1 : 1 complexes[1117, 1259] and (XXXI) for 2 : 1 complexes.[1259]

Amino-substituted bis(2-pyrazolin-5-ones) have been prepared in which the rings are linked by carbon chains or by nitrogen atoms. The former are listed in Tables VIII and IX and the latter in Tables VII and VIII. In most of those cases in which carbon chains link the two rings the amino substituents are introduced as they are in mono-pyrazolinones.[255,494] Eisner, Elvidge and Linstead[419] have prepared some amino bis(2-pyrazolin-5-ones) by direct cyclization (eq. 190).

$$(C_2H_5OOC)_2CHCOCH{=}CHCOCH(COOC_2H_5)_2 + C_6H_5NHNH_2$$

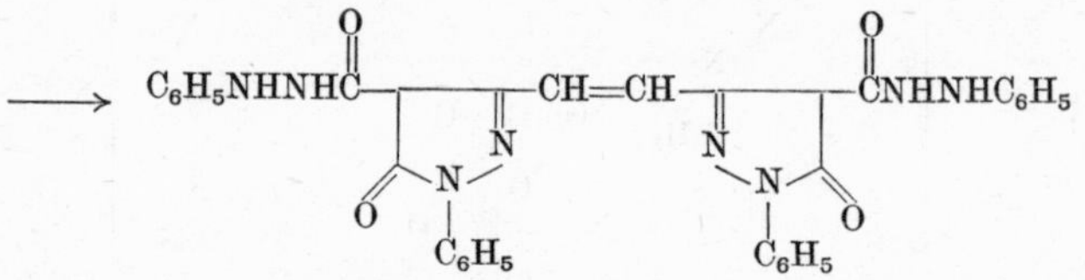

$$\longrightarrow C_6H_5NHNHC(=O)\text{—[pyrazolinone ring, N–}C_6H_5\text{]—}CH{=}CH\text{—[pyrazolinone ring, N–}C_6H_5\text{]—}C(=O)NHNHC_6H_5 \qquad (190)$$

Some 1,1′-bis(4-arylideneamino-2-pyrazolin-5-ones) have been prepared by Furuya and Ueno[494] by treating bis(2-pyrazolin-5-ones) with oxidizing agents in the presence of arylamines.

The best known series of amino bis(2-pyrazolin-5-ones) is the rubazonic acid series. In this case the two rings are linked by a single nitrogen atom. The preparation of rubazonic acid itself by oxidation of 4-amino-3-methyl-1-phenyl-2-pyrazolin-5-one with ferric chloride has already been mentioned (eq. 178).[809] This is a general method for the preparation of rubazonic acids,[333,397,611] although other oxidizing agents are sometimes used.[480] Votocek and Wichterle[1567] have reported the isolation of a rubazonic acid analog as a side-product in the reduction of 4-oximino-3-phenyl-1-(2-phenethyl)-2-pyrazolin-5-one to the corresponding amine using zinc and acetic acid. The reduction of 4-phenylazo-2-pyrazolin-5-one has also been found to give a rubazonic acid.[1552] Wohl and Doll[1576] have prepared rubazonic acid analogs by the reaction of an α,β-diketoester with hydrazine (eq. 191) and a some-

$$R^1COCOCOOR^2 + H_2NNH_2 \longrightarrow R^1\text{—[pyrazolinone ring, NH]}{=}N\text{—[pyrazolinone ring, NH]—}R^1 \qquad (191)$$

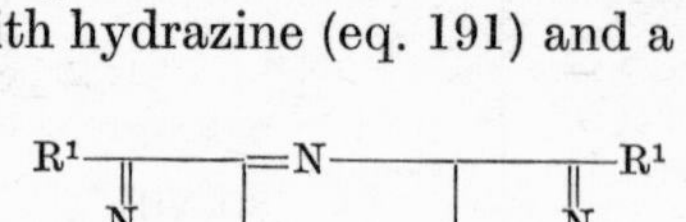

what analogous method has been reported by Wislicenus and Grob.[1642] Moureu, Choivin and Petit[1022] have obtained a very low yield of a rubazonic acid by the reaction of ethyl α-bromocinnamate with phenylhydrazine. 4,4′-Bis(2-pyrazolin-5-ones) linked by a single azo group and by —N=N—R—N=N— have been reported, although these compounds are very few. Diazotization of 4-amino-2-pyrazolin-5-ones followed by coupling with an appropriate acetoacetic ester derivative and cyclization gives 4,4′-azobis(2-pyrazolin-5-ones).[1062] von Walther and Rothacker[1564] have claimed that the reaction of 4,4-dichloro-3-methyl-1-phenyl-2-pyrazolin-5-one and 3-methyl-1-phenyl-2-pyrazolin-5-one in the presence of hydrazine gives the same type of product. The compounds having two azo groups in the chain are prepared by coupling of tetrazotized diamines with acetoacetic esters followed by cyclization to 2-pyrazolin-5-ones,[767] coupling of tetrazotized diamines with pyrazolinones,[727,1245,1359] or a combination of these.[259] Priewe and Poljak[1147] reduced 5-oxo-2-pyrazolin-4-oximes with hydrogen or sodium hyposulfite and obtained 4,4′-bis(5-oxo-2-pyrazolin-4-yl)hydrazines. Oxidation of these compounds gave 4,4′-azo derivatives. 3,3′-Imino bis(2-pyrazolin-5-ones) have been prepared by condensation of 3-amino-1-aryl-2-pyrazolin-5-ones (1-aryl-5-imino-2-pyrazolidinones) with ammonia or amines (eq. 192).[595,596]

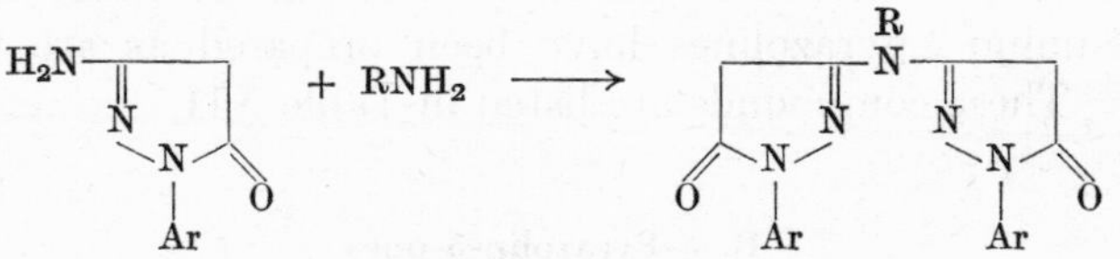

H_2N–(pyrazolinone, N–Ar, =O) + RNH_2 ⟶ bis(pyrazolinone) linked by N–R (each ring N–Ar, =O) (192)

The most interesting of the aminobispyrazolinones are the rubazonic acids having the =N— linkage. These compounds are quite strong acids, although no quantitative data on this are available. As would be expected, reduction of the extranuclear C=N— occurs readily with stannous chloride to give the corresponding tertiary amine. Rubazonic acid is decomposed completely by sodium hydroxide and reverts to a monomer (eq. 193) upon treatment with phenylhydrazine.[809,992] The

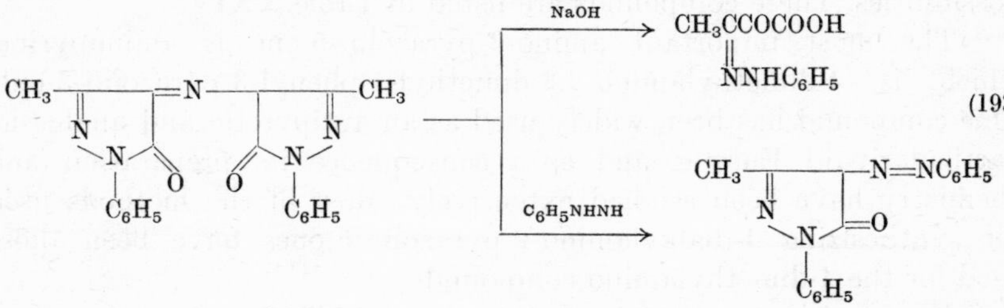

CH_3–(pyrazolinone, N–C_6H_5)=N–(pyrazolinone, N–C_6H_5)–CH_3 —NaOH⟶ $CH_3CCOCOOH$ (=$NNHC_6H_5$); —C_6H_5NHNH⟶ CH_3–(pyrazolinone, N–C_6H_5, =O)–N=NC_6H_5 (193)

3,3′-iminobis(2-pyrazolin-5-ones) react with formaldehyde and ethyl orthoformate at the reactive 4,4′-positions to give tricyclic compounds.[595] If there is no substituent on the linking nitrogen atom, reaction with dimethyl sulfate causes methylation at this nitrogen.[705]

Treatment with chlorosulfonic acid gives sulfonation in the benzene ring, when present.[705]

Michaelis and co-workers[990] have prepared 3-methyl-1-phenyl-4-phenylazo-2-pyrazolin-5-thione by coupling of the corresponding pyrazolinthione with phenyldiazonium chloride.

5-Imino-2-pyrazolines having nitrogen substituents at the 4-position have been reported by Michaelis and co-workers.[995,996,1002] The 4-amino compounds have been prepared by reduction of 4-oximino analogs[1002] and by reduction of arylazopyrazoles[995] (eq. 194) with

$$\text{3-}CH_3\text{-4-}(N{=}NC_6H_5)\text{-5-imino-1-}C_6H_5\text{-pyrazoline} \longrightarrow \text{3-}CH_3\text{-4-}NH_2\text{-5-}(NC_6H_5)\text{-1-}C_6H_5\text{-pyrazoline} \quad (194)$$

mild reducing agents, such as sodium hydrosulfite. These amino compounds react with ketones and isocyanates as do other amines. 4-Arylazo-5-imino-2-pyrazolines have been prepared as are the 5-oxo analogs.[996] These compounds are listed in Table XII.

B. 3-Pyrazolin-5-ones

3-Pyrazolin-5-ones having nitrogen substituents in the 3- or 4-positions, except primary amino, secondary amino, amido having hydrogen on the nitrogen, nitroso and nitro are discussed in this section. Although primary and secondary amino- and amido-3-pyrazolin-5-ones undoubtedly exist as the 3-pyrazolin-5-one tautomer, they are discussed under the heading of the 4-imino-3-pyrazolidinone and 5-imino-3-pyrazolidinone tautomers because of the convention adopted in this discussion regarding compounds having such tautomeric possibilities. These compounds are listed in Table XXIV.

The most important amino-3-pyrazolin-5-one is aminopyrine, which is 4-dimethylamino-2,3-dimethyl-1-phenyl-3-pyrazolin-5-one. This compound has been widely used as an antipyretic and analgesic, particularly in Europe, and as a consequence its preparation and chemistry have been studied extensively. Most of the methods used for synthesizing 4-dialkylamino-2-pyrazolin-5-ones have been those used for the 4-dimethylamino compounds.

Most syntheses of tertiary amino-3-pyrazolin-5-ones are based on an alkylation by one means or another of the primary or secondary amino analogs. In some cases simultaneous reduction of a nitroso or nitro compound or of a Schiff base and alkylation of the amine so formed is carried out. 4-Dimethylamino-3-pyrazolin-5-ones (aminopyrine and analogs) have been synthesized by application of the Eschweiler–Clarke procedure to 4-amino-3-pyrazolin-5-ones (eq. 195).[548,860,941] Other alkylating agents used have been alkyl

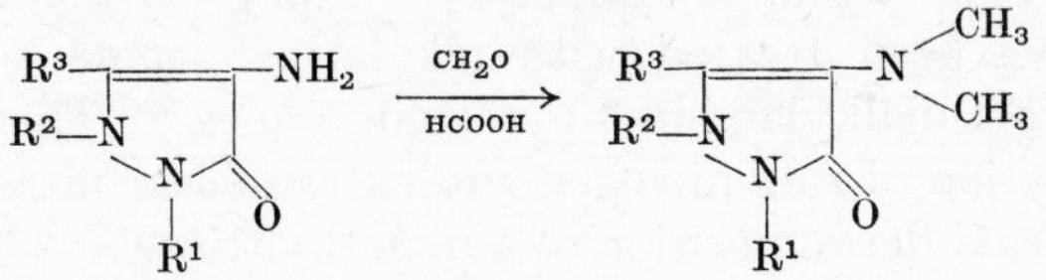

(195)

halides,[130,984] dimethyl sulfate[984,992] and methyl-*p*-toluenesulfonate.[1175] 3-Pyrazolin-5-ones dialkylated at N–4 have frequently been prepared by alkylation of the primary amine by such means as treatment with an aldehyde[111,172] and reduction of the Schiff base followed by alkylation. The final alkylation has been achieved by treatment with an alkyl halide,[524,1298] by heating with an amine hydrochloride[111] and by treatment with an aldehyde followed by reduction.[860] A special type of alkylation of secondary amines is that reported by Bochmühl and Stein.[105] Secondary amines were treated with formaldehyde and sulfur dioxide or an alkali bisulfite to give an aminomethanesulfonic acid (eq. 196). Several patents have reported the synthesis of amino-

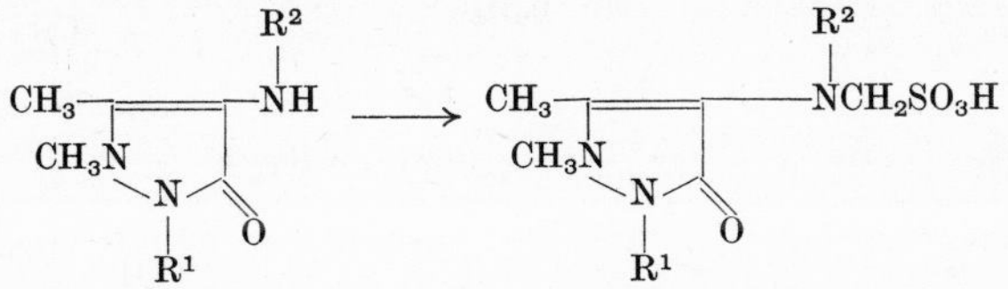

(196)

pyrine starting with reduction of 4-nitroso-2,3-dimethyl-3-pyrazolin-5-one with sodium bisulfite to give the 4-sulfamino analog (eq. 197). This

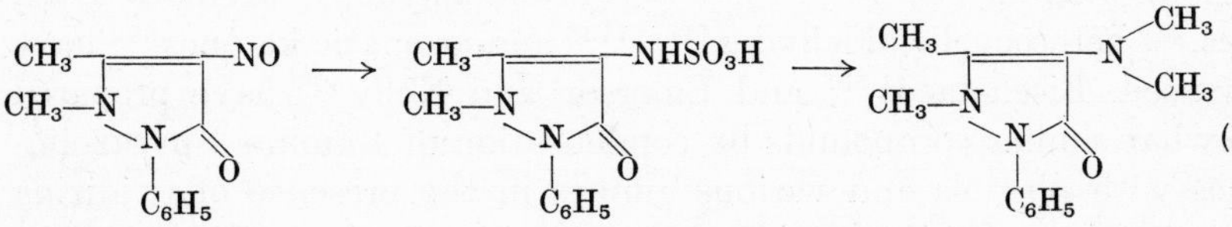

(197)

is then methylated by various means. The most common method is use of formaldehyde and formic acid.[150,661,781,860,1174] Alkylation with dimethyl sulfate[144,1256] and electrolysis in the presence of formaldehyde and sulfuric acid[691] have also been used.

Reduction of 4-nitroso-2,3-dimethyl-1-phenyl-3-pyrazolin-5-one with zinc or iron and acid[554,550,915] or catalytically[551] in the presence of formaldehyde also gives aminopyrine. The analogous 4-nitro compound can also be reduced catalytically in the presence of formaldehyde to form aminopyrine.[860,1356] Sonn and Litten[1320] have replaced the bromine atom in 4-bromo-3-benzyl-2-methyl-1-phenyl-3-pyrazolin-5-one with dimethylamine.

A variety of 4-amino-5-alkoxy- and acyloxy-1,3-disubstituted-pyrazoles have been treated with alkylating agents such as alkyl halides to give 4-dialkylamino-3-pyrazolin-5-ones.[525] There is a simultaneous alkylation of ring nitrogen and extranuclear nitrogen.

The reported decomposition of 4-dimethyltriazeno-2,3-dimethyl-1-phenyl-3-pyrazolin-5-one to aminopyrine[527] has been shown by Stoltz[1353] to be incorrect.

Most 4-amido-3-pyrazolin-5-ones have been prepared either by acylation of secondary amines[537,618,1471] (4-alkylimino-3-pyrazolidinones) or by acylation of the primary amine[1471] followed by alkylation.[537] Shimidzu[1297] has reported the replacement of a methyl group by a cyano group and conversion of this to a thiourea (eq. 198).

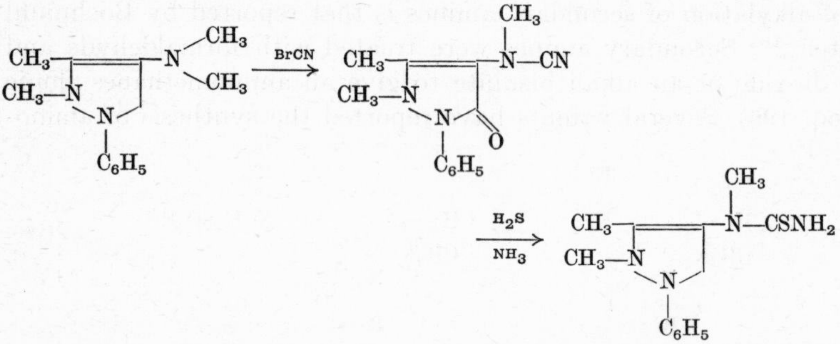

$$\xrightarrow{\text{BrCN}} \qquad \xrightarrow[\text{NH}_3]{\text{H}_2\text{S}} \qquad (198)$$

4-Amino-3-pyrazolin-5-ones (4-imino-3-pyrazolidinones) react with aldehydes and ketones to form 4-alkylidene- and arylideneamino-3-pyrazolin-5-ones.[424,984,1001,1365,1592] Formaldehyde,[172] aromatic aldehydes,[430] heterocyclic aldehydes[1184,1186] and aromatic ketones[992] have been used. Eisenstaedt[417] and Emerson and Kelly[426] have prepared somewhat similar compounds by condensation of 4-amino-3-pyrazolin-5-ones with phenols and various amines in the presence of oxidizing agents, such as ferric chloride and potassium ferricyanide (eq. 199).

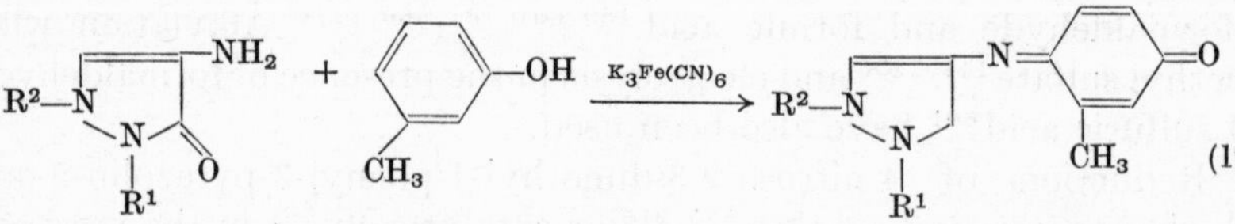

$$\xrightarrow{\text{K}_3\text{Fe(CN)}_6} \qquad (199)$$

The same type of condensation occurs with 2-pyrazolin-5-ones having no substituent in the 4-position.[424] Here, of course, it is unnecessary for the aromatic ring to assume a quinnooid form, as the 3-pyrazolin-5-one analogs do, since two active hydrogen atoms are present on the C–4. 4-Amino-2-pyrazolin-5-ones react with Schiff bases to form the 4-arylideneamino-3-pyrazolin-5-ones.[954] Rubtsov[1217] reports the condensation of this amine with sodium 1,2-naphthoquinone-4-sulfonate to give a quinoneimine by replacement of the sulfonate group. The 4-arylideneamino substituent has been introduced by condensation of a 4-nitroso-3-pyrazolin-5-one with fluorenes.[270] The condensation occurs at the active methylene group of the fluorene. Michaelis and coworkers[1001] have prepared a compound which they believe to have a sulfur-nitrogen double bond at least formally similar to the >C=N— substituents discussed here. This was prepared by condensation of a 4-amino-3-pyrazolin-5-one with thionyl chloride and supposedly gave a 4-OS=N— substituent. However, it appears unlikely that this type of compound was actually prepared.

The only amino 4,4′-bis(3-pyrazolin-5-one) reported is *N*,*N*′-[bis(2,3-dimethyl-1-phenyl-5-oxo-3-pyrazolin-4-yl)]-*N*,*N*′-dimethylmethylenediamine prepared by acid treatment of the sodium salt of *N*-sulfomethyl-*N*-methylaminoantipyrine with acid.[1572]

4-Amino-3-pyrazolin-5-ones (4-imino-3-pyrazolidinones) react with nitrous acid as do ordinary aromatic amines to form diazonium salts.[426,984,1353] These then couple readily with aromatic amines,[1017,1018,1060] phenols[992,1323] and aliphatic compounds having active hydrogen atoms,[426,1017] such as acetoacetic esters. The products are 4-azo-3-pyrazolin-5-ones (eq. 200). The diazonium salts also couple

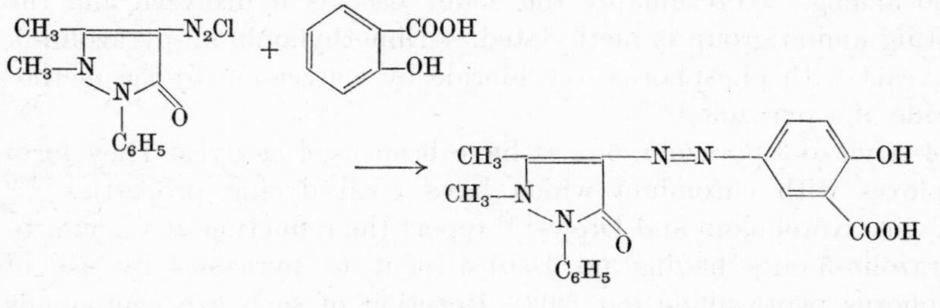

$$\text{(2,3-dimethyl-1-}C_6H_5\text{-3-pyrazolin-5-one-4-}N_2Cl) + C_6H_4(COOH)(OH) \longrightarrow \text{(2,3-dimethyl-1-}C_6H_5\text{-3-pyrazolin-5-one-4-})N{=}N{-}C_6H_3(OH)(COOH) \qquad (200)$$

with 2-pyrazolin-5-ones in the 4-position.[426] Similar compounds can be prepared by the coupling of an aromatic diazonium salt with a 3-pyrazolin-5-one. Coupling occurs in these cases either at the 3- or the 4-position, whichever is unsubstituted.[972,1004] Huebner and Link[670] prepared 4-arylazo-3-pyrazolin-5-ones by reaction of 2,3,4-trioxochromane-3,4-bis(phenylhydrazone) and 3-arylhydrazone with phenylhydrazine. The 3-arylhydrazone group becomes the 4-arylazo group in the final product.

The preparation of 1-(2,3-dimethyl-1-phenyl-5-oxo-3-pyrazolin-4-yl)-3,3-dialkyltriazenes has been accomplished by reaction of 2,3-dimethyl-1-phenyl-5-oxo-3-pyrazolin-4-diazonium chloride with dialkylamines (eq. 201).[1353] The previously reported method of preparation[527] was found to be in error.

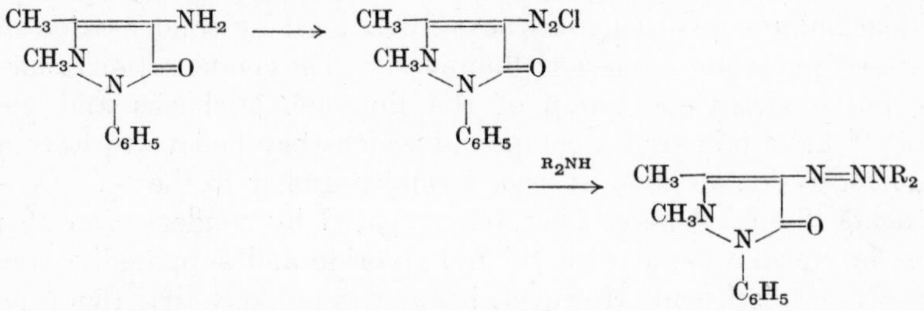

$$\text{4-}NH_2\text{ pyrazolinone } (CH_3, CH_3N, C_6H_5, =O) \longrightarrow \text{4-}N_2Cl \xrightarrow{R_2NH} \text{4-}N{=}NNR_2 \qquad (201)$$

2,3-Dimethyl-1-phenyl-5-oxo-3-pyrazolin-4-diazonium chloride reacts with hydrazoic acid to form the corresponding 4-azide.[456] This azide decomposed to form 4-(2,3-dimethyl-1-phenyl-5-oxo-3-pyrazolin-4-yl)azo-2,3-dimethyl-1-phenyl-3-pyrazolin-5-one.

Dihlmann[371] has determined the R_f values of 4-amino- and 4-amido-3-pyrazolin-5-ones by using butanol–acetic acid–water as solvent and ferric chloride or *p*-dimethylaminobenzaldehyde as developer.

The rearrangement of 4-dimethylamino-2,3-dimethyl-1-phenyl-3-pyrazolin-5-one to a 2-pyrazolin-5-one has already been mentioned (eq. 169). 4-Benzylideneamino-2,3-dimethyl-1-phenyl-3-pyrazolin-5-one reacts with dimethyl sulfate in aqueous media to give the 4-methylamino analog.[940] Presumably the Schiff base is hydrolyzed and the resulting amino group is methylated. 4-Dimethylamino-3-pyrazolin-5-ones react with phosphorus oxychloride by conversion to the methochloride of a pyrazole.[1000]

4-Arylazo-3-pyrazolin-5-ones have been used as dyes. They form complexes with chromium which have good dyeing properties.[1060] Michaelis, Kotelmann and Drews[984] report the reduction of 4-aryl-azo-3-pyrazolin-5-ones having no 1-substituent to pyrazoles by use of phosphorus pentasulfide (eq. 202). Reaction of such azo compounds

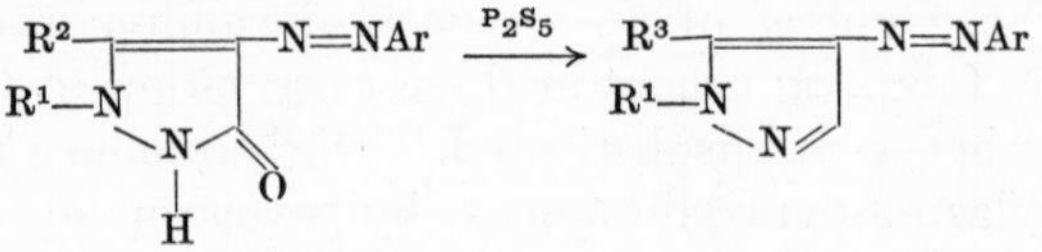

$$\text{R}^2, \text{R}^1\text{–N}, \text{N–H}, =O, \text{–N=NAr} \xrightarrow{P_2S_5} \text{R}^3, \text{R}^1\text{–N}, \text{N}, \text{–N=NAr} \qquad (202)$$

with phosphorus oxychloride leads to the corresponding 5-chloropyrazole.[972]

The only 4-dialkylamino-3-pyrazolin-5-thione reported in the literature[986,1000] was prepared by the action of sodium sulfide or potassium hydrogen sulfide on the methochloride of the corresponding 5-chloropyrazole.

A very few bis(3-pyrazolin-5-ones) in which the two rings are connected by the azo group have been prepared. The preparation of these *via* the 4-azido-3-pyrazolin-5-ones[456] has already been mentioned. These bispyrazolinones have also been prepared by coupling diazonium salts with 3-pyrazolin-5-ones (eq. 203).[984,1001] Scott and co-workers[1284]

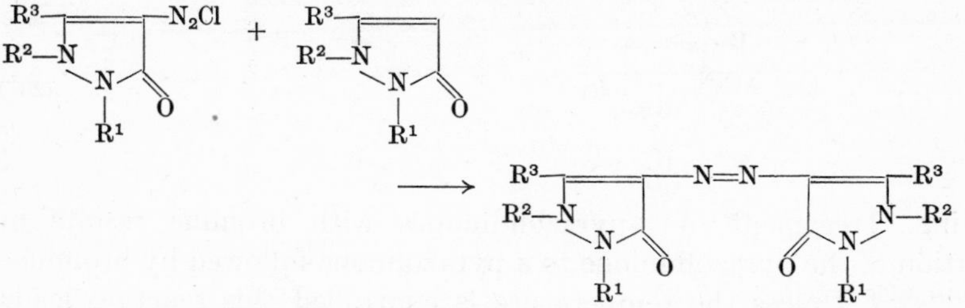

(203)

have reported a bis(3-pyrazolin-5-one) having a very extended bridge system prepared by reaction of a 3-pyrazolin-5-one diazonium chloride with *N,N′*-dibenzylidenediaminoguanidine.

5. Halogen Substituted Derivatives

A. 2-Pyrazolin-5-ones

Halogenated 2-pyrazolin-5-ones having halogen at N–1, C–3 and C–4 are known, but by far the largest number of such compounds have the halogen atom at C–4. Such compounds are usually prepared by direct halogenation with elemental halogen. Chlorination or bromination of 2-pyrazolin-5-ones having no 4-substituent with one equivalent of halogen gives the 4-monohalogeno product (eq. 204), but an excess of halogen gives the 4,4-dihalo derivative.[355,809,1605]

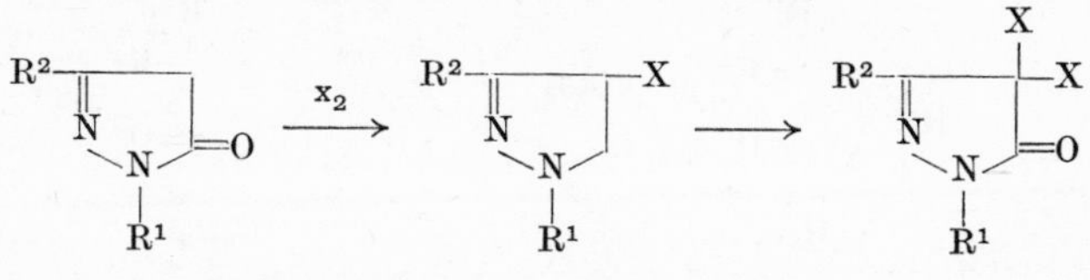

(204)

4-Iodo- and 4,4-di-iodo-2-pyrazolin-5-ones can be prepared by treatment of 2-pyrazolin-5-ones with iodine–potassium iodide in an alkaline solution.[1307] Here, again, either the mono or the dihalogeno product is formed, depending upon the amount of halogen used.

Extremely good yields have been reported in these halogenations.[1605] 4-Alkyl-2-pyrazolin-5-ones react with halogens readily, but even with an excess only monohalogenated products have been obtained.[1605] Smith and co-workers[1309] have found that 1,3-dimethyl-2-pyrazolin-5-one reacts with bromine to give both the expected 4-bromo product and also 1-bromo-3-methyl-2-pyrazolin-5-one. This same compound was obtained by bromination of 3-methyl-2-pyrazolin-5-one with *N*-bromosuccinimide.[1309] 4-Bromo-2-pyrazolin-5-ones have been prepared by bromination of 2-nitroso-3-pyrazolin-5-ones[1209] (eq. 205) with

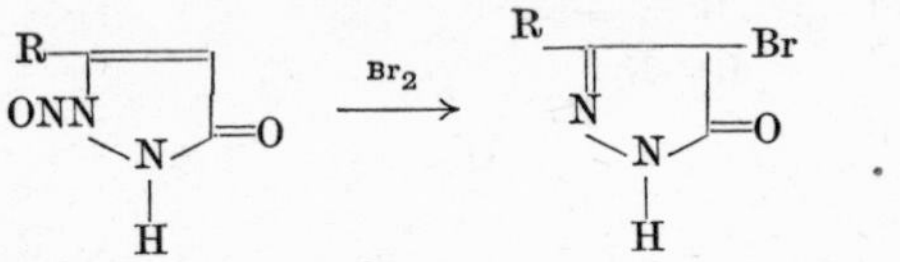

$$\text{R-C}_3\text{(ONN)(NH)C{=}O} \xrightarrow{Br_2} \text{R,Br-C}_3\text{N(NH)C{=}O} \quad (205)$$

bromine. Treatment of 3-pyrazolidinones with bromine results in oxidation of the pyrazolidinone to a pyrazolinone followed by bromination.[816,1028] Unless the temperature is controlled this reaction leads to a mixture of mono-, di- and tribromo-2-pyrazolin-5-ones. However, Muckermann[1028] was able to obtain the monobromo derivative at 0° and the dibromo at room temperature.

A number of reagents other than elemental halogen have been used for the introduction of halogen into 2-pyrazolin-5-ones. Treatment of 2-pyrazolin-5-ones with phosphorus pentachloride[333,809,980] or with sodium hypochlorite[1004] forms 4,4-dichloro-2-pyrazolin-5-ones. An analogous reaction is the formation of 4,4-dibromo analogs by use of phosphorus tribromide.[333] The methods already discussed for halogenation of 2-pyrazolin-5-ones lead exclusively to the 4-substituted products, but 3-halogenated-2-pyrazolin-5-ones are known. These have been prepared by Michaelis and co-workers[994,998] by reaction of one molar equivalent of phosphorus oxychloride with 1-phenyl-3,5-pyrazolidinediones (eq. 206) or with 3-methoxy-1-phenyl-2-pyrazolin-5-ones.

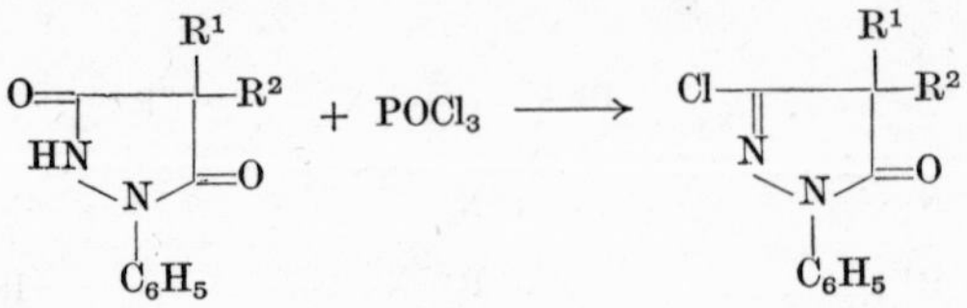

$$\text{O=C}_3\text{(HN)(N-}C_6H_5\text{)C{=}O}(R^1)(R^2) + POCl_3 \longrightarrow \text{Cl-C}_3\text{N(N-}C_6H_5\text{)C{=}O}(R^1)(R^2) \quad (206)$$

Some halogenated 2-pyrazolin-5-ones have been prepared by cyclization of various aliphatic compounds. Darapsky, Berger and Neuhaus[353] have treated a β-hydrazino hydrazide with bromine to achieve cyclization, oxidation and halogenation in one step (eq. 207).

The cyclization of a β-phenylazo-α,β-unsaturated ester with hydrochloric acid has been reported by van Alphen[1513,1514] to give a 4-chloro-2-pyrazolin-5-one.

$$\underset{\textstyle NHNH_2}{R^1\overset{|}{C}HCH_2CONHNH_2} \xrightarrow{Br_2} \text{4,4-dibromo-3-}R^1\text{-2-pyrazolin-5-one} \quad (207)$$

These compounds are listed in Table XXV.

The 4,4-dichloro-2-pyrazolin-5-ones are reduced with hydriodic acid to the corresponding monochloro compound.[1605] The 4-monohalogenated-2-pyrazolin-5-ones react readily with another mole of the same compound or with unhalogenated 2-pyrazolin-5-ones to give bis(2-pyrazolin-5-ones). In the former case the two rings are linked by a double bond,[1307] and in the latter by a single bond.[1528]

Only two halogenated bis(2-pyrazolin-5-ones) have been reported (Table VI). One of these is prepared by bromination of 4,4′-methylidyne-bis(3-methyl-1-phenyl-2-pyrazolin-5-one) with bromine to give the 4-bromo analog.[1682] In the second case[1109] bromine is added to a diolefinic system connecting two 2-pyrazolin-5-one rings.

A number of halogenated 5-imino-2-pyrazolines have been reported. These are included in Table XII. They are usually prepared by direct halogenation.[996,1655] Another preparative method which has been used is treatment of a 5-imino-3-pyrazolidinone with phosphorus oxychloride.[391] Michaelis has reported the treatment of a compound, which he believed to have the azipyrazole structure (XXVI, p. 45), with halogen acids to give halogenated 5-imino-2-pyrazolines.[996] 4-Chloro-3-dichloromethyl-1-phenyl-5-phenylimino-2-pyrazoline has been prepared by treatment of 1,1-bisanilino-2,4,4-trichloro-1-buten-3-one with phenylhydrazine.[1201] The reactions of halogenated iminopyrazolinones are essentially the same as of those having no halogen.

B. 3-Pyrazolin-5-ones

These compounds are listed in Table XXVI.

As is the case with 2-pyrazolin-5-ones, direct bromination of 3-pyrazolin-5-ones can be used to prepare the 4-bromo derivatives. This bromination is not complicated by substitution of a second bromine at the same carbon atom, but further bromination occurs to give 3-pyrazolin-5-ones containing two or three atoms of bromine. In spite of considerable investigation of these polybrominated 3-pyrazolin-5-ones, their structures have not been conclusively established and several very bizarre suggestions as to their nature have been made. Knorr[809] and other early workers[978,981] found that reaction of one mole of bromine with one mole of a 3-pyrazolin-5-one gave a compound whose molecular formula was that to be expected from addition of the bromine to the ring double bond to give 4,5-dibromo-3-pyrazolidinones and it was suggested that this was the structure of the products. This view was held for many years[1320] until Kitamura and Sunagawa[793,794] suggested that these compounds might be the hydrobromides of 4-bromo-3-pyrazolin-5-ones in the betaine form. The ready conversion of these dibromo-3-pyrazolin-5-ones to the corresponding 4-bromo-3-pyrazolin-5-ones by treatment with base and the reaction of the monobromo compounds with hydrogen bromide to give the dibromo derivatives make the argument of Kitamura and Sunagawa very compelling. Westoo[1605] has agreed with this proposal and it seems very likely to be correct. Reaction of excess of bromine with 3-pyrazolin-5-ones leads to the compounds called perbromides, generally considered to be tribromo compounds, although Komada[844] claimed to have obtained tetrabromo derivatives also. These claims have been discounted by others.[794] These perbromides have usually been considered as a molecular complex of the halogen and 4-bromo-3-pyrazolin-5-ones. Kitamura and Sunagawa[794] have proposed more definite structures involving dimerization, with the dimers bound by resonance. However, their suggested structure seems inherently improbable. Whatever may be the structures of these compounds, two of the bromine atoms must be very loosely held, as they are lost by treatment with water,[794,992] giving a 4-bromo-3-pyrazolin-5-one. Direct chlorination[988] and iodination[540,981] with the elemental halogens to give 4-halogeno-3-pyrazolin-5-ones have also been reported. Ledrut and co-workers[362,899] have found that bromination of 3-pyrazolin-5-ones having hydroxymethyl, formyl and carboxyl groups at C–4 results in replacement of the 4-substituent by bromine. Michaelis[978] earlier had reported this replacement if a 4-nitro group was present.

A variety of other halogenating agents have been used to prepare 4-halogeno-3-pyrazolin-5-ones. *N*-Bromosuccinimide[362,899] replaces hydrogen or other substituents in the 4-position with bromine. Hydrobromic acid in the presence of peroxide[907] and bromocyanogen[1491] also bring about bromination. 4-Chloro-2,3-dimethyl-1-phenyl-3-pyrazolin-5-one is obtained in excellent yield by chlorination of 2,3-dimethyl-1-phenyl-3-pyrazolin-5-one with sodium hypochlorite.[795,907,908] 5,5-Dimethyl-1,3-dichlorohydantoin also gives 4-chlorination of 3-pyrazolin-5-ones.[362] 4-Iodo-3-pyrazolin-5-ones have been obtained by replacement of a 4-chloromercuri group with iodine.[1001,1155] 3,4-

Dichloro-2-phenyl-3-pyrazolin-5-one has been prepared by treatment of perchloro-1-penten-3-one with phenylhydrazine.[1201]

The halogen in these 3-pyrazolin-5-ones is readily replaced with hydrogen by catalytic reduction[697,698] or by treatment with acetone.[793]

A few halogenated 3-pyrazolin-5-thiones are known (Table XVIII). These are prepared from the methyl chlorides of 3- or 4,5-dichloropyrazole by reaction with sodium sulfide or potassium hydrogen sulfide.[795,981] Michaelis[988,992] has reported that 3-pyrazolin-5-selenones form dichlorides and di- and tetrabromides when treated with chlorine or bromine. No specific structures were suggested.

6. Nitroso Substituted Derivatives

A. 2-Pyrazolin-5-ones

Although the compounds obtained by introduction of a nitroso group at C–4 in 2-pyrazolin-5-ones are considered as 4-nitroso-2-pyrazolin-5-ones for purposes of classification in this discussion, they actually exist as the oximino isomers (eq. 208) and are usually so

R²— N=N(R¹)—C(=O) ring + HNO_2 ⟶ R²— ring with =NOH, =O, N—R¹ (208)

considered in the literature. These compounds are always strongly colored, being light yellow to deep red. Such compounds are listed in Table XXVII.

Knorr[809] first prepared 4-oximino-2-pyrazolin-5-ones by treatment of 2-pyrazolin-5-ones with nitrous acid (eq. 208) and this has remained the standard method of preparation.[25,413,446,818,1004,1549] If an excess of nitrous acid is used, the nitroso substituent introduced is oxidized further to a nitro substituent.[992] Amyl nitrite[9] and nitrogen trioxide[355,406] have also been used as nitrosating agents, though not extensively.

The standard β-ketoester–hydrazine reaction for preparation of 2-pyrazolin-5-ones has been used for direct synthesis of the 4-oximino derivatives by starting with an α-oximino-β-ketoester.[269,1125,1534,1536] In a modification of this by Bülow and Bozenhardt[258] a hydrazone of the α-oximino-β-ketoester was used. Ponzio and Ruggeri[1125] have used α-oximino-β-hydrazonohydroxamic acids and hydrazines, and other oximino compounds, as illustrated in eq. 209.

It has been claimed that 3-pyrazolidinones can be converted to 4-oximino-2-pyrazolin-5-ones by treatment with nitrous acid.[816,1550] However, later workers[911,1342,1491] report that this reaction gives

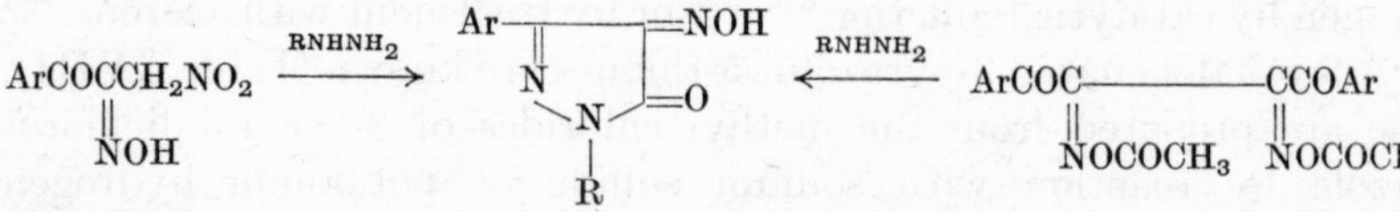

$$ArCOC(=NOH)CH_2NO_2 \xrightarrow{RNHNH_2} \text{[1-R-3-Ar-4-oximino-2-pyrazolin-5-one]} \xleftarrow{RNHNH_2} ArCOC(=NOCOCH_3)-C(=NOCOCH_3)COAr \quad (209)$$

nitrosation at N–1. Since neither Knorr and Duden[816] nor von Rothenburg[1550] give sufficient physical data to identify their products, it may well be that they were actually 1-nitroso-3-pyrazolidinones. Curtius and Bleicher[335] have isomerized 1-nitroso-3-pyrazolidinones by boiling with dilute sulfuric acid, thus causing rearrangement of the nitroso group to the 4-position and oxidation to a pyrazolinone (eq. 210). Qvist[1153] has

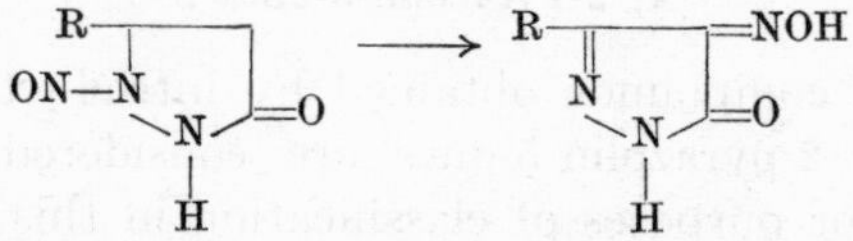

$$\text{[5-R-1-nitroso-3-pyrazolidinone (N-H)]} \longrightarrow \text{[3-R-4-oximino-2-pyrazolin-5-one (N-H)]} \quad (210)$$

rearranged 3-hydrazino-4-nitroso-5-arylisoxazoles to 4-oximino-2-pyrazolin-5-ones by heating in aqueous sodium hydroxide.

Freri[478,480] has reported a very interesting synthesis of 4-oximino-3-methyl-2-pyrazolin-5-one. This consisted in the treatment of citraconic acid hydrazide with nitrous acid (eq. 211). The physical data which

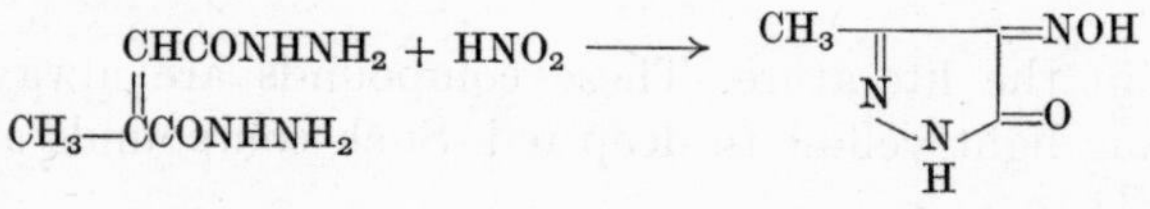

$$CHCONHNH_2{=}C(CH_3)CONHNH_2 + HNO_2 \longrightarrow \text{[3-methyl-4-oximino-2-pyrazolin-5-one (N-H)]} \quad (211)$$

were reported for the product were consistent with those reported by other workers for the same compound. The reaction may go by preferential Curtius rearrangement of one hydrazide to form β-aminocrotonic acid hydrazide which cyclizes and is nitrosated.

Treatment with nitrous acid of a 4-substituted-2-pyrazolin-5-one having no substituent on N–1 gives the 1-nitroso derivative.[262]

In the section dealing with 4-amino-2-pyrazolin-5-ones the reduction of 4-oximino-2-pyrazolin-5-ones and their reaction with active hydrogen atoms of heterocyclic compounds (eq. 174, p. 68) have been discussed. The oximino group is readily oxidized to the nitro group by ozone[478,480] or nitric acid.[809,992] The hydrogen of the oximino group can be replaced by silver by use of silver nitrate[866,1553] and the silver salt thus formed can be alkylated to form an *O*-alkyl oxime. The oximino group can be replaced by a hydrazino group.[1549]

Only one oximinobis(2-pyrazolin-5-one) is known.[459] This is 2,3-bis(4-oximino-3-phenyl-5-oxo-2-pyrazolin-1-yl)naphthalene prepared by nitrosation with nitrous acid.

4-Nitroso-5-imino-2-pyrazolines are capable of existing in several tautomeric forms, (XXXII), (XXXIII) and (XXXIV). Although there

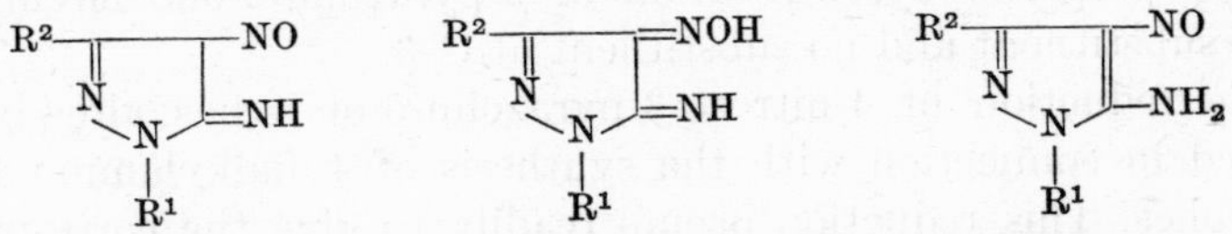

(XXXII) (XXXIII) (XXXIV)

is little experimental evidence concerning structures, these compounds have usually been considered to exist in the oximino–imino form (XXXIII).[996,1002]

Preparation has usually been by the nitrosation of the 5-imino-2-pyrazolines with nitrous acid.[340,996,1002,1010] Qvist[1153] has prepared them by thermal rearrangement of nitrosoisoxazoles (eq. 212). The

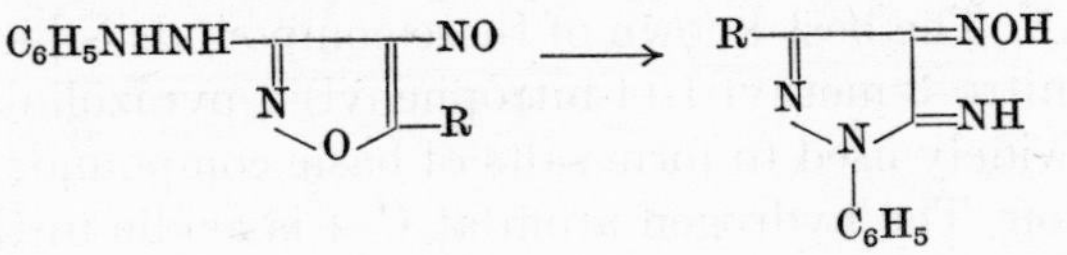

$$C_6H_5NHNH\text{-isoxazole(NO, R)} \longrightarrow \text{pyrazoline}(R, =NOH, =NH, N\text{-}C_6H_5) \quad (212)$$

4-oximino-5-imino-2-pyrazolines may be reduced to amines or oxidized with potassium permanganate to nitro compounds, similarly to their 5-oxo analogs.[1010] However, oxidation with sodium hypochlorite forms furoxazans (eq. 213).[1010]

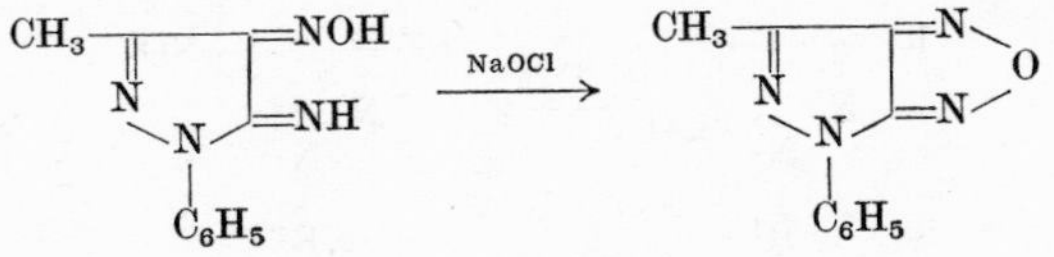

$$\text{pyrazoline}(CH_3, =NOH, =NH, N\text{-}C_6H_5) \xrightarrow{NaOCl} \text{furazanopyrazole}(CH_3, N\text{-}C_6H_5) \quad (213)$$

B. 3-Pyrazolin-5-ones

3- and 4-Nitroso-3-pyrazolin-5-ones can only exist as the nitroso compounds. They are green, as would be expected, and somewhat unstable to heat. In many cases they melt with deflagration. They are basic enough to form stable hydrochlorides, which are usually red. This probably means that these hydrochlorides are actually alkyl chloride salts of 4-oximino-2-pyrazolin-5-ones. The 4-nitroso-3-pyrazolin-5-ones have been of great commercial interest because 4-nitroso-2,3-dimethyl-1-phenyl-3-pyrazolin-5-one is an intermediate in the preparation of the analgesic, aminopyrine. The 4-nitroso-3-pyrazolin-5-ones are listed in Table XXVIII.

The 4-nitroso-3-pyrazolin-5-ones are always prepared by nitrosation of 3-pyrazolin-5-ones with nitrous acid.[99,103,145,647,781,807,809,854,888,972,978,984] Only one 3-nitroso-3-pyrazolin-5-one has been reported.[972] This was prepared by nitrosation of 3-pyrazolin-5-one having a 4-methyl substituent and no substituent at C–3.

The reduction of 4-nitroso-3-pyrazolin-5-ones has already been discussed in connection with the synthesis of 4-dialkylamino-3-pyrazolin-5-ones. This reduction occurs readily to give the corresponding amine when catalytic hydrogenation or various chemical combinations[461,992,1174,1175] are used. Oxidation of nitroso to nitro occurs in the presence of excess of nitrous acid or by use of nitric acid.[984,992]

7. Nitro Substituted Derivatives

A. 2-Pyrazolin-5-ones

Only a few 4-nitro-2-pyrazolin-5-ones are known. They are listed in Table XXIX. The best-known of these compounds is picrolonic acid, which is 4-nitro-3-methyl-1-(4-nitrophenyl)-2-pyrazolin-5-one. This compound is widely used to form salts of basic compounds for isolation or identification. The hydrogen atom at C–4 is acidic in the 4-nitro-2-pyrazolin-5-ones because of the two adjacent electron-withdrawing groups. This hydrogen is easily replaced by metals when treated with metal alkoxides[1642] and reacts with diazomethane.[478]

The usual synthesis of the 4-nitro-2-pyrazolin-5-ones is by nitration of 2-pyrazolin-5-ones under mild conditions (eq. 214).[61,672,690,1004,1683]

$$\text{2-pyrazolin-5-one } (R^1 \text{ at N-1}, R^2 \text{ at C-3}) \xrightarrow{HNO_3} \text{4-}NO_2\text{ derivative} \quad (214)$$

In the case of picrolonic acid further nitration can be brought about to give the 4,4-dinitro compound.[690] The oxidation of 4-nitroso-2-pyrazolin-5-ones has already been mentioned in the section dealing with the nitroso compounds. Ajello[9] has been able to nitrate 3-methyl-2-pyrazolin-5-one using amyl nitrite in acetone or ether for several days. Hill and Black[653] have reported the cyclization of *N*,*N*′-diacetylnitromalondialdimine with base to give 4-nitro-2-pyrazolin-5-one, but such a course for this reaction seems unlikely. The reaction of furlones with sodium nitrite and sulfuric acid to give as one of the products 4-nitro-2-pyrazolin-5-ones[1607] has already been illustrated in eq. 62 (p. 33).

The alkylation of 4-nitro-2-pyrazolin-5-ones at C–4 with diazomethane[478] has already been mentioned. This hydrogen atom is also replaceable with bromine.[1642] Reduction of the nitro group with stannous chloride forms the corresponding amine.[478,480] Picrolonic acid condenses with itself to form a bis(2-pyrazolin-5-one) connected by a double bond at the 4,4′-position, with elimination of two moles of nitrous acid.[690] Condensation also occurs in the presence of phenylhydrazine, but 4,4′-bis[3-methyl-1-(4-nitrophenyl)-2-pyrazolin-5-one] is formed.[690]

Two 4-nitro-5-imino-2-pyrazolines are listed in Table XII. One of these was prepared by permanganate oxidation of the 4-oximino compound[1010] and the other by direct nitration.[1656] These compounds were believed to be aminopyrazoles rather than 5-imino-2-pyrazolines.

B. 3-Pyrazolin-5-ones

The 4-nitro-3-pyrazolin-5-ones are listed in Table XXVIII. They have been prepared most frequently by direct nitration of 3-pyrazolin-5-ones, usually with concentrated nitric acid.[807,809,860,888,1001,1320] The oxidation of 4-nitroso-3-pyrazolin-5-ones to give the 4-nitro compounds has been mentioned in connection with reactions of the 4-nitroso compounds. Nitration of 3-pyrazolin-5-ones with nitrogen tetroxide has been accomplished.[1491]

The nitro group of 4-nitro-3-pyrazolin-5-ones is readily reduced to an amino group by metal–acid combinations.[984,1001]

8. Aldehydes and Ketones

A. 2-Pyrazolin-5-ones

A large number of 2-pyrazolin-5-one aldehydes and ketones are known. These are listed in Table XXX. It is possible to have both 3- and 4-formyl and acyl substituents and both are known, although only one 5-oxo-2-pyrazoline-3-carboxaldehyde has been reported. There has been very little study of the effect of 4-acyl substituents on the structure of 2-pyrazolin-5-ones, but it seems probable that such compounds would tend to exist to a large extent as the 5-hydroxypyrazoles since they would be 1,3-dicarbonyl compounds.

The preparation of the 5-oxo-2-pyrazolinecarboxaldehydes is usually done by procedures which are not applicable to preparation of the acyl homologues. The most extensively used method for preparing the aldehydes is hydrolysis of their Schiff bases,[824,1089,1092,1186,1188] illustrated in eq. 215. R^3 is usually aromatic, although it may be hydrogen.[586,1188] This hydrolysis occurs in the presence either of base or of acids. A second method of preparation is treatment of 4-(2,2,2-trichloro-1-hydroxyethyl)-2-pyrazolin-5-ones, obtained by reaction of

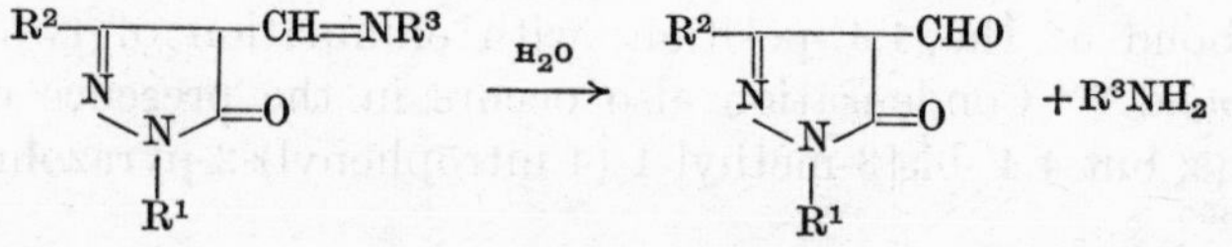

$$\text{R}^2\text{-pyrazolinone-4-CH=NR}^3 \ (\text{1-R}^1) \xrightarrow{H_2O} \text{R}^2\text{-pyrazolinone-4-CHO} \ (\text{1-R}^1) + R^3NH_2 \quad (215)$$

2-pyrazolin-5-ones with chloral, with potassium carbonate.[107] von Rothenburg[1546] has reported that heating of the calcium salt of 5-oxo-2-pyrazolin-3-carboxylic acid in the presence of calcium oxide and calcium formate formed 5-oxo-2-pyrazolin-3-carboxaldehyde. However, his product was not well characterized and the work has not been confirmed.

4-Acyl-2-pyrazolin-5-ones have been synthesized by three general methods. These are cyclization of aliphatic compounds, conversion of other 2-pyrazolin-5-ones and conversion of other heterocycles. As might be expected the reaction of β-ketoesters with hydrazines has been utilized.[124,1124,1532,1533] In this case the β-ketoester has an α-acyl substituent (eq. 216). Both Borsche and Lewinsohn[124] and Vila[1533]

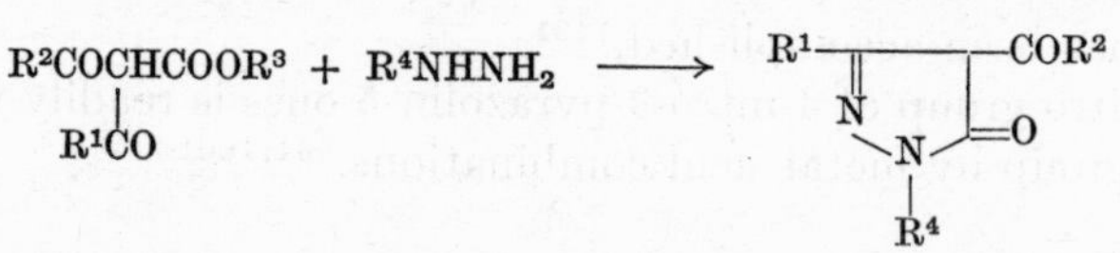

$$R^2COCH(COR^1)COOR^3 + R^4NHNH_2 \longrightarrow \text{3-R}^1\text{-4-COR}^2\text{-1-R}^4\text{-2-pyrazolin-5-one} \quad (216)$$

have used α-hydrocinnamoylacetoacetic ester in this reaction. The former workers claim that the 4-acetyl products are obtained, while Vila reported the products were 4-hydrocinnamoyl-2-pyrazolin-5-ones. 4-Acetyl-2-pyrazolin-5-ones have been obtained by cyclization of hydrazones of β-ketoesters with acetic anhydride.[1009] Kendall and Fry[767] have obtained 3-acyl-2-pyrazolin-5-ones by the reaction sequence shown in eq. 217. The reaction of β,γ-diketoesters with hydrazines also forms 3-acyl-2-pyrazolin-5-ones.[837]

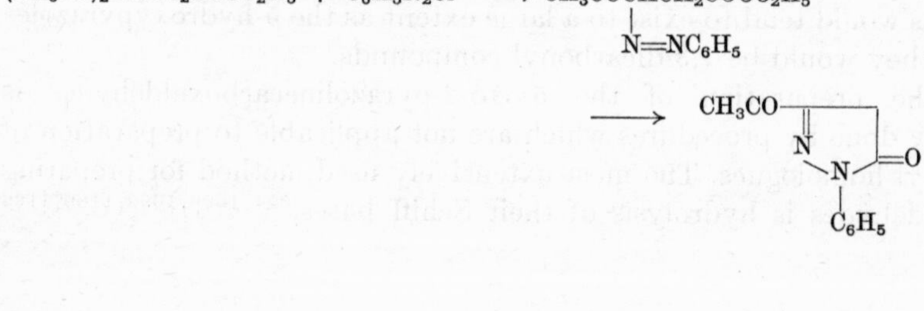

$$(CH_3CO)_2CHCH_2COOC_2H_5 + C_6H_5N_2Cl \longrightarrow CH_3COCH(N{=}NC_6H_5)CH_2COOC_2H_5$$

$$\longrightarrow \text{3-CH}_3\text{CO-1-C}_6\text{H}_5\text{-2-pyrazolin-5-one} \quad (217)$$

Acylation of 2-pyrazolin-5-ones leads to 4-acyl-2-pyrazolin-5-ones. This has been done by treatment with aromatic acid chlorides[110] and with ethyl oxalate in the presence of potassium. A modification of this procedure is acylation of 2-pyrazolin-5-ones to give 4-acyl-5-acyloxy-pyrazoles[591,977] or 2,4-diacyl-3-pyrazolin-5-ones[1056] followed by hydrolytic removal of the *N*-acyl or *O*-acyl groups. The 4-acyl compounds can also be prepared by hydrolysis of their Schiff bases as shown in eq. 215.

The reaction of hydrazine with appropriately substituted isoxazolones or isoxazolinones also forms 4-acyl-2-pyrazolin-5-ones (eq. 218).[947,1295]

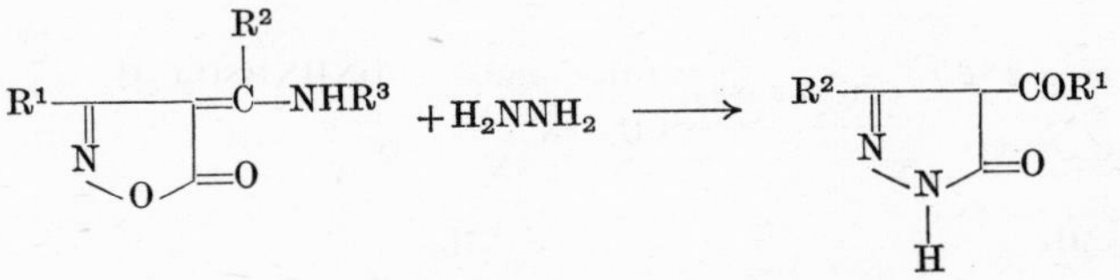

R¹ | N | O | =O | =C—NHR³ | R² $+ H_2NNH_2$ ⟶ R² | COR¹ | N | N | =O | H (218)

5-Oxo-2-pyrazolin-4-carboxaldehydes are oxidized to the corresponding acid by permanganate.[107] These aldehydes under various conditions form 4,4′-methylidynebis(2-pyrazolin-5-ones), and heating alone brings about this reaction (eq. 219).[1089,1093,1188] This same type

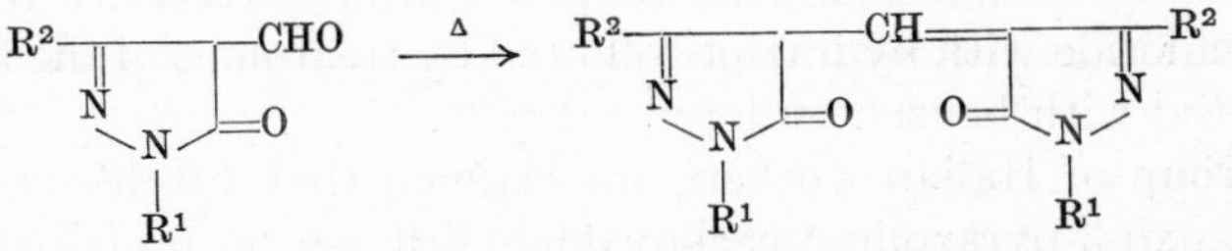

R² | CHO | N | N | =O | R¹ $\xrightarrow{\Delta}$ R² | CH= | R² | N | N | =O | O= | N | N | R¹ | R¹ (219)

of product is obtained by the reaction of the 2-pyrazolin-5-one aldehydes with 2-pyrazolin-5-ones.[1093] Reaction of these aldehydes with 2-methylindole also gives the bis(2-pyrazolin-5-ones).[1185] Such aldehydes react normally with amines and hydroxylamines to give Schiff bases and oximes.[1188] The 4-acyl-2-pyrazolin-5-ones undergo the Mannich reaction.[1098] Treatment of acylpyrazolinones with diazonium salts results in replacement of the acyl group by an arylazo group.[591]

Kendall and Fry[768,770] have prepared 3-acetyl-4-phenylazo-2-pyrazolin-5-one by the reaction of ethyl β-acetyl-δ-oxovalerate with two equivalents of phenyldiazonium chloride.

4-Benzoyl-3-methyl-1-phenyl-2-pyrazolin-5-thione has been prepared by Michaelis and co-workers[977,990] by the reaction of sodium and potassium hydrogen sulfide with 4-benzoyl-5-chloro-3-methyl-1-phenyl-pyrazole. The thiono compound forms a methiodide and gives the characteristic reactions of both ketones and 2-pyrazolin-5-thiones.

B. 3-Pyrazolin-5-ones

There has been considerable interest in the preparation of 5-oxo-3-pyrazolin-4-carboxaldehydes (listed in Table XXXI) because of their close relationship to antipyrine (2,3-dimethyl-1-phenyl-3-pyrazolin-5-one). The most frequently used preparation of these compounds has already been mentioned (eq. 135, p. 54). This consists of treating the condensation products of 3-pyrazolin-5-ones and chloral with base.[107,196,889,893,896,901,1190] The McFadyen–Stevens aldehyde synthesis has been applied to the preparation of both 5-oxo-3-pyrazolin-3-carboxaldehydes[698] and -4-carboxaldehydes.[204,892,1634] This is illustrated in eq. 220. The final step is usually carried out in glycerol at

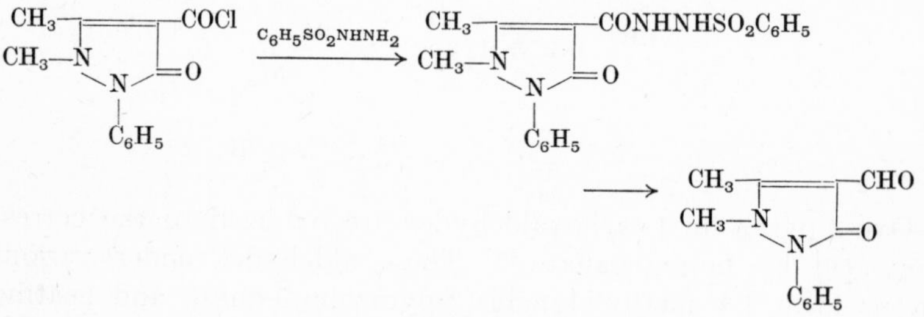

$$\text{(}CH_3\text{, }CH_3\text{–N, N–}C_6H_5\text{, =O)–COCl} \xrightarrow{C_6H_5SO_2NHNH_2} \text{(}CH_3\text{, }CH_3\text{–N, N–}C_6H_5\text{, =O)–}CONHNHSO_2C_6H_5 \longrightarrow \text{(}CH_3\text{, }CH_3\text{–N, N–}C_6H_5\text{, =O)–CHO} \qquad (220)$$

elevated temperatures in the presence of sodium carbonate. The acylsulfonylhydrazide has been prepared alternatively by reaction of the acid chloride with hydrazine followed by treatment of the hydrazide so produced with benzenesulfonyl chloride.

A group of Italian workers has claimed that 1,3-disubstituted-2-methyl-5-oxo-3-pyrazolin-4-carboxaldehydes can be prepared through methylation of the Schiff bases derived from aromatic amines and 1,3-disubstituted-2-pyrazolin-5-ones.[1097] The methylation is carried out with methyl iodide which methylates the ring at N–2, and this is followed by hydrolysis of the Schiff bases with alkaline solutions (eq. 221). Passerini and Losco[1092,1093,1097] and Ridi[1181] claimed to have

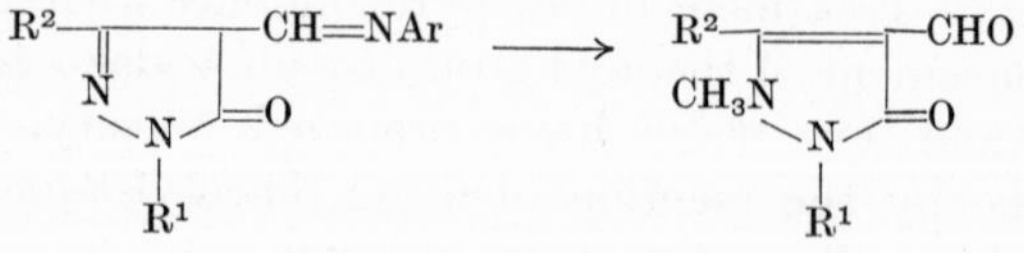

$$\text{(}R^2\text{, N, N–}R^1\text{, =O)–CH=NAr} \longrightarrow \text{(}R^2\text{, }CH_3N\text{, N–}R^1\text{, =O)–CHO} \qquad (221)$$

prepared 2,3-dimethyl-2-phenyl-5-oxo-2-pyrazolin-4-carboxaldehyde in this fashion. Ridi[1180] has also reported the preparation of similar compounds by the same procedure. However, various other workers[108,696,897,902] have reported that in the presence of base 2,3-dimethyl-1-phenyl-5-oxo-2-pyrazolin-4-carboxaldehyde isomerized to 4-acetyl-2-methyl-

1-phenyl-3-pyrazolin-5-one (eq. 222), presumably by hydrolytic ring

$$\text{4-CHO-3-}CH_3\text{-2-}CH_3N\text{-1-}C_6H_5\text{-pyrazolin-5-one} \longrightarrow \text{4-}COCH_3\text{-2-}CH_3N\text{-1-}C_6H_5\text{-pyrazolin-5-one} \qquad (222)$$

cleavage and reclosure. Ledrut, Combes and Sweikert[902] have shown that the reaction depicted in eq. 221, in which $R^1 = C_6H_5$ and $R^2 = CH_3$, does lead to the acetyl derivative, although other substituents give the expected product. A British patent[201] has appeared claiming that alkaline hydrolysis of the presumed 2-methyl intermediate in eq. 221 actually can be made to give the aldehyde by using dilute base and mild conditions. In summary it would appear that the various claims of Passerini, Losco and Ridi are largely correct.

A few miscellaneous preparations of 5-oxo-3-pyrazolincarboxaldehydes have been reported. Ito[698] has prepared 3-carboxaldehydes and 3,4-dicarboxaldehydes by manganese dioxide oxidation of the corresponding alcohols. The 4-carboxaldehydes have also been prepared in this way.[1370] Treatment of antipyrine with dimethylformamide in the presence of phosphorus oxychloride has also been used.[696] Passerini and Losco[1093] have reported methylation of 3-methyl-1-phenyl-5-oxo-2-pyrazolin-4-carboxaldehyde to the corresponding 3-pyrazolin-4-carboxaldehyde. However, the melting point given for their product is that of 4-acetyl-2-methyl-1-phenyl-3-pyrazolin-5-one, so it is probable that isomerization occurred.

Only 4-acetyl-3-pyrazolin-5-ones are known. Most of those prepared are antipyrine derivatives. The most common method for preparing these is by a Friedel–Crafts reaction on 3-pyrazolin-5-ones with acid chlorides and aluminum chloride,[88] zinc chloride[735] or no condensing agent.[737] 2,3-Dimethyl-1-phenyl-5-oxo-3-pyrazolin-4-carboxylic acid and its acid chloride have been condensed with various aromatic compounds to give ketones.[740] Treatment of 4-benzoyl-5-chloro-3-methyl-1-phenylpyrazole or 4-benzoyl-3-methyl-1-phenyl-2-pyrazolin-5-one with dimethyl sulfate gives rise to 4-benzoyl-2,3-dimethyl-1-phenyl-3-pyrazolin-5-one.[977] Phenylhydrazine reacts with isoxazolidones to give what may be 4-acetyl-2-phenyl-3-pyrazolin-5-one.[1295]

The 4-formyl and 4-acyl-3-pyrazolin-5-ones react like normal carbonyl compounds with active methylene groups,[696,1190] amines,[107,1190] hydroxylamine,[196] hydrazines[196,201] and semicarbazide,[201] although some fail to react with thiosemicarbazide.[799] They also form bisulfite addition compounds.[107] Isomerization of 5-oxo-3-pyrazolin-4-carboxaldehydes to 4-acyl-3-pyrazolin-5-ones by base treatment has already been discussed. 4-Acyl-3-pyrazolin-5-ones can be reduced to the corresponding alcohol by sodium–mercury amalgam. Bromination of 5-oxo-3-pyrazolin-4-carboxaldehydes leads to replacement of the formyl group with bromine.[362] Bodendorf, Mildner and Lehman[107] have reported the condensation of 2,3-dimethyl-1-phenyl-5-oxo-3-pyrazolin-4-carboxaldehyde with itself and with 2,3-dimethyl-

CH_3 CHO CH_3N N O C_6H_5 + CH_3 CH_3N N O C_6H_5 + CH_3 CHO CH_3N N O C_6H_5 → (CH_3 CH_3N N O C_6H_5)$_3$CH (223)

1-phenyl-3-pyrazolin-5-one (eq. 223) to form a trimeric 3-pyrazolin-5-one. Passerini and co-workers[1093,1097] have reported that the reaction of 4-acetyl-2-methyl-1-phenyl-3-pyrazolin-5-one with 3-methyl-1-phenyl-2-pyrazolin-5-one gives, in addition to 4,4′-methylidynebis(3-methyl-1-phenyl-2-pyrazolin-5-one), some 2,3-dimethyl-1-phenyl-3-pyrazolin-5-one (eq. 224) and this has been confirmed by Curatolo.[331]

CH_3 N N O C_6H_5 + $COCH_3$ CH_3N N O C_6H_5

→ CH_3 N N C_6H_5 =CH— O N N C_6H_5 CH_3 + CH_3 CH_3N N O C_6H_5 (224)

It may be that there is a transfer of the $CH_3\overset{|}{N}$—$\overset{|}{N}$—C_6H_5 moiety of the 3-pyrazolin-5-one molecule to the 2-pyrazolin-5-one, or it may be that the N–2 methyl group acts as a methylating agent.

Various bis(3-pyrazolin-5-ones) having acyl substituents are known. In all cases the acyl group is part of a 4,4′-bridge between the 3-

pyrazolin-5-one rings. The condensation of 2,3-dimethyl-1-phenyl-5-oxo-3-pyrazolin-4-carboxaldehyde with 4-acetyl-2-methyl-1-phenyl-3-pyrazolin-5-one gives rise to such a compound.[108,696,902] Antipyrine and its 4-carboxyl derivative condense to form diantipyryl ketone.[740] Sodium 2,3-dimethyl-1-phenyl-5-oxo-3-pyrazolin-4-carboxylate reacts with 4-chloroacetyl-3-pyrazolin-5-ones to give bis compounds.[741] 4-Acyl-3-pyrazolin-5-ones dimerize by an aldol condensation.[901]

4-Benzoyl-2,3-dimethyl-1-phenyl-5-imino-3-pyrazoline is prepared by treating the methiodide of 4-benzoyl-3-methyl-1-phenyl-5-imino-2-pyrazoline with base.[977]

9. Carboxylic Acids and Derivatives

A. 2-Pyrazolin-5-ones

A large number of 5-oxo-2-pyrazolin-3- and 4-carboxylic acids and their derivatives have been prepared. These are listed in Tables XXIII, XXXII and XXXIII. These compounds have been of considerable commercial interest because they are the basis for many azo and azomethine dyes.

The usual procedure for preparing the 5-oxo-2-pyrazolin-3-carboxylic acids is reaction of oxaloacetic acid or esters with hydrazines (eq. 225). Several modifications of this reaction have been used. The

$$R^2OOCC(=O)CH(R^1)COOR + R^3NHNH_2 \longrightarrow \text{[5-oxo-2-pyrazoline: } R^2OOC \text{ at C-3, } R^1 \text{ at C-4, C=O at C-5, } N\text{-}R^3\text{]} \qquad (225)$$

common method is to use the ester in which $R = R^2 = CH_3$ or C_6H_5 and either hydrolyze the ester first obtained ($R^2 = CH_3$ or C_2H_5 to $R^2 = H$) with base to give the acid[498,1544,1547] or to use base for the cyclization with concomitant hydrolysis of the ester to give acid directly.[87,312,837,1635] The acid ester in which $R = H$ and $R^2 = C_2H_5$ as starting material gives the acid directly.[347,624] Oxaloacetic acid has been used and it also gives the acid.[43] Of course, hydrolysis of alkyl 5-oxo-2-pyrazolin-3-carboxylates obtained by other means can also be used, as can the hydrolysis of the hydrazide.[337] 5-Oxo-2-pyrazolin-4-carboxylic acids are most frequently prepared by hydrolysis of the corresponding esters.[306,1228,1230] Oxidation of 4-hydroxymethyl-2-pyrazolin-5-ones[24] and 5-oxo-2-pyrazolin-4-carboxaldehydes[107] with permanganate also gives the acid.

Esters of 5-oxo-2-pyrazolin-3-carboxylic acid are prepared by treatment of the esters of four-carbon dicarboxylic acids with hydrazines or diazonium salts. By far the most frequently used method has been the condensation of oxaloacetic esters (esters of α-oxosuccinic acid) with various hydrazines, as shown in eq. 225.[358,1544] This is of course merely a variation of the classical 2-pyrazolin-5-one synthesis. The ester can be substituted[43] to give various 4-substituents in the product and various hydrazines[2,153,499] can be used. The reaction mixture can be heated[594] or mild bases can be used as condensing agents.[414] The hydrazone can first be prepared and then cyclized with acid.[43] Usually the 3-carboxylic acid hydrazide is obtained as a by-product.[1544] As is the case with other α,β-acetylenic esters, the condensation of diethyl acetylenedicarboxylate with hydrazine forms 2-pyrazolin-5-ones but the dicarboxylic esters give products having 3-carbethoxy substituents.[1547,1549] In a very similar type of reaction diethyl chlorofumarate and hydrazines are used.[1220] Treatment of diethyl α-acetylsuccinate with phenyldiazonium chloride forms ethyl 1-phenyl-5-oxo-2-pyrazolin-3-carboxylates (eq. 226).[37,767]

$$CH_3COCH(COOC_2H_5)\text{—}CH(R)COOC_2H_5 + C_6H_5N_2^+Cl^- \longrightarrow \text{1-}C_6H_5\text{-3-}(H_5C_2OOC)\text{-4-R-2-pyrazolin-5-one} \quad (226)$$

The synthesis of alkyl 5-oxo-2-pyrazolin-4-carboxylates is carried out by reaction of hydrazines with various esters having β-substituents or α,β-unsaturation and also an α-carbalkoxy substituent. These methods are quite analogous to ones used generally for this type of ring formation, being modified only to introduce the carboxylate function at the appropriate place. The reaction of acylmalonic esters[138,418,419,563,1222,1223] and their thiono analogs[1008] with hydrazines (eq. 1, p. 9, $R^2 = COOR$ and $R^3 = H$) gives this type of pyrazolinone and is the most frequently used synthesis. Ethoxymethylenemalonic esters[306] and aminomethylidynemalonic esters[604,1231] also react with hydrazines to form alkyl 5-oxo-2-pyrazolin-4-carboxylates. Further syntheses are illustrated in eqs. 227a, 227b and 228. The thio analogs[89]

$$(H_5C_2OOC)_2C{=}CHCH(COOC_2H_5)_2 \xrightarrow{RNHNH_2} \text{1-R-4-}COOC_2H_5\text{-2-pyrazolin-5-one} \quad (227a)$$

$$[HNCH{=}CH(COOC_2H_5)_2]_2 \xrightarrow{RNHNH_2} \text{1-R-4-}COOC_2H_5\text{-2-pyrazolin-5-one} \quad (227b)$$

of these esters are synthesized by reaction of 2-pyrazolin-5-ones with carbon disulfide and ethyl bromide (eq. 229).

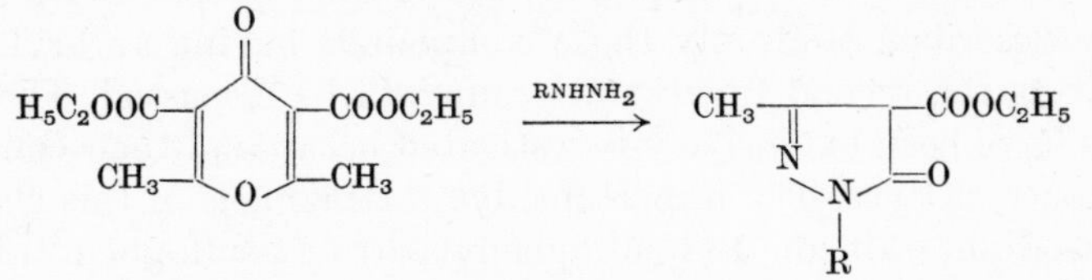

$$H_5C_2OOC,\ CH_3\text{-pyranone-}COOC_2H_5,\ CH_3 \xrightarrow{RNHNH_2} CH_3\text{-pyrazolinone}(COOC_2H_5)(=O)(N\text{-}R) \qquad (228)$$

The usual acid derivatives of 5-oxo-2-pyrazolin-3- and 4-carboxylic acids are known. Amides are prepared by reaction of esters and ammonia,[1339] by the reaction of urea with 2-pyrazolin-5-ones, and by the reaction of azides with ammonia and amines. Hydrolysis of nitriles

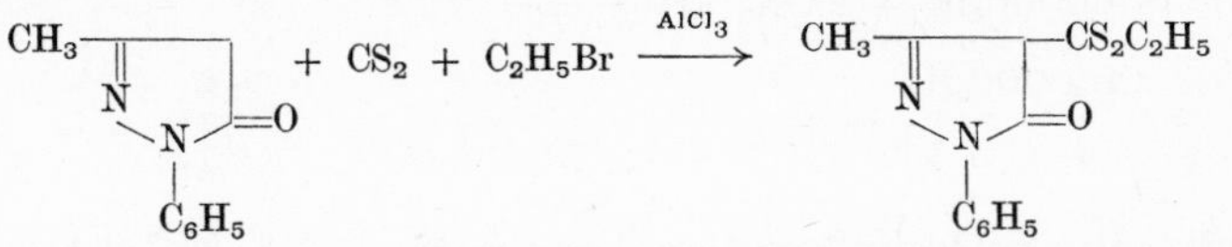

$$CH_3\text{-pyrazolinone}(=O)(N\text{-}C_6H_5) + CS_2 + C_2H_5Br \xrightarrow{AlCl_3} CH_3\text{-pyrazolinone}(CS_2C_2H_5)(=O)(N\text{-}C_6H_5) \qquad (229)$$

also gives amides.[924] The reaction of oxaloacetic esters with excess of hydrazine leads to formation of the hydrazide of 5-oxo-2-pyrazolin-3-carboxylic acid.[1544] Fenton and Jones[443] have reported the same product obtained from oxaloacetic acid, but their melting point differs from the melting point reported by others for this compound. The 3-hydrazide is also obtained by the reaction of hydrazine with diethyl bromosuccinate.[337] A number of hydrazides have been prepared by standard reactions, such as reaction of esters[594] and acid chlorides[498] with hydrazine. Acid chlorides are prepared by reaction of acids with thionyl chlorides.[498] Azides have been synthesized by treatment of hydrazides with nitrous acid[498] and by reaction of acid chlorides with sodium azides.[498] 5-Oxo-2-pyrazolin-4-carbonitriles are prepared by condensation of acylcyanoacetic esters with hydrazine,[1310] by dehydration of the 4-carboxaldehyde oxime[925] and by direct introduction of a nitrile group. The nitrile group has been introduced by treatment of 2-pyrazolin-5-ones with either cyanogen bromide in the presence of aluminum chloride[24] or with mercuric fulminate (eq. 230).[924,1186] Ridi

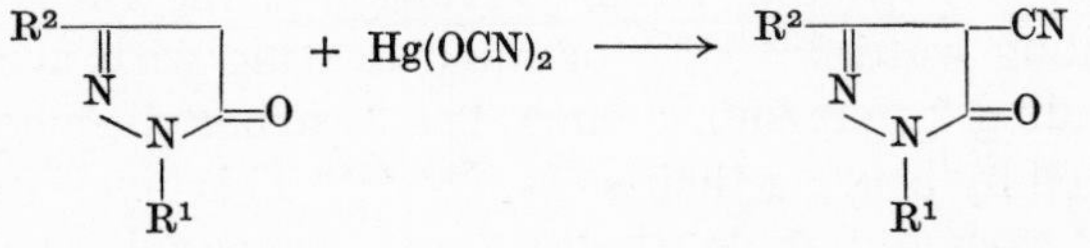

$$R^2\text{-pyrazolinone}(=O)(N\text{-}R^1) + Hg(OCN)_2 \longrightarrow R^2\text{-pyrazolinone}(CN)(=O)(N\text{-}R^1) \qquad (230)$$

and Checchi[1190] described a similar reaction but claimed to have obtained the isonitrile.

A variety of 2-pyrazolin-5-ones having carboxyl or carboxyl derivatives as substituents and a second functional group are known (Table XXXIII). Such compounds are usually prepared by methods already described, and only those compounds having an arylazo substituent as the second functional group will be discussed. These compounds have been extensively investigated because of their commercial importance as dyes. The important dye tartrazine is of this class. It is the trisodium salt of 4-(4-sulfophenylazo)-1-(4-sulfophenyl)-5-oxo-2-pyrazolin-3-carboxylic acid. These dyes exist largely as enol isomers. The principal means of preparation is coupling of a diazonium salt with a 5-oxo-2-pyrazolin-3-carboxylic acid or its derivatives. Another important preparation of these compounds (eq. 231) is by the reaction of

$$CH_3COCH(CH_2COOC_2H_5)COOC_2H_5 + 2ArN_2^+Cl^- \longrightarrow \text{3-}(H_5C_2OOC)\text{-4-}(N{=}NAr)\text{-1-Ar-2-pyrazolin-5-one} \quad (231)$$

diazonium salts with dialkyl acetylsuccinates.[37,444,768,770,1240,1661] In this method the two aryl groups are the same. Various derivatives of succinic acid or its esters such as α-keto-α'-hydroxy,[44] α,α'-diketo[291,293] or their hydrates (dihydroxytartaric acid and esters)[71,1628,1662] react with hydrazines to give the 4-arylazo-5-oxo-2-pyrazolin-3-carboxylic acid derivatives. Treatment of various oxaloacetic acid derivatives[126,285,1066] with diazonium salts, followed by treatment with hydrazines is another method of preparation (eq. 232).

$$H_5C_2OOCCH_2COCOOC_2H_5 + Ar^2N_2^+Cl^- \longrightarrow H_5C_2OOCC(=NNHAr^2)COCOOC_2H_5$$

$$\xrightarrow{Ar^1NHNH_2} \text{3-}(H_5C_2OOC)\text{-4-}(N{=}NAr^2)\text{-1-}Ar^1\text{-2-pyrazolin-5-one} \quad (232)$$

The 5-oxo-2-pyrazolin-3- and 4-carboxylic acids give the normal reactions of 2-pyrazolin-5-ones and of acids. Their derivatives also react as would be expected. Decarboxylation of the 4-carboxylic acids occurs in boiling water,[1228,1230] or upon heating with acid[306] to give the corresponding 2-pyrazolin-5-ones. The 3-carboxylic acids have been decarboxylated by heating their salts.[1544,1549] This gives, in addition to simple loss of carbon dioxide, the bis(5-oxo-2-pyrazolin-4-yl) ketone.

5-Imino-2-pyrazolin-4-carbonitriles and 4-carboxamides have been prepared by Taylor by reaction of hydrazines with malononitrile.[1478]

This presumably goes by dimerization of the malononitrile to give a substituted β-amino-crotononitrile. This dimer also reacts with hydrazines to give 5-imino-2-pyrazolin-4-carbonitriles. These can be hydrolyzed to amides.

A number of bis(2-pyrazolin-5-ones) having carboxyl groups or carboxyl derivatives as substituents have been prepared. Compounds linked at the 4,4′-positions by a single bond are usually formed by oxidation of a 5-oxo-2-pyrazolin-3-carboxylate with hydrazines (eq. 45).[1082,1229] The usual process is to start with a compound, such as an oxaloacetic ester, and treat this with excess of hydrazine. The monomeric pyrazolinone is formed and oxidized to the dimer by the excess of hydrazine present. Another cyclization procedure resulting in dimeric pyrazolinones containing carbethoxy groups is the reaction of hydrazines with α,α′-dicarbethoxy-β,β′-dioxoglutaric esters.[1222] Dimerization of 5-oxo-2-pyrazolin-3-carboxylic acids or their derivatives has been achieved by reaction with formamide to give 4,4′-methylidynebis(5-oxo-2-pyrazolin-3-carboxylic acids).[1262] 5-Oxo-2-pyrazolin-3-carboxylic acids having a 1-(*X*-aminophenyl)-substituent have been dimerized by reaction with phosgene to give a urea which links the two monomers.[152,511] Some 4,4′-bis(2-pyrazolin-5-ones) of the pyrazole blue type, i.e. having an olefin linkage at the 4,4′-positions, have been converted to nitriles by treatment with hydrogen cyanide which adds across the double bond.[1612] Bis compounds having both carboxyl or carboxyl derivatives and arylazo substituents have been prepared analogously to the mono compounds, except for the use of tetrazonium salts.[727,767]

Only a few 5-imino-2-pyrazolinecarboxylic acid derivatives are known. One rather interesting synthesis is oxidation of the 3-methyl group of a 2-pyrazolin-5-one to a 3-carboxyl group with potassium permanganate,[325] illustrating the stability of the 2-pyrazolin-5-one ring to oxidation. Treatment of 3-methyl-1-phenyl-5-phenylimino-2-pyrazoline with phenyl isocyanate gives the corresponding 4-carboxamide.[826] The third method for synthesizing such compounds is shown in eq. 233.

$$NCCH_2COCOOC_2H_5 \xrightarrow{C_6H_5N_2Cl} \underset{\displaystyle N{=}NC_6H_5}{NCCHCOCOOC_2H_5} \xrightarrow{C_6H_5NHNH_2}$$

$$\underset{\displaystyle N{=}NC_6H_5}{NCCH}\text{———}\underset{\displaystyle NNHC_6H_5}{\overset{}{C}COOC_2H_5} \longrightarrow \text{(pyrazoline: } H_5C_2OOC\text{ at C-3, } N{=}NC_6H_5 \text{ at C-4, } {=}NH \text{ at C-5, } N\text{-}C_6H_5 \text{ at N-1)} \quad (233)$$

B. 3-Pyrazolin-5-ones

A large number of 5-oxo-3-pyrazolin-3- and 4-carboxylic acids, acid derivatives and their sulfur analogs are known and are listed in Tables XXXIV and XXVI. The acids are synthesized by methylation of the N–2 of 5-oxo-2-pyrazolin-3-carboxylic acids[108] or by conversion of 4-substituents to 4-carboxyl groups. These conversions involve oxidation of hydroxyl,[17,107,697] formyl[107] and carbon chain substituents,[108] hydrolysis of esters[109,370,993] and hydrolysis of a 4-trichloroacetyl group.[896] Esters have been prepared by reaction of *N*,*N'*-diphenylhydrazine with ethyl oxaloacetate[370] and with dimethyl acetylenedicarboxylate,[370] similarly to the previously mentioned 5-oxo-2-pyrazolin-3-carboxylate analogs. Diethyl ethoxymethylenemalonate and *N*-phenyl-*N'*-acetylhydrazine react to form ethyl 2-phenyl-5-oxo-3-pyrazolin-4-carboxylate.[993] Methylation of 2-pyrazolin-5-one esters at N–2, as expected, gives the 3-pyrazoline analogs.[1228,1230] These esters are also obtained by direct esterification of the acids[18,697,698] and by reaction of acid chlorides with alcohols.[741] The 5-oxo-2-pyrazolin-3- and 4-carboxamides are synthesized by treatment of the appropriate acid chloride,[107,741] anhydride[23] or ester[697,826,1339] with an amine. Partial hydrolysis of nitriles has also given the amides.[925] Treatment of 3-pyrazolin-5-ones with ureas or isocyanates gives the 4-carboxamides.[826] Hydrazides have been prepared from 5-oxo-3-pyrazolinecarboxylic acid chlorides[204,892,1634] or esters[697,698] and hydrazines. Azides are obtained by treatment of hydrazides with nitrous acid.[167,1387] Various dehydrations of 5-oxo-3-pyrazolin-4-carboxaldehyde oximes have been used to prepare nitriles.[925,1181,1183] The N–2 methylation of 5-oxo-2-pyrazolin-carbonitriles has also been employed.[1183] Acid chlorides,[18,109] anhydrides[741] and acyl nitriles[741] have been synthesized by the usual procedures.

Sulfur analogs of 5-oxo-3-pyrazolin-4-carboxylic acids, esters and amides are known. The usual synthesis of both thio and dithio acids is by alkaline hydrolysis of the dithioesters,[109,831] as shown in eq. 234.

$$\text{(ring: } R^3, R^2\text{–N, N–}R^1, =O) + \begin{matrix} C_2H_5Br \\ \text{or} \\ ClCOOC_2H_5 \end{matrix} + CS_2 \xrightarrow{AlCl_3} \text{(ring: } R^3, \text{–}CS_2C_2H_5, R^2\text{–N, N–}R^1, =O)$$

$$\xrightarrow[C_2H_5CH]{OH^-} \text{(ring: } R^3, \text{–COSH}, R^2\text{–N, N–}R^1, =O) + \text{(ring: } R^3, \text{–}CS_2H, R^2\text{–N, N–}R^1, =O) \quad (234)$$

Also shown in the same equation is the synthesis of esters by the reaction of 3-pyrazolin-5-ones with carbon disulfide and either ethyl bromide or ethyl chloroformate in the presence of aluminum chloride.[89,109] The monothio acids have been synthesized by reaction of acid chlorides with hydrogen sulfide.[109] Kocwa[826,829,830,831] has studied the preparation of amides and hydrazides of these thio acids and found that two types exist. In one type the compounds are thioamides but in the other they are iminothiolic acids. Treatment

$$(\text{—}\overset{\overset{\Large S}{\|}}{C}\text{—NHR}) \qquad (\text{—}\overset{\overset{\Large SH}{|}}{C}\text{=NR})$$

of dithioesters and monothio acids with amines results in a mixture of products. The reaction of 3-pyrazolin-5-ones with *N*,*N'*-diphenylthiourea or thioisocyanates forms the thioamides.[826] Hydrolysis of the iminothiolic acids with base gives amides no longer containing sulfur.[826] Mixed anhydrides of sulfonic acids and 5-oxo-3-pyrazolin-4-carboxylic acids have been prepared by the reaction of the sodium salt of the carboxylic acid with benzenesulfonyl chloride.[741]

The 5-oxo-3-pyrazolincarboxylic acids react normally. A number of their reactions have already been discussed in connection with the synthesis of analogous aldehydes and ketones. The Curtius rearrangement of the azide will be discussed in more detail in the section concerning 5-imino-3-pyrazolidinones. Both the 3- and 4-carboxylic acids decarboxylate at elevated temperatures.[107,108,370] Hydrolysis of 4-carboxanilides with hydrochloric acid first forms the acid which then loses carbon dioxide.[826]

A few 5-phenylimino-3-pyrazolin-4-carboxanilides and thioanilides are known (Table XIX). These were prepared by the reaction of phenylisothiocyanates or *N*,*N*-diphenylthiourea with the corresponding 5-imino-3-pyrazoline[826] or by methylation at N–2 of a 5-imino-2-pyrazolin-4-carboxanilide.[826]

10. Sulfonic Acids and Derivatives

A. 2-Pyrazolin-5-ones

The only compounds of this kind which have been reported are 5-oxo-2-pyrazolin-4-sulfonic acids (Table XXXV). They are prepared by direct sulfonation, usually with fuming sulfuric acid.[684,685,1671,1672,1674] Sulfonation occurs at temperatures as low as 10–15°,[684] but it takes place much more rapidly at higher temperatures. If an aryl group is present as a 1-substituent, this too may be sulfonated at higher temperatures.

The sulfonic acid group is readily replaced by a number of reagents, such as nitrous acid[684] and aryldiazonium salts. It is readily removed by acid hydrolysis.[684]

B. 3-Pyrazolin-5-ones

5-Oxo-3-pyrazolin-4-sulfonic acids (Table XXXVI) are prepared by direct sulfonation[738,745] with sulfuric acid and acetic anhydride or by chlorosulfonation with chlorosulfonic acid, followed by hydrolysis to the acid.[1248,1249] The reaction of 2,3-dimethyl-1-phenyl-5-oxo-3-pyrazolin-4-sulfonyl chloride with urea forms a bis(5-oxo-2-pyrazolin-4-sulfonic acid) derivative,[1249] the only such bis derivative reported. Reduction of the sulfonic acid chlorides with zinc and acid forms the corresponding mercapto compound.[1249]

11. Functional Group Substituents on Nitrogen

A. 2-Pyrazolin-5-ones

Functional group substituents on N–1 of 2-pyrazolin-5-ones (Table XXXVII) are acyl, sulfonyl and various carboxyl derivatives, such as carbalkoxy, amides, thioamides, hydrazides, thiohydrazides and amidines. The usual synthesis of these compounds is by the classical 2-pyrazolin-5-one synthesis, reaction of a β-ketoester with a hydrazine. In these cases the hydrazines are special types such as hydrazide, semicarbazide, carbazide or their imino or thio analogs.[61,65,97,275,357,358,359,497,602,716,718,719,720,1012,1013,1067,1222,1345,1568,1632] This synthesis is illustrated in eq. 235. Hydrazides of sulfonic acids can also be

$$R^1COCH_2COOR^2 + R^3CXNHNH_2 \longrightarrow \text{1-}(R^3CX)\text{-3-}R^1\text{-2-pyrazolin-5-one} \qquad (235)$$

R^3 = alkyl, aralkyl, aryl, NH_2, NH_2NH, C_6H_5NHNH
X = O, S, NH

used.[716] Sometimes the hydrazone intermediates are isolated and cyclized by heating.[264,355,358] If R^3 is aralkyl or aryl it is necessary to operate at room temperature, otherwise deacylation occurs.[6] A β-ketoamide can be used instead of a β-ketoester.[692] 2-Pyrazolin-5-ones having no N–1 substituent have been acylated by various procedures (eq. 236). Weissberger and Porter[1598] have studied such acylations using acetic anhydride and found that a side-product is formed by acylation of both

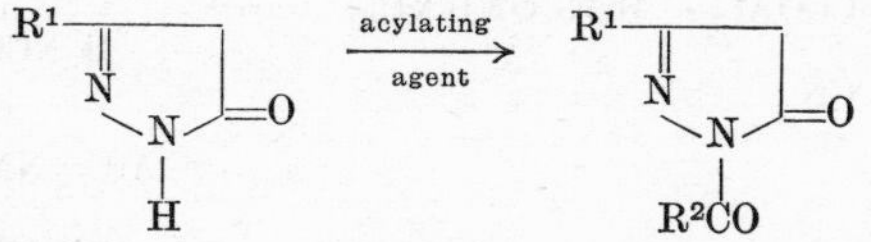

$$\text{R}^1\text{-pyrazolin-5-one (N–H)} \xrightarrow[\text{agent}]{\text{acylating}} \text{R}^1\text{-pyrazolin-5-one (N–COR}^2\text{)} \quad (236)$$

N–1 and O. Other acylating agents used have been arylsulfonyl chlorides[1199] and alkylchloroformates.[61] Isocyanates react with N–1 of 2-pyrazolin-5-ones having no 1-substituent to form 5-oxo-2-pyrazolin-1-carboxanilides. Treatment of 1-acyl-5-acyloxypyrazoles with piperidine in ethanol removes the O-acyl to give 1-acyl-2-pyrazolin-5-ones.[1598]

A number of such compounds having a functional group on carbon atoms of the ring are known. Compounds having nitro[61] and carboxyl[497] substituents are prepared by the above procedures with appropriate substituents in the starting materials. Those compounds having bromine,[355,357] nitroso[355,357,1296] and phenylazo[355,1499] substituents are prepared by the usual methods for introducing such substituents into the 2-pyrazolin-5-one ring.

The N–1 acyl substituted 2-pyrazolin-5-ones react as do the other classes of 2-pyrazolin-5-ones since the hydrogen atoms at C–4 are active.[519,1296] The *N*-acyl substituents are readily removed by hydrolysis[264,355] or treatment with aniline.[6] Pyridine and acetic acid cause a rearrangement of *N*-acetyl groups to the oxygen atom.[1598]

A few bis(1-acyl-2-pyrazolin-5-ones) are known. Those linked through N–1 have been prepared by reaction of carbazide with two equivalents of a β-ketoester[1037,1632] either with[255] or without isolation of the intermediate hydrazone. The bis compounds linked at C–3 or C–4 are prepared by reaction of bis(β-ketoesters) with semicarbazide.[357,1222]

The 5-imino-2-pyrazolines having no N–1 substituents can be acylated with acetic anhydride to form the 1-acyl derivatives,[301,342,391] as can their 5-oxo analogs. Compounds of this type having a 3-acetoxy substituent have been prepared by reaction of 3-amino-2-pyrazolin-5-ones (5-imino-3-pyrazolidinones) with acetic anhydride (eq. 237).[594,1598] Cusmano and Sprio[343,344] have treated α-benzylidene-β-ketonitriles

$$\text{3-}H_2N\text{-pyrazolin-5-one (N–H)} + (CH_3CO)_2O \longrightarrow \text{3-}CH_3COO\text{-1-}CH_3CO\text{-5-}(=NCOCH_3)\text{-pyrazoline} \quad (237)$$

(eq. 238) with semicarbazide to give products which may be 5-imino-

$$C_6H_5CH{=}C(CN)COAr + H_2NCONHNH_2 \longrightarrow \text{Ar-pyrazoline (=NH, N-CONH}_2\text{)} \text{ or } ArC(CH_2CN){=}NNHCONH_2 \quad (238)$$

2-pyrazolin-1-carboxamides, although they may be isomeric open-chain compounds.

B. 3-Pyrazolin-5-ones

Many 3-pyrazolin-5-ones having acyl substituents on N–1 or N–2 or on both have been reported and are listed in Table XXXVIII. Most of these compounds have been prepared by acylation of 2-pyrazolin-5-ones with acyl chlorides or anhydrides. Usually it was assumed that acylation occurred on one or the other of the nitrogen atoms and *O*-acylation was not considered. However, Weissberger and Porter[1598] have found that acylation occurs quite readily on the oxygen, and have shown that the compound reported by von Rothenburg[1557] to be 1,2-diacetyl-3-phenyl-3-pyrazolin-5-one was actually 1-acetyl-3-phenyl-5-acetoxypyrazole. In view of this work it is probable that many of the compounds believed to be 1- or 2-acyl-3-pyrazolin-5-ones are 5-acetoxypyrazoles. Henry and Dehn[643] have obtained a product from 3-methyl-1-phenyl-2-pyrazolin-5-one and phenylisocyanate which may be 3-methyl-1-phenyl-2-phenylcarbamyl-3-pyrazolin-5-one but it may be a product of reaction of the enolic hydroxyl group.

4,4′-Bis(3-methyl-2-benzoyl-1-phenyl-3-pyrazolin-5-one) has been reported as the product obtained from treatment of 4,4′-bis(3-methyl-1-phenyl-2-pyrazolin-5-one) with benzoyl chloride.[1056]

The reaction of 5-imino-3-pyrazolidinones with acetic anhydride forms 2-acetyl-3-acetoxy-5-acetimido-3-pyrazolin-5-ones as well as the 5-imino-2-pyrazoline derivatives already mentioned.[594,1599]

12. Mercury Substituted Derivatives

A. 2-Pyrazolin-5-ones

Only one mercurated 2-pyrazolin-5-one has been reported. This was prepared by Schrauth and Bauerschmidt[1275] and its structure is not completely known (eq. 239).

$$\text{C}_6\text{H}_5\text{-pyrazolinone (N-H)} \xrightarrow{\text{Hg(OCOCH}_3)_2} (\text{CH}_3\text{COOHg})_2\text{C}_6\text{H}_3\text{-}\ldots\text{-HgOCOCH}_3 \quad (239)$$

B. 3-Pyrazolin-5-ones

A few mercurated 3-pyrazolin-5-ones have been prepared by Ragno[1155] (Table XXXIX). Antipyrine was treated with mercuric acetate or mercuric ammonobasic chloride, giving mercury-containing substituents in the 4-position. The chloromercuri and acetoxymercuri compounds obtained were converted into others by treatment with hydrochloric acid, potassium bromide, potassium iodide, iodine or sodium hydroxide. More vigorous treatment with mercuric acetate introduced a second acetoxymercuri substituent which was in the phenyl ring.

13. Metallic and Non-metallic Complexes

A. 2-Pyrazolin-5-ones

2-Pyrazolin-5-ones react with salts of various metals to form compounds in which the pyrazolinone has reacted in its enolic form with replacement of the enolic hydrogen to give a salt and having semipolar bonds formed by donation of electrons to the metal by the nitrogen atoms[393,394] Usually these compounds contain the number of pyrazolinone residues corresponding to the valence of the metal atom. Such salts as cuprous iodide, ferric iodide, cobaltous iodide, silver iodide and silver diiodide participate in such reactions.[393,394] In addition, complexes may be formed in which there has been no elimination of a small molecule between the reactants and no formation of ionic bonds.[482]

Various substituted 2-pyrazolin-5-ones react with metal salts with replacement of hydrogen and formation of semipolar bonds with electron donating atoms. The most important of these compounds are the metal complexes of 4-arylazo-2-pyrazolin-5-ones. These complexes are widely used in the dye industry to give desired properties to 4-arylazo-2-pyrazolin-5-one dyes. Although a large number of metal–dye complexes have been used in dyeing, only a few such compounds have been characterized and reported in the literature. Usually a solution of the azo compound and an appropriate salt such as cupric chloride or nickel sulfate are mixed in solution and heated.[326] The reaction is shown in eq. 240 together with the structure of the final product. In some cases the formation of an intermediate, as shown in eq. 240, has been reported.[1038-1040] The structures of complexes with chromium are shown in formulas (XXX) and (XXXI). Brady and Porter[139] have

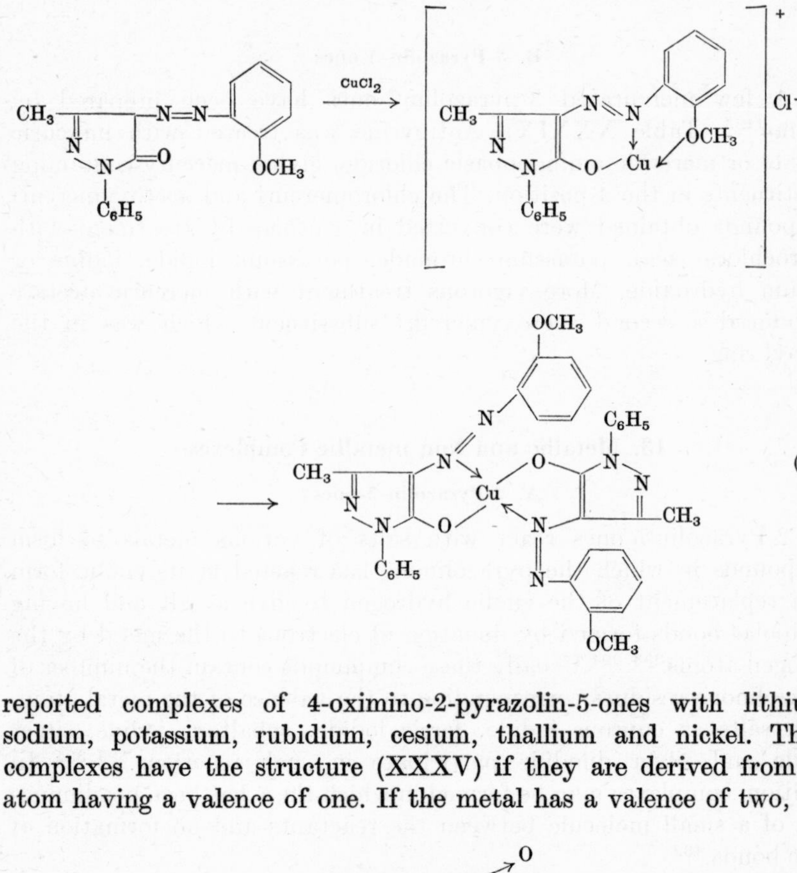

(240)

reported complexes of 4-oximino-2-pyrazolin-5-ones with lithium, sodium, potassium, rubidium, cesium, thallium and nickel. These complexes have the structure (XXXV) if they are derived from an atom having a valence of one. If the metal has a valence of two, the

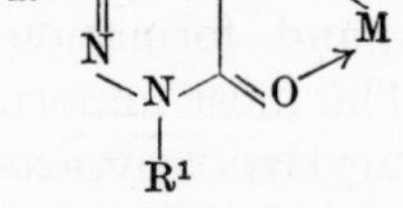

(XXXV)

complex is a dimer of (XXXV). Giva[573] has prepared the thallous salt of picrolonic acid, 4-nitro-3-methyl-1-(4-nitrophenyl)-2-pyrazolin-5-one. This is reported to have a structure similar to (XXXV), with the metal replacing the hydrogen of the pseudo-acid form of the nitro group.

Dains, O'Brien and Johnson[351] have added bromine to various 4-arylaminomethylidyne-1-aryl-3-alkyl- and 3-aryl-2-pyrazolin-5-ones. Whether this is a complex or an addition to a carbon–nitrogen double bond is uncertain. The bromine is very loosely held and is probably not bound covalently.

The formation of various complexes between 1-methyl-3-phenyl-2-pyrazolin-5-one and organic compounds has been reported.[1164] These were 1:1 complexes with *m*- and *p*-nitrophenol, *o*-cresol, picric acid, trinitrobenzene, α-naphthol, hydroquinone, hydroxy- and halogeno-aliphatic acids and aromatic acids. It was claimed that these did not behave as salts. Similar complexes of other 2-pyrazolin-5-ones with trinitrobenzene have been reported.[1368]

B. 3-Pyrazolin-5-ones

3-Pyrazolin-5-ones form complexes with both inorganic and organic compounds much more readily than do the 2-pyrazolin-5-ones. The most extensive series of complexes is that formed with a variety of metallic salts. Antipyrine (2,3-dimethyl-1-phenyl-3-pyrazolin-5-one) forms a series of complexes with salts of divalent, trivalent and tetravalent metals. Two molecules of antipyrine form a complex with one molecule of copper, cadmium, cobalt and zinc salts.[266,868,1116] Complexes prepared from metallic nitrates are usually hydrated.[1322] There also exists a series of complexes in which three molecules of antipyrine form a complex with one or two molecules of metallic salts. Such complexes form with two molecules of simple ferric salts[272] or with one of complex iron cyanides.[608] Nitrates of thorium, lanthanum, cerium and samarium also give such complexes.[841] This ratio also occurs in some antipyrine complexes with cadmium and zinc thiocyanate.[266] A number of salts of rare earths and iron which have complex anions such as thiosulfate, thiocyanate, dithionic acid and complex iron cyanides form complexes in which six molecules of antipyrine are present.[405,408,608,841,950] Stannic chloride forms salts containing three or four molecules of antipyrine and hydrochloric acid.[46]

Aminopyrine (4-dimethylamino-2,3-dimethyl-1-phenyl-3-pyrazolin-5-one) forms complexes similar to those of antipyrine, but usually containing fewer molecules of the 3-pyrazolin-5-one. Complexes with mercury, cadmium, antimony, zinc and cobalt salts include only one molecule of aminopyrine. A number of complexes with cobalt, zinc and calcium salts have two molecules of aminopyrine, some also containing acid and water of hydration.[736,1322] The complex with cerous nitrate contains three molecules of aminopyrine.[1238] A few other substituted antipyrine–metal salt complexes of a similar nature have been reported.[869,1158,1322] These metallic salt complexes are decomposed by sodium hydroxide[868] or by boiling with water.[1158]

Several complexes of 3-pyrazolin-5-ones with iodine are known.[321,429] These contain varying proportions of the pyrazolinones and iodine and always contain hydrogen iodide. The iodine is readily lost by heating or by recrystallization. Iodine complexes with bis(2,3-dimethyl-1-phenyl-5-oxo-3-pyrazolin-4-yl)mercury have been reported.[433]

A number of organic compounds form complexes with antipyrine and aminopyrine. Usually these are in a 1 : 1 ratio, although those with diethylbarbituric acid,[1112] phenylethylbarbituric acid[1484] and diphenylhydantoin[491] may contain two molecules of pyrazolinone, and a complex having two molecules of diphenylhydantoin to one of antipyrine has been reported.[1021] A series of complexes with phenols, aromatic acids, and hydroxy and halogeno aliphatic acids have been reported.[1164] These products do not behave like salts. Benzenesulfonyl chloride forms a complex with antipyrine in a 2 : 1 ratio.[1281] Pfeiffer and Seydel[1115] claim that complexes of antipyrine and aminopyrine with 2,2,2-trichloroethyl carbamate and its *N*-phenyl homologue involve bonding at the amide group in the pyrazolinone. Taboury[1467] reaches the same conclusion regarding the chloral–antipyrine complex on the basis of Raman spectra.

14. Miscellaneous Derivatives

This section comprises a few 3-pyrazolin-5-ones which do not fit well in other sections and some polymeric 2-pyrazolin-5-ones.

2-Pyrazolin-5-ones have been incorporated into a number of polymers for use in color photography. Many of these are prepared by reaction of a functional group in a polymer with some reactive group in a pyrazolinone. Some are prepared by linking polymers with pyrazolinones through aldehydes, and frequently bifunctional pyrazolinones are made to react with aldehydes to give condensation polymers. In one case a hydrazino group is formed in a copolymer of *p*-aminostyrene and maleic acid and this polymer is condensed with ethyl acetoacetate giving a polymeric pyrazolinone.[16]

Several pyrazolinone polymers have been prepared by linking polymers and pyrazolinones by amide linkages. This has been done by treating copolymers containing maleic anhydride with 1-(aminophenyl)-2-pyrazolin-5-ones[162,1273] and by treating the acid chloride of 1-(3-carboxyphenyl)-3-methyl-2-pyrazolin-5-one with polymeric amines.[483,484] A similar type of polymer is that obtained from poly-*p*-chlorosulfostyrene and 1-(aminophenyl)-2-pyrazolin-5-one, except that a sulfonamide linkage is obtained.[1005]

Quite a variety of polymeric pyrazolinones have been prepared by reaction of polymers having amide or hydroxyl groups with aldehydes and pyrazolinones. Some of the pyrazolinones have contained amino groups. The linkages involved are probably acetal for the most part. In one of these cases the aldehyde group is incorporated in the 1-aryl group of the pyrazolinone and the polymer is a polyvinyl alchohol.[385] Presumably the polyvinyl alcohol forms an acetal of the formyl group. Woodward[1647,1648] has prepared polymers from polyhydroxy compounds such as polyvinyl alcohols and methyl cellulose combined with aldehydes and pyrazolinones. The linkages here are no doubt formed by conversion of the aldehydes to acetals and may be derived from the enolic form of the 2-pyrazolin-5-ones. Jennings[708] and McQueen[966] have prepared similar polymers. Condensation of polyvinyl alcohol with 1-(3-aminophenyl)-3-methyl-2-pyrazolin-5-one in the presence of dialdehydes such as glyoxal and terephthaldehyde has given polymeric pyrazolinones.[710] The linkage is probably a combination of Schiff's base and acetal formation. A polymer has been prepared by reaction of a polyamide with formaldehyde, 3-methyl-1-phenyl-2-pyrazolin-5-one and butanol.[965] It seems likely that the amide nitrogen of the polymer is connected by a methylene group with C–4 of the pyrazolinone. Jennings, Murray and White[712] have obtained a polymer of uncertain structure from polyvinyl alcohol, *m*-aminobenzaldehyde and 1-phenyl-5-oxo-2-pyrazolin-3-carboxylic acid. There are a number of possibilities for linking groups which may be present in this polymer but, in any case, some must be of acetal or ether type.

Bisamides of amino-2-pyrazolin-5-ones react with aldehydes such as formaldehyde and *p*-hydroxybenzaldehyde to give polymers.[797,1041] Presumably the linking group is $>\mathrm{N\overset{|}{C}H{-}N}<$. Bisamides of 1-(aminophenyl)-2-pyrazolin-5-ones and of 3-amino-2-pyrazolin-5-ones have been used. 1-(3-Aminophenyl)-3-methyl-2-pyrazolin-5-one reacts with many aldehydes and ketones to form polymers.[964] Probably condensation occurs at C–4 and the amino group. The product of reaction of *p*-cresol with formaldehyde has been found to react with 1-(4-hydroxyphenyl)-3-methyl-2-pyrazolin-5-one to give a polymer that must have the aromatic and pyrazolinone rings connected by ether linkages.[1269]

Kirby[780] has linked a polymer with a pyrazolinone by forming the quaternary salt of 1-(3-bromoacetamidophenyl)-3-methyl-2-pyrazolin-5-one with a polyamine.

Jennings[709] has linked pyrazolinones with zein by means of formaldehyde and dimethylolurea. It was suggested that a linkage is formed from amino groups in the zein to C–4 or an amino group in the pyrazolinone.

Verkade and Dhont[1531] have treated 3,4-dimethyl-2-pyrazolin-5-one and 4-methyl-3-phenyl-2-pyrazolin-5-one with phenyldiazonium chloride, forming respectively 3,4-dimethyl-2-phenylazo-3-pyrazolin-5-one, m.p. 273°, and 4-methyl-3-phenyl-2-phenylazo-3-pyrazolin-5-one, m.p. 212°. 2,3-Dimethyl-1-phenyl-3-pyrazolin-5-one reacts with thiocyanogen to give its thiocyanate salt and 2,3-dimethyl-1-phenyl-4-thiocyanato-3-pyrazolin-5-one, m.p. 125°.[742]

2,3-Dimethyl-1-phenyl-5-oxo-3-pyrazolin-4-carboxaldehyde reacts with 2,3-dimethyl-1-phenyl-3-pyrazolin-5-one to give tris(2,3-dimethyl-1-phenyl-5-oxo-3-pyrazolin-4-yl)methane.[107] Mannich and Krosche[946] have treated 2,3-dimethyl-1-aryl-2-pyrazolin-5-ones with hexamethylenetetramine to give compounds of the type shown in eq. 241. The aryl groups were phenyl and *p*-tolyl. The reaction of 2,3-

CH3, CH3—N, N, O, Ar + $(CH_2)_6N_4$ ⟶ (CH3, CH2—, CH3—N, N, O, Ar)$_3$N (241)

dimethyl-1-phenyl-3-pyrazolin-5-one with ethylene diamine and formaldehyde gives (XXXVI).[945] 2,3-Dimethyl-1-phenyl-3-pyrazolin-5-one reacts with mercuric oxide to give bis(2,3-dimethyl-1-phenyl-5-oxo-3-pyrazolin-4-yl) mercury, m.p. 180°,[433] and with selenium or selenium dioxide to give the corresponding selenide, m.p. 240°.[545]

CH3, CH2—N—CH2, CH3, CH3—N, O, CH2, O, N—CH3, N, N, C_6H_5, CH2, C_6H_5

CH3, CH2—N—CH2, CH3, CH3—N, O, O, N—CH3, N, N, C_6H_5, C_6H_5

(XXXVI)

CHAPTER III

2-Pyrazolin-4-ones

Relatively few 2-pyrazolin-4-ones are known, and most of our knowledge of these compounds has been furnished by Chattaway, Ashworth and co-workers who published an extensive series of papers on this subject in the thirties. These compounds are basic, forming salts with acids and alkyl halides, and they are also acids, giving salts with bases. They form colored complexes with ferric chloride. Four structures are possible for 2-pyrazolin-4-one, (XXXVII), (XXXVIII), (XXXIX) and (XL), but substitution at C–3 and C–5 makes possible

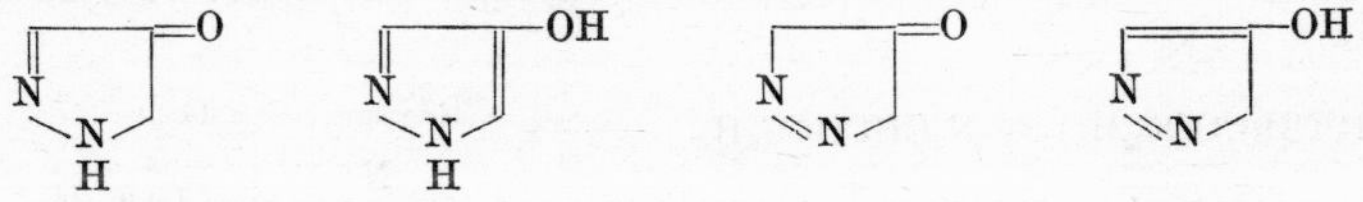

(XXXVII) (XXXVIII) (XXXIX) (XL)

several more isomers. If a substituent is present at N–1, only two isomers, (XXXVII) and (XXXVIII), are possible. It has usually been considered that 2-pyrazolin-5-ones have the hydroxypyrazole structure (XXXVIII).[286–290] Wolff[1644] has postulated this structure on the basis of the alcohol derivatives formed by these compounds. However, Emerson and Beegle[425] have found that 4-oxo-2-pyrazolin-3-carboxylic acid forms two derivatives by reaction with 4-amino-2,3-dimethyl-1-phenyl-3-pyrazolin-5-one (2,3-dimethyl-1-phenyl-4-imino-3-pyrazolidinone). This was interpreted to mean that the 2-pyrazolin-4-ones exist in two forms. One of these would be either (XXXVII) or (XXXVIII) with a carboxyl group at C–3, or a mixture of these two forms, and the other would be either (XLI) or (XLII), or a mixture of these. Bertho

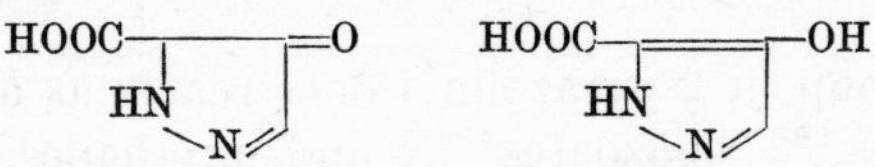

(XLI) (XLII)

and Nüssel[92] have argued that 2-pyrazolin-4-ones exist as keto–enol tautomers. 2-Pyrazolin-4-ones having substituents at N–1 and C–3 and disubstituted at C–5 would necessarily exist in the oxo-form (XXXVII). The 2-pyrazolin-4-ones are listed in Table XL.

Only two procedures are known for direct synthesis of the 2-pyrazolin-4-one ring system and one of these has been used very little. The chief method employed has been cyclization of the 1-arylhydrazone of 3-substituted-1,2-dioxo compounds (eq. 242) using basic cyclizing

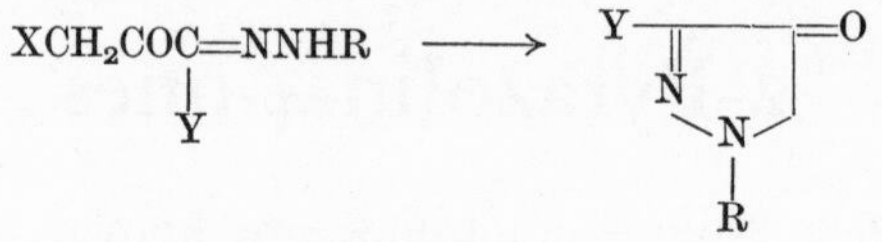

$$XCH_2COC(Y){=}NNHR \longrightarrow \text{1-R-3-Y-2-pyrazolin-4-one} \qquad (242)$$

X = halogen or R′COO
Y = $COOC_2H_5$ or R′CO
R = Ar or SO_3Na

agents.[286-290,295,1292,1644] In the case in which $R = SO_3Na$, the R is lost and in the final product R = H. The only other method of ring formation is that reported by Bertho and Nüssel[92] in which malonic esters are treated with ethyl diazoacetate (eq. 243). If R^1 is H, the substituent R^2 in the product is carbethoxyl, but otherwise $R^1 = R^2$.

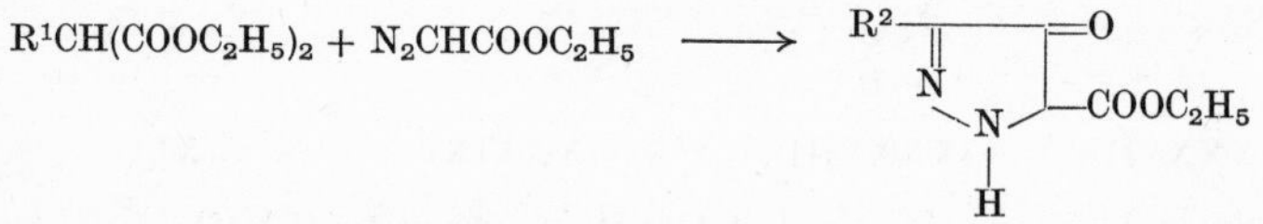

$$R^1CH(COOC_2H_5)_2 + N_2CHCOOC_2H_5 \longrightarrow \text{3-}R^2\text{-5-}COOC_2H_5\text{-2-pyrazolin-4-one (N–H)} \qquad (243)$$

Treatment of 2-pyrazolin-4-ones with chlorine results in formation of 5,5-dichloro-2-pyrazolin-4-ones.[287,288,290] Reaction of the 5,5-dichloro compound with hydrogen iodide[287] or potassium iodide[288,290] removes one chlorine atom to give 5-chloro-2-pyrazolin-4-ones. Bromination does not follow the same course as chlorination, but instead forms 5-bromo-2-pyrazolin-4-ones.[286,290,1292] Carboxyl-containing 2-pyrazolin-4-ones can be obtained by hydrolysis of the esters obtained, as shown in eq. 243, or directly by the cyclization procedure of eq. 242. These acids can then be decarboxylated at elevated temperatures.[92,1644] Heating the methiodide of 2-pyrazolin-4-one gives methylation at N–1. 2-Pyrazolin-4-ones couple with diazonium salts to give 5-arylazo substituents.[1644]

The oxo group in 2-pyrazolin-4-ones reacts as a hydroxyl group, forming acetates,[286] benzoates[1644] and urethanes.[1644] Reaction of 2-pyrazolin-4-ones with phosphorus oxychloride results in replacement of the oxygen to give 4-chloropyrazoles.[1644] Treatment of 2-pyrazolin-4-ones with nitrous acid gives substitution of an oximino group at C–5.

Ethyl 1-aryl-5,5-dichloro-4-oxo-2-pyrazolin-3-carboxylates react with alcohols and alkali by cleavage of the ring and formation of mono-arylhydrazones of diketosuccinic acid and its esters.[287,290]

For purposes of classification the 4-aminopyrazoles are considered to be 4-imino-2-pyrazolines and analogs of 2-pyrazolin-4-ones. These compounds are listed in Table XL. Such compounds can be prepared by direct cyclization using ethyl diazoacetate and ethyl cyanoacetate.[92] This is the same as eq. 243, except that the malonic ester is replaced by ethyl cyanoacetate. Purines can be hydrolyzed to 4-imino-2-pyrazolines by using strong acid.[1210,1646] By far the most frequently used preparation is reduction of appropriately substituted pyrazoles, such as 4-nitro,[368,812,819,1015,1019,1049] 4-nitroso[1165] or 4-arylazo.[671,974,995] The hydrolysis of the carbethoxy 4-imino-2-pyrazolines derived from ethyl cyanoacetate and ethyl diazoacetate forms 4-imino-2-pyrazolin-3-carboxylic acid which is readily decarboxylated to the parent compound.[92]

The 4-imino-2-pyrazolines react as would be expected of 4-amino-pyrazoles. For example, acylation[368,1043] and diazotization[812,819] occur readily.

Only two bis(4-imino-2-pyrazolines) have been prepared. These were reported by Michaelis and Schäfer.[995]

CHAPTER IV

2-Pyrazolin-4,5-diones

Only half-a-dozen of these compounds are known (Table XLI) and at least this number of methods of preparing them have been reported. Borsche and Manteuffel[125] have found that 2-pyrazolin-4,5-diones are formed as the by-products when α-ketoesters are treated with aryldiazonium salts. The principal products are 4-arylazo-2-pyrazolin-5-ones. Nitric acid oxidation of 3-methyl-1-phenyl-2-pyrazolin-5-one forms the corresponding 4,5-dione.[809] Wislicenus and Göz[1642] heated 4-bromo-4-nitro-1-(4-bromophenyl)-3-methyl-2-pyrazolin-5-one in water and obtained the analogous 4-oxo compound. Acid hydrolysis of rubazonic acids, which are 4-imino-2-pyrazolin-5-ones, leads to 2-pyrazolin-4,5-diones.[424, 809] Oxidation of 4,4′-bis(2-pyrazolin-5-ones) or of rubazonic acids with nitric acid[809] forms the 4,5-diones.

CHAPTER V

3-Pyrazolidinones

In recent years there has been extensive work in the field of 3-pyrazolidinones because of their use as photographic developers.[750,758,1176,1630] This phase of 3-pyrazolidinone chemistry will be considered in more detail in a later section. The 3-pyrazolidinones are monoacidic bases[911,1550] forming various salts. They are not acidic,[1550] in contrast to the 2-pyrazolin-5-ones. They reduce Fehling's solution and give colors with ferric chloride.[1550] Jensen[713] found that 5-phenyl-3-pyrazolidinone absorbs infrared light in the carbonyl region at 5.83 μ and at 5.91 μ in solution or at 5.97 μ in the solid state. The absorption was markedly different from that of noncyclic hydrazides. These compounds are listed in Table XLII.

As was mentioned previously (eq. 4, p. 10), the principal method used for synthesis of 3-pyrazolidinones is the reaction of hydrazines with α,β-unsaturated acids,[446,816,911,1342,1550] α,β-unsaturated esters[581,762,911,1209,1569] and α,β-unsaturated amides.[758] In many cases these reactions do not give 1-substituted-3-pyrazolidinones, as shown in eq. 4, but the isomeric 2-substituted-3-pyrazolidinones, as shown for one particular case in eq. 244. Most frequently aryl hydrazines have

$$CH_3CH{=}CHCOOH + C_6H_5NHNH_2 \longrightarrow \text{(5-methyl-2-phenyl-3-pyrazolidinone: ring } CH_3\text{–C, HN, N(}C_6H_5\text{), C=O)} \qquad (244)$$

been used in this synthesis, but in a few cases hydrazine has been used.[911,1209,1550] In this situation isomerism is not a problem. Only a few acids have been used in these reactions, but these have all given the 2-isomer (eq. 244).[446,816,1550] Acrylamide, methacrylamide, crotonamide and β,β-dimethylacrylamide and various aryl hydrazines have been condensed in anhydrous solvents in the presence of strong bases. In all cases the 1-isomer (eq. 4) has been obtained.[758] Kendall, Duffin and

Axford[762] have found that the reaction of various esters with phenylhydrazine in the presence of sodium ethoxide led to the 1-isomers (eq. 4). Under somewhat similar conditions, but using sodium methoxide as the condensing agent, Vystrčil and Stejskal[1569] found that methyl crotonate and phenylhydrazine did not give a 3-pyrazolidinone but rather pyrazolinones. These latter authors studied the condensation of methyl methacrylate and methyl crotonate with phenylhydrazine in the presence of hydroquinone. The chief products were the 2-isomers (eq. 244), but 1-isomers were usually formed in very small yields.

Another widely used procedure for the preparation of 3-pyrazolidinones is one closely related to the preceding one. This method is treatment of a β-substituted acid, lactone, amide or acid chloride with an aryl hydrazine. Substituted β-chloropropionyl chlorides have been used, giving 1-aryl-3-pyrazolidinones.[15] The same kind of product was obtained with a β-bromopropionic acid.[1327] Condensation of β,β-dimethylglycidamide with phenylhydrazine at 150° gave 5,5-dimethyl-4-hydroxyl-2-phenyl-3-pyrazolidinone.[156,1260,1261] Kendall[750] has claimed that arylhydrazines react with β-propiolactone to give 1-aryl-3-pyrazolidinones. Reynolds and Tinker[1177] have stated that this reaction does not occur. However, Gresham and co-workers[599] have reported that β-propiolactone and phenylhydrazine form the phenylhydrazide of β-hydroxypropionic acid, and Reynolds and Tinker have converted this compound into 1-phenyl-3-pyrazolidinone. Furthermore, the physical constants claimed by Kendall for his products are the same as those reported by others for the same compounds. From these facts it seems likely that Kendall did obtain 3-pyrazolidinones by the procedure claimed.

Cyclization of α,β-unsaturated acid hydrazides[319] or β-hydroxypropionic acid hydrazides[1177,1327] forms 3-pyrazolidinones. The β-hydroxy acid derivatives have usually been cyclized with acid at elevated temperatures. If the hydrazides of aryl hydrazines are used, N–1 substitution occurs. It has been reported that α,β-unsaturated acid hydrazines cyclize by treatment of the hydrazide with nitrous acid (eq. 245),[335,479,1028,1029] leading to formation of 1-nitroso-

$$\text{RCH{=}CHCONHNH}_2 \xrightarrow{\text{HNO}_2} \text{(1-nitroso-5-R-3-pyrazolidinone: R, ONN, N–H, =O)} \qquad (245)$$

pyrazolidinones. However, Godtfredsen and Vangedal[581] have shown that in some cases the starting materials were pyrazolidinones, rather than hydrazides, and this may be true in all cases, so that cyclization by this procedure probably does not occur.

Cyclization of β-hydrazino acids under acid conditions has been used by Lederer[888] and by Stolz[1351] to obtain 3-pyrazolidinones. Treatment of an analogous nitrile with concentrated hydrochloric acid also gives a 3-pyrazolidinone.[1122] Vystričil and Stejskal[1569] have reported that heating a mixture of methyl α-piperidinobutyrate and phenylhydrazine at 170° gave 4-methyl-2-phenyl-3-pyrazolidinone.

The reaction of 2-phenyl-4-benzylidene-5-oxazolone with hydrazine forms 4-benzamido-5-phenyl-3-pyrazolidinone.[319,1342] Both 2-pyrazolin-5-ones and 3-pyrazolin-5-ones have been reduced catalytically to 3-pyrazolidinones.[1491,1592] Heymons and Rohland[647] have treated 3-methyl-1,2-diphenyl-3-pyrazolin-5-one with sodium and carbon dioxide and claimed to have obtained a carboxylic acid, presumably by intermediate addition of sodium to the double bond (eq. 246). A number of

$$\text{3-}CH_3\text{-1,2-}(C_6H_5)_2\text{-3-pyrazolin-5-one} \xrightarrow[CO_2]{Na} \text{3-}CH_3\text{-3-}COOH\text{-1,2-}(C_6H_5)_2\text{-5-pyrazolidinone} \qquad (246)$$

conversions of variously modified ring systems into 3-pyrazolidinones have been reported. 3-Iminopyrazolidines have been hydrolyzed with acid to the analogous oxo compounds. Rondestvedt and Chang[1209] have found that treatment of *N,N*-diethyl-1-pyrazolin-3-sulfonamide with bromine forms 3-pyrazolidinones. The first step is probably the replacement of the sulfonamide portion by bromine; the bromopyrazoline could then go to the pyrazolidinone by hydrolysis. 3-Pyrazolidinone was also obtained by the reaction of ethylenesulfonyl chloride with diazomethane,[1209] which also probably passes through a halogenated pyrazoline stage. Tsumaki[1501] has claimed that acid hydrolysis of 1,2-diphenyl-3,5-pyrazolidinedione formed 3,4-dihydroxy-1,2-diphenyl-3-pyrazolidinone.

The oxidation of 3-pyrazolidinones to 2-pyrazolin-5-ones has been mentioned (eq. 22). The 3-pyrazolidinones are also oxidized by Fehling's solution[1550] and cupric sulfate.[581] The oxidation of 1-aryl-3-pyrazolidinones to 3-pyrazolin-5-ones has been mentioned.[56,888]

Substitution in the 3-pyrazolidinone molecule occurs preferentially on one of the nitrogen atoms, if this is possible, although reagents such as bromine may oxidize the 3-pyrazolidinone to a 2-pyrazolin-5-one, and then substitute at C–4. Alkylation of 3-pyrazolidinones with alkyl halides and alkyl sulfates and bases usually occurs at N–2,[335,1029] but if substituents are present here, alkylation occurs at N–1.[888,1261]

Alkylation of 4-methyl-3-pyrazolidinone with butyl ethylenesulfonate gave alkylation at N–1 with addition of nitrogen at the β-position of the α,β-unsaturated system.[1209] Earlier workers have claimed that nitrosation of 3-pyrazolidinones leads to either substitution at C–4[446] or oxidation to 2-pyrazolin-5-ones followed by substitution at C–4.[816,1550] However, later workers uniformly report that nitrosation occurs at N–1 (eq. 247).[911,1342,1491] Treatment of 3-pyrazolidinones

$$\text{4-}CH_3\text{-1-}C_6H_5\text{-3-pyrazolidinone (HN)} \xrightarrow{HNO_2} \text{4-}CH_3\text{-1-}C_6H_5\text{-2-nitroso-3-pyrazolidinone (ONN)} \quad (247)$$

with bromine results in oxidation to 2-pyrazolin-5-ones followed by substitution of one or two bromine atoms at C–4.[335,1028] Acetic anhydride reacts with 3-pyrazolidinones to give 1-acetyl derivatives.[888,1569] Aldehydes react with 3-pyrazolidinones at N–1, giving products which are zwitterions.[581]

In the presence of sulfuric acid 1-nitroso-3-pyrazolidinones lose nitrous acid by elimination, giving 2-pyrazolin-5-ones which are then nitrosated at C–4.[335,1028] The amino group in 4-amino-3-pyrazolidinones is diazotizable and the resulting diazonium salt undergoes coupling.[12]

A number of mercury-containing 3-pyrazolidinones have been prepared by Schrauth and Bauerschmidt.[1275] Treatment of 1-aryl-3-pyrazolin-5-ones having no substituent at C–4 with mercuric acetate in methanol causes addition of acetoxymercuri and methoxy groups at the 3,4-double bond, substitution of acetoxymercuri at C–4 and mercuration in the aryl rings (eq. 248). 2-Pyrazolin-5-ones also undergo

$$\text{3-}CH_3\text{-2-}CH_3\text{-1-}C_6H_5\text{-3-pyrazolin-5-one} \longrightarrow \text{3-}CH_3\text{-3-}HgOCOCH_3\text{-4-}OCH_3\text{-4-}HgOCOCH_3\text{-2-}CH_3\text{-1-}C_6H_3(HgOCOCH_3)_2\text{-pyrazolidin-5-one} \quad (248)$$

this reaction, behaving as if they were 3-pyrazolin-5-ones. Substituents at C–4 change the course of the reaction. In these cases reaction does not occur at low temperatures but does at 160° to give addition of acetoxymercuri and hydroxyl at the 3,4-double bond. The 4-acetoxymercuri substituents are replaced by hydrogen in the presence of hydrochloric acid, but the same substituents at C–5 are converted to chloromercuri.

Only three bis(3-pyrazolidinones) have been reported in the literature. These are 5,5′-bis(4,4-dimethyl-1-phenyl-3-pyrazolidinone),[15] 4,4′-bis(3-oxopyrazolidin-1-yl)dibenzyl ether[1177] and 1,4-bis(2-nitroso-3-oxopyrazolidin-5-yl)benzene.[1226] These are made by procedures already discussed.

A number of 3-iminopyrazolidines have been reported and are listed in Table XLIII. It has generally been believed that these compounds exist as 3-aminopyrazolines, although equilibrium between the two forms has been suggested.[757] Actually the correct structure of these compounds has not been established and it may well be that they exist primarily as the imino isomer.

The reaction of α,β-unsaturated nitriles[396,757,760] or β-alkoxypropionitriles[757] with hydrazines gives 3-iminopyrazolidines. If the hydrazine is substituted, the substituent appears at N–1 (eq. 249). The

$$R^1R^2C{=}C(R^3)CN + R^4NHNH_2 \longrightarrow \text{3-imino-pyrazolidine } (R^1, R^2 \text{ at C-5};\ R^3 \text{ at C-4};\ R^4 \text{ at N-1};\ =NH \text{ at C-3};\ N^2\text{-H}) \tag{249}$$

same type of product is obtained by cyclization of a β-hydrazinopropionitrile.[1122] Reduction of 3-arylazopyrazolines also forms 3-iminopyrazolidines.[396,757] The imino group of these compounds is readily acylated, and the acyl derivatives can be reduced with lithium aluminum hydride to 3-alkyliminopyrazolidines. The acid hydrolysis of 3-iminopyrazolidines has already been discussed.

CHAPTER VI

3,4-Pyrazolidinediones

For purposes of classification, 4-hydroxy-, 4-mercapto- and 4-amino-3-pyrazolin-5-ones, except 4-amino having no hydrogen on the nitrogen, have been considered to be 3,4-pyrazolidinediones or derivatives thereof. These compounds could theoretically exist as the 4-oxo, 4-thiono or 4-imino forms but do exist largely, if not exclusively, as the hydroxy, mercapto and amino isomers. The amino compounds will be named as 4-amino-3-pyrazolin-5-ones. They are listed in Table XLIV.

1,5-Dimethyl-2-phenyl-3,4-pyrazolidinedione and its 1,5-diphenyl-2-methyl analog are the only compounds of their class known. The former has been synthesized by treatment of 1-(2,3-dioxobutyryl)-1-phenyl-2-methyl-2-nitrosohydrazine hydrate with sodium bisulfite[99] and by methylation of 4-hydroxy-3-methyl-1-phenyl-2-pyrazolin-5-one.[820] The latter compound has been prepared in the same way.[1243] The dimethyl phenyl compound has also been isolated from urine as a metabolic product of 4-dimethylamino-2,3-dimethyl-1-phenyl-3-pyrazolin-5-one[617] and it is formed by treatment of the same compound with sulfuric acid.[618] The 4-thiono analog is also known. Reduction of 2-3-dimethyl-1-phenyl-5-oxo-3-pyrazolin-4-sulfonic acid using zinc in acid gives 1,5-dimethyl-2-phenyl-4-thiono-3-pyrazolidinone.[1249]

There has been a great deal of interest in 4-amino-3-pyrazolin-5-ones because of their pharmacological activity. These compounds are closely related to antipyrine and aminopyrine and a great many of them have considerable antipyretic and analgesic activity. By far the most widely used method of preparation of 4-amino-3-pyrazolin-5-ones has been reduction of the corresponding nitroso compounds (eq. 250).

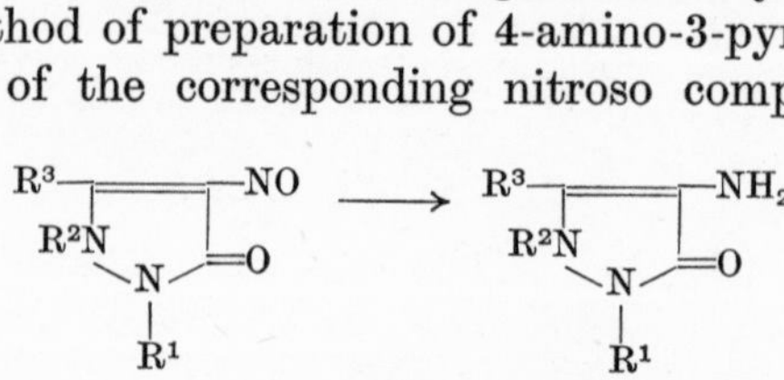

R³—C═C—NO (ring: R²N, N—R¹, C═O) ⟶ R³—C═C—NH₂ (ring: R²N, N—R¹, C═O) (250)

Catalytic hydrogenation,[145,1491] zinc–acetic acid,[992,1001,1504] zinc–sodium bisulfite,[1174,1175] and a mixture of sodium sulfide, sodium hydrogen sulfide and sodium[461] have been used. Reduction of 4-nitroso-3-pyrazolin-5-ones with sodium bisulfite forms the 4-sulfamino acid or its sodium salt (eq. 197). The reduction of 4-nitro-3-pyrazolin-5-ones with zinc and acetic acid also gives the 4-amino compounds.[984,992,1001] Reduction of 4-arylazo-3-pyrazolin-5-ones with hydrogen[670] and of iminoquinones in which the imino nitrogen is substituted by a 5-oxo-3-pyrazolin-4-yl[417] are means of obtaining 4-amino-3-pyrazolin-5-ones.

A few other methods of preparing 4-amino-3-pyrazolin-5-ones have been reported but none has been used extensively. Methylation of the N–2 of 2-pyrazolin-5-ones, the classical 3-pyrazolin-5-one synthesis, has been reported only once.[536] Emerson and co-workers[426] have hydrolyzed iminotoluquinone substituted by antipyrine to give the 4-amino compound. A rather similar reaction, hydrolysis of 4-benzylideneamino-2,3-dimethyl-1-phenyl-3-pyrazolin-5-one in the presence of dimethyl sulfate, forms the 4-methylamino analog.[940] 3-Pyrazolin-5-ones react with urea and acylureas at elevated temperatures, introducing the urea moiety as a substituent at C–4 (eq. 251).[1300,1367] 4-Amino-

$$\text{3-pyrazolin-5-one}(R^1, R^2, R^3) + R^4NHCONH_2 \longrightarrow \text{4-}(NHCONHR^4)\text{-3-pyrazolin-5-one}(R^1, R^2, R^3) \quad (251)$$

antipyrine has been isolated as one of the metabolic products of antipyrine.[617,618]

The amino group of 4-amino-3-pyrazolin-5-ones reacts normally. Acylation occurs readily with a wide variety of acylating agents. Amides are formed by reaction with acid chlorides,[50,533,984,1414,1473] acids[618,984,1471] and esters in the presence of phosphorus pentoxide.[1471] Thioformamides have been prepared by reaction with dithioformic acid and its salts.[472,556,1374] Sulfonyl chlorides react to form sulfonamides.[98,489,984,1249,1504] Chlorophosphates react with 4-amino-3-pyrazolin-5-ones to form phosphoramide derivatives.[509,1496]

The alkylation of 4-amino-3-pyrazolin-5-ones has already been discussed to a considerable extent in connection with the preparation of such compounds having two substituents on the extranuclear nitrogen atom (see p. 76). The most straightforward alkylation is that with alkyl halides.[101,431] Alkylation by means of formation of the Schiff base with aldehydes or ketones followed by catalytic reduction has frequently been used.[111,131,1303] Treatment of 4-amino-2,3-dimethyl-1-phenyl-3-pyrazolin-5-one with formaldehyde and sodium bisulfite in basic solution forms sulfamipyrine (Melubrin),[145,164,541] formerly used as an antipyretic and analgesic (eq. 252). The 4-methylamino derivative

$$\text{4-}NH_2\text{-2,3-}(CH_3)_2\text{-1-}C_6H_5\text{-3-pyrazolin-5-one} \xrightarrow[\text{NaHSO}_3]{\text{CH}_2\text{O}} \text{4-}NHCH_2SO_3H\text{-2,3-}(CH_3)_2\text{-1-}C_6H_5\text{-3-pyrazolin-5-one} \quad (252)$$

gives Dypyrone (Novalgin) used outside the U.S.A. Other aldehydes have also been used in this reaction to give analogous products.[542] If sulfurous acid and formaldehyde are used in this reaction, the product is the sulfinic acid.[164] The use of formaldehyde and hydrogen cyanide introduces a cyanomethyl substituent on the nitrogen.[524] A number of acridine and quinoline substituents have been introduced into the 4-amino group by reaction of 4-amino-3-pyrazolin-5-ones with chlorinated acridines and quinolines.[69,390,547,717] These compounds were studied for their antimalarial activity.

The amino group of 4-amino-3-pyrazolin-5-ones can be diazotized easily and the resulting diazonium salt couples with the usual reagents. Other diazonium salts couple with 4-amino-3-pyrazolin-5-ones at the amino group. Mercuric halides replace the amino hydrogen in 2,3-dimethyl-1-phenyl-4-sulfamino-3-pyrazolin-5-one.[543] The 4-amino groups react normally with isothiocyanates,[49] epoxides,[1261] ureas[1367] and nitrosamines.[527]

Only a few bis(4-imino-3-pyrazolidinones) are known and most of these are linked through the imino nitrogen atoms. The only exceptions to this are three compounds (Table XLVI) which are linked through arsenic atoms in the *p,p'*-positions of 1,1'-aryl substituents.[546,1362] These compounds are prepared by way of 1-(4-arsinophenyl)-2,3-dimethyl-4-nitroso-3-pyrazolin-5-one. This compound is reduced, giving 4,4'-amino groups and reducing the arsenic atoms to give the —As=As— linkage connecting the two rings. The amino groups are then alkylated. The type formula and the remaining bis(4-imino-3-pyrazolidinones) are listed in Table XLV. These have been prepared by reaction of 4-amino-3-pyrazolin-5-ones with dihalides such as phosgene,[589] ethylene dibromide[992] and β,β'-dichloromethyl ether, with carbon disulfide[992,1001] and with ketones.[984]

The only 3,4-di-iminopyrazolidine known is the 5-(3-pyridyl) compound prepared by chemical reduction of 3-(3-pyridyl)-4,5-dinitropyrazole.[932]

CHAPTER VII

3,5-Pyrazolidinediones

1. Introduction

The 3,5-pyrazolidinediones have become of increasing importance in recent years owing to the medical use of 4-butyl-1,2-diphenyl-3,5-pyrazolidinedione which is marketed as Butazolidin (phenylbutazone) and used widely in the treatment of rheumatoid arthritis and various other diseases. A large number of analogs have been prepared for further investigation of their pharmacological and therapeutic properties. 3,5-Pyrazolidinediones have also been of interest as color formers in color photography. The 5-imino-3-pyrazolidinones, contrary to usual practice in this discussion, will be treated separately in the next chapter. This is due to the very large number that are known and the extensive knowledge concerning them and also to the fact that they exist much more as 3-aminopyrazolinones than as 5-imino-3-pyrazolidinones.

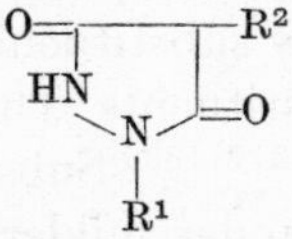

(XLIII) 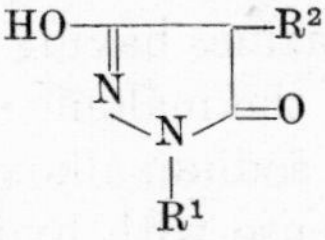 (XLIV) 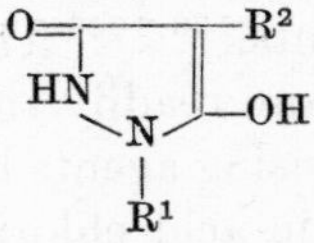 (XLV)

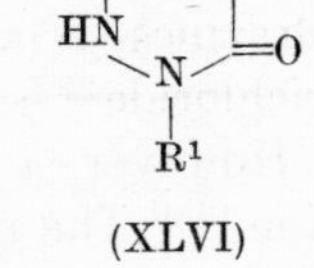

(XLVI) 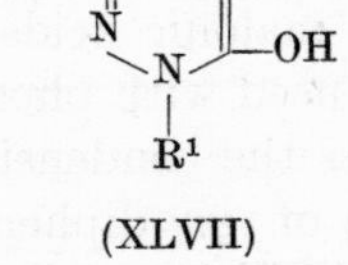 (XLVII)

Five isomeric forms of 3,5-pyrazolidinediones are theoretically possible. These are (XLIII), (XLIV), (XLV), (XLVI) and (XLVII)

when R^1 is not hydrogen. When $R^1 = H$ (XLV) and (XLVI) are identical but the fifth isomer, 3,5-dihydroxypyrazole, is still possible. In those instances in which there are substituents on both nitrogen atoms, only forms (XLIII) and (XLV), which would be identical with (XLVI), are possible if both substituents are the same. Different substituents on the nitrogen atoms would then make possible a third form (XLVI). Compounds having four substituents could exist only in form (XLIII). In view of the acidity of 3,5-pyrazolidinediones[1501,1512] and the ready *O*-alkylation which they undergo, it was suggested by Michaelis and Röhmer[994] that they must exist in form (XLV). Gagnon and coworkers[504,506] from a study of their ultraviolet spectra proposed that a mixture of tautomers (XLIV), (XLV) and (XLVI) occurs. The strong absorption of infrared light in the carbonyl regions by 3,5-pyrazolidinediones[919] is indicative of the presence of only a very small amount of form (XLVII) or perhaps of its complete absence. In summary, it would appear that the 3,5-pyrazolidinediones tend to exist as an equilibrium mixture of 2-pyrazolin-5-one forms and 3-pyrazolin-5-one forms if the existence of such forms is possible.

2. Alkyl, Aralkyl, Heterocyclicalkyl and Aryl Substituted Derivatives

By far the most widely used synthesis of 3,5-pyrazolidinediones is the condensation of malonic acids or esters or acid chlorides with hydrazines (eq. 5, p. 10). A large variety of malonic esters have been used. Esters having monoalkyl,[188,969] monoaryl,[222] aralkyl,[504] dialkyl,[388] diaralkyl,[339] alkyl and aralkyl[504] and alkyl and aryl[388] substituents have been used. The larger the substituents the lower the yields. The hydrazines used have had alkyl,[222] aryl[506] and diaryl substituents.[188,1338] Those hydrazines having less bulky substituents react the more readily the smaller the malonic ester substituents. The usual condensing agents have been sodium alkoxides.[496,1312,1339] Substituted malonic acid chlorides condense with hydrazines under milder conditions than do the esters. The malonic acid chlorides used have had monoalkyl[252,1032] or monoaryl[1031,1032] substituents. Only symmetrical diarylhydrazines have been used.[1032,1338] In most cases involving condensation of malonic acids with hydrazines, *N*-aryl-*N*-acylhydrazines have been used with phosphorus trichloride[222,997] or phosphorus oxychloride[998] as the condensing agent. However, a Swiss patent has reported the use of *sym*-diphenylhydrazine.[1440] The malonic acid may be unsubstituted,[997] or monoalkyl,[998] dialkyl[997] or monoaryl[222] substituted. A modification of these methods is the use of carbon suboxide instead of the malonic acid derivatives.[1512] Although Tsumaki[1501] has reported poor yields from carbon suboxide, Quintilla[1150] claimed yields of 80–90 per cent. Phenylhydrazine and *sym*-diphenylhydrazine have been condensed with carbon suboxide. The use of *N*,*N'*-diphenyl-*N*-butylhydrazine[1150] led to the formation of 4-butyl-1,2-diphenyl-3,5-pyrazolidinedione (eq. 253).

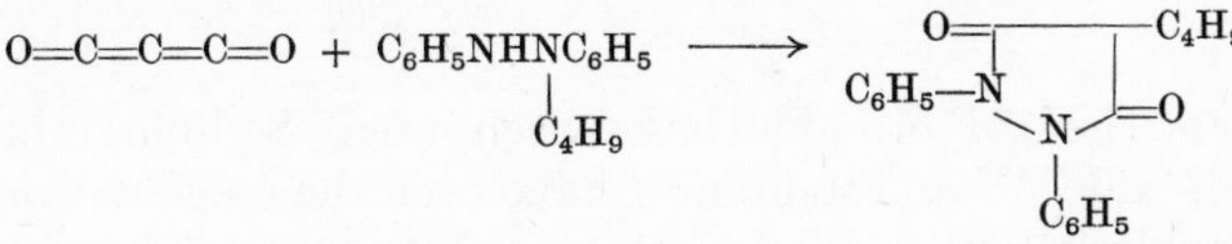

$$O{=}C{=}C{=}C{=}O + C_6H_5NHN(C_4H_9)C_6H_5 \longrightarrow \text{4-}C_4H_9\text{-1,2-}(C_6H_5)_2\text{-3,5-pyrazolidinedione} \quad (253)$$

Three other methods of forming the 3,5-pyrazolidinedione ring system have been reported. One of these involves oxidation of malonic acid amides with potassium hypochlorite[952] or with sulfur and aluminum chloride (eq. 254).[1324] The second method is cyclization of

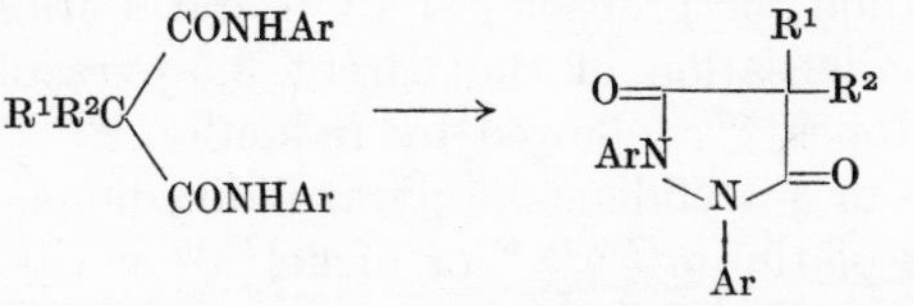

$$R^1R^2C(CONHAr)_2 \longrightarrow \text{4-}R^1\text{-4-}R^2\text{-1,2-}Ar_2\text{-3,5-pyrazolidinedione} \quad (254)$$

malonic acid half-ester hydrazides with base.[976] A rather similar method, published recently, is that of Hallman, Ringhardtz and Fischer.[619] This involves the sequence of reactions shown in eq. 254a.

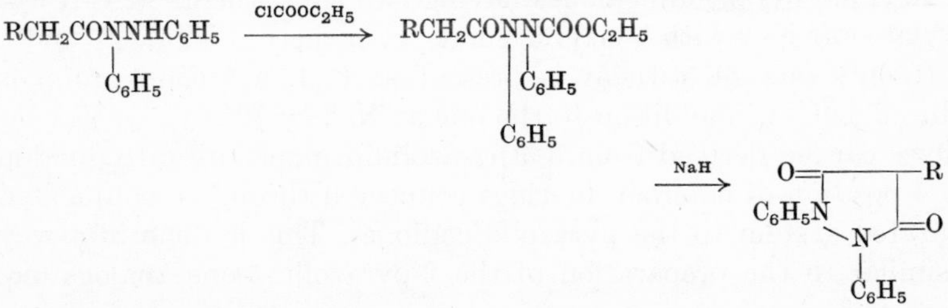

$$RCH_2CONN(C_6H_5)HC_6H_5 \xrightarrow{ClCOOC_2H_5} RCH_2CON(C_6H_5)N(C_6H_5)COOC_2H_5 \xrightarrow{NaH} \text{4-R-1,2-}(C_6H_5)_2\text{-3,5-pyrazolidinedione} \quad (254a)$$

Modification of this synthesis can be achieved by treating the hydrazide with diethyl carbonate or diethyl thiocarbonate. In the latter case the products are 5-thiono-3-pyrazolidinones.

Synthetic methods involving conversion of other, but similar, ring systems to 3,5-pyrazolidinediones have been reduction of 1,2-diphenyl-3,4,5-pyrazolidinetrione with tin and hydrochloric acid[63] and hydrolysis of 5-imino-3-pyrazolidinones (3-amino-2-pyrazolin-5-ones) with acid.[1339, 1596]

A variety of 4-substituted-3,5-pyrazolidinediones has been prepared by alkylation of 3,5-pyrazolidinediones in various ways. The hydrogen atoms at the 4-position are active and direct alkylation with alkyl halides and a base is possible (eq. 255).[222] Usually the lower alkyl

$$\text{3,5-pyrazolidinedione }(R^1\text{ on N-1}, R^2\text{ on N-2}) + R^3X \longrightarrow \text{4-}R^3\text{-3,5-pyrazolidinedione} \qquad (255)$$

bromides and benzyl bromide have been used. Sodium ethoxide,[63] sodium hydroxide[1437] and sodium[304] have been the reagents employed. Either monoalkylation or dialkylation at C–4 can be achieved. In all cases in which this procedure has been used for alkylation, both nitrogen atoms have been substituted. A Wurtz–Fittig reaction on 4-bromo-3,5-pyrazolidinedione using alkyl halides and sodium, zinc or magnesium gives the same type of product.[1325] Probably the most widely used method for preparing 4-alkyl and 4-aralkyl-3,5-pyrazolidinediones is condensation of the parent 3,5-pyrazolidinedione with aldehydes or ketones[1501] followed by reduction.[188] The first product is a 4-alkylidene- or 4-arylidene-3,5-pyrazolidinedione. Catalytic reduction using either platinum[615,1439] or nickel[1430] as catalyst gives alkyl or aralkyl analogs. A large number of aliphatic aldehydes and ketones, cycloalkanones and such aromatic carbonyl compounds as benzaldehyde, acetophenone and benzophenone[188,615,976,1439,1501,1502] give aldol condensations with 3,5-pyrazolidinediones.

1-Aryl-3,5-pyrazolidinediones having two substituents at C–4 can be alkylated at N–2 with benzyl bromide[248] or methyl iodide[998] and a base. If only one substituent is present at C–4, a second group is introduced at C–4 in addition to the one at N–2.[222,998]

Dyes can be derived from 3,5-pyrazolidinediones by introduction at the 4-position of heterocyclic rings connected through a conjugated unsaturated system to the pyrazolidinediones. This is done in a way very similar to the preparation of the 2-pyrazolin-5-one analogs (eq. 256).[1330,1670]

The 3,5-pyrazolidinediones undergo the Mannich reaction[919] and can be readily alkylated in this way.

These compounds are listed in Table XLVII.

Owing to the active hydrogen atoms at C–4 in 3,5-pyrazolidinediones various substitutions at C–4 can be accomplished. Reaction with acid chlorides in the presence of aluminum chloride gives 4-acyl-3,5-pyrazolidinediones.[919,976] However, if two groups are already present at C–4, the enolic form of the dione is acylated on the oxygen atom to give 3-acyloxy-2-pyrazolin-5-ones.[998] Treatment of 3,5-pyrazolidinediones with nitrous acid gives nitrosation at C–4.[976] The nitroso derivative is thought to exist as the oximino isomer. Reaction with aryldiazonium salts[976] results in introduction of a 4-arylazo group.

O= R²N N =O R¹ + X + N I⁻ C₂H₅ —CH=CHNC₆H₅ COCH₃

or

X + N I⁻ C₂H₅ —CH₃ + HC(OC₂H₅)₃

⟶ O= R²N N =O R¹ =CHCH= X N C₂H₅ (256)

Bromination occurs readily with formation of 4-bromo-3,5-pyrazolidinediones.[1031,1032,1048] A 4-phenyliminomethinyl substituent can be introduced[1190] by reaction with *N*,*N′*-diphenylformamidine (eq. 257).

O= HN N =O C_6H_5 + HC(=NC_6H_5)(NHC_6H_5) ⟶ O= HN N =O C_6H_5 —CH=NC_6H_5 (257)

3,5-Pyrazolidinediones having either no substituent at N–2 or at least one hydrogen atom at C–4 form 3-alkoxy-2- or 3-pyrazolin-5-ones by reaction with potassium hydroxide and methyl iodide.[994] In addition, alkylation occurs at C–4. Arndt, Loewe and Ergener[41] have studied alkylation of 3,5-pyrazolidinediones with diazomethane. 1-Phenyl-3,5-pyrazolidinedione reacted to give 3-methoxy-2-phenyl-3-pyrazolin-5-one. However, if two substituents were present at C–4, the product was a 3-methoxy-2-pyrazolin-5-one in addition to methylation of the unsubstituted nitrogen atom. Similarly, treatment of 4-ethyl-4-phenyl-3,5-pyrazolidinedione with hot acetic anhydride gave 3-acetoxy-4-ethyl-4-phenyl-2-pyrazolin-5-one.[1234] One or both of the nuclear oxygen atoms in 3,5-pyrazolidinediones are replaced by chlorine upon reaction with phosphorus oxychloride.[994,998] Reaction of 1-phenyl-3,5-pyrazolidinedione with one mole of phosphorus oxychloride forms 3-chloro-1-phenyl-2-pyrazolin-5-one. A second mole of phosphorus oxychloride gives 1-phenyl-2,4-dichloropyrazole.

Acid hydrolysis of 3,5-pyrazolidinediones opens the ring, giving under mild conditions a half-hydrazide of malonic acid. Under more vigorous conditions degradation goes further.[976] 4-Ethyl-4-phenyl-3,5-pyrazolidinedione undergoes an interesting dimerization[1234] under oxidative conditions to form a bicyclic compound (eq. 258).

$$\text{4-}C_2H_5\text{-4-}C_6H_5\text{-3,5-pyrazolidinedione} \xrightarrow{Br_2} \text{bicyclic dimer (N–N linked, with } C_2H_5, C_6H_5 \text{ on each ring)} \tag{258}$$

3. Hydroxy and Alkoxy Substituted Derivatives

Only two hydroxy- and alkoxy-3,5-pyrazolidinediones are known (Table XLVIII). 4-Butyl-4-hydroxy-1,2-diphenyl-3,5-pyrazolidinedione is formed as a by-product in the synthesis of 4-butyl-1,2-diphenyl-3,5-pyrazolidinedione by condensation of diethyl butylmalonate with *sym*-diphenylhydrazine in the presence of sodium ethoxide.[1312] The reaction of 4-bromo-1,2-diphenyl-3,5-pyrazolidinedione with 2-dimethylaminoethanol forms 4-(2-dimethylaminoethoxy)-1,2-diphenyl 3,5-pyrazolidinedione.[1048]

4. Amino and Azo Substituted Derivatives

These compounds are listed in Table XLVIII. 4-Amino-3,5-pyrazolidinediones have been prepared by reduction of the corresponding 4-oximino compounds.[981,1048,1339] The preparation of 4-arylazo-3,5-pyrazolidinediones by direct introduction of this substituent has already been mentioned in Section 2 of this chapter.[976,1048] Bülow and Bozenhardt[257] have prepared 4-phenylazo-3,5-pyrazolidinedione by cyclization of the phenylhydrazone of mesoxalic acid hydrazide in acetic acid (eq. 259). Stepanov and Kuzin[1340] have suggested that the

$$C_6H_5NHN{=}C(CONHNH_2)_2 \longrightarrow \text{4-}(N{=}NC_6H_5)\text{-3,5-pyrazolidinedione} \tag{259}$$

product obtained in the reaction of chloral hydrate with *p*-nitrophenylhydrazine is 1,4-bis(4-nitrophenylazo)-3,5-pyrazolidinedione, but there is very little evidence for this and it seems highly unlikely.

5. Halogen Substituted Derivatives

4-Halogeno-3,5-pyrazolidinediones are listed in Table XLVIII. Preparation by direct halogenation has already been discussed. This has been done with bromine and chlorine[458,1031,1032,1048] and only monohalogeno products have been obtained. A number of 4-halogeno-3,5-pyrazolidinediones have been prepared by condensation of halogenomalonylchloride with *sym*-diphenylhydrazine.[1033]

The replacement of halogen by alkoxy was mentioned in Section 3. The halogen atom is readily replaced by hydrogen upon treatment with *sym*-diphenylhydrazine[1031,1032] thus reversing halogenation.

6. Nitroso Substituted Derivatives

These are listed in Table XLVIII. The nitrosation of 3,5-pyrazolidinediones has already been mentioned (Section 2). A second method of preparation of the 4-nitroso-3,5-pyrazolidinediones (which are usually considered to have the tautomeric oximino form) has been used by Michaelis and Kirstein.[981] This involves treatment of 3-chloro-3-pyrazolin-5-ones with nitrous acid (eq. 260). A third method of syn-

Cl ; CH_3N ; N ; =O ; C_6H_5 $\xrightarrow{HNO_2}$ O= ; =NOH ; CH_3N ; N ; =O ; C_6H_5 (260)

thesis is hydrolysis of 3-amino-4-oximino-2-pyrazolin-5-ones (4-oximino-5-imino-3-pyrazolidinones).[1339] The reduction of these nitroso compounds has already been discussed (Section 4).

7. C-Acyl Substituted Derivatives

The structure of 4-acyl-3,5-pyrazolidinediones has been studied by use of infrared absorption spectra.[919] These studies indicate that one nuclear oxygen exists in its enolic form and the hydrogen is bonded to acyl oxygen in a chelate ring (XLVIII). These compounds are listed in Tables XLVII and XLVIII.

R ; C ; O= ; O ; C_6H_5N ; H ; N ; O ; C_6H_5

(XLVIII)

The preparation of 4-acyl-3,5-pyrazolidinediones by acylation of 3,5-pyrazolidinediones has already been discussed in Section 2.

4-Acetyl-1-methyl-2-phenyl-5-thiono-3-pyrazolidinone[89,109] has been prepared by hydrolysis of ethyl 2,3-dimethyl-1-phenyl-5-oxo-3-pyrazolin-4-thiocarboxylate with alcoholic potassium hydroxide. This presumably involves ring opening and reclosure.

8. N-Acyl Substituted Derivatives

These compounds are listed in Table XLVIII. *N*-Acyl-3,5-pyrazolidinediones are prepared either by acylation with acid chlorides,[976] in which case acylation at C–4 occurs, or by cyclization.[506,976] Cyclization involves condensation of semicarbazides with malonic esters or cyclization of 3-acylsemicarbazides.

CHAPTER VIII

5-Imino-3-pyrazolidinones

1. Introduction

The compounds considered in this section as 5-imino-3-pyrazolidinones can, at least theoretically, have a number of tautomers. Of this number the four structures shown here, (XLIX), (L), (LI) and (LII),

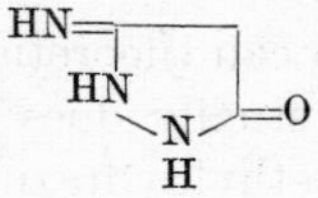

(XLIX) 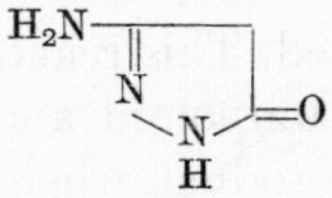 (L) 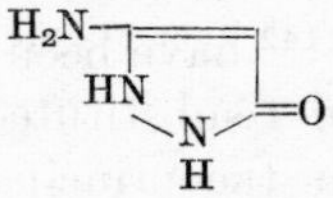 (LI) 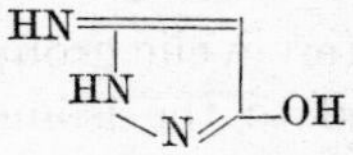 (LII)

are those usually considered to describe adequately the isomers actually occurring. In most cases the structure has not been determined but has been considered to be the 3-amino-2-pyrazolin-5-one form (L). In those cases which have been studied the form (L) and the 3-amino-3-pyrazolin-5-one form (LI) have usually been the ones occurring. Gagnon, Boivin and others,[120,497,499,507] as a part of their general investigation of the ultraviolet absorption spectra of 2-pyrazolin-5-ones, have studied 5-imino-3-pyrazolidinones. No generalization as to structure can be drawn from their findings, but they show the existence of forms (XLIX), (L) and (LI). Weissberger, Porter and Graham[594,1597,1599] have shown that some 5-imino-3-pyrazolidinones actually exist as the isomeric hydroxyiminopyrazoline form (LII). In some cases[1597] the two isomeric forms (L) and (LII) have been isolated. Of course, various combinations of substituents make certain of these tautomeric forms impossible. Four substituents on N–1, N–2 and C–4 would make form (XLIX) the only possible one. Two substituents at N–1 and N–2 would preclude forms (L) and (LII). Two C–4 substituents would likewise eliminate form (LI).

In recent years a great deal of research on 5-imino-3-pyrazolidinones has been done because of their use as color couplers in color photography. Weissberger, Porter, Graham and others at the Kodak Research Laboratories have been particularly active in this field. This point will be discussed in more detail in the section devoted to dyes.

2. Alkyl, Alicyclic, Aralkyl, Heterocyclicalkyl, Heterocyclic and Aryl Substituted Derivatives

The most frequently used procedures for preparation of 5-imino-3-pyrazolidines can all be considered as variations of cyclization of malonic acid derivatives. Various hydrazines react with ethyl β-amino-β-ethoxyacrylate to form 2-substituted-5-imino-3-pyrazolidinones (eq. 261). Complex alkyl groups,[705] aryl groups[693,695,922,1140,1601] and

$$H_5C_2OC(NH_2){=}CHCOOC_2H_5 + RNHNH_2 \longrightarrow \text{HN}{=}\overline{\text{C}-\text{CH}_2-\text{C}}(=\text{O})-\text{N(R)}-\text{NH} \quad (261)$$

heterocyclic groups[1142] have been used. This reaction can theoretically lead to the isomeric 1-substituted compound and actually does give such a compound as the principal product when methylhydrazine is used.[594] A variation of this procedure is to isolate the product resulting from replacement of the ethoxyl group by the hydrazine and cyclization of this product to the 5-imino-3-pyrazolidinone.[871,1142,1603,1604] A somewhat similar method is that used by Weissberger, Porter and Gregory[1597,1601] and by Worrall.[1649,1651] In this method phenyliso-thiocyanate is condensed with ethyl acetoacetate and the resulting thioamide is treated with hydrazine, giving the 5-imino-3-pyrazolidinone (eq. 262). Other isocyanates can be used in this synthesis[1649,1651] and both aliphatic and aromatic hydrazines have been used.

$$C_6H_5NCS + CH_3COCH_2COOC_2H_5 \longrightarrow C_6H_5NHCSCH(COCH_3)COOC_2H_5$$

$$\xrightarrow{RNHNH_2} C_6H_5N{=}\overline{\text{C}-\text{CH}_2-\text{C}}(=\text{O})-\text{N(H)}-\text{N}-\text{R} \quad (262)$$

In the preceding methods only compounds having substituents on the nitrogen atoms can be obtained. In order to introduce substituents at C–4, substituted cyanoacetic esters and cyanoacetic hydrazides have been used (eq. 263). Two isomeric products are possible in this reaction,

R^3 being either at N–1 or N–2. Gagnon and co-workers[498] report that unsubstituted cyanoacetic esters yield the N–2 isomers, while substituted esters give N–1 substituents. Other workers have also found

$$R^1R^2C(CN)COOC_2H_5 + R^3NHNH_2 \longrightarrow \text{HN=}\underset{\text{HN—N(R}^3\text{)—C=O}}{\text{C—CR}^1\text{R}^2} \tag{263}$$

that unsubstituted cyanoacetic esters give the 2-substituted-5-imino-3-pyrazolidinones.[870,1141,1600] Hydrazine,[391] arylhydrazines[498,872,1141] and heterocyclic hydrazines[1142,1600] have been used. Monoalkyl, monoaryl and dialkyl[391] cyanoacetic esters undergo this reaction. The usual condensing agents have been sodium alkoxides. A modification of this procedure is isolation of the intermediate cyanoacetic hydrazide and cyclization of this with base[498,1138] or acid.[506] Unsubstituted,[594,644] mono-substituted[120,500,508] or disubstituted[501] cyanoacetic esters can be used and either hydrazine[594] or phenylhydrazine.[1596]

One of the most widely used methods for the preparation of 5-imino-3-pyrazolidinones is from 5-oxo-3-pyrazolin-3-carboxylic acids or their derivatives by use of the Hofmann[167,697] or Curtius[167,1387,1395] rearrangements (eq. 264). A similar synthesis is from the analogous

$$\text{R}^4\text{OOC-pyrazolinone (R}^1\text{, R}^2\text{N, R}^3\text{)} \rightarrow \begin{cases} \text{H}_2\text{NOC-pyrazolinone} \longrightarrow \text{HN=pyrazolidinone (R}^1\text{, R}^2\text{N, R}^3\text{)} \\ \text{N}_3\text{OC-pyrazolinone} \longrightarrow \text{H}_5\text{C}_2\text{OOCHN-pyrazolinone} \uparrow \end{cases} \tag{264}$$

2-pyrazolin-5-ones by way of the Curtius rearrangement.[497,499,594,1595] The amides and azides are formed by the usual procedures. The usual Hofmann and Curtius conditions are employed and the yields are frequently quite good. The azide rearrangement is usually carried out in ethanol and the carbamate derivatives of 5-imino-3-pyrazolidinones, *N*-(5-oxo-2- or 3-pyrazolin-3-yl) carbamates are prepared as intermediates.[506,594,1387,1395,1595] If 3-pyrazolin-5-ones are used as starting materials in this synthesis, the products can have only one substituent at C–4 and are actually 3-amino-3-pyrazolin-5-ones. Use of 2-pyrazolin-5-ones leads to compounds unsubstituted at N–1. In all cases the products obtained by these syntheses have had substituents at N–2.

A number of 5-substituted imino-3-pyrazolidinones have been prepared by reaction of various reagents with 5-imino-3-pyrazolidinone. For example, 5-alkylimino compounds can be prepared by reduction of 3-benzylideneimino-3-pyrazolin-5-ones.[1052] The benzylidene derivatives are prepared by reaction of benzaldehyde with 5-imino-3-pyrazolidinone.[1052] The same products can be obtained by direct alkylation of 5-imino-3-pyrazolidinone with benzyl chloride and an analogous reaction has been reported by Jennen[704,705] with halogenated heterocycles. Various 5-substituted imino-3-pyrazolidinones have been prepared by reaction of the corresponding 5-imino compounds with various amines.[595,596,1597] This reaction must occur by way of the 5-imino form rather than an amino form and the compounds involved must be at least partially in the 5-imino, rather than the amino, forms. This reaction has been carried out with aniline[1595,1597] and ethylamine,[595] although in the latter case a 4,4′-ethyliminobis(2-pyrazolin-5-one) is the chief product. A variation of this is the condensation of 2-phenyl-5-imino-3-pyrazolidinone with ammonia,[595,596] as shown in eq. 265. The reaction of phenylisocyanate with 2-phenyl-5-imino-3-

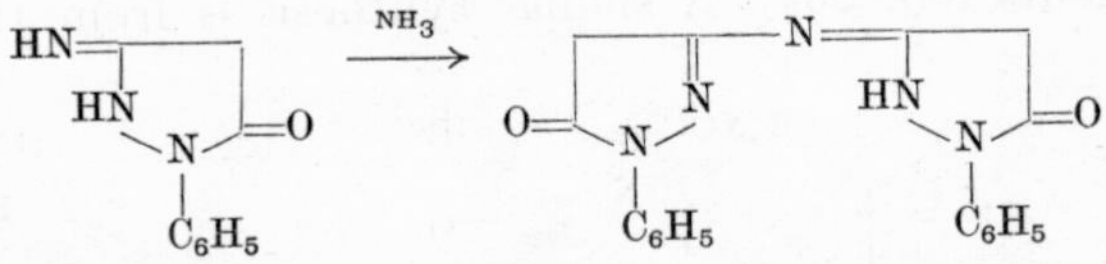

HN=, HN, N, =O, C_6H_5 $\xrightarrow{NH_3}$ O=, N, N, –N=, HN, N, =O, C_6H_5, C_6H_5 (265)

pyrazolidinone leads to the corresponding 5-phenylcarbamyl derivative.[1595] Phenylisothiocyanate reacts in the same way but *p*-tolylisothiocyanate in the presence of pyridine has been reported to cyclize to give 2-phenyl-5-[2-(5-methylbenzothiazolyl)imino]-3-pyrazolidinone.[705]

Acylation of 5-imino-3-pyrazolidinone can occur at several places. Most commonly reaction occurs at the 5-imino group and further reaction then may occur by acylation of the enol form of the 5-oxo group.

In compounds which have no substituents at N–1 or N–2 nuclear acylation also occurs and under some conditions acylation occurs at C–4. The use of 2-alkyl- or aryl-5-imino-3-pyrazolidinones, which exist as the 3-amino-2-pyrazolin-5-one isomer, with an equivalent of acid chloride, either aliphatic or aryl, leads to 3-acylamides (eq. 266),[14,67,594,695,1247,1594,1595] although in some cases a side-reaction gives both *N*- and *O*-acylation.[1595] Under the same conditions 3-hydroxy-5-imino-2-pyrazolinones give *O*-acylation.[1599] The reaction of aromatic acid chlorides in excess[594,1599,1604] or of acetic anhydride[693,1595] with the same types of compounds leads to both *N*- and

H_2N–(ring: N, N–R^1, =O) + R^2COCl ⟶ R^2CONH–(ring: N, N–R^1, =O) (266)

O-acylation. These amide-esters can be hydrolyzed with base to the *N*-acyl derivatives (eq. 267). Hepner and Fajersztejn[644] have reported

HN=(ring: R^2N, N–R^1, =O) $\xrightarrow[\text{or } (R^3CO)_2O]{R^3COCl}$ R^3CON=(ring: R^2N, N–R^1, –$OCOR^3$) $\xrightarrow{OH^-}$ R^3CON=(ring: R^2N, N–R^1, =O) (267)

that acetic anhydride and benzoyl chloride react with 5-imino-3-pyrazolidinones to give acylation on nuclear nitrogen and diacylation at C–4. Graham, Porter and Weissberger[594] have investigated this reaction and have found that acylation does not occur at C–4 but at the 5-imino group and the 5-oxo group (eq. 268). A similar acylation occurs

HN=(ring: HN, N–H, =O) $\xrightarrow{(CH_3CO)_2O}$ CH_3CON=(ring: CH_3CON, N=, –$OCOCH_3$) + CH_3CONH–(ring: N, N–$COCH_3$, –$OCOCH_3$) (268)

with 1-phenyl-5-imino-3-pyrazolidinone to give 2-acetyl-3-acetoxy-1-phenyl-5-acetimido-3-pyrazoline if pyridine is present.[1599] Otherwise a mixture is obtained, but the chief product is 3-acetoxy-4-acetyl-1-phenyl-5-imino-2-pyrazoline.[1599]

The reactions undergone by 5-imino-3-pyrazolidinones are in general very similar to those of 2-pyrazolin-5-ones. The hydrogen atoms at C–4 are active and this position is the reactive center in the nucleus of these molecules. Condensation with aldehydes and ketones occurs with formation of benzylidene[644,1083] or 4,4′-benzylidenebis compounds[1603] rather than Schiff bases which are formed with the amino substituent. However, when β-ketoesters or β-ketoacids are used the carbonyl group does react with the amino group and then cyclizes at the C–4 position (eq. 269).[1085] Reaction with nitrous acid forms, at

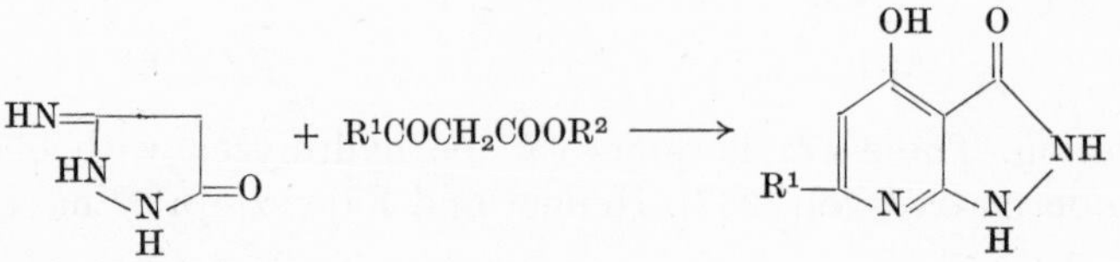

$$\text{5-imino-3-pyrazolidinone} + R^1COCH_2COOR^2 \longrightarrow \text{4-hydroxy-6-}R^1\text{-pyrazolo[3,4-b]pyridin-3-one} \quad (269)$$

least in compounds having no substituents at C–4, 4-oximino-5-imino-3-pyrazolidinones.[644] In compounds substituted at C–4 reaction with nitrous acid leads to loss of nitrogen.[501] Coupling occurs with aryldiazonium salts to give 4-arylazo-5-imino-3-pyrazolidinones.[594] Papini and Venturini[1085] have found that 5-imino-3-pyrazolidinone reacts with *N,N'*-diphenylformamidine at 150° to introduce at C–4 the phenyliminomethylidyne group. 5-Imino-3-pyrazolidinones react with sulfur dichloride to give the 4,4'-bis sulfide.[693,921] Sulfur monochloride reacts to give the analogous disulfide.[693] As is the case with 2-pyrazolin-5-ones, the 5-imino-3-pyrazolidinones undergo condensation at C–4 with *p*-amino-*N,N*-dimethylaniline in the presence of an oxidizing agent to form a magenta dye. Those 5-imino-3-pyrazolidinones which have no N–2 substituent react as enols with phosphorus oxychloride to give 3-chloro-5-imino-2-pyrazolines.[391] They also give positive color tests with ferric chloride.[500,501] They are methylated at N–2 by dimethyl sulfate.[391] As mentioned previously, the 5-imino group can be hydrolyzed with acid to give 3,5-pyrazolidinediones.[1339,1596]

The known bis(5-imino-3-pyrazolidinones) are listed in Tables XLVI and L and are of three types: (1) linked at the 4,4'-positions directly, (2) linked at the 4,4'-positions by a carbon chain, and (3) linked through the nitrogen of the 5-imino group. The compounds of the first type are prepared by reaction of 3-acylamido-1-aryl-4-arylimino-2-pyrazolin-5-ones with the corresponding 3-acylamido-1-aryl-2-pyrazolin-5-ones, the 5-imino-3-pyrazolidinones being considered to exist in this case as their 3-amino-2-pyrazolin-5-one tautomers (eq. 270).[1538] The second type is usually synthesized by reaction of a 3-amido-2-pyrazolin-5-one with an aromatic aldehyde to give a 4-arylidene derivative, followed either by addition of a second mole of the original pyrazolinone to give a symmetrical bis compound (eq. 68)[1255,1603] or by addition of a different pyrazolinone to give an unsymmetrical bis compound.[1254] Most of those compounds which are linked through the 5-imino nitrogen are prepared by reaction of 5-imino-3-pyrazolidinones with the acid chloride of a dibasic acid.[797] However, a bis compound connected only by a carbonyl group has been

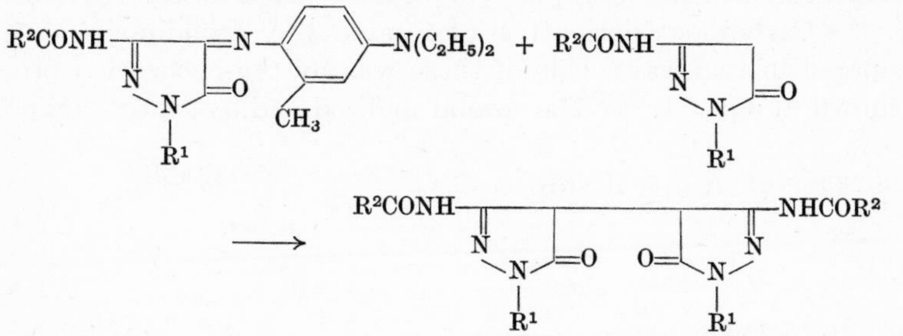

R^2CONH—(pyrazolinone ring: N, N—R^1, =O)=N—(C₆H₃, CH_3)—$N(C_2H_5)_2$ + R^2CONH—(pyrazolinone ring: N, N—R^1, =O)

⟶ R^2CONH—(pyrazolinone ring: N, N—R^1, =O)—(pyrazolinone ring: N, N—R^1, O=)—$NHCOR^2$ (270)

obtained as a by-product in the Curtius rearrangement of an azide to give a 5-imino-3-pyrazolidinone.[1387] It would appear that part of the intermediate isocyanate reacts with some of the final product.

3. Functional Group Derivatives

5-Imino-3-pyrazolidinones having functional group substituents are listed in Sections B and C of Table XLIX. These compounds are usually synthesized by procedures which are used for introduction of the same substituents into previously discussed pyrazolinone and pyrazolidinone systems.

4-Bromo-5-imino-3-pyrazolidinones are synthesized by Curtius rearrangement of the azides of 4-bromo-5-oxo-3-pyrazolin-3-carboxylic acids.[697] 4-Nitroso-5-imino-3-pyrazolidinones are believed to exist as the oximino tautomers.[337] They are usually prepared by direct nitrosation with nitrous acid.[644,1339,1649] A Curtius rearrangement of 4-oximino-5-oxo-2-pyrazolin-3-carboxylic acid azide has also been used.[337]

4-Amino-5-imino-3-pyrazolidinones have been synthesized by reduction of the corresponding oximes.[644,1339] Such amines form ureas and thioureas by reaction with potassium cyanate in acid solution and with phenyl isothiocyanate.[644] 4-Arylimino-5-imino-3-pyrazolidinones have been prepared by reaction of the 5-imino-3-pyrazolidinones with *p*-amino-*N*,*N*-diethylaniline in the presence of silver salts as oxidizing agents (eq. 172).[244,519,1255,1538] 4-Arylazo-5-imino-3-pyrazolidinones have most frequently been prepared by reaction of 5-imino-3-pyrazolidinones with aryldiazonium chlorides, as is usual for the preparation of similar compounds.[591,594,920,1087,1255,1339,1539,1649] One such compound has been prepared by the Curtius rearrangement of the corresponding 4-arylazo azide.[594]

The preparation of C–4 acyl and N–1 and N–2 acyl 5-imino-3-pyrazolidinones has been partially discussed in the preceding section. 4-Acetyl-5-imino-3-pyrazolidinones have been prepared by reaction of ethyl acetylcyanoacetate with phenylhydrazine (eq. 263, $R^1 = CH_3CO$, $R^2 = H$).[498] 4-Carbethoxy derivatives of 5-imino-3-pyrazolidinones have been prepared in two ways. One of these was by the cyclization procedure shown in eq. 271.[1650] The second method is direct introduction

$$RNHCSCH(COOC_2H_5)_2 + H_2NNH_2 \longrightarrow \text{(RN=, HN, N–H ring with } COOC_2H_5 \text{ and =O)} \quad (271)$$

by using ethyl chloroformate.[1083] In addition to the *N*-acylations already discussed, 1-acyl-5-imino-3-pyrazolidinones have been prepared by treatment of 1-acyl-3-acyloxy-5-imino-2-pyrazolines with piperidine.[1598] The acyl group on oxygen is preferentially removed. 1-Acyl-5-imino-3-pyrazolidinones also have been prepared by reaction of cyanoacetic esters with acylhydrazines such as benzoyl hydrazide[497] or semicarbazides (eq. 263, $R^3 = C_6H_5CO$, H_2NCO or C_6H_5NHCO).[498,506] Such compounds can also be prepared by the Curtius rearrangement.[497]

4-Amino-5-imino-3-pyrazolidinones react with formaldehyde at the 4-amino group giving methylol derivatives.[644] The 4-arylimino derivatives are reduced catalytically to give 4-arylamino analogs.[1538] An interesting reaction of the 4-arylazo-5-imino-3-pyrazolidinones is the replacement of the 4-arylazo group by arylimino (eq. 272).[1255,1296]

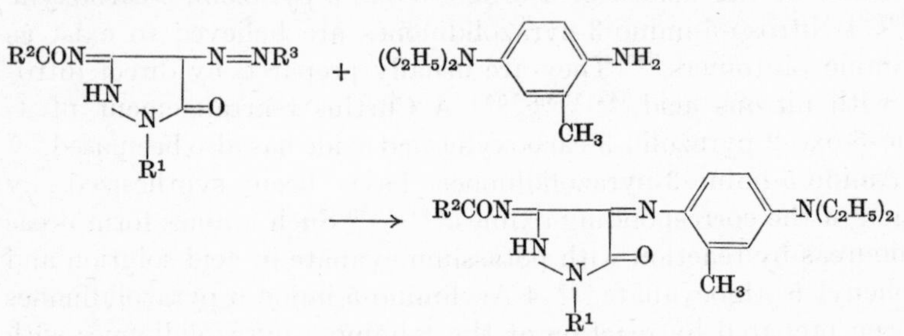

$$\text{(}R^2CON\text{=, HN, N–}R^1\text{ ring with –N=NR}^3\text{ and =O)} + (C_2H_5)_2N\text{–}C_6H_3(CH_3)\text{–}NH_2 \longrightarrow \text{(}R^2CON\text{=, HN, N–}R^1\text{ ring with =N–}C_6H_3(CH_3)\text{–}N(C_2H_5)_2\text{ and =O)} \quad (272)$$

It seems likely that this occurs by way of the hydrazono tautomer of the azo compound.

Bis(5-imino-3-pyrazolidinones) linked at the 4,4′-positions by one or two atoms of sulfur are known (Table L) and their preparation was mentioned in the previous section.

CHAPTER IX

Miscellaneous 3,5-Pyrazolidinediones and Analogs

3,4,5-Pyrazolidinetrione has been prepared by oxidation of the anilide of mesoxalic acid with hydrogen peroxide in alkaline solution.[63]

Six 3,5-di-iminopyrazolidines have been prepared. These compounds are usually considered to exist as diaminopyrazoles, although their structure has not been investigated. The parent compound, 3,5-di-iminopyrazolidine or 3,5-diaminopyrazole, has been reported[473,1561] as the product obtained by reaction of malononitrile and hydrazine. However, Taylor[1478] has claimed that these same reactants give a different product, derived from dimerization of the malononitrile followed by reaction with hydrazine. Knorr[819] has prepared 3,5-di-iminopyrazolidine by the Curtius rearrangement starting with diethyl pyrazole-3,5-dicarboxylate. Two acyl derivatives and the intermediate carbamates were also prepared. Phenylhydrazine and malononitrile do not give a diaminopyrazole as reported.[1478,1561] 2-Methyl-1-phenyl-3,5-bis(phenylimino)pyrazolidine results from the action of aniline on the methiodide of 2,5-dichloro-1-phenylpyrazole.[981]

PART 2

APPLICATIONS

CHAPTER I

Medical

Since the synthesis of antipyrine (2,3-dimethyl-1-phenyl-3-pyrazolin-5-one) by Knorr in 1883 pyrazolinones have been widely used in medicine as analgesics and antipyretics. The discovery of this drug led to a widespread search for other pyrazolinones, having the same type of action but more satisfactory properties, and to a very intensive investigation of the biological properties of pyrazolinones. This investigation resulted in the discovery of aminopyrine, which is the 4-dimethylamino analog of antipyrine, and phenylbutazone (4-butyl-1,2-diphenyl-3,5-pyrazolidinedione) and their employment in medicine. Many other pyrazolinones have been synthesized and studied and a number of these have been used as drugs, but these three have been by far the most important and most of this discussion will be concerned with them.

Although antipyrine has been used as an antipyretic and analgesic for many years, it finds very little use today. In part this has been due to the introduction of the more effective aminopyrine, but largely it has been due to replacement by the salicylates. At the present time it is used chiefly in Europe, South America and the Near East where approximately 50,000 lb. per year is consumed. Antipyrine definitely has analgesic activity[842] but this appears to be of a rather low order.[265] It is absorbed rapidly from the gastrointestinal tract and blood plasma levels are at a maximum in 1–2 hours. Metabolism is rather rapid, with disappearance occurring at the rate of 6 per cent per hour. Water solubility is high and distribution in the tissues is in proportion to their water content. This property has been used as a basis for determining the water content of various tissues. About 30–40 per cent of ingested antipyrine is converted to 4-hydroxyantipyrine and excreted in the urine conjugated with glucuronic acid.[587]

At present aminopyrine is little used in the United States but is still widely used in Europe, South America and the Near East. World production is 250,000–300,000 lb. per year. It is somewhat more effective than antipyrine and is administered in doses of 0.3 or 0.6 g. every four hours. Absorption occurs from the gastrointestinal tract and blood levels reach a maximum in 1–2 hours and then the drug disappears at the rate of 10–30 per cent per hour. A large proportion of it is demethylated in the liver to 4-aminoantipyrine[230,617,618] and this is acetylated and excreted in the urine.[617,618] A small amount, about 9 per cent, is excreted as 4-aminopyrine and about 5 per cent as 4-hydroxyantipyrine.[617,618] As is the case with antipyrine the fate of about half of the aminopyrine ingested is unknown. Its primary effect is on the autonomic nervous system which it depresses[1235,1495] and its analgesic action is exerted through this system.[1479] The mechanism of action of aminopyrine is not known. It does not appear to act through its metabolite, 4-aminoantipyrine,[587] but it may act through some as yet unknown metabolite. The action of aminopyrine in rheumatic fever is equal to that of the salicylates[587] and it is effective in reduction of inflammation due to edema and necrosis.[1625] The chief toxic manifestation of aminopyrine is agranulocytosis. This occurs only in a small minority of those taking the drug, but it may be extremely severe and there is a high death rate among those in whom agranulocytosis occurs. In some individuals there seems to be a hypersensitivity to this drug. Other toxic effects are central nervous system involvement, rash and hemoglobin alterations.

Aminopyrine forms complexes with barbiturates containing one or two molecules of aminopyrine for each molecule of barbiturate. These complexes have a synergistic action on the analgesic activity of the pyrazolinone.[265] Two of these complexes have been marketed as analgesics under the names Allonal and Veramon. The former is a 1 : 1 complex with phenylisopropylbarbituric acid and the latter is a 2 : 1 complex with diethylbarbituric acid. A complex of aminopyrine with trichloroethylurethan has been sold as an analgesic under the trade name Compral.

A tremendous number of 3-pyrazolin-5-ones have been tested for activity as antipyretics and analgesics. Of these many have been found to have such activity, most of them being rather closely related to antipyrine.[58,249,490,530,532,859,1337,1476] Many of these have been claimed to be superior to anipyrine and aminopyrine, but only a few have been used to any extent. Dypyrone (Novalgin) is perhaps the most widely used of these, although on a small scale and almost exclusively outside the U.S.A. This compound has the antipyrine nucleus, but the 4-substituent is $NaO_3SCH_2(CH_3)N$. Sulphamipyrine (Melubrin) is similar to this but lacks the methyl group attached to the side-chain nitrogen atom and is very little used at present. A pyrazolinone which has enjoyed some use as an analgesic is 2,3-dimethyl-4-isopropyl-1-phenyl-3-pyrazolin-5-one. This compound is very closely analogous to aminopyrine and is of the same order of activity.[842]

The most interesting of the pyrazolinones and pyrazolidinones from the medical standpoint at the present time is phenylbutazone. This was synthesized by H. Stenzl in the laboratories of J. R. Geigy, S.A. in 1946 and was shortly found to have activity in various rheumatoid and arthritic conditions. Phenylbutazone was then marketed as the sodium salt under the trade name of Butazolidin. It has also been marketed as a mixture with aminopyrine under the name Irgapyrine. Since then practically every aspect of the biological activity of phenylbutazone has been investigated and a large number of analogs have been synthesized. Hemming and Kuzell[639] have published an excellent review of the biological properties and medical uses of phenylbutazone and most of the material reported here is drawn from that publication.

After oral administration phenylbutazone is completely absorbed in a short time and high plasma concentrations are reached in about two hours. Intramuscular injection gives a much slower peak concentration in the plasma, requiring six to eight hours. The usual dose is about 800 mg. per day and under this regime a stable plasma concentration is reached in three or four days. A considerable amount of phenylbutazone is bound by plasma protein and this acts as a reservoir. The drug is metabolized at a rate of 15–25 per cent per day in the human but dogs and rats metabolize it much more rapidly. The metabolic products are 4-(3-hydroxybutyl)-1,2-diphenyl-3,5-pyrazolidinedione and 4-butyl-1-(4-hydroxyphenyl)-2-phenyl-3,5-pyrazolidinedione.[267] It has been suggested that the former metabolite is responsible for the effect of phenylbutazone on uric acid excretion and the latter metabolite has the antirheumatic effect and causes sodium chloride retention.[1663] Some phenylbutazone is excreted in the urine.[1335]

Several workers have found that phenylbutazone has a pronounced effect upon electrolyte balance.[435, 597, 1626] A decrease in urine volume occurs with retention of sodium and chloride ions. This is apparently caused by increased reabsorption in the renal tubules.[1626] After discontinuance of the drug diuresis occurs and the edema disappears.

Phenylbutazone brings about a number of changes in the blood. In rabbits it decreases total protein albumin, but increases globulin.[1500] There is frequently a drop in the platelet count, mild anemia, occasionally hemorrhage from the gastrointestinal tract and sometimes granulocytopenia. The most serious blood reaction is the occurrence of agranulocytosis.[779,906] This occurs infrequently but may result from moderately low doses and therefore must be kept constantly in mind. It has been reported that concurrent administration of ferrous iron reverses the agranulocytosis.[392] Some physicians have regarded this toxic manifestation as being so serious that they recommend the complete discontinuance of the use of phenylbutazone.

The principal action of phenylbutazone is its inhibition of inflammatory action, although it is also a mild analgesic and antipyretic. It has a very striking clinical effect in many arthritic cases, giving rapid and complete relief from pain. There is also significant improvement of joint function and objective remission of the arthritic condition. Its field of usefulness is very similar to that of the corticosteroids, and as a consequence it has been suggested that it may be a stimulant of the pituitary–adrenal system. However, its failure to affect urinary ketosteroid excretion, eosinophil count and the erythrocyte sedimentation rate make this action unlikely. It may be that it acts by a cortisone-sparing mechanism. Korns and others[852] have suggested this because of their finding that phenylbutazone prevents the inactivation of cortisone by rat liver slices. Wallenfels and Sund[1587] believe that phenylbutazone may be transported to inflamed tissue as a complex with the zinc attached to dehydrogenase systems. In these tissues the complex may be broken down owing to the relatively acid conditions and phenylbutazone enter the intracellular space where it inhibits dehydrogenases.

Phenylbutazone has been found to be clinically useful in several forms of arthritis. It is particularly effective in acute gouty arthritis, in which it is superior to any other drug. In several series of patients it has been claimed that nearly all patients are improved by phenylbutazone treatment. This is probably a result of its ability to increase urate clearances.[1664] In such diseases as rheumatoid arthritis, osteoarthritis and rheumatoid spondylitis phenylbutazone affords prompt relief of pain in something like 75 per cent of cases in which it is used. Although there is considerable disagreement as to the incidence of measurable objective improvement, it is probable that this occurs in at least 50 per cent of patients using phenylbutazone. The objective improvement is reduction in swelling and increased mobility. Some have claimed that improvement is due to analgesic effect, but the beneficial effect is too pronounced for mere analgesia and must be due to a specific antirheumatic effect of phenylbutazone. An amazing number of other conditions, usually arthritic, have been reported to be improved by phenylbutazone, although its use is as yet not completely established in many of these. Some of these diseases are psoriatic arthritis, osteoporosis of the spine, acute peritendonitis, acute myofibritis, degenerative diseases of the hip, bursitis, fibrositis, postmenopausal arthralgia, scleroderma with arthropathy and lumbrosacral sprain. Phenylbutazone has also been used in arthritic conditions in veterinary medicine.

The clinical efficacy of phenylbutazone has been well established but the high percentage of side-effects resulting from it has severely curtailed its usefulness. In many of the arthritic conditions for which it is used treatment for long periods of time is necessary and drug toxicity is particularly disadvantageous. It has been found that 25 per cent of patients taking phenylbutazone are subject to toxic reaction, many so severe as to prevent further use of the drug. The most common of these are gastrointestinal upset, edema and drug rash. Of other side-effects, as already mentioned, the most dangerous is agranulocytosis. A number of phenylbutazone analogs have been studied in attempts to decrease side-effects and retain potency,[233,1624] and it is to be hoped that these studies will be successful. In the case of phenylbutazone it seems that the drug can be used effectively, but only with great care and conservatively. Its tendency to reactivate peptic ulcers contraindicates its use in patients who have ulcers. Periodic blood counts should be made, and the patient should be under close supervision of a physician. In order to overcome some of these side-effects phenylbutazone has been marketed mixed with aluminum hydroxide, magnesium trisilicate and homatropine methyl bromide.

Various publications have appeared in which pyrazolinones, either alone or as mixtures with other materials, have been claimed to be effective as germicides,[26] in influenza,[377] as antimicrobial agents,[571] as fungicides,[676] as antiactinics,[1151] and as antidiuretics.[663,1078] At present it appears that none of these claims have led to clinical use.

CHAPTER II

Color Photography

The pyrazolinones and pyrazolidinones are extensively employed in photography as color couplers, sensitizers, supersensitizers, developers and antihalation agents. A number of pyrazolinones which have been prepared for use as sensitizers are listed in Tables LI and LII.

The most important use of pyrazolinones in photography is their utilization as color couplers. The reaction of *p*-phenylenediamines with 2-pyrazolin-5-ones in the presence of oxidizing agents, in this case silver ions, forms magenta azomethine dyes (eq. 172, p. 67). These magenta dyes are then used to reproduce the green component in pictures. Two processes have been devised to form the magenta dye at the appropriate place on the developed film. In one process one coating of a three-coated film contains a substance sensitizing that coating to green light. After the film has been exposed it is developed in a solution containing a *p*-phenylenediamine developer, usually a *p*-amino-*N*,*N*-diethylaniline, and a 2-pyrazolin-5-one. The silver halide which has been affected by light acts as an oxidizing agent to couple the two compounds, hence the name color coupler, and a magenta color appears at those points where green light has been absorbed. This can then be reprinted as green. In the second method, which is now much more extensively used, a three-layer film is used. The middle layer contains a green-sensitized emulsion and a 2-pyrazolin-5-one. Upon exposure to a developer an azomethine magenta dye is formed.

The chemistry involved in the formation of these azomethine dyes has been extensively investigated by Vittum and others.[244,1538,1539a] The present interpretation of the reactions involved is that the primary amino group of the developer is oxidized to give a quinonediimine cation which then reacts with the anion of the coupler to form a leuco dye. Subsequent oxidation converts the leuco dye to a colored form (LIII). This may be done by silver ion or by the oxidized form of the developer. The over-all reaction requires the reduction of four silver ions.

The azomethine dyes have two absorption bands in the visible region.[244, 519] One, of much higher intensity, is in the green region at wave lengths of 510–560 mμ. A lower intensity band occurs in the blue region at 420–450 mμ. The second band is undesirable in photographic applications and can be suppressed to a certain extent by modifications in the group at C–3. Amide substitutions at this position are effective for this purpose. The structures contributing to the resonance hybrid responsible for the absorption of the dyes are considered to be (LIII)–(LVII). The forms (LIII) and (LV) represent the ground state. Transitions of these to the forms (LVI) and (LVII) are responsible for absorption at the longer wave lengths, while transitions to form (LIV) give rise to the shorter wave length, less intense band. Electropositive and electronegative substituents at C–3 have considerable effect upon the electron density at N–2 and thus alter the light absorption of the 2-pyrazolin-5-ones.

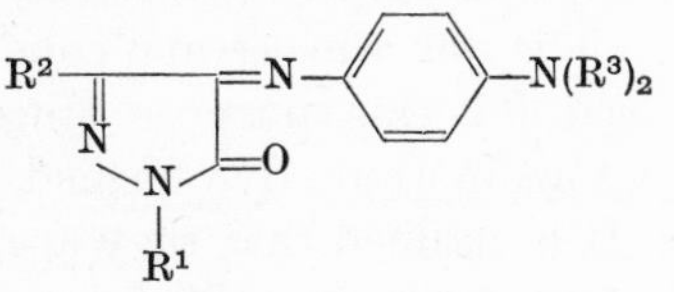

(LIII) 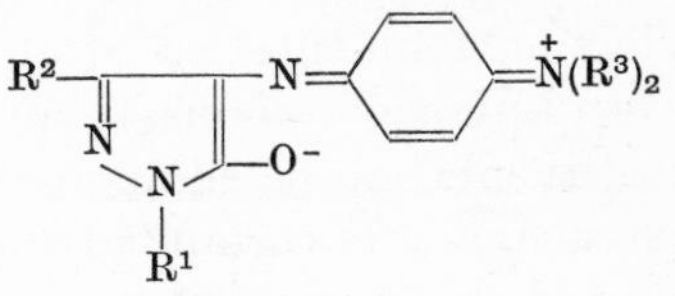 (LIV)

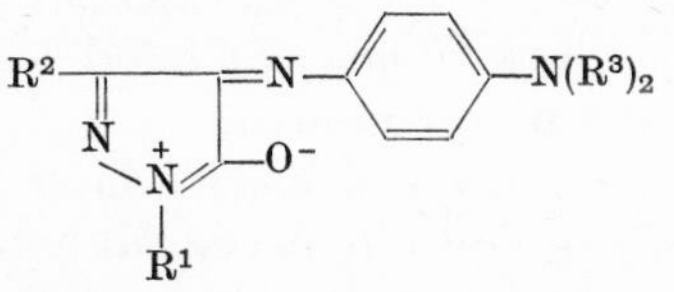

(LV) 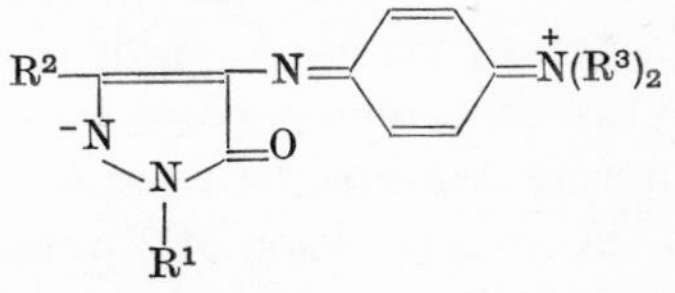 (LVI)

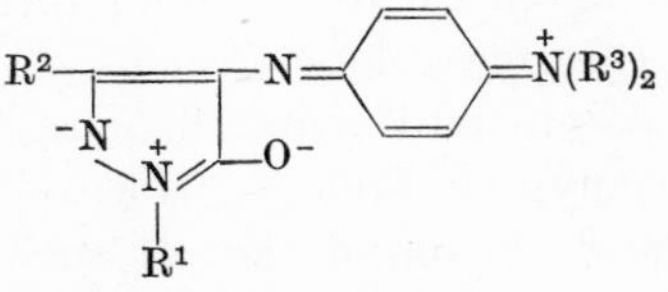

(LVII)

A very large number of compounds have been claimed to be useful as color couplers.[492, 493, 634, 705, 766, 769, 797, 870, 921, 922, 965, 966, 1041, 1138–1140, 1142, 1247, 1684] Weissberger and Edens[1593] have reported very complex amides which are useful as color couplers, but are so complex that they are listed in none of the tables. In the color photography process employing the 2-pyrazolin-5-one in solution in the developer, low molecular weight compounds were used. These, being acidic, are soluble in the alkaline developer solution. When the 2-pyrazolin-5-one is incorporated in one layer of the film, diffusion from layer to layer is a serious problem. In order to prevent this, large groups are introduced in the molecule, usually at N–1 or at C–3. The substituent at N–1 is always aromatic and may have very complex substituents. Frequently it has a carboxyl or sulfonic acid group to assist in dispersion in the gelatin. One of the most successful approaches to the problem of diffusion is that developed by Weissberger and co-workers. Their solution to the problem was use of 1-aryl-3-amino-2-pyrazolin-5-ones (2-aryl-5-imino-3-pyrazolidinones). In order to increase the bulk of the molecule the amino group was acylated[592,870,921,922] or carried a heterocyclic substituent.[704] 2-Pyrazolin-5-ones having a carboxyl substituent as an amide at C–3 are also satisfactory. Kendall and Fry[766,769] have suggested the use of 3,5-pyrazolidinediones as color couplers.

Although by far the majority of 2-pyrazolin-5-ones used as color couplers have no substituent at C–4, this is not a necessary condition. 4,4′-Bis(2-pyrazolin-5-ones) can be used for this purpose since the 4-substituents can be eliminated and an azomethine dye formed. Such couplers may offer certain advantages. It is claimed that they are more stable and also they make it possible to form two azomethine dyes if the two portions of the molecule are different. Weissberger, Vittum and Porter[1540,1603] have patented a number of 4,4′-arylidenebis(2-pyrazolin-5-ones) for use as color couplers. Gluck[580] has suggested 4,4′-bis-(2-pyrazolin-5-ones) linked by sulfur which he prepared.

Another approach to prevention of diffusion of color couplers has been the incorporation of 2-pyrazolin-5-ones into some type of polymer. The pyrazolone can be incorporated directly in the polymer by utilizing a polymer-forming derivative such as a 1-(amino or hydroxyphenyl)pyrazolone in a phenol (or aniline)–formaldehyde polymerization. Alternatively, the pyrazolone nucleus can be combined with a synthetic or natural polymer by reaction of a functional group in the pyrazolone with the polymer. Thus, a 1-formylphenyl type is used to form a polyvinyl acetal. A compilation of such reactions is given in Part 1, Chapter II, Section 14, pp. 108–110.

In many photographic processes it has been found advantageous to use a colored coupler. In these processes a 4-arylazo-2-pyrazolin-5-one is the coupler and it reacts with a developer as shown in eq. 272 (p. 138).[1539] This results in the formation of an azomethine dye which counteracts the overlapping absorption of the negative image dyes present and leads to improved color reproduction. These compounds usually have a negative substituent at N–1[1058,1305] as this enhances the rate of reaction.[1539] Amide substituents at C–3 have the same effect.

Another important use for pyrazolinones in photography is as sensitizers and supersensitizers. Addition of certain dyes to silver halide gelatin emulsions increases the sensitivity of the silver halide to the green or red regions of the spectrum and a number of methine dyes derived from pyrazolinones have been used for this purpose. These compounds sensitize at 475–700 mμ, although their maximum absorption is at somewhat shorter wave lengths. Both 2-pyrazolin-5-ones[488,707,747,749,765,771,772,1069,1195] and 3-pyrazolin-5-ones[765,1516,1517] have been used. These nuclei are connected through one or more unsaturated groups to heterocyclic rings such as benzoxazoline, benzimidoazoline or benzothiazoline rings.[747,749,771] Frequently the pyrazolinone is a substituent on the unsaturated chain of a cyanine dye (Table LIII).[765,1516] The more extended the unsaturated chain is the longer are the wave lengths at which sensitization occurs. A variety of substituents have been used at C–3. Among these are methyl,[488,747] carbethoxy,[772] amino[1330] and hydroxyl.[1330] Supersensitization occurs in some cases by addition of a second dye which is synergistic with the first. Brooker and White have patented a number of azomethine 2-pyrazolin-5-ones for this purpose.[240]

There has been a great deal of interest in Great Britain in 1-phenyl-3-pyrazolidinone (phenidone) and some of its analogs as photographic developers. In combination with various weak developers, pyrazolinones greatly enhance their developing powers. Such compounds as ascorbic acid, gallic acid, glucose, dihydropyrogallol and various reductones show this property.[57,640,641,1630] Reynolds[1176] in the United States has also reported such a phenomenon with iminoascorbic acid. A number of 3-pyrazolidinones having various aryl substituents at N–1 and hydrogen or alkyl groups at C–4 have been reported to be effective.[701,750,756,758,1176,1630,1631] It has been claimed by Kendall[57,751] that in the course of development 1-phenyl-3-pyrazolidinone is oxidized to 2-phenyl-3-pyrazolin-5-one. A number of compounds having two alkyl substituents at C–4[701,1176,1630] or at C–5[758] have been reported to be photographic developers and these could not undergo such an oxidation.

A number of 2-pyrazolin-5-ones have been reported in patents to be useful as color filters and for antihalation. Most of these are colored compounds, in two cases merocyanine dyes[1301] and in others various methine dyes having heterocyclic rings at the end of unsaturated chains.[776] van Dormael and van der Aurwa[1518] have reported that a mixture of the product of reaction between aromatic amines and furfural with 3-methyl-1-phenyl-2-pyrazolin-5-one is useful for antihalation.

CHAPTER III

Textile and Fabric Dyes

The most important commercial use for pyrazolinones is as dyes. They have been extensively employed for this purpose since tartrazine (Table LIV) was synthesized by Ziegler and Locher in 1884[1681a] and this dye is still widely used today as an approved coloring for foodstuffs. Almost all pyrazoline dyes are azo dyes having an arylazo group substituted at the 4-position of a 2-pyrazolin-5-one and frequently having two, three or four azo groups in the entire molecule. The preparation of these compounds has already been discussed in the section dealing with 4-arylazo-2-pyrazolin-5-ones. A tremendous variety of 1-aryl-2-pyrazolin-5-ones have been used to prepare azo dyes, although most of the commercially important dyes have been derived from 1-aryl-2-pyrazolin-5-ones having methyl, carboxyl groups or carboxyl derivatives substituted at C–3. The 1-aryl substituents have been so greatly varied that no generalizations can be made. Most dyes contain at N–1 substituted phenyl groups which frequently have sulfonic groups as substituents. The arylazo groups also have been extremely varied and in many cases are very complex. The majority of pyrazolinone azo dyes are either acid dyes or dyes which are complexed with metals. The acid dyes are compounds having carboxylic and/or sulfonic acid functions and can be used to dye fabrics directly, while the metal complexes are formed with various metals either before or after deposition on the material to be dyed. The outstanding feature of the pyrazolinone dyes is their excellent fastness to light and to severe wet treatments. A number of pyrazolinone dyes are produced in very large quantities. In the U.S.A. the production of tartrazine in 1960 was 437,000 lb. and the production of many more is in the tens of thousands of pounds. In Table LIV are listed the trade names and structures of a number of representative commercially important dyes. It is generally considered that pyrazolinone azo dyes have one or more of the structures (LVIII),

(LIX) and (LX) but other structures are theoretically possible. Little research has been published to indicate which of these structures is the correct one, although the usual methods of preparation would allow

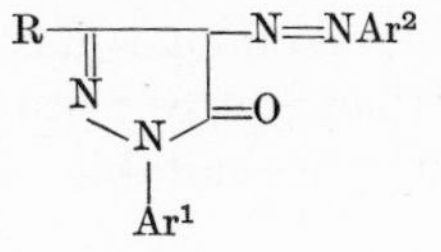

(LVIII) 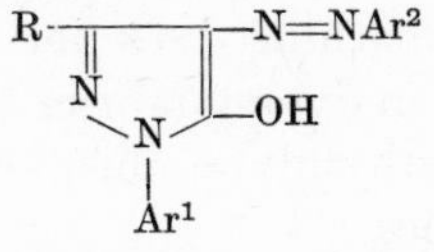 (LIX)

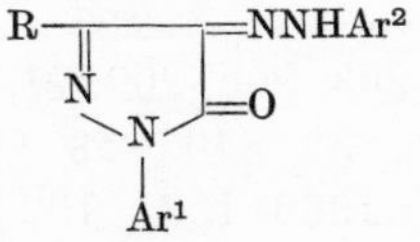

(LX)

any of the three. In the case of dyes complexed with various metals it is believed that (LIX) is the usual structure. In these cases it is probable that the metal reacts with the enol form of the pyrazolinone and with a hydroxyl group at the *ortho*-position in the arylazo group—formulas (XXX) and (XXXI).[1259] This is then stabilized by electron donation by the nitrogen atoms of the azo group.[326] However, in most uncomplexed dyes it has not been established which form is the correct one. A few 4-arylazo-3-pyrazolin-5-ones have been patented for use as dyes.[1060]

The earlier pyrazolinone azo dyes were used to dye wool yellow,[81, 214, 217, 312, 582, 1384, 1424] but this situation has changed so that by use of suitable complexes almost any color can be obtained with almost any material it is desired to dye. A very large variety of orange dyes are available[199, 207, 475, 622, 840, 1449, 1459, 1617] as well as brown,[169, 576, 856, 1446] red,[312, 803, 839, 1119] green,[630, 1060, 1291] violet,[186, 189] gray[205] and intermediate shades.[190, 208, 221, 577] In addition to wool other materials which can be dyed with pyrazolinone azo dyes are cotton and its derivatives such as rayon,[169, 177, 205, 215, 453, 877, 963, 1326, 1449, 1451] synthetic polyamides,[216, 865, 1117] silk,[453, 582, 1117, 1457] leather[39, 1117, 1457] and rubber.[476, 577] Complexed metal dyes are not suitable for polyesters and polyacrylonitriles.

As already mentioned, numerous pyrazolinone azo dyes form complexes with metals. This can be done either before or after deposition but is usually done after the azo dye has been used to treat the fabric. In those dyes which are applied to wool the usual metal employed is chromium.[77, 177, 213, 441, 935, 1061, 1259, 1421, 1448] For cotton dyes it is more common to use copper.[38, 177, 276, 622, 879, 1429, 1619] Cobalt,[207, 276] lead,[213] nickel[213,276] and iron[177,276] have also been used. Many metal salts and oxides can be used for the metallizing operation. In the case of chromium, various salts of chromosalicylic acid have been widely used[186,207,1384,1426] as well as sulfates, fluorides and others.

The polymethine dyes derived from pyrazolinones have not been of importance in dyeing fabrics because of their lack of fastness to light. However, methylidyne bispyrazolinones are suitable for dyeing polyester fabrics.

The following list of references is made up of those reporting azo dyes having structures so complex that it was considered inadvisable to include them in the tables:

168, 174, 177, 179, 182, 203, 205, 209, 215, 218, 220, 221, 224, 227, 477, 486, 487, 635, 657, 782, 839, 840, 853, 886, 904, 958, 1020, 1062, 1121, 1267, 1326, 1358, 1361, 1366, 1381, 1394, 1398, 1403, 1408, 1412, 1415, 1416, 1419, 1420, 1429, 1449, 1451, 1465.

CHAPTER IV

Analytical Reagents

The use of various pyrazolinones as reagents in qualitative and quantitative analysis has been proposed, although these procedures have not been widely applied. Calcium ions form an insoluble precipitate with picrolonic acid. They can therefore be determined by using excess of the acid and back titration.[313] Sodium, potassium, ammonium, copper, zinc and strontium ions form crystalline salts with picrolonic acid and these salts can be used for identification of the ions.[415,416] Trivalent and tetravalent plutonium ions form insoluble salts of picrolonic acid and can be isolated as such.[1099] Hovorka and Śykora[665,666] have studied the use of various 4-nitroso-2-pyrazolin-5-ones in the gravimetric determination of a number of metal ions. It was found that the 3-methyl, 3-phenyl and 1,3-diphenyl compounds give precipitates with silver, mercuric, cuprous, cupric, plumbous, cadmium, ferrous, ferric, manganous, nickel and cobalt ions. However, only silver was precipitated quantitatively. The cupric ion could also be precipitated quantitatively by use of 3-methyl- or 3-phenyl-4-nitroso-1-(2-phenethyl)-2-pyrazolin-5-one. In the presence of ammonium thiocyanate cobalt gives a blue color with antipyrine[1369] or 4,4′-methylenebis(2,3-dimethyl-1-phenyl-3-pyrazolin-5-one)[1678] which can then be used to determine the cobalt colorimetrically. It is claimed that cobalt can be determined in concentrations of one part per million,[1369] but iron, copper and bismuth interfere. 4,4′-Methylenebis(2,3-dimethyl-1-phenyl-3-pyrazolin-5-one) also forms insoluble complexes with various ions and this can be used to determine the ions gravimetrically. Cadmium forms such a complex in the presence of bromide ion[1306,1678] and cobalt, copper, zinc, ferric, cadmium and mercury ions form such complexes in the presence of ammonium thiocyanate.[1679]

Cyanides and cyanogen halides in the presence of pyridine and 3-methyl-1-phenyl-2-pyrazolin-5-one give a color which can be used for their determination.[436] The cyanides must be converted to cyanogen halides. The determination depends on conversion of pyridine to glutaconaldehyde which reacts with the pyrazolinone to form a colored compound.

The ferricyanide ion forms an insoluble complex with 4,4′-benzylidene-bis(2,3-dimethyl-1-phenyl-3-pyrazolin-5-one). This complex can be used to determine the ion gravimetrically if other complex ions are not present.[609] A green color is formed by the ferricyanide ion in the presence of aminopyrine and can be used for determination because of its fluorescence.[1212] The ferrocyanide ion does not interfere.

Emerson, Kelly, Beegle and Beacham[423, 425, 427] have studied the coupling of various phenols with 4-aminoantipyrine and suggest the use of this reaction as a volumetric test for phenols. Phenols having no *para*-substituent or such *para*-substituents as carboxyl, sulfo, hydroxy or methoxy groups couple, in the presence of mild oxidizing agents such as potassium ferricyanide, with the pyrazolinone to give a color which can be used as the basis for determination of the phenol.

CHAPTER V

Miscellaneous

Various pyrazolinones have been reported in patents and publications to have a variety of applications and activities. For example, both 2-pyrazolin-5-ones and 3-pyrazolin-5-ones have been reported to cause abnormal mitosis in plants and to inhibit their growth.[1489,1565] Howland[667] has reported that a number of 2-pyrazolin-5-ones are effective antioxidants for rubber and linseed oil. The same property is probably responsible for their inhibition of odor formation in synthetic detergents.[454] The perchlorate of antipyrine has been patented for use as an explosive.[933] Matsumoto[953] has found that aminoantipyrine (probably the 4-amino) is an effective catalyst for decarboxylation.

5-Methyl-2-(3-sulfophenyl- and 2-chloro-3-sulfophenyl)-3-pyrazolidinone forms complexes with choromethylcumene to give surface-active textile assistants.[1388]

The use of antipyrine as an agent for the concentration of tannin in tannin extracts has been proposed.[66] Antipyrine forms a water-insoluble complex with tannin and the complex is easily decomposed by treating an aqueous suspension with organic solvents. These properties can be utilized for tannin concentration.

APPENDIX

SYSTEMATIC TABLES OF PYRAZOLONES AND THEIR DERIVATIVES

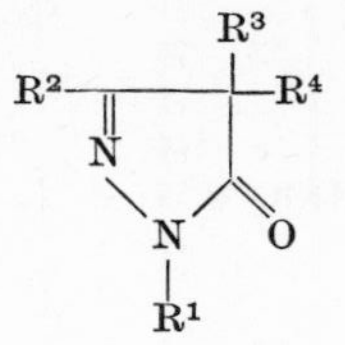

TABLE II. 2-Pyrazolin-5-ones

Section A. Alkyl and Alicyclic Substituents

R^1	R^2	R^3	R^4	M.p.	Reference
H	H	H	H	165°	457, 813, 1228, 1232, 1522, 1544, 1546, 1547, 1548, 1550, 1553, 1555
H	CH_3	H	H	215°	6, 54, 61, 338, 354, 359, 479, 480, 1047, 1075, 1085, 1199, 1485, 1553, 1622
H	H	CH_3	H	226°	51, 457
H	C_3H_7	H	H	207°	360, 1012
H	iso-C_3H_7	H	H	183°	1012
H	*t*-C_4H_9	H	H	210°	354, 1522
H	C_5H_{11}	H	H	198°	1024
H	C_6H_{13}	H	H	201°	1024
H	C_9H_{19}	H	H	187°	855

(*Table continued*)

TABLE II, Section A (*continued*)

R^1	R^2	R^3	R^4	M.p.	Reference
H	$C_{11}H_{23}$	H	H	67°	135
H	$C_{16}H_{33}$	H	H	108°	1480
H	$C_2H_5OOC(CH_2)_3$	H	H	149°	96
H	F_3C	H	H	208°	564
H	$(CH_3)_3SiCH_2CH_2$	H	H	203°	1317
H	$C_2H_5OOCCH_2$	H	H	189°	866
H	H	$C_2H_5OOCCH_2$	H	167°	962
H	$H_2NNHCOCH_2$	H	H	180°	866
H	$C_6H_5CH{=}NNHCOCH_2$	H	H	> 190°	866
H	$2\text{-}HOC_6H_4CH{=}NNHCOCH_2$	H	H	> 200°	866
H	$3\text{-}NO_2C_6H_4CH{=}NNHCOCH_2$	H	H	> 145°	866
H	$C_6H_5CH{=}CHCH{=}NNHCOCH_2$	H	H	> 145°	866
H	$HOOCCH_2CH_2$	H	H	222°	1221
H	$CH_3OOCCH_2CH_2$	H	H	168°	1221
H	$H_2NHNOCCH_2CH_2$	H	H	178°	1221
CH_3	CH_3	H	H	117°	788, 985, 1522
C_2H_5	CH_3	H	H	109°	250
C_3H_7	CH_3	H	H	115°	250
iso-C_3H_7	CH_3	H	H	99°	250
C_4H_9	CH_3	H	H	56°, 86°	206, 250, 1681
iso-C_4H_9	CH_3	H	H	120°	250
C_8H_{17}	CH_3	H	H	59°	206
$C_{10}H_{21}$	CH_3	H	H	65°	206
$HOOCCH_2CH(CH_3)$	CH_3	H	H	209°	1118, 1119
$HOOCCH_2CH_2$	CH_3	H	H	164°	1119
H	CH_3	$C_2H_5OOCCH_2$	H	166°	962
$C_4H_9OOCCH_2CH_2$	CH_3	H	H	52°	1118, 1119
$C_2H_5OOCCH_2CH_2$	CH_3	H	H	106°	1118, 1119
$NCCH_2CH_2$	CH_3	H	H	—	1119
$NH_2COCH_2CH_2$	CH_3	H	H	167°	1119

$NCCHCH_2$ (with CH_3 on the CH)	CH_3	H	H	146°	1119
iso-$C_8H_{17}OOCCH_2CH_2$	CH_3	H	H	liquid	1119
$HO_3SCH_2CH_2$	CH_3	H	H	—	1684
$HO_3SCH_2CH_2$	$C_{17}H_{35}$	H	H	—	1684
$HO_3SCH_2CHCH_2$ (with OH on the CH)	CH_3	H	H	—	1684
$HO_3SCH_2CHCH_2$ (with OH on the CH)	$C_{17}H_{35}$	H	H	—	1684
H	CH_3	CH_3	H	272°	61, 358, 359, 692, 1012, 1531, 1645
H	CH_3	C_2H_5	H	229°	61, 358, 359, 660, 729, 1012, 1645
H	C_2H_5	CH_3	H	232°	730
H	CH_3	C_3H_7	H	211°	359, 720, 1522, 1645
H	CH_3	iso-C_3H_7	H	182°	250
H	CH_3	C_3H_5	H	193°	883, 1522, 1546
H	CH_3	C_4H_9	H	197°	1526
H	CH_3	s-C_4H_9	H	158°	917
H	CH_3	C_5H_{11}	H	198°	1012
H	CH_3	$C_{12}H_{25}$	H	178°	1505
H	CH_3	$HOCH_2CH_2$	H	182°	60, 1171
H	CH_3	CH_3CH (with OH on the CH)	H	273°	513, 514, 515
H	CH_3	$HOOCCH_2$	H	240°	349
H	CH_3	$C_2H_5OOCCH{=}C$ (with CH_3 on the C)	H	188°	1288

(Table continued)

TABLE II, Section A (*continued*)

R^1	R^2	R^3	R^4	M.p.	Reference
H	CH_3	$NH_2NHCOCH(CH_3)$	H	212°	1277
H	CH_3	$NO_2CH_2C(CH_3)_2$	H	—	64
H	CH_3	CH_3–C(=N–NH–C(CH_3)=C)–CH_2 (3,5-dimethylpyrazol-4-ylmethyl)	H	285°	1169
CH_3	CH_3	CH_3	H	133°	51, 1531
CH_3	CH_3	C_2H_5	H	94°	1522
CH_3	CH_3	C_3H_7	H	84°	1522
CH_3	CH_3	C_3H_5	H	71°	1522
C_2H_5	CH_3	iso-C_3H_7	H	113°	250
C_3H_7	CH_3	iso-C_3H_7	H	85°	250
iso-C_3H_7	CH_3	iso-C_3H_7	H	84°	250
C_4H_9	CH_3	iso-C_3H_7	H	83°	250
iso-C_4H_9	CH_3	iso-C_3H_7	H	74°	250
H	CH_3	CH_3	CH_3	109°, 268°	61, 358, 359, 759, 1012, 1531, 1560
H	CH_3	CH_3	C_2H_5	76°	61
H	CH_3	C_2H_5	C_2H_5	105°	61, 759, 1522
H	⬡	H	H	224°	1579

⬠	CH_3	H	H	152°	101
⬡	CH_3	H	H	139°	101, 103, 161, 859, 1280
H	CH_3	⬡	H	255°	1526
H	CH_3	$—CH_2CH_2—$		195°	1546

TABLE II (*continued*)

Section B. Monoaryl, Alkyl, and Alicyclic Substituents

R^1	R^2	R^3	R^4	M.p.	Reference
C_6H_5	H	H	H	118°	306, 810, 858, 1002, 1230, 1350, 1351, 1554, 1559
H	C_6H_5	H	H	244°	181, 610, 992, 1023, 1024, 1085, 1205, 1431, 1522, 1549, 1552, 1553, 1578

(*Table continued*)

TABLE II, Section B (*continued*)

R^1	R^2	R^3	R^4	M.p.	Reference
2-$CH_3C_6H_4$	H	H	H	177°	1004
4-IC_6H_4	H	H	H	126°	446
H	4-$NO_2C_6H_4$	H	H	217°	798
3-(4-$CH_3C_6H_4SO_2NH$)C_6H_4	H	H	H	210°	467
H	3-NO_2-4-$CH_3OC_6H_3$	H	H	225°	181
2,4,6-$(CH_3)_3C_6H_2$	H	H	H	290° (dec.)	835
H	1-$C_{10}H_7$	H	H	233°	1577
H	3-CH_3O-2-$C_{10}H_6$	H	H	205°	1575
6-HO_3S-8-HO-2-$C_{10}H_5$	H	H	H	—	522
C_6H_5	CH_3	H	H	127°	68, 95, 629, 723, 788, 805, 806, 809, 811, 816, 838
C_6H_5	H	CH_3	H	142°	1569
CH_3	C_6H_5	H	H	207°	54, 992, 1560
H	C_6H_5	CH_3	H	127°, 213°	54, 1531, 1560
C_6H_5	CF_3	H	H	—	564
C_6H_5	C_2H_5	H	H	100°	1686
C_6H_5	H	C_2H_5	H	99°	303
H	C_6H_5	C_2H_5	H	165°	505
C_6H_5	C_3H_7	H	H	110.5°	1686
H	C_6H_5	C_3H_7	H	186°	505
C_6H_5	iso-C_3H_7	H	H	81°	1588
H	C_6H_5	iso-C_3H_7	H	182°	1294
H	iso-C_3H_7	C_6H_5	H	191°	1640
C_6H_5	C_4H_9	H	H	83°	1686
H	C_6H_5	C_4H_9	H	180°	505
C_6H_5	iso-C_4H_9	H	H	79°, 107°	97, 448, 1589, 1590
C_6H_5	*t*-C_4H_9	H	H	110°	1582, 1589, 1590

C_6H_5	C_5H_{11}	H	H	95°	1023, 1589, 1590, 1686
H	C_6H_5	C_5H_{11}	H	139°	505
C_6H_5	$CH_3{-}C(CH_3)(CH_3){-}CH_2$	H	H	138°	1588, 1589, 1590
C_6H_5	C_6H_{13}	H	H	84°	1023, 1024, 1589, 1590
H	C_6H_5	C_6H_{13}	H	116°	505
C_6H_5	C_7H_{15}	H	H	82°	143
H	C_6H_5	C_7H_{15}	H	108°	505
C_6H_5	C_8H_{17}	H	H	65°	143
H	C_6H_5	C_8H_{17}	H	110°	505
C_6H_5	C_9H_{19}	H	H	—	143
H	C_6H_5	C_9H_{19}	H	100°	505
C_6H_5	$C_{10}H_{21}$	H	H	67°	143
H	C_6H_5	$C_{10}H_{21}$	H	95°	505
C_6H_5	$C_{11}H_{23}$	H	H	240°	42
C_6H_5	$C_{15}H_{31}$	H	H	75°	636
$HOOCCH_2CH_2$	C_6H_5	H	H	185°	1118
C_6H_5	$CH_3OOCCH_2CH_2$	H	H	79.5°	1221
C_6H_5	$C_2H_5OOCCH_2CH_2$	H	H	107.5°	1341
C_6H_5	$H_2NOCCH_2CH_2$	H	H	172°	1221
C_6H_5	CH_2 / $CH_2{-}CH{-}$ (ring)	H	H	115°	274, 1477
C_6H_5	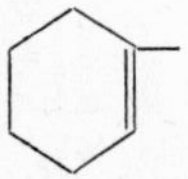	H	H	126°	778

(Table continued)

TABLE II, Section B (*continued*)

R^1	R^2	R^3	R^4	M.p.	Reference
C_6H_5	$C_5H_4FeC_5H_5$	H	H	186°	628
2-$CH_3C_6H_4$	CH_3	H	H	143°, 183°	806, 838, 1524, 1584
3-$CH_3C_6H_4$	CH_3	H	H	104°	723, 838
3-$CH_3C_6H_4$	CH_2 CH_2—CH—	H	H	103°	1477
4-$CH_3C_6H_4$	CH_3	H	H	91.5°, 140°	68, 723, 806, 838
4-$CH_3C_6H_4$	CH_2 CH_2—CH—	H	H	104°	1477
4-$CH_3OC_6H_4$	CH_3	H	H	122°	838
4-$C_2H_5OC_6H_4$	CH_3	H	H	—	902
4-$C_3H_7OC_6H_4$	CH_3	H	H	132°	1149
3-$NH_2C_6H_4$	CH_3	H	H	—	197
4-$NH_2C_6H_4$	CH_3	H	H	—	192
3-[3,5-$(HO)_2C_6H_3NH$]C_6H_4	CH_3	H	H	—	470
4-$HSCH_2CONHC_6H_4$	CH_3	H	H	—	492
4-[2,3-$(HO)_2$-1-$C_{10}H_7CONH$]C_6H_4	CH_3	H	H	260°	863
2-ClC_6H_4	CH_3	H	H	182°, 199°	192, 296, 838, 1494
3-ClC_6H_4	CH_3	H	H	131°	296, 838
4-ClC_6H_4	CH_3	H	H	172°	296, 838, 1002

3-BrC_6H_4	CH_3	H	H	134°	1683
4-BrC_6H_4	H	CH_3	H	233°	1569
4-BrC_6H_4	H	C_2H_5	H	170°	303
4-IC_6H_4	CH_3	H	H	196°	446
3-$NO_2C_6H_4$	CH_3	H	H	185°	837
4-$NO_2C_6H_4$	CH_3	H	H	220°	777, 838, 1282, 1372
4-$NO_2C_6H_4$	H	C_2H_5	H	212°	303
$HO_3SCH_2CH_2$	4-$NO_2C_6H_4$	H	H	—	1684
$HO_3SCH_2CH(OH)CH_2$	4-$NO_2C_6H_4$	H	H	—	1684
4-(4-C_6H_5CO)C_6H_4	CH_3	H	H	170°	1497
2-$HOOCC_6H_4$	CH_3	H	H	189°	1004, 1520
3-$HOOCC_6H_4$	$C_{17}H_{35}$	H	H	—	165, 1270
4-$HOOCC_6H_4$	CH_3	H	H	278°	356
4-$C_2H_5OOCC_6H_4$	CH_3	H	H	145°	1490
4-(3-HOOC-4-HOC_6H_3NHCO)C_6H_4	CH_3	H	H	—	1361
2-$HO_3SC_6H_4$	CH_3	H	H	—	1305
3-$HO_3SC_6H_4$	C_8H_{17}	H	H	265°	593
3-$HO_3SC_6H_4$	$C_{17}H_{35}$	H	H	—	1348
4-$HO_3SC_6H_4$	CH_3	H	H	306°	191, 356, 684, 1163
4-$HO_3SC_6H_4$	$C_{15}H_{31}$	H	H	> 300°	694
4-$NaO_3SC_6H_4$	$C_{16}H_{33}$	H	H	—	1481
4-$H_2NO_2SC_6H_4$	CH_3	H	H	237°	324, 328, 356, 695, 1475, 1476, 1628
4-(2-pyridyl-$NHSO_2$)C_6H_4	CH_3	H	H	248°	25

(*Table continued*)

TABLE II, Section B (*continued*)

R^1	R^2	R^3	R^4	M.p.	Reference
4-$HO_2AsC_6H_4$	CH_3	H	H	—	546
4-(3-$CH_3C_6H_{10}$)C_6H_4	CH_3	H	H	150°	141
4-(3-$H_2NC_6H_4$)C_6H_4	CH_3	H	H	—	197
4-(4-$H_2NC_6H_4$)C_6H_4	CH_3	H	H	194°	163, 1377
4-(4-$CH_3CONHC_6H_4$)C_6H_4	CH_3	H	H	—	163
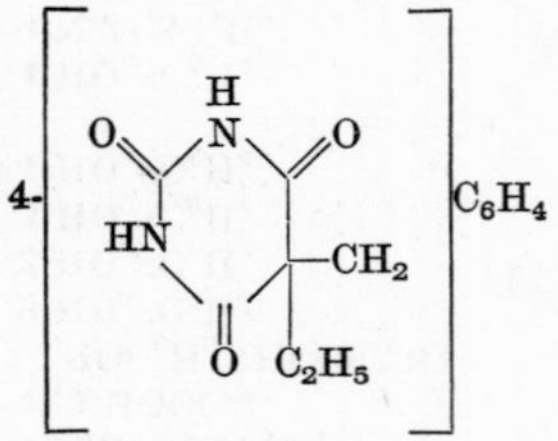	CH_3	H	H	—	1160
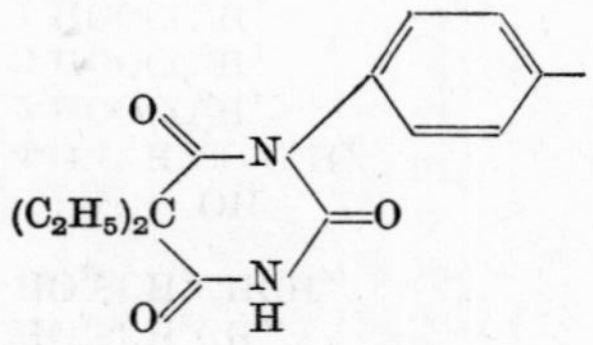	CH_3	H	H	190°	517
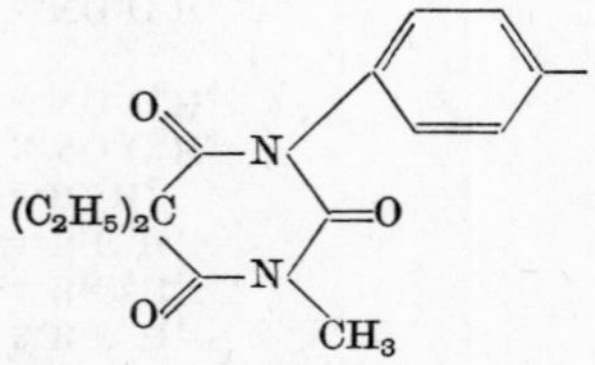	CH_3	H	H	198°	517

$2,5(CH_3)_2C_6H_3$	CH_3	H	H	164°	679
$2\text{-}CH_3\text{-}4\text{-}IC_6H_3$	CH_3	H	H	194°	446
$2\text{-}C_2H_5\text{-}4\text{-}HOC_6H_3$	CH_3	H	H	—	1389
$2\text{-}HO\text{-}5\text{-}HO_3SC_6H_3$	CH_3	H	H	—	539
$2\text{-}HO_3S\text{-}4\text{-}CH_3OC_6H_3$	CH_3	H	H	—	1162
$2\text{-}C_2H_5O\text{-}5\text{-}NO_2C_6H_3$	CH_3	H	H	—	364
$3\text{-}HO_3S\text{-}4\text{-}C_6H_5OC_6H_3$	$C_{15}H_{31}$	H	H	>300°	694
$3\text{-}HO_3S\text{-}4\text{-}C_6H_5OC_6H_4$	$C_{17}H_{35}$	H	H	—	1348
$2,4\text{-}Cl_2C_6H_3$	CH_3	H	H	178°	296, 885
$3,4\text{-}Cl_2C_6H_3$	CH_3	H	H	164°	80
$3\text{-}HO_3S\text{-}4\text{-}ClC_6H_3$	$C_{17}H_{35}$	H	H	—	1348
$2,4\text{-}I_2C_6H_3$	CH_3	H	H	153°	446
$2,4\text{-}(NO_2)_2C_6H_3$	CH_3	H	H	144°, 126°	723, 777, 1207
$4\text{-}(2\text{-}H_3OS\text{-}4\text{-}NH_2C_6H_3$ $CH{=}CH)\text{-}3\text{-}HO_3SC_6H_3$	CH_3	H	H	—	197
$4\text{-}CH_3\text{-}3\text{-}NO_2\text{-}5\text{-}HO_3SC_6H_2$	CH_3	H	H	—	123
$2,4,6\text{-}Cl_3C_6H_2$	CH_3	H	H	—	312
$2,5\text{-}Cl_2\text{-}4\text{-}HO_3SC_6H_2$	CH_3	H	H	—	1393
$2,4,6\text{-}(NO_2)_3C_6H_2$	CH_3	H	H	211°	777
$1\text{-}C_{10}H_7$	CH_3	H	H	190°	806
$2\text{-}C_{10}H_7$	CH_3	H	H	190°	806
$4\text{-}HO_3S\text{-}1\text{-}C_{10}H_7$	CH_3	H	H	—	238, 239
$X,Y\text{-}(HO_3S)_2\text{-}2\text{-}C_{10}H_5$	CH_3	H	H	—	534
$X—HO_3S—Y—HO\text{-}2\text{-}C_{10}H_5$	CH_3	H	H	—	534
$5\text{-}HO\text{-}7\text{-}HO_3S\text{-}2\text{-}C_{10}H_5$	CH_3	H	H	—	71
	CH_3	H	H	—	1251

(*Table continued*)

TABLE II, Section B (*continued*)

R^1	R^2	R^3	R^4	M.p.	Reference
C_6H_5	CH_3	CH_3	H	127°	95, 809, 811, 814, 1056, 1299
C_6H_5	CH_3	C_2H_5	H	107°	95, 814, 1007, 1522, 1524
C_6H_5	C_2H_5	CH_3	H	111.5°	1277, 1589, 1590
C_6H_5	CH_3	C_3H_7	H	101°	53, 1522
C_6H_5	CH_3	iso-C_3H_7	H	116°	53, 249, 1336
C_6H_5	$\underset{CH_2—CH—}{\overset{CH_2}{\diagup\diagdown}}$	iso-C_3H_7	H	—	1477
C_6H_5	$\underset{CH_2—CH—}{\overset{CH_2}{\diagup\diagdown}}$	$CH_2=CHCH_2$	H	$b_{0.006}$ 148–151°	1477
C_6H_5	CH_3	C_4H_9	H	95°	53, 560
C_6H_5	CH_3	iso-C_4H_9	H	118°	560, 1336
C_6H_5	CH_3	s-C_4H_9	H	92°	1336
C_6H_5	t-C_4H_9	CH_3	H	114.5°	1582
C_6H_5	C_5H_{11}	CH_3	H	80.4°	277
C_6H_5	CH_3	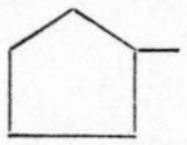 (cyclopentyl ring)	H	133°	1239
C_6H_5	CH_3	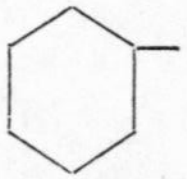 (cyclohexyl ring)	H	130°	1336
C_6H_5	CH_3	$HOCH_2CH_2$	H	94°	1171
C_6H_5	CH_3	$BrCH_2CH_2CH_2$	H	190°	583

C_6H_5	CH_3	$(C_2H_5)_2NCH_2CH_2$	H	145°	574
C_6H_5	CH_3	CH_3COCH_2	H	114°	113
C_6H_5	CH_3	$CH_3C(=NOH)CH_2$	H	105°	113
C_6H_5	CH_3	$CH_3C(=O)CH_2C(CH_3)_2$	H	142°	686
C_6H_5	CH_3	$CH_3C(=O)CH{=}CH$	H	181°	721
C_6H_5	CH_3	$HOOCCH_2$	H	178°	814
C_6H_5	CH_3	$C_2H_5OOCH_2$		138°	309
C_6H_5	CH_3	$C_2H_5OOCCH_2CH_2$	H	$b_3$215°	814
C_6H_5	CH_3	$C_2H_5OOCCH{=}C(CH_3)$	H	246°	1288
C_6H_5	CH_3	$(CH_3)_2C{=}$		117°	809
C_6H_5	CH_3	$—CH_2CH_2—$		94°, 138° (2 forms)	872
C_6H_5	CH_3	OH; CH_3—; CH_3 (ring) =		110°	753
C_6H_5	CH_3	$CH_3C(CH_2COOC_2H_5){=}$		98°	1347

(Table continued)

TABLE II, Section B (*continued*)

R^1	R^2	R^3	R^4	M.p.	Reference
C_6H_5	CH_3	(bicyclic structure: CH_3; C=O; CH_3—CH_3; O; C=) or (bicyclic structure: CH_3; C=; CH_3—CH_3; O; C=O)		195°	1237
C_6H_5	CH_3	(structure: benzene ring fused to a five-membered ring; ring O; =O; =)		212°	1279
C_6H_5	CH_3	$4\text{-}(CH_3)_2NC_6H_4N{=}CHC{=}$ (CH_3)		184°	1131
C_6H_5	CH_3	$CH_3C{=}$, C=NOH, $COOC_2H_5$		198°	1347
C_6H_5	CH_3	$C_6H_5NH(CH{=}CH)_2CH{=}$		182°	1070
C_6H_5	CH_3	$C_6H_5N{=}NCH_2C{=}$ (CH_3)		173°	1130, 1131
C_6H_5	CH_3	$4\text{-}NO_2C_6H_4N{=}NCH_2C{=}$ (CH_3)		234°	1130
C_6H_5	CH_3	$2,5\text{-}Cl_2C_6H_3N{=}NCH_2C{=}$ (CH_3)		194°	1130

C_6H_5	CH_3	$3\text{-}HOOCC_6H_4N{=}NCH_2C{=}$ (with CH_3 on C)	235°	1130
C_6H_5	CH_3	$2,5\text{-}Cl_2C_6H_3N{=}NCH_2C{=}$ (with C_6H_5 on C)	185°	1130
C_6H_5	CH_3	$4\text{-}NO_2C_6H_4N{=}NCH_2C{=}$ (with C_6H_5 on C)	235°	1130, 1131
C_6H_5	CH_3	$2\text{-}NO_2\text{-}4\text{-}ClC_6H_3N{=}NCH_2C{=}$ (with C_6H_5 on C)	226°	1130
C_6H_5	CH_3	$C_6H_5N{=}NCH_2C{=}$ (with C_6H_5 on C)	118°	1130, 1131
C_6H_5	CH_3	$2\text{-}HOOCC_6H_4N{=}NCH_2C{=}$ (with C_6H_5 on C)	214°	1130
C_6H_5	CH_3	$4\text{-}NO_2C_6H_4N{=}NCH_2C{=}$ (with $3\text{-}NO_2C_6H_5$ on C)	231°	1130, 1131
C_6H_5	CH_3	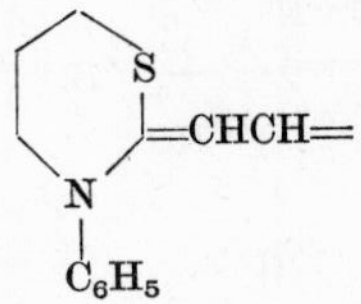 ring (S, N–C_6H_5) $=CHCH=$	177°	389
C_6H_5	CH_3	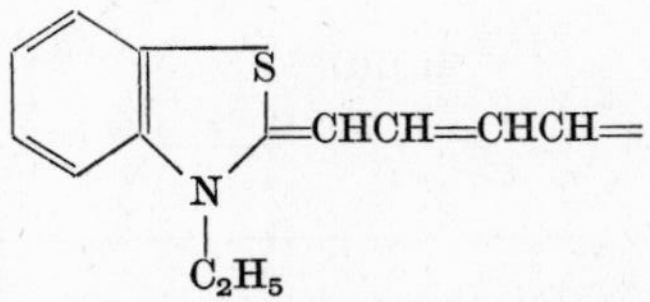 benzo-fused ring (S, N–C_2H_5) $=CHCH{=}CHCH=$	—	166

(*Table continued*)

TABLE II, Section B (*continued*)

R^1	R^2	R^3	R^4	M.p.	Reference
C_6H_5	CH_3	S, N, C_2H_5, =CHCH=		218°	675
C_6H_5	CH_3	CH_3, CH_3, =CHC=, N—CH_3, CH_3, CH_3S, N		146°	759
C_6H_5	CH_3	H, N, O, O, HN, O, CH=		297°	1191
C_6H_5	CH_3	H, N, S, O, HN, O, CH=		305°	1187

C_6H_5	CH_3	H N O O C_6H_5N O CH=		308°	1188
2-$CH_3C_6H_4$	CH_3	CH_3	H	179°	1004
2-$CH_3C_6H_4$	CH_3	C_2H_5	H	82.5°	1524
4-$C_2H_5OC_6H_4$	CH_3	H N O O C_6H_5N O CH=		> 300°	1188
4-$NH_2C_6H_4$	CH_3	CH_3	H	—	535
4-FC_6H_5	CH_3	$(CH_3)_2C=$		136°	1263
4-$NO_2C_6H_4$	CH_3	C_2H_5	H	—	532
4-$NO_2C_6H_4$	$C_{11}H_{23}$	CH_3	H	85°	136
4-$NO_2C_6H_4$	CH_3	$HOCH_2CH_2$	H	159°	1171
2-$HOOCC_6H_4$	CH_3	C_2H_5	H	196°	1520
1-$C_{10}H_7$	CH_3	iso-C_3H_7	H	—	849
2-$C_{10}H_7$	CH_3	iso-C_3H_7	H	160°	849
C_6H_5	CH_3	CH_3	CH_3	55°	95, 785, 809, 1056
C_6H_5	CH_3	CH_3	C_2H_5	25.5°	53
C_6H_5	CH_3	CH_3	C_3H_7	b_{13}185°	53
C_6H_5	CH_3	CH_3	iso-C_3H_7	66°	53
C_6H_5	CH_3	CH_3	C_3H_5	b_{12}189°	53
C_6H_5	CH_3	CH_3	C_4H_9	b_{20}205°	53
C_6H_5	C_2H_5	CH_3	CH_3	b_{11}177°	53

(Table continued)

TABLE II, Section B (*continued*)

R^1	R^2	R^3	R^4	M.p.	Reference
C_6H_5	CH_3	C_2H_5	C_2H_5	39°, 51°	53, 95
C_6H_5	CH_3	C_2H_5	C_3H_7	b_{12}181°	53
C_6H_5	CH_3	C_3H_7	C_3H_7	b_{12}184°	53
C_6H_5	CH_3	C_3H_5	C_3H_5	b_{11}192°	53, 1321
C_6H_5	C_2H_5	C_2H_5	C_3H_7	b_{30}203°	53
1-(4-$NH_2C_6H_5$)	CH_3	CH_3	CH_3	—	538
1-[4-$(CH_3)_2NC_6H_5$]	CH_3	CH_3	CH_3	—	538

TABLE II (*continued*)

Section C. Aralkyl, Heterocyclicalkyl, Aryl, and Alkyl Substituents

R^1	R^2	R^3	R^4	M.p.	Reference
H	$C_6H_5CH_2$	H	H	197°	1320
H	H	$C_6H_5CH=$		180°	813
$C_6H_5CH=CH$	H	H	H	216°	181
$C_6H_5CH_2$	CH_3	H	H	174°	54, 250, 333
$C_6H_5CH_2CH_2$	CH_3	H	H	134°	1566
2-$CH_3OC_6H_4CH_2$	CH_3	H	H	82°	334
3,4-$(OCH_2O)C_6H_4CH_2$	CH_3	H	H	155°	334
H	CH_3	$C_6H_5CH_2$	H	213°, 218°, 230°	302, 660, 729
H	CH_3	$C_6H_5CH=CH$	H	214°	883
H	CH_3	$C_6H_5CH_2CH_2CH_2$	H	176°	883

H	CH_3	C_6H_5CH | $CH{=}CH_2$	H	184°	882
H	CH_3	C_6H_5CH | C_2H_5	H	193°	882, 883
H	CH_3	$C_6H_5CH{-}CH$ | | NO_2 C_6H_5	H	235°	383
C_2H_5	CH_3	$C_6H_5CH_2$	H	177°	302
$C_6H_5CH_2$	CH_3	iso-C_3H_7	H	74°	250
$C_6H_5CH_2$	CH_3	$C_6H_5CH{=}$		111°	333
C_6H_5	$C_6H_5CH_2$	H	H	—	1320
C_6H_5	H	$C_6H_5CH_2$	H	146°	1236, 1320
$C_6H_5CH_2$	C_6H_5	H	H	204°	333
H	C_6H_5	$C_6H_5CH_2$	H	184°	505
H	$C_6H_5CH_2$	C_6H_5	H	172°	1200
C_6H_5	H	$C_6H_5CH{=}$		170°	306
H	C_6H_5	$C_6H_5CH{=}$		> 250°	1552, 1560
C_6H_5	$C_6H_5CH_2CH_2$	H	H	133°	1534
$C_6H_5CH_2CH_2$	C_6H_5	H	H	145.5°	1567
C_6H_5	$C_6H_5CH{=}CH$	H	H	148°	124, 1334
C_6H_5	$C_6H_5O(CH_2)_3$	H	H	115°	246
C_6H_5	$C_6H_5O(CH_2)_4$	H	H	118.5°	246
C_6H_5	H	C_6H_5CH | C_6H_5	H	220°	1639
H	C_6H_5	$HOOCC{=}C$ | C_6H_5	H	145°	1050
2,4-$(CH_3)_2C_6H_3CH_2$	C_6H_5	H	H	162°	334
3,4-$(OCH_2O)C_6H_3CH_2$	C_6H_5	H	H	144.5°	334
4-$NO_2C_6H_4$	H	$C_6H_5CH_2$	H	176°	1236
2,4-$(NO_2)C_6H_3$	$C_6H_5CH{=}CH$	H	H	171°	1334
H	2,4,6-$(CH_3)_3C_6H_2$	$C_6H_5CH{=}$		280°	835

(Table continued)

TABLE II, Section C (*continued*)

R^1	R^2	R^3	R^4	M.p.	Reference
C_6H_5	CH_3	2,4,6-$(CH_3)_3$-3-HO-5-$CH_3COOC_6CH_2(CH_3)_2C{=}$		208°	1308
C_6H_5	CH_3			116°	1128
C_6H_5	CH_3	$C_6H_5CH_2$	H	140°	1321, 1584
C_6H_5	CH_3	2-CH_3-5-iso-C_3H_7-$C_6H_3CH_2$	H	143°	1148
C_6H_5	CH_3	$C_6H_5CH{=}$		106°	686, 809, 1250
C_6H_5	CH_3	$C_6H_5CH{=}CHCH{=}$		139°	809
C_6H_5	CH_3	$C_6H_5CH{=}C(C_6H_5){-}$	H	220°	1522
C_6H_5	CH_3	$HON{=}CHC(C_6H_5){=}$		208°	1131
C_6H_5	CH_3	$HON{=}CHC(3\text{-}NO_2C_6H_4){=}$		235°	1131
C_6H_5	CH_3	$H_2NCONHN{=}CHC(C_6H_5){=}$		227°	1131
C_6H_5	CH_3	4-$(CH_3)_2NC_6H_4N{=}CHC(C_6H_5){=}$		181°	1131
C_6H_5	CH_3	4-$(CH_3)_2NC_6H_4N{=}CHC(3\text{-}NO_2C_6H_4){=}$		185°	1131
C_6H_5	CH_3	3-$NO_2C_6H_4C(CH_3){=}$		150°	1128
C_6H_5	$C_6H_5CH_2$	$C_6H_5CH_2$	H	139°	1320
C_6H_5	C_6H_5	$C_6H_5CH{=}$		147°	818
C_6H_5	C_6H_5	$C_6H_5CH_2$	H	178°	505
C_6H_5	$C_6H_5CH_2$	C_6H_5	H	229°	1200
C_6H_5	$C_6H_5CH_2CH_2$	C_6H_5	H	163°	1227
C_6H_5	CH_3	4-$CH_3OC_6H_4CH{=}$		127°	1254, 1255

C_6H_5	CH_3	4-$H_2NC_6H_4CH_2$	H	oil	110
C_6H_5	CH_3	4-$CH_3CONHC_6H_4CH_2$	H	185°	110
C_6H_5	CH_3	3-$(CH_3)_2NC_6H_4CH$=		117°	311
C_6H_5	CH_3	4-$(CH_3)_2NC_6H_4CH$=		196°	376
C_6H_5	CH_3	4-$(CH_3N)C_6H_4CH$= | CH_2CH_2Cl		154°	34
C_6H_5	CH_3	4-$(C_2H_5N)C_6H_4CH$= | CH_2CH_2Cl		117°	34
C_6H_5	CH_3	4-$(ClCH_2CH_2)_2NC_6H_4CH$=		167°	34
C_6H_5	CH_3	2-$NO_2C_6H_5CH$=		—	633
C_6H_5	CH_3	3-$NO_2C_6H_5CH$=		162°	633
C_6H_5	CH_3	4-$NO_2C_6H_5CH$=		180°, 209°	110, 376, 633
C_6H_5	CH_3	2-$H_5C_2OOCCH_2OC_6H_4CH$=		122°	832
C_6H_5	CH_3	3-CH_3O-4-HOC_6H_3CH=		169°	22
C_6H_5	CH_3	3-CH_3O-4-$HOC_6H_3CH_2$	H	240°	24
C_6H_5	CH_3	3,4-$(CH_3O)_2C_6H_3CH$=		157°	22
C_6H_5	CH_3	2,4-$[(CH_3)_2N]_2C_6H_3CH$=		181°	1241
C_6H_5	CH_3	3-NO_2-4-$(CH_3)_2CHC_6H_3CH$=		205°	1123
C_6H_5	CH_3	3,5-$(CH_3O)_2$-4-HOC_6H_2CH=		208°	956
C_6H_5	CH_3	3,4,5-$(CH_3O)_3C_6H_2CH$=		141°	955
C_6H_5	CH_3	2-NO_2-3-CH_3O-4-HOC_6H_2CH=		192°	702
C_6H_5	CH_3	$[4-(CH_3)_2NC_6H_4]_2C$=		265°	1073
C_6H_5	CH_3	4-$(CH_3)_2NC_6H_4]_2CH$	H	185°	836
C_6H_5	CH_3	2,4-$(NO_2)_2C_6H_4N$=CHCH=CHCH=CH	H	247°	1114
C_6H_5	CH_3	$(C_6H_5)_3C$	H	209°	567
C_6H_5	CH_3	4-$(CH_3)_2NC_6H_4C$ | $(C_6H_5)_2$	H	179°	570
C_6H_5	CH_3	$[4-(CH_3)_2NC_6H_4]_2C$ | C_6H_5	H	162°	570
C_6H_5	CH_3	$[4-(CH_3)_3NC_6H_4]_2CH$	H	193°	570

(Table continued)

TABLE II, Section C (*continued*)

R[1]	R[2]	R[3]	R[4]	M.p.	Reference
C_6H_5	CH_3	$[4\text{-}(CH_3)_2NC_6H_4]_3C$	H 67	154°	567
C_6H_5	CH_3	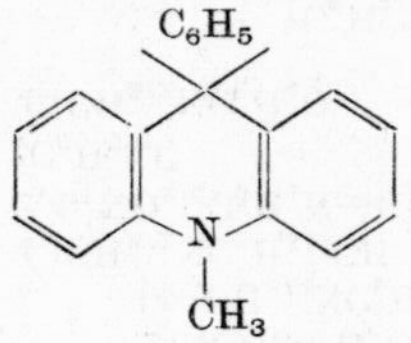 C_6H_5; N; CH_3	H	188°	567
C_6H_5	CH_3	O; $CH_3\overset{\|}{C}CH_2CH$; C_6H_5	H	161°	686
C_6H_5	CH_3	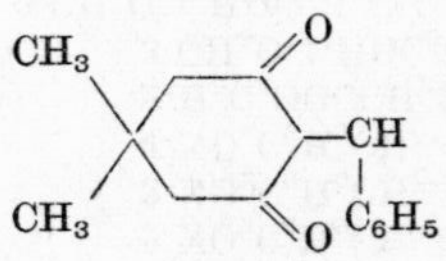 CH_3; CH_3; O; O; –CH; C_6H_5	H	220°	686
C_6H_5	CH_3	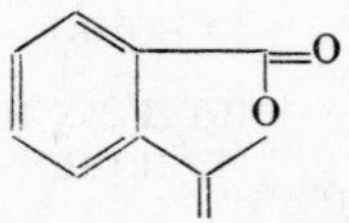 O; O		—	1202
C_6H_5	CH_3	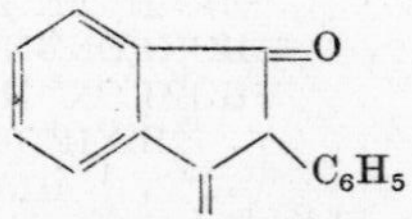 O; C_6H_5		272°	1204

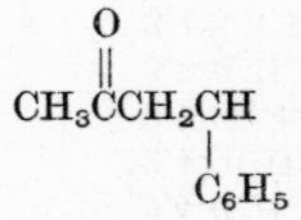

C_6H_5	CH_3	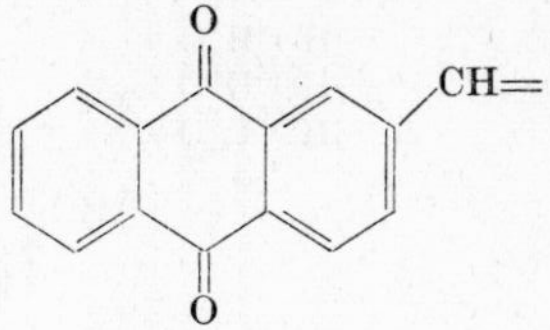 O, O, CH=		243°	1219
C_6H_5	CH_3	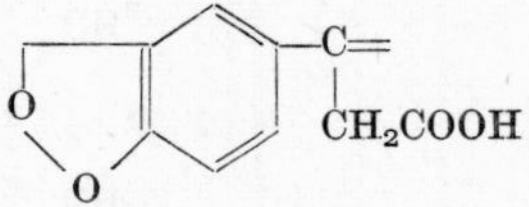 O, O, C=, CH_2COOH		145°	957
C_6H_5	CH_3	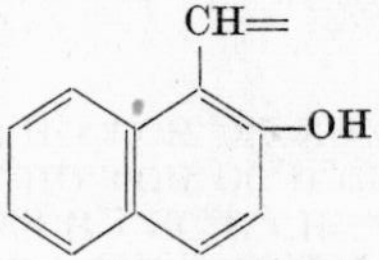 CH=, OH		—	948
C_6H_5	CH_3	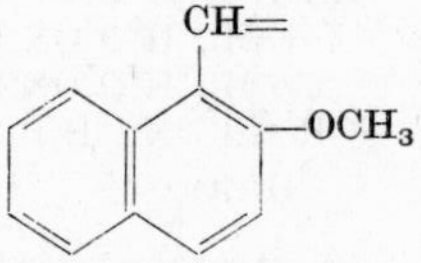 CH=, OCH_3		219°	1036
C_6H_5	CH_3	$C_6H_5CH(COC_6H_5)CH(C_6H_5)$	H	212°	689
C_6H_5	CH_3	$4\text{-}CH_3OC_6H_4CH(COC_6H_5)CH(C_6H_5)$	H	200°	689

(Table continued)

TABLE II, Section C (*continued*)

R^1	R^2	R^3	R^4	M.p.	Reference
C_6H_5	CH_3	$3,4\text{-}(CH_2O_2)C_6H_3CH(C_6H_5)CH(COC_6H_5)$	H	206°	689
C_6H_5	CH_3	$4\text{-}(CH_3)_2NC_6H_4CH(C_6H_5)CH(COC_6H_5)$	H	201°	689
$2\text{-}CH_3C_6H_4$	CH_3	$4\text{-}(CH_3)_2NC_6H_4CH{=}$		140°	702
$2\text{-}CH_3C_6H_4$	CH_3	$2\text{-}NO_2C_6H_4CH{=}$		183°	702
$2\text{-}CH_3C_6H_4$	CH_3	$3\text{-}NO_2C_6H_4CH{=}$		176°	702
$2\text{-}CH_3C_6H_4$	CH_3	$3,4\text{-}(CH_3O)_2C_6H_3CH{=}$		222°	702
$4\text{-}CH_3C_6H_4$	CH_3	$4\text{-}(CH_3)_2NC_6H_4CH{=}$		142°	702
$4\text{-}CH_3C_6H_4$	CH_3	$4\text{-}HO\text{-}3\text{-}CH_3OC_6H_3CH{=}$		183°	702
$4\text{-}CH_3C_6H_4$	CH_3	$4\text{-}HO\text{-}3\text{-}CH_3O\text{-}2\text{-}NO_2C_6H_2CH{=}$		209°	702
$4\text{-}C_2H_5OC_6H_4$	CH_3	(2-furyl)CH_2	H	—	378
$4\text{-}H_2NC_6H_4$	CH_3	(2-furyl)CH_2	H	—	378
$4\text{-}CH_3CONHC_6H_4$	CH_3	(2-furyl)CH_2	H	244°	378
$2\text{-}ClC_6H_4$	CH_3	$C_6H_5CH{=}$		159°	296, 1494
$3\text{-}ClC_6H_4$	CH_3	$C_6H_5CH{=}$		128°	296
$4\text{-}ClC_6H_4$	CH_3	$C_6H_5CH{=}$		156°	296

R¹	R²	R³	R⁴	M.p.	Reference
7* 4-BrC_6H_4	CH_3	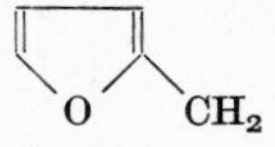 $C_4H_3O{-}CH_2$ (2-furyl-CH_2)	H	—	378
4-$NO_2C_6H_4$	CH_3	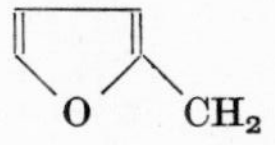 $C_4H_3O{-}CH_2$ (2-furyl-CH_2)	H	—	378
2-$HOOCC_6H_4$	CH_3	$C_6H_5CH{=}$		243°	1004
3-$HOOCC_6H_4$	CH_3	$C_6H_5CH{=}$		251°	980
4-$HOOCC_6H_4$	CH_3	$C_6H_5CH{=}$		281°	980
4-$HO_3SC_6H_4$	CH_3	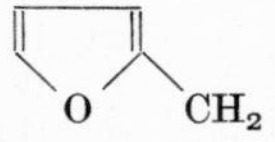 $C_4H_3O{-}CH_2$ (2-furyl-CH_2)	H	—	378
2,4-$Cl_2C_6H_3$	CH_3	$C_6H_5CH{=}$		131°	296
1-$C_{10}H_7$	CH_3	$C_6H_5CH_2$	H	168°	849
2-$C_{10}H_7$	CH_3	$C_6H_5CH_2$	H	153°	849
C_6H_5	$C_6H_5CH_2$	4-$NO_2C_6H_5CH_2$	H	160°	1313
C_6H_5	CH_3	$C_6H_5CH_2$	CH_3	81°	53
C_6H_5	CH_3	$C_6H_5CH_2$	$C_6H_5CH_2$	91°	1321

TABLE II (*continued*)

Section D. Polyaryl Substituents

R¹	R²	R³	R⁴	M.p.	Reference
C_6H_5	C_6H_5	H	H	136°	777, 818, 1023, 1522, 1524, 1552

(*Table continued*)

TABLE II, Section D (*continued*)

R^1	R^2	R^3	R^4	M.p.	Reference
C_6H_5	H	C_6H_5	H	195°	506, 1636
C_6H_5	$4\text{-}F_3CC_6H_4$	H	H	140°	673
C_6H_5	$4\text{-}C_2H_5OC_6H_4$	H	H	152°	1588, 1589, 1590
C_6H_5	$2\text{-}ClC_6H_4$	H	H	113°	1580
C_6H_5	$3\text{-}ClC_6H_4$	H	H	144°	1580
C_6H_5	$4\text{-}ClC_6H_4$	H	H	140°, 161°	1580, 1589
C_6H_5	$4\text{-}NO_2C_6H_4$	H	H	209°	340
C_6H_5	$4\text{-}HOOCC_6H_4$	H	H	—	857
C_6H_5	H	$2\text{-}HSC_6H_4$	H	195°	578
C_6H_5	H	$2\text{-}HS\text{-}4\text{-}C_2H_5OC_6H_3$	H	243°	578
C_6H_5	$1\text{-}C_{10}H_7$	H	H	199°	1577
C_6H_5	$2\text{-}C_{10}H_7$	H	H	127.5°	1577
C_6H_5	H	$2\text{-}C_{10}H_7$	H	219°	1640
C_6H_5	$3\text{-}CH_3O\text{-}2\text{-}C_{10}H_6$	H	H	235°	1575
C_6H_5	$4\text{-}(4\text{-}CH_3COOC_6H_4O)C_6H_4$	H	H	128°	1585
C_6H_5	$3\text{-}CH_3C(=NNHC_6H_5)C_6H_4$	H	H	230°	1225
C_6H_5	$4\text{-}CH_3SO_2C_6H_4$	H	H	215°	455
$2\text{-}CH_3C_6H_4$	C_6H_5	H	H	191°	1004, 1524
$3\text{-}CH_3OC_6H_4$	C_6H_5	H	H	124°	1581
$4\text{-}CH_3OC_6H_4$	C_6H_5	H	H	137°	1581
$4\text{-}BrC_6H_4$	C_6H_5	H	H	154°	351
$3\text{-}NO_2C_6H_4$	C_6H_5	H	H	174°	777, 1003
$4\text{-}NO_2C_6H_4$	C_6H_5	H	H	207.5°	777
$2\text{-}HOOCC_6H_4$	C_6H_5	H	H	196°	1520
$4\text{-}HOOCC_6H_4$	C_6H_5	H	H	—	857
$2\text{-}HO_3SC_6H_4$	C_6H_5	H	H	—	469, 857
$3\text{-}HO_3SC_6H_4$	C_6H_5	H	H	—	857
$4\text{-}HO_3SC_6H_4$	C_6H_5	H	H	—	857
$4\text{-}H_2NO_2SC_6H_4$	C_6H_5	H	H	236°	695

4-(4-$CH_3CONHC_6H_4$)C_6H_4	C_6H_5	H	H	—	163
2-CH_3-4-$HO_3SC_6H_3$	C_6H_5	H	H	—	857
2-Cl-4-$HO_3SC_6H_3$	C_6H_5	H	H	—	857
2-Cl-5-$HO_3SC_6H_3$	C_6H_5	H	H	—	857
2,4-$(NO_2)_2C_6H_3$	C_6H_5	H	H	160°	777
4-NO_2-2-$HO_3SC_6H_3$	C_6H_5	H	H	—	469, 857
2-NO_2-4-$HO_3SC_6H_3$	C_6H_5	H	H	—	857
2,5-$(HO_3S)_2C_6H_3$	C_6H_5	H	H	—	857
2-HO-3-HOOC-5-$HO_3SC_6H_2$	C_6H_5	H	H	—	857
3-CH_3-4-Cl-6-$HO_3SC_6H_2$	C_6H_5	H	H	—	857
2,5-Cl_2-4-$HO_3SC_6H_2$	C_6H_5	H	H	—	857
2,4,6-$(NO_2)_3C_6H_2$	C_6H_5	H	H	223°	777
2-(4-HO-3-$HOOCC_6H_2SO_2$)-4-$HO_3SC_6H_3$	C_6H_5	H	H	—	857
2-CH_3-4,5-$(HO_3S)_2C_6H_2$	C_6H_5	H	H	—	857
4-$CH_3OC_6H_4$	4-$NO_2C_6H_4$	H	H	204°	1581
4-$NO_2C_6H_4$	2-ClC_6H_4	H	H	203°	1580
4-$NO_2C_6H_4$	3-ClC_6H_4	H	H	189°	1580
4-$NO_2C_6H_4$	4-ClC_6H_4	H	H	200°	1580
4-$NO_2C_6H_4$	4-$HOOCC_6H_4$	H	H	—	857
4-$NO_2C_6H_4$	1-$C_{10}H_7$	H	H	228°	1577
4-$NO_2C_6H_4$	2-$C_{10}H_7$	H	H	235°	1577
4-$NO_2C_6H_4$	3-CH_3O-2-$C_{10}H_6$	H	H	235°	1575
3-$HOOCC_6H_4$	4-$NO_2C_6H_4$	H	H	—	694
3-$HOOCC_6H_4$	4-$H_2NC_6H_4$	H	H	—	694
3-$HOOCC_6H_4$	4-$C_{15}H_{33}CONHC_6H_4$	H	H	256°	694
3-$HOOCC_6H_4$	4-$HOOCC_6H_4$	H	H	—	857
4-$HOOCC_6H_4$	3-$C_{15}H_{33}CONHC_6H_4$	H	H	256°	694
2-$HO_3SC_6H_4$	4-$HOOCC_6H_4$	H	H	—	857
3-$HO_3SC_6H_4$	4-$HOOCC_6H_4$	H	H	—	469
4-$HO_3SC_6H_4$	4-$HOOCC_6H_4$	H	H	—	857
2-Cl-5-$HO_3SC_6H_3$	4-$HOOCC_6H_4$	H	H	—	469, 857
2,4-$(NO_2)_2C_6H_3$	3-$(CH_3)_2NC_6H_4$	H	H	243°	229

(Table continued)

TABLE II, Section D (*continued*)

R[1]	R[2]	R[3]	R[4]	M.p.	Reference
2-HO-3-HOOC-5-$HO_3SC_6H_2$	4-$HOOCC_6H_4$	H	H	—	857
1-HO_3S-2-$C_{10}H_6$	4-$HOOCC_6H_4$	H	H	—	857
C_6H_5	C_6H_5	CH_3	H	204°	505
C_6H_5	CH_3	C_6H_5	H	199°	1522
C_6H_5	H	C_6H_5	CH_3	57°	1643
C_6H_5	C_6H_5	C_2H_5	H	213°	505
C_6H_5	C_6H_5	C_3H_7	H	198°	505
C_6H_5	C_3H_7	C_6H_5	H	151°	1276
C_6H_5	iso-C_3H_7	C_6H_5	H	192°	1640
C_6H_5	C_6H_5	C_4H_9	H	192°	505
C_6H_5	iso-C_4H_9	C_6H_5	H	170°	1276
C_6H_5	C_6H_5	C_5H_{11}	H	174°	505
C_6H_5	C_6H_5	C_6H_{13}	H	158°	505
C_6H_5	C_6H_5	C_7H_{15}	H	134°	505
C_6H_5	C_6H_5	C_8H_{17}	H	144°	505
C_6H_5	C_6H_5	C_9H_{19}	H	133°	505
C_6H_5	C_6H_5	$C_{10}H_{21}$	H	116°	505
C_6H_5	C_6H_5	[furan ring]—CH_2	H	130°	378
4-$CH_3C_6H_5$	C_6H_5	[furan ring]—CH_2	H	135°	378
4-$NO_2C_6H_5$	C_6H_5	[furan ring]—CH_2	H	203°	378

3-HOOC-4-HOC_6H_3	CH_3	2-HO_3S-4-(4-$NO_2C_6H_4CONH$)C_6H_5	H	—	1361
C_6H_5	C_6H_5	C_6H_5	H	204°	3, 1640
C_6H_5	C_6H_5	CH_3	CH_3	45	1343
4-BrC_6H_4	C_6H_5	$C_6H_5CH=$		> 265	351
2-$HOOCC_6H_4$	C_6H_5	$C_6H_5CH=$		241°	1004
4-$HO_3SC_6H_4$	4-$HO_3SC_6H_4$	4-(4-$HO_3SC_6H_4CH_2NH$)-3-$CH_3C_6H_3CH=$		—	1371

TABLE II (*continued*)

Section E. Heterocyclic, Alkyl, and Aryl Substituents

R^1	R^2	R^3	R^4	M.p.	Reference
H	O	H	H	223°	1498, 1499
H	S	H	H	205°	662
H	N, N, N, O	H	H	265°	358

(*Table continued*)

TABLE II, Section E (*continued*)

R^1	R^2	R^3	R^4	M.p.	Reference
H	N	H	H	219°	308
H	N	H	H	268°	307
H	N	H	H	286°	1659
H	N N	H	H	245°	437
CH_3 N $COOC_2H_5$	CH_3	H	H	180°	1296
CH_3 N S	CH_3	H	H	190°	94

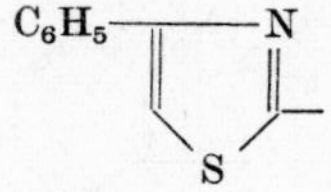 C_6H_5 N S	CH_3	H	H	196°	94
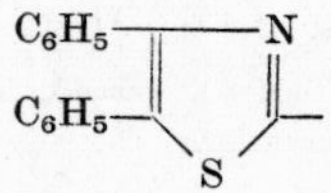 C_6H_5 C_6H_5 N S	CH_3	H	H	198°	94
H	CH_3	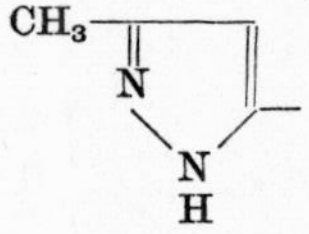 CH_3 N N H	H	260°	1347
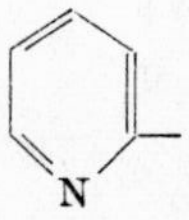 N	CH_3	H	H	110°	438
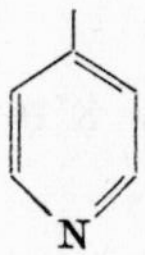 N	CH_3	H	H	198°	833
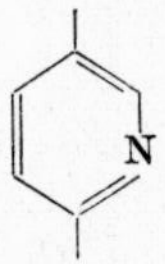 N	CH_3	H	H	128°	1687

(*Table continued*)

TABLE II, Section E (*continued*)

R^1	R^2	R^3	R^4	M.p.	Reference
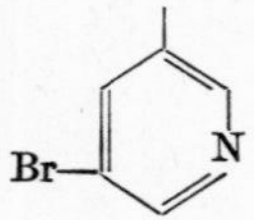 Br, N	CH_3	H	H	191°	1687
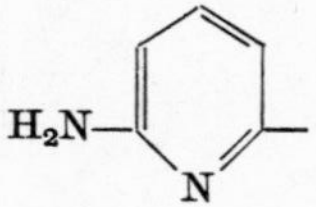 H_2N, N	CH_3	H	H	188°	91
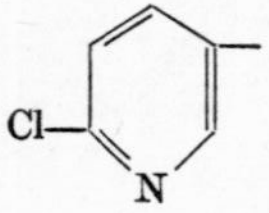 Cl, N	CH_3	H	H	175°	1120
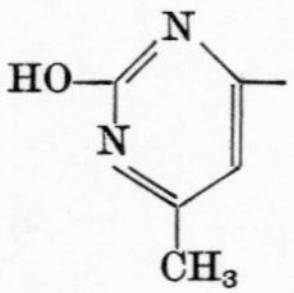 HO, N, N, CH_3	CH_3	H	H	205°	1570
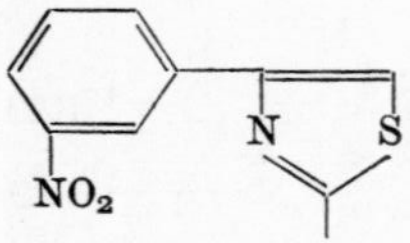 NO_2, N, S	CH_3	H	H	235°	421
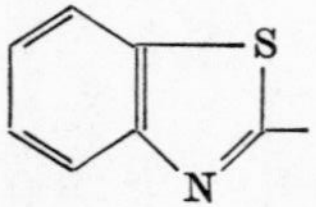 S, N	CH_3	H	H	231°	74, 413

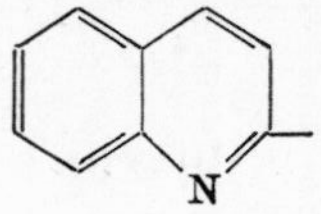	CH_3	H	H	140°	438
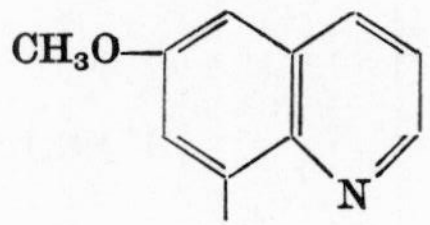	CH_3	H	H	135°	1053
C_6H_5	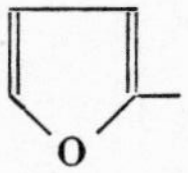	H	H	178°	912, 1215, 1499
C_6H_5	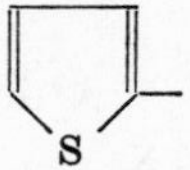	H	H	137°	662, 909
C_6H_5	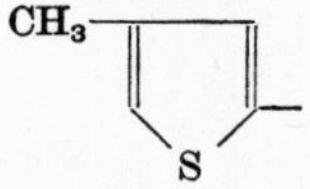	H	H	136°	662
C_6H_5	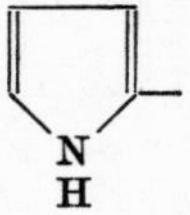	H	H	193°	1067
C_6H_5	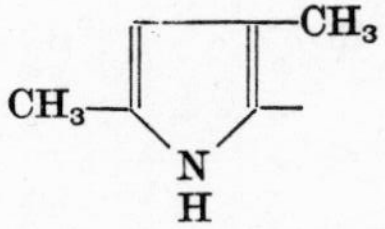	H	H	141°	682

(*Table continued*)

TABLE II, Section E (*continued*)

R^1	R^2	R^3	R^4	M.p.	Reference
C_6H_5	CH_3, CH_3, N, H	H	H	225°	1068
C_6H_5	N	H	H	188°	307
C_6H_5	NH_2, N, N, H_2N, N	H	H	261°	1492
C_6H_5	CH_3, N, H	H	H	258°	10
4-BrC_6H_4	O	H	H	160°	1499
3-$NO_2C_6H_4$	O	H	H	174°	1499

4-$HO_3SC_6H_4$	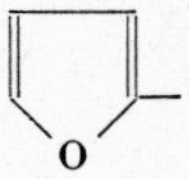 O	H	H	> 295°	1499
H	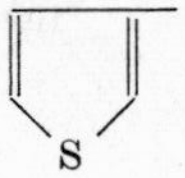 S	CH_3	CH_3	118°	662
C_6H_5	CH_3	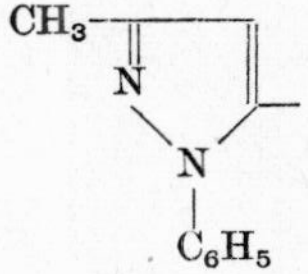 CH_3, N, N, C_6H_5	H	260°	1347
C_6H_5	CH_3	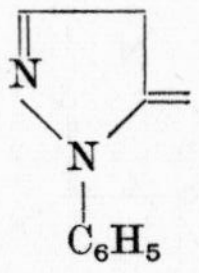 N, N, C_6H_5		258°	323, 688
C_6H_5	CH_3	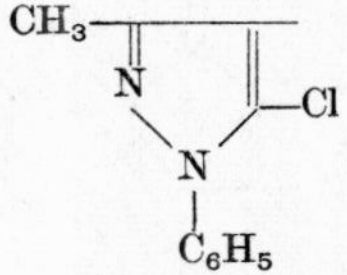 CH_3, N, Cl, N, C_6H_5	H	240°	991
C_6H_5	CH_3	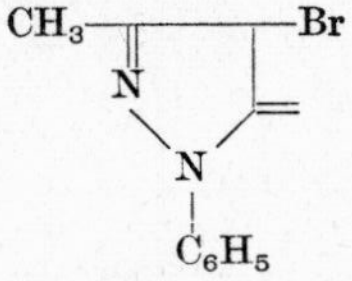 CH_3, Br, N, N, C_6H_5		214°	323

(Table continued)

TABLE II, Section E (*continued*)

R^1	R^2	R^3	R^4	M.p.	Reference
C_6H_5	CH_3	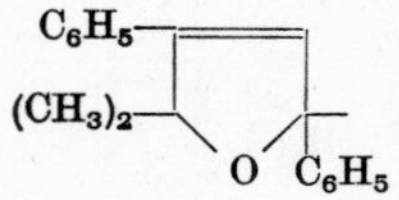 C_6H_5, $(CH_3)_2$, O, C_6H_5	H	137°	1530
C_6H_5	CH_3	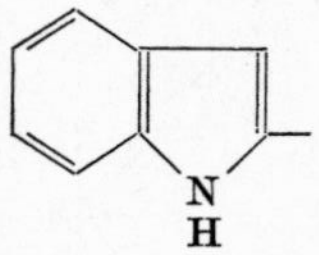 N, H	H	238°	559
C_6H_5	CH_3	S, N, CH_3	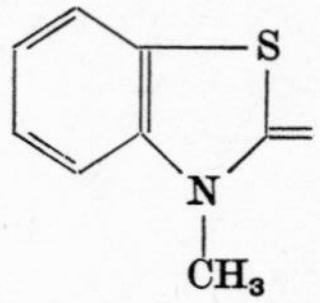	177°	1072
C_6H_5	CH_3	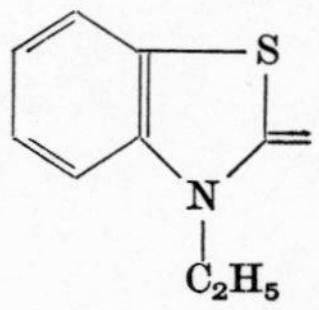 S, N, C_2H_5		143°	1072
C_6H_5	CH_3	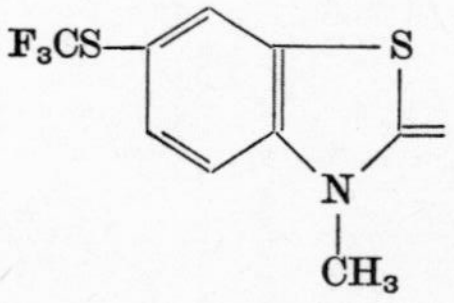 F_3CS, S, N, CH_3		175°	1658

C_6H_5	CH_3	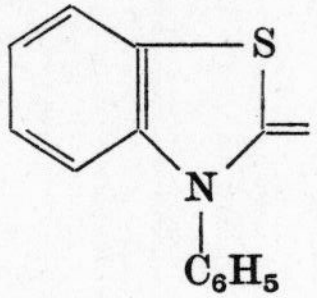 S, N, C_6H_5		280°	1072
C_6H_5	CH_3	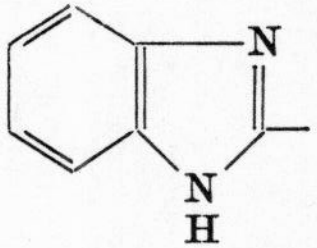 N, N, H	H	172°	558
C_6H_5	CH_3	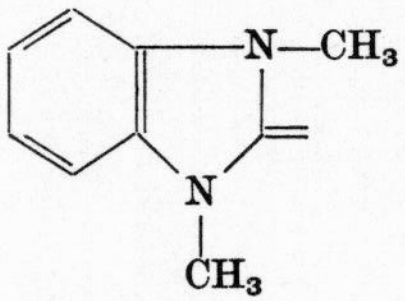 N—CH_3, N, CH_3		153°	1195
C_6H_5	CH_3	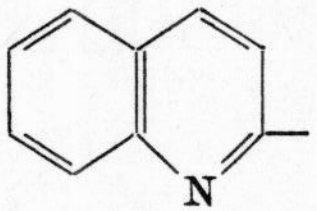 N	H	159°	796
C_6H_5	CH_3	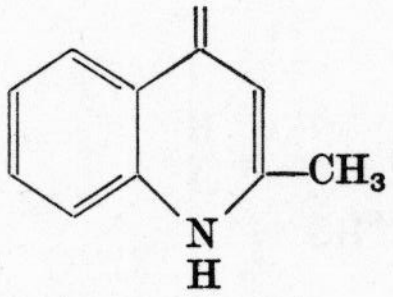 —CH_3, N, H		320°	971
C_6H_5	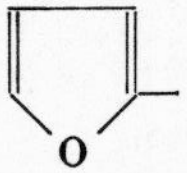 O	C_6H_5CH=		210°	1499

(Table continued)

TABLE II, Section E (*continued*)

R^1	R^2	R^3	R^4	M.p.	Reference
4-$CH_3C_6H_4$	CH_3	N H —CH_3	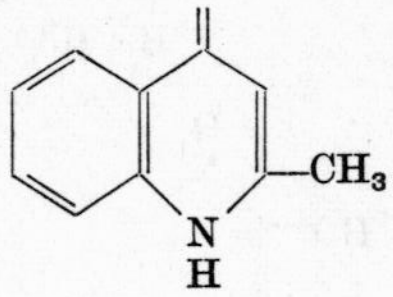	302°	971
4-$C_2H_5OC_6H_4$	CH_3	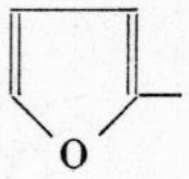 O	H	—	378
4-$NH_2C_6H_4$	CH_3	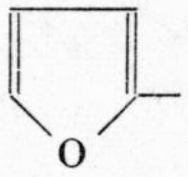 O	H	—	378
4-$CH_3CONHC_6H_4$	CH_3	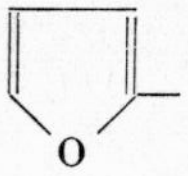 O	H	244°	378
4-BrC_6H_5	CH_3	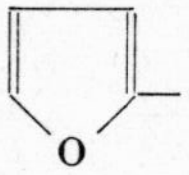 O	H	—	378
4-$NO_2C_6H_4$	CH_3	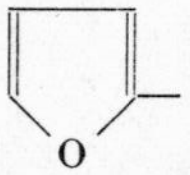 O	H	—	378

		O			
C_6H_5	C_6H_5	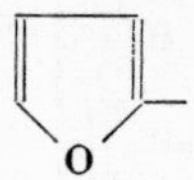 O	H	136°	378
C_6H_5	C_6H_5	CH_3, N, H		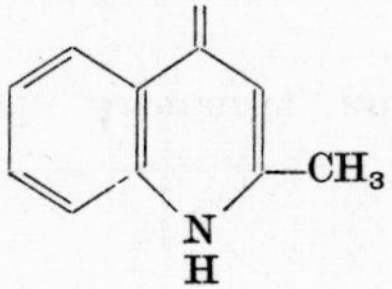 207°	971
$4\text{-}CH_3C_6H_4$	C_6H_5	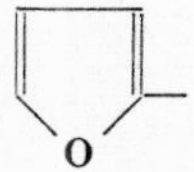 O	H	203°	378
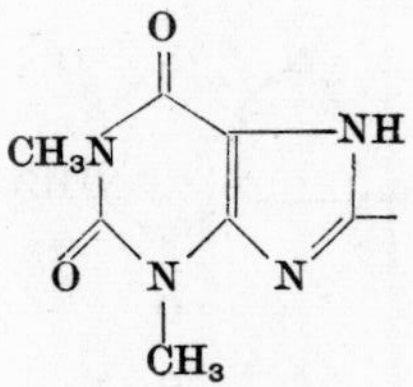 O, CH_3N, NH, O, N, N, CH_3	CH_3	H	H	310°	1147
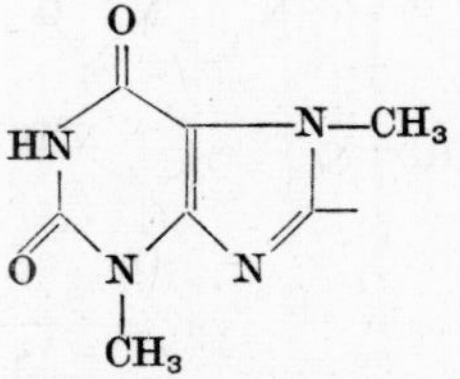 O, HN, N—CH_3, O, N, N, CH_3	CH_3	H	H	267°	1147

(Table continued)

TABLE II, Section E (*continued*)

R^1	R^2	R^3	R^4	M.p.	Reference
O; CH_3N; N—CH_3; O; N; H; N	CH_3	H	H	292°	1147
O; CH_3N; N—CH_3; O; N; N; CH_3	CH_3	H	H	216°	1147

TABLE II (*continued*)

Section F. α-Hydroxy- and α-Alkoxyalkyl, Alkyl, Aralkyl, Aromatic, and Heterocyclic Substituents

R^1	R^2	R^3	R^4	M.p.	Reference
H	$C_2H_5OCH_2$	H	H	148°	1315
H	$C_2H_5OCH_2$	H	CH_3	135°	1314
H	$C_2H_5OCH_2$	H	C_2H_5	99°	1314

H	$C_2H_5OCH_2$	H	$C_6H_5CH_2$	—	1315
H	C_6H_5	O=C–N–C(=O)–C(OH)–C(=O)–N (ring)	H	254°	1194
C_6H_5	$C_2H_5OCH_2$	H	H	82°	1316
$4\text{-}NO_2C_6H_5$	$HOCH_2$	H	H	—	532
C_6H_5	CH_3	$HOCH_2$	H	158°	24
C_6H_5	CH_3	Cl_3CCH–OH	H	189°	895
CH_3	C_6H_5	Cl_3CCH–OH	H	184°	1190
$4\text{-}CH_3C_6H_4$	CH_3	Cl_3CCH–OH	H	191°	107
C_6H_5	CH_3	$C_2H_5OC=$ CH_3		129°	764
C_6H_5	CH_3	$C_2H_5OC=$ C_2H_5		120°	764
C_6H_5	CH_3	$C_2H_5OC=$ C_6H_5		130°	764
C_6H_5	CH_3	O=C–NH–C(=O)–C(OH)–C(=O)–NH (ring)	H	196°, 243°	1194, 1253

(*Table continued*)

TABLE II, Section F (*continued*)

R^1	R^2	R^3	R^4	M.p.	Reference
C_6H_5	C_4H_3O (2-furyl)	$C_2H_5OC(CH_3)=$		90°	764
C_6H_5	$C_6H_5OCH_2$	C_6H_5	H	145°	1562
C_6H_5	$C_6H_5OCH_2$	$4\text{-}ClC_6H_5$	H	166°	1562

TABLE II (*continued*)

Section G. α-Amino- and α-Iminoalkyl Alkyl, and Aryl Substituents

R^1	R^2	R^3	R^4	M.p.	Reference
H	CH_3	$CH_3C(=NH)$	H	280°	1193
H	CH_3	$C_6H_5C(=NH)$	H	> 300°	1193
H	CH_3	$C_6H_5C(=NNHC_6H_5)$	H	230°	1193
C_6H_5	$2\text{-}HOOCC_6H_4CONHCH_2$	H	H	164°	138
C_6H_5	$C_6H_4(CO)_2NCH_2$	H	H	192°	138

H	C_6H_5	HN=CH	H	283°	1188, 1189
H	C_6H_5	$C_6H_5N{=}CH$	H	263°	1188
H	C_6H_5	$4\text{-}C_2H_5OC_6H_4N{=}CH$	H	240°	1188
H	C_6H_5	$NH_2CONHNHCH(COOCH_3)$	H	172°	1179
H	C_6H_5	$NH_2CONHNHCH(COOC_2H_5)$	H	171°	1179
C_6H_5	CH_3	$ONCH_2$	H	170°	925
C_6H_5	CH_3	HN=CH	H	155°	1189
CH_3	C_6H_5	HN=CH	H	210°	1189
C_6H_5	CH_3	$(CH_3)_2NCH_2$	H	221°	1098
C_6H_5	CH_3	$(C_2H_5)_2NCH_2$	H	221°	1098
C_6H_5	CH_3	(piperidino)NCH_2	H	224°	1098
C_6H_5	CH_3	$CH_3C{=}NH$	H	172°	1192, 1193
C_6H_5	CH_3	$C_2H_5C{=}NH$	H	68°	1193
C_6H_5	CH_3	$C_3H_7C{=}NH$	H	137°	1193
C_6H_5	CH_3	$H_2NN{=}CH$	H	201°	1206
C_6H_5	CH_3	$C_6H_5N{=}CH$	H	184°	348, 823, 824, 923, 1070, 1088, 1089, 1090
CH_3	C_6H_5	$C_6H_5N{=}CH$	H	110°	1189

(Table continued)

TABLE II, Section G (*continued*)

R^1	R^2	R^3	R^4	M.p.	Reference
C_6H_5	CH_3	$C_6H_5N{=}C(CH_3)$	H	183°	947, 1192
C_6H_5	CH_3	2,4,5-$(CH_3)_3C_6H_4N{=}CH$	H	162°	348
C_6H_5	CH_3	3,4-$(NH_2)_2C_6H_3N{=}CH$	H	173°	351
C_6H_5	CH_3	2-$C_2H_5OC_6H_4N{=}CH$	H	170°	351
C_6H_5	CH_3	4-$C_2H_5OC_6H_4N{=}CH$	H	144°	1092
C_6H_5	CH_3	2-$NH_2C_6H_4N{=}CH$	H	—	1190
C_6H_5	CH_3	4-$BrC_6H_4N{=}CH$	H	164°	348
C_6H_5	CH_3	3-$NO_2C_6H_4N{=}CH$	H	175°	351
C_6H_5	CH_3	4-$NO_2C_6H_4N{=}CH$	H	170°	351
C_6H_5	CH_3	4-$C_6H_5CH_2OC_6H_4N{=}CH$	H	181°	350
C_6H_5	CH_3	4-$C_6H_5N{=}NC_6H_4N{=}CH$	H	203°	923
C_6H_5	CH_3	1-$C_{10}H_7N{=}CH$	H	122°	348
C_6H_5	CH_3	2-$C_{10}H_7N{=}CH$	H	171°	348
C_6H_5	CH_3	$C_6H_5NHC(C_6H_5){=}$		161°	947
C_6H_5	CH_3	(3-methyl-1-phenyl-pyrazol-5-yl: CH_3, N, N, C_6H_5)$-NH-C(2\text{-}HOOCC_6H_4){=}$		242°	1202
C_6H_5	CH_3	$C_6H_5NHN{=}C(CH_3)$	H	197°, 210°	559, 1192
C_6H_5	CH_3	$C_6H_5NHN{=}C(C_2H_5)$	H	168°	1193
C_6H_5	CH_3	$C_6H_5NHN{=}C(C_3H_7)$	H	185°	1193

C_6H_5	CH_3	$C_6H_5NHN{=}C$ | C_6H_5	H	204°	1193
C_6H_5	CH_3	$C_6H_5NHN{=}C$ | $COOC_2H_5$	H	182°	1641
C_6H_5	CH_3	$C_6H_5NHN{=}C$ | $COOH$	H	205°	1641
C_6H_5	CH_3	$4\text{-}BrC_6H_4NHN{=}C$ | $COOC_2H_5$	H	213°	1641
C_6H_5	CH_3	$(C_6H_5)_2NNHC{=}$ | $COOC_2H_5$		137°	1641
$2\text{-}CH_3C_6H_4$	CH_3	$C_6H_5N{=}CH$	H	140°	351
$2\text{-}CH_3C_6H_4$	CH_3	$3\text{-}CH_3C_6H_4N{=}CH$	H	232°	351
$2\text{-}CH_3C_6H_4$	CH_3	$4\text{-}C_2H_5OC_6H_3N{=}CH$	H	160°	351
$4\text{-}CH_3C_6H_4$	CH_3	$3\text{-}CH_3C_6H_4N{=}CH$	H	122°	351
$4\text{-}CH_3C_6H_4$	CH_3	$2,5\text{-}(CH_3)_2C_6H_3N{=}CH$	H	249°	349
$4\text{-}CH_3C_6H_4$	CH_3	$2\text{-}C_2H_5OC_6H_4N{=}CH$	H	133°	351
$4\text{-}CH_3C_6H_4$	CH_3	$4\text{-}BrC_6H_4N{=}CH$	H	196°	351
$4\text{-}CH_3C_6H_4$	CH_3	$C_6H_5NHN{=}C$ | $COOH$	H	217°	1641
$4\text{-}CH_3C_6H_4$	CH_3	$C_6H_5NHN{=}C$ | $COOC_2H_5$	H	195°	1641
$4\text{-}CH_3C_6H_4$	CH_3	$C_6H_5NHNHC{=}$ | $COOC_2H_5$		209°	1641
$4\text{-}C_2H_5OC_6H_4$	CH_3	$HON{=}CH$	H	182°	1186
$4\text{-}C_2H_5OC_6H_4$	CH_3	$C_6H_5N{=}CH$	H	155°	902

(Table continued)

TABLE II, Section G (*continued*)

R^1	R^2	R^3	R^4	M.p.	Reference
$4\text{-}C_2H_5OC_6H_4$	CH_3	$4\text{-}C_2H_5OC_6H_4N{=}CH$	H	132°	1186
$4\text{-}C_2H_5OC_6H_4$	CH_3	$CH_3C(=NH)$	H	235°	1193
$4\text{-}C_2H_5OC_6H_4$	CH_3	$C_6H_5C(=NH)$	H	177°	1193
$4\text{-}C_2H_5OC_6H_4$	CH_3	$2\text{-}NH_2C_6H_4N{=}CH$	H	190°	1190
C_6H_5	C_6H_5	$NH_2C(H){=}$		175°	1189
C_6H_5	C_6H_5	$HON{=}CH$	H	254°	902
C_6H_5	C_6H_5	$C_6H_5N{=}CH$	H	195°, 140°	348, 902
C_6H_5	C_6H_5	$2\text{-}CH_3C_6H_4N{=}CH$	H	146°	348
C_6H_5	C_6H_5	$2\text{-}NH_2C_6H_4N{=}CH$	H	215°	1190
C_6H_5	C_6H_5	$4\text{-}BrC_6H_4N{=}CH$	H	184°	600
C_6H_5	C_6H_5	$2\text{-}C_{10}H_7N{=}CH$	H	192°	348
C_6H_5	C_6H_5	$C_6H_5NHN{=}C(COOC_2H_5)$	H	208°	1641
$2\text{-}CH_3C_6H_4$	C_6H_5	$C_6H_5N{=}CH$	H	169°	351
$2\text{-}CH_3C_6H_4$	C_6H_5	$2,4\text{-}(CH_3)_2C_6H_3N{=}CH$	H	142°	351
$2\text{-}CH_3C_6H_4$	C_6H_5	$4\text{-}ClC_6H_4N{=}CH$	H	181°	351
$2\text{-}CH_3C_6H_4$	C_6H_5	$3\text{-}BrC_6H_4N{=}CH$	H	148°	351
$2\text{-}CH_3C_6H_4$	C_6H_5	$4\text{-}BrC_6H_4N{=}CH$	H	142°	351
$4\text{-}BrC_6H_4$	C_6H_5	$C_6H_5N{=}CH$	H	188°	351
C_6H_5	$C_6H_5NCH_2(C_2H_5)$	CH_3	CH_3	77°	512

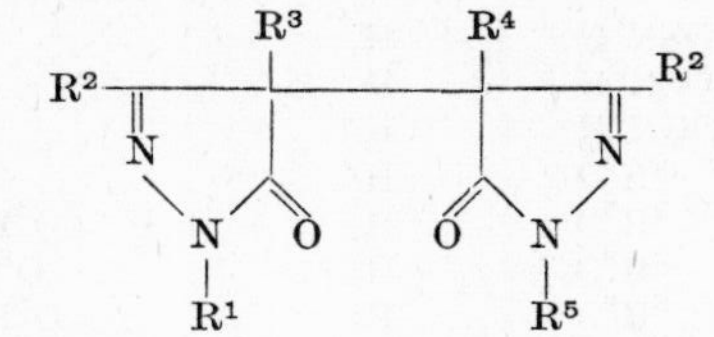

TABLE III. 4,4′-Bis(2-pyrazolin-5-ones) Linked by a Single Bond

R^1	R^2	R^3	R^4	R^5	M.p.	Reference
H	H	H	H	H	>360°	725
CH_3	H	H	H	H	>360°	725
H	CH_3	H	H	H	—	1485
CH_3	H	H	H	CH_3	>375°	72, 725
$HO_3SCH_2CH_2$	CH_3	H	H	$HO_3SCH_2CH_2$	—	72
C_6H_5	CH_3	H	H	C_6H_5	dec. without melting, 290°, 320°	114, 807, 809, 815, 885, 925, 1090, 1091, 1096, 1185, 1192, 1513, 1522, 1538, 1612
C_6H_5	$t\text{-}C_4H_9$	H	H	C_6H_5	>290°	1582
C_6H_5	$C_{15}H_{31}$	H	H	C_6H_5	238°	636
C_6H_5	$C_{17}H_{35}$	H	H	C_6H_5	—	72
C_6H_5	$H_5C_2OOCCH_2$	H	H	C_6H_5	—	72
$4\text{-}CH_3C_6H_4$	CH_3	H	H	$4\text{-}CH_3C_6H_4$	—	72
$4\text{-}C_2H_5OC_6H_4$	CH_3	H	H	$4\text{-}C_2H_5OC_6H_4$	—	72
$4\text{-}ClC_6H_4$	CH_3	H	H	$4\text{-}ClC_6H_4$	dec.	296
$4\text{-}NO_2C_6H_4$	CH_3	H	H	$4\text{-}NO_2C_6H_4$	255° (dec.)	690
$3\text{-}HOOCC_6H_4$	$C_{17}H_{35}$	H	H	$3\text{-}HOOCC_6H_4$	—	72
$4\text{-}HO_3SC_6H_4$	CH_3	H	H	$4\text{-}HO_3SC_6H_4$	—	72
$4\text{-}HO_3SC_6H_4$	$C_{17}H_{35}$	H	H	$4\text{-}HO_3SC_6H_4$	—	72

(*Table continued*)

TABLE III (*continued*)

R^1	R^2	R^3	R^4	R^5	M.p.	Reference
$2\text{-}C_{10}H_7$	$4\text{-}ClC_6H_4NHCOCH_2$	H	H	$2\text{-}C_{10}H_7$	—	72
$4\text{-}HO_3S\text{-}1\text{-}C_{10}H_6$	CH_3	H	H	$4\text{-}HO_3S\text{-}1\text{-}C_{10}H_6$	—	72
$C_6H_5CH_2$	CH_3	H	H	$C_6H_5CH_2$	> 280°	333
C_6H_5	C_6H_5	H	H	C_6H_5	> 330°	72, 129, 818, 1022
C_6H_5	$4\text{-}CH_3OC_6H_4$	H	H	C_6H_5	—	129
C_6H_5	CH_3	CH_3	CH_3	C_6H_5	166°	729, 809, 1299, 1528, 1606, 1611
C_6H_5	CH_3	C_2H_5	C_2H_5	C_6H_5	149°, 161°	809, 1526, 1528, 1645
$1\text{-}C_{10}H_7$	CH_3	$C_6H_5CH_2$	$C_6H_5CH_2$	$1\text{-}C_{10}H_7$	215°	849
C_6H_5	CH_3	C_2H_5	H	C_6H_5	161°	1522
C_6H_5	CH_3	NCHC— (with $COOC_2H_5$ on C)	H	C_6H_5	116°	1613
C_6H_5	CH_3	NCHC— (with COOH on C)	H	C_6H_5	160° (dec.)	1613
C_6H_5	CH_3	$HOOCCH_2$	H	C_6H_5	213° (dec.)	1613
C_6H_5	CH_3	$NCCH_2$	H	C_6H_5	160°	1613
C_6H_5	CH_3	H_5C_2OOCCH (with $COCH_3$ on C)	H	C_6H_5	106°	1613
C_6H_5	CH_3	$(CN)_2CH$	H	C_6H_5	230° (dec.)	1614
C_6H_5	CH_3	NCCH (with $CONH_2$ on C)	H	C_6H_5	—	1614
C_6H_5	CH_3	C_2H_5O	H	C_6H_5	94° (dec.)	1609
C_6H_5	CH_3	CH_3O	H	C_6H_5	—	1609
C_6H_5	CH_3	C_3H_7O	H	C_6H_5	—	1609
C_6H_5	CH_3	NC	H	C_6H_5	—	1612
H_2NOC	CH_3	H	H	H_2NOC	128°	73, 357
H_2NSC	CH_3	H	H	H_2NSC	197°	73, 357
H_2NSC	$C_{17}H_{35}$	H	H	H_2NSC	—	73

H_5C_6HNSC	CH_3	H	H	H_5C_6HNSC	191°	357
$4\text{-}CH_3C_6H_5NHSC$	CH_3	H	H	$4\text{-}CH_3C_6H_5NHSC$	201°	357
C_2H_5NHSC	CH_3	H	H	C_2H_5NHSC	191°	357
C_6H_5	H_5C_2OOC	H	H	C_6H_5	272°	1082, 1229
C_6H_5	CH_3	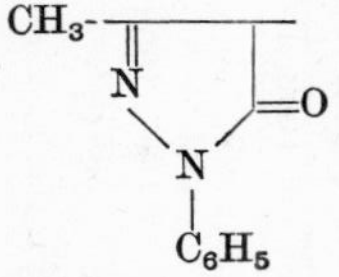 CH_3-, N, N, =O, C_6H_5	H	C_6H_5	262°, 200° (dec.)	688, 1607, 1609
C_6H_5	CH_3	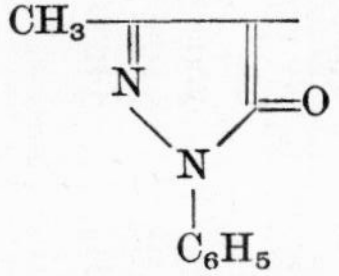 CH_3, N, N, =O, C_6H_5	H	$4\text{-}BrC_6H_4$	200° (dec.)	1607

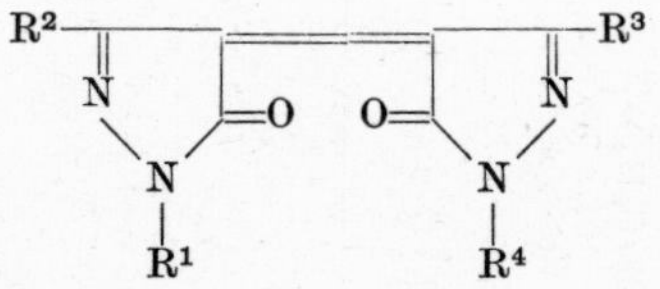

TABLE IV. 4,4′-Bis(2-pyrazolin-5-ones) Linked by a Double Bond

R^1	R^2	R^3	R^4	M.p.	Reference
H	C_6H_5	C_6H_5	H	—	1560
C_6H_5	CH_3	CH_3	C_6H_5	230°	323, 807, 809, 816, 1090, 1091
3-ClC_6H_4	CH_3	CH_3	3-ClC_6H_4	—	296
4-ClC_6H_4	CH_3	CH_3	4-ClC_6H_4	300°	296
C_6H_5	CH_3	CH_3	4-BrC_6H_4	219°	1607, 1608
$C_6H_5CH_2$	CH_3	CH_3	$C_6H_5CH_2$	142°	333

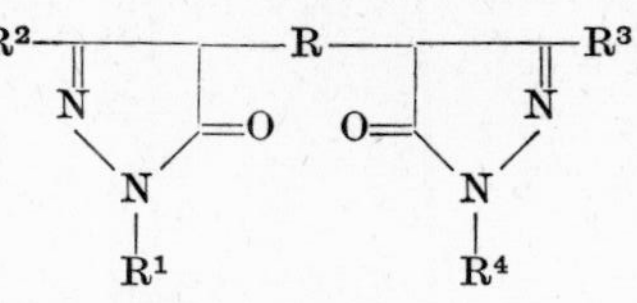

TABLE V. 4,4′-Bis(2-pyrazolin-5-ones) Linked by a Carbon Chain

Section A. 1,1′-Phenyl-3,3′-methyl Substituents

R	M.p.	Reference
—CH=	185°	93, 117, 365, 611, 675, 825, 926, 1070, 1088, 1089, 1093, 1185, 1187, 1188, 1189, 1190, 1193, 1262, 1669, 1682
$—CH_2—$	220°	22, 24, 117, 300, 1262
$—C(CH_3)_2—$ (printed as CH_3CCH_3 with bonds above and below)	138°	809
$—CH_2CH_2—$	—	451
—CH=CHCH=CHCH=	205°	1070
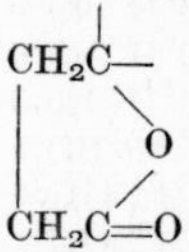 $CH_2C—$ / O / $CH_2C{=}O$ (ring: CH_2–C(–)–O–C(=O)–CH_2)	184°	297
$C_6H_5CH<$	174°	686, 977, 1135
$4\text{-}CH_3C_6H_4CH<$	166° ($0.5\ C_2H_5OH$)	1094

(Table continued)

TABLE V, Section A (*continued*)

R	M.p.	Reference
2-$HOC_6H_4CH<$	228°	93, 1135
3-$HOC_6H_4CH<$	181°	1135
4-$HOC_6H_4CH<$	162°	1135
4-$CH_3OC_6H_4CH<$	175°	1094, 1255
2-$ClC_6H_4CH<$	231°	1135
3-$ClC_6H_4CH<$	149°	1135
4-$ClC_6H_4CH<$	208°	1135
2-$NO_2C_6H_4CH<$	146° (dec.), 203°	633, 1135
3-$NO_2C_6H_4CH<$	150° (dec.), 227° (164° enol)	376, 633, 1134
4-$NO_2C_6H_4CH<$	226°	110
2-$HOOCC_6H_4CH<$	208°	1279
2-$CH_3OOCC_6H_4CH<$	178°	1279
2-$C_2H_5OOCCH_2OC_6H_4CH<$	204°	832
4-HO-3-$CH_3OC_6H_3CH<$	191°	22
3,4-$(CH_3O)_2C_6H_3CH<$	122°	22
2,4,6-$(CH_3O)_3C_6H_2CH<$	204°	1036
3-CH_3O-4-HO-5-$HO_3SC_6H_2CH<$	—	22
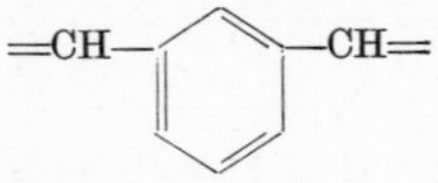 =CH—C_6H_4—CH= (meta)	220°	1224
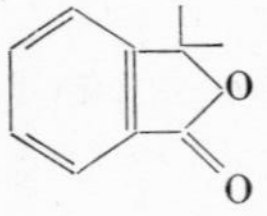 (phthalidylidene: O, O)	212°	297
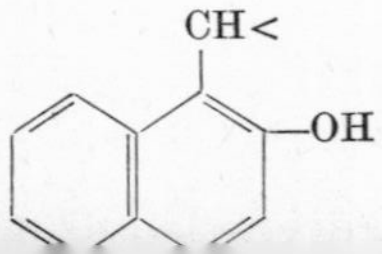 CH< (2-hydroxy-1-naphthyl, —OH)	118–140°	93

2-methoxy-1-naphthyl: $CH<$ on C-1, $-OCH_3$ on C-2	195°	1036
$=C(OC_2H_5)-C(OC_2H_5)=$	163°	1109
$=C(OCH_3)-C(OCH_3)=$	193°	1109
$-C(=O)-C(=O)-$	237°	1109
$-CH(OC_2H_5)-CH(OC_2H_5)-$	208°	1109
ring: $CH_3-C{=}N-N(C_6H_5)-C{=}$, $=C-$ (C–C bond closing ring)	175°	187
ring: $(CH_3)_2C<$, $CH_2-C(-)=CH-C(=)-CH_2$	—	187

(*Table continued*)

TABLE V, Section A (*continued*)

R	M.p.	Reference
Indene ring: benzene fused to a five-membered ring, C(—)=CCOOH—C(<)	—	187

TABLE V (*continued*)

Section B. Alkyl and Aryl Substituents

R	R^1	R^2	R^3	R^4	M.p.	Reference
—CH=	H	CH_3	CH_3	H	130–140°, 315° (dec.)	93, 923, 925, 1262
$—CH_2—$	H	CH_3	CH_3	H	326°	1154
$CH_3CH<$	H	CH_3	CH_3	H	253°	514
$—CH_2CH_2—$	H	CH_3	CH_3	H	250°	1154
$HOOCCH_2CH<$	C_6H_5	H	H	C_6H_5	—	1351
$H_5C_2OOCCH_2CH<$	C_6H_5	H	H	C_6H_5	173°	1351

HN—N=C(CH$_3$) (pyrazole ring)	H	CH_3	CH_3	H	—	703
—CH=	H	C_6H_5	C_6H_5	H	>300°	1188, 1189
—CH_2—	H	C_6H_5	C_6H_5	H	280° (dec.)	1154, 1188
$C_6H_5CH<$	H	C_6H_5	C_6H_5	H	—	1154
—CH=	2-$CH_3C_6H_4$	CH_3	CH_3	2-$CH_3C_6H_4$	190°	351
—CH=	4-$CH_3C_6H_4$	CH_3	CH_3	4-$CH_3C_6H_4$	249°	351
—CH=	4-$C_2H_5OC_6H_4$	CH_3	CH_3	4-$C_2H_5OC_6H_4$	202°	1186
—CH_2—	4-$C_2H_5OC_6H_4$	CH_3	CH_3	4-$C_2H_5OC_6H_4$	202°	1097
$(CH_3)_2C<$	4-FC_6H_4	CH_3	CH_3	4-FC_6H_4	141°	1263
2-$NO_2C_6H_4CH<$	2-ClC_6H_4	CH_3	CH_3	2-ClC_6H_4	249°	1494
CH_3—(pyrazole ring)—N—C_6H_5	C_6H_5	CH_3	CH_3	4-$HO_3SC_6H_4$		187
CH_3—(pyrazole ring)—N—4-$HO_3SC_6H_4$	C_6H_5	CH_3	CH_3	4-$HO_3SC_6H_4$		187
(cyclohexane ring)=CH—	4-$HO_3SC_6H_4$	CH_3	CH_3	4-$HO_3SC_6H_4$	—	187

(Table continued)

TABLE V, Section B (*continued*)

R	R[1]	R[2]	R[3]	R[4]	M.p.	Reference
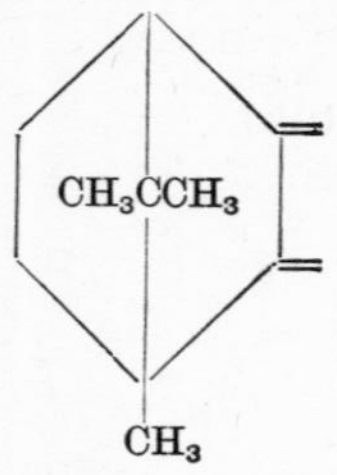 CH_3CCH_3, CH_3	4-$HO_3SC_6H_4$	CH_3	CH_3	4-$HO_3SC_6H_4$	—	187
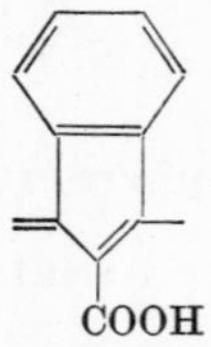 COOH	4-$HO_3SC_6H_4$	CH_3	CH_3	4-$HO_3SC_6H_4$	—	187, 703
—CH=	C_6H_5	C_6H_5	C_6H_5	C_6H_5	249°	93, 923, 925, 1185, 1188, 1189, 1262
—CH_2CH_2—	C_6H_5	C_6H_5	C_6H_5	C_6H_5	—	1189
C_6H_5CH	C_6H_5	C_6H_5	C_6H_5	C_6H_5	220°	818
—CH=	2-$CH_3C_6H_4$	C_6H_5	C_6H_5	2-$CH_3C_6H_4$	179°	351
—CH=	4-BrC_6H_4	C_6H_5	C_6H_5	4-BrC_6H_4	>265°	351
C_6H_5CH	4-BrC_6H_4	C_6H_5	C_6H_5	4-BrC_6H_4	290° (dec.)	1154
—CH=	C_6H_5	COOH	COOH	C_6H_5	248° (dec.)	1262

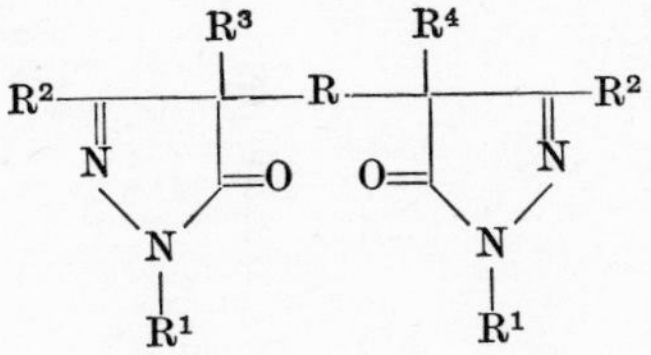

TABLE VI. Miscellaneous 4,4′-Bis(2-pyrazolin-5-ones)

R	R^1	R^2	R^3	R^4	M.p.	Reference
$—CH=$	C_6H_5	CH_3	Br		138°	1682
$—C(OC_2H_5)(Br)—C(OC_2H_5)(Br)—$	C_6H_5	CH_3	Br	Br	80°	1109
$CH_3CH<$	H	CH_3	$CH_3CH(OH)—$	H	267°	513
$3\text{-}NO_2C_6H_4CH<$	C_6H_5	CH_3	CH_3	CH_3	178°	1134
$C_6H_5CH<$	H	CH_3	CH_3	CH_3	129°	1560

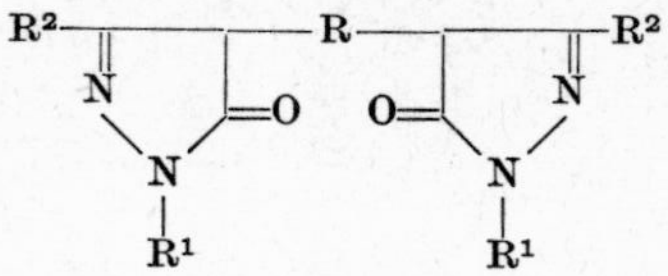

$$R^2-C \cdots R \cdots C-R^2$$

TABLE VII. 4,4′-Bis(2-pyrazolin-5-ones) Linked by Chains Containing N and S

R^1	R^2	R	M.p.	Reference
C_6H_5	CH_3	S	181°	579, 580
C_6H_5	H	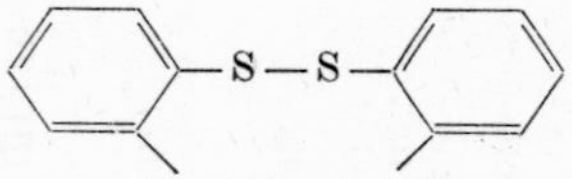 —S—S— (between two ring structures)	257°	578
C_6H_5	H	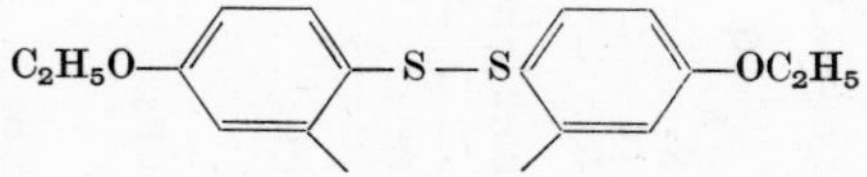 C_2H_5O—(ring)—S—S—(ring)—OC_2H_5	270°	578
C_6H_5	CH_3	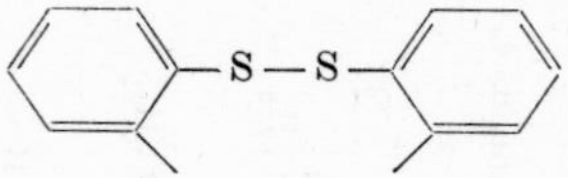 —S—S— (between two ring structures)	281°	578
H	CH_3	=N—	238° (dec.)	262
H	CH_3	—NH—	247° (dec.) (HCl)	480
H	C_2H_5	=N—	235° (dec.)	1576
H	C_3H_7	=N—	260° (dec.)	1576
$C_6H_5CH_2$	CH_3	=N—	160°	333
$C_6H_5CH_2CH_2$	CH_3	=N—	95°	1566
H	C_6H_5	=N—	124°, 267° (dec.)	1552, 1576

C_6H_5	CH_3	=N—	181°	327, 611, 809
C_6H_5	$HOCH_2$	=N—	199°	397
$C_6H_5CH_2CH_2$	C_6H_5	=N—	165°	1567
4-BrC_6H_4	CH_3	=N—	305°	1642
C_6H_5	C_6H_5	=N—	251°	1022, 1552
C_6H_5	2-HOC_6H_4	=N—	222°	670
C_6H_5	CH_3	—N=N—	184°, 260°	995, 1564
3-$HO_3SC_6H_4$	C_8H_{17}	—N=N—	> 200°	593
4-$HO_3SC_6H_4$	CH_3	—N=N—	> 250°	593
4-$NaO_3SC_6H_4$	CH_3	—N=N—	—	1062
C_6H_5	CH_3	$CONH(CH_2CH_2)_3NHCO$	104°	1111
C_6H_5	H	—N=N—C_6H_4—C_6H_4—N=N—	—	782
C_6H_5	H	—N=N—$C_6H_3(OCH_3)$—$C_6H_3(OCH_3)$—N=N— (OCH₃ ortho to each N=N)	—	782
C_6H_5	H	—N=N—C_6H_3Cl—C_6H_3Cl—N=N— (Cl ortho to the ring–ring bond)	—	782
C_6H_5	H	—N=N—C_6H_4—CH_2—C_6H_4—N=N—	—	782
C_6H_5	CH_3	—N=N—C_6H_4—C_6H_4—N=N—	98°	327

(Table continued)

TABLE VII (*continued*)

R[1]	R[2]	R	M.p.	Reference
C_6H_5	CH_3	$—N{=}N—C_6H_3(OH)—C_6H_3(OH)—N{=}N—$	—	1359
$3\text{-}NO_2C_6H_4$	CH_3	$—N{=}N—C_6H_3(OH)—C_6H_3(OH)—N{=}N—$	—	1359
$3\text{-}H_2NO_2SC_6H_4$	CH_3	$—N{=}N—C_6H_3(OH)—C_6H_3(OH)—N{=}N—$	—	1359
$3\text{-}HOOC\text{-}4\text{-}HOC_6H_3$	CH_3	$—N{=}N—C_6H_3(OH)—C_6H_3(OH)—N{=}N—$	—	1359
C_6H_5	CH_3	$—N{=}N—C_6H_4—SO_2—C_6H_4—N{=}N—$	—	1245
C_6H_5	C_6H_5	$—N{=}N—C_6H_4—N{=}N—$	> 270°	259
$3\text{-}NH_2C_6H_4$	HOOC	$—N{=}N—$(benzimidazol-2-yl)CCH_2CH_2C(benzimidazol-2-yl)$—N{=}N—$ (N, N—H ring atoms)	—	727

2-Cl-4-$HO_3SC_6H_3$	HOOC	—N=N— (benzimidazole, N, NH)–C_6H_4–(benzimidazole, N, NH) —N=N—	—	727
2,5-Cl_2-4-$HO_3SOCH_2CH_2O_2SC_6H_4$	CH_3	N=N–C_6H_4–CH(C_6H_5)–C_6H_4–N=N	—	651
C_6H_5	H_5C_2OOC	—N=N–C_6H_4–N=N—	250°	767
C_6H_5	CH_3	CH=N–C_6H_4–N=CH	260°	1190
C_6H_5	C_6H_5	CH=N–C_6H_4–N=CH	221°	1190
(purine ring: O, CH_3N, NCH_3, O, N, N, CH_3)	CH_3	—N=N—	298° (dec., Na salt)	1147
(purine ring: O, CH_3N, NCH_3, O, N, N, CH_3)	CH_3	—NHNH—	272° (dec.)	1147

(Table continued)

TABLE VII (*continued*)

R¹	R²	R	M.p.	Reference
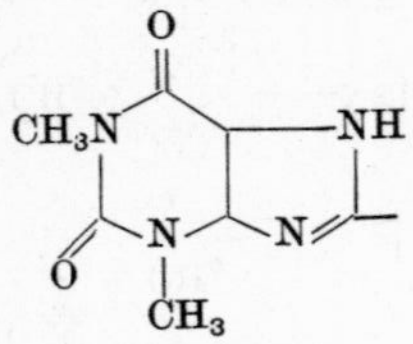	CH_3	—NHNH—	224°	1147
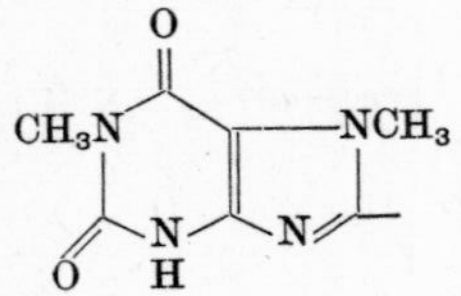	CH_3	—NHNH—	330° (dec.)	1147

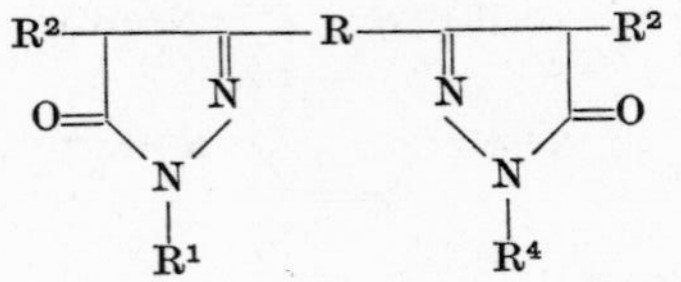

TABLE VIII. 3,3′-Bis(2-pyrazolin-5-ones)

R	R¹	R²	R³	R⁴	M.p.	Reference
C=O	H	H	H	H	b_{760} 203°	1549

$C_6H_5NHN{=}C<$	H	H	H	H	113°	1549
[structure]	C_6H_5	H	H	C_6H_5	263°	1225
[structure]	4-$HO_3SC_6H_4$	H	H	4-$HO_3SC_6H_4$	—	462
[structure]	2-HO_3S-4-$NO_2C_6H_3$	H	H	2-HO_3S-4-$NO_2C_6H_3$	—	462
$—CH_2CH_2—$	C_6H_5	H_5C_2OOC	H_5C_2OOC	C_6H_5	188°	1222
$—CH_2CH_2—$	H_2NOC	H_5C_2OOC	H_5C_2OOC	H_2NOC	207° (dec.)	1222
$—CH_2CH_2—$	H_2NOC	$H_2NCONHNHCOCH_2CH_2$	$H_2NCONHNHCOCH_2CH_2$	H_2NOC	—	1222
$—HC{=}CH—$	C_6H_5	C_6H_5NHNH	C_6H_5NHNH	C_6H_5	291° (dec.)	419
$—NH—$	C_6H_5	H	H	C_6H_5	290°	595, 596
$—N(C_2H_5)—$	C_6H_5	H	H	C_6H_5	265°	595, 596
$—N(C_4H_9)—$	C_6H_5	H	H	C_6H_5	223°	595, 596
$—N(C_5H_{11})—$	C_6H_5	H	H	C_6H_5	227°	595, 596

Table continued)

TABLE VIII (*continued*)

R	R¹	R²	R³	R⁴	M.p.	Reference
$-N(CH_2C_6H_5)-$	C_6H_5	H	H	C_6H_5	245°	595, 596
$-N(H)-$	4-(4-*t*-$C_4H_9C_6H_4O)C_6H_4$	H	H	4-(4-*t*-$C_4H_9C_6H_4O)C_6H_4$	260°	595, 596
$-N(CH_3)-$	4-$HO_3SC_6H_4$	H	H	C_6H_5	—	705

R¹—C=N—N(—R—)—C(=O)—C—R²   R²—C—C(=O)—N(—R—)—N=C—R¹

TABLE IX. 1,1′-Bis(2-pyrazolin-5-ones)

R	R¹	R²	M.p.	Reference
$-C_6H_4-NHCONH-C_6H_4-$ (*p*,*p*′)	H	H	—	656
$-C(=O)-$	CH_3	H	183°	1037, 1632

1,3-C_6H_4	CH_3	H	185°	116
1,4-C_6H_4	CH_3	H	—	116
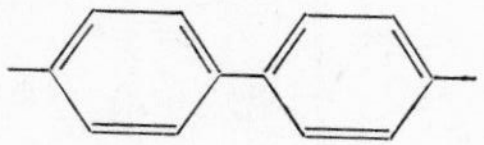	CH_3	H	—	386, 849
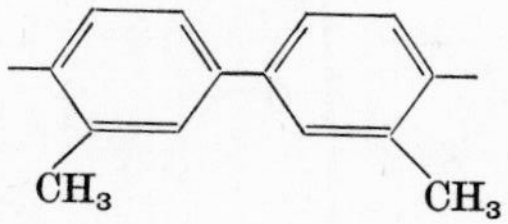 CH_3 CH_3	CH_3	H	—	386
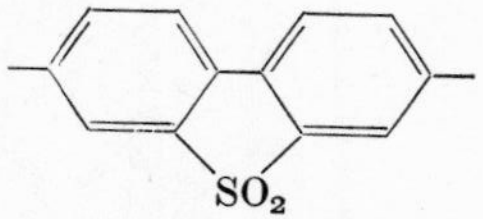 SO_2	CH_3	H	—	711
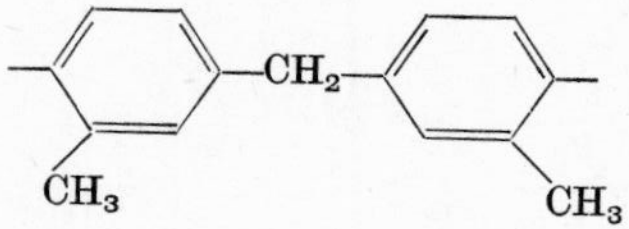 CH_2 CH_3 CH_3	CH_3	H	—	544
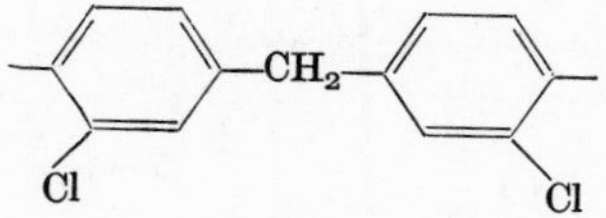 CH_2 Cl Cl	CH_3	H	—	544
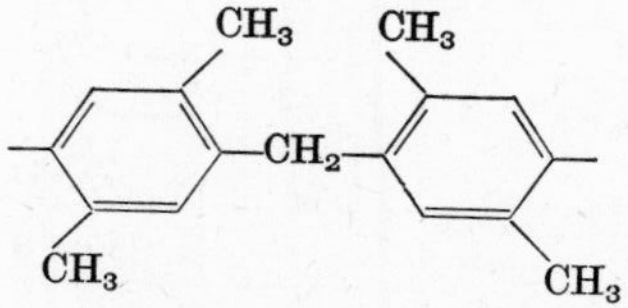 CH_3 CH_3 CH_2 CH_3 CH_3	CH_3	H	—	544

(*Table continued*)

TABLE IX (*continued*)

R	R^1	R^2	M.p.	Reference
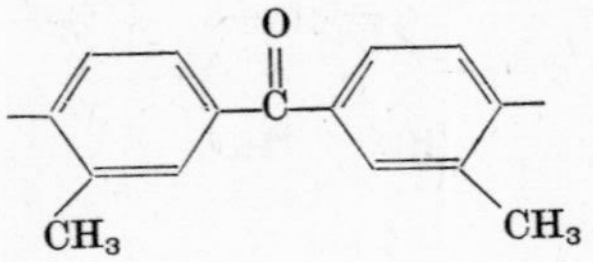 [structure: O, C, CH_3, CH_3]	CH_3	H	—	544
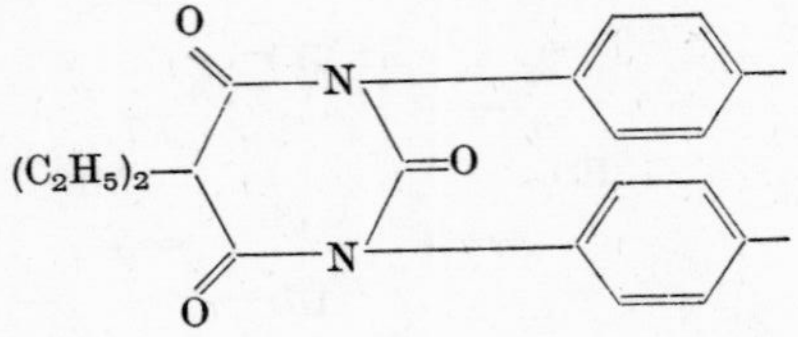 [structure: O, N, O, $(C_2H_5)_2$, N, O]	CH_3	H	220	517
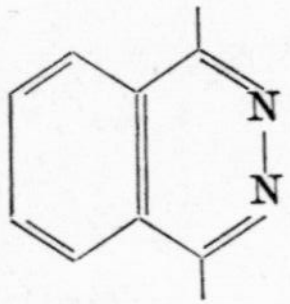 [structure: N, N]	CH_3	H	—	212
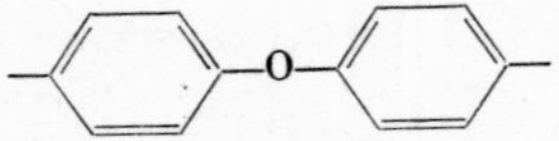 [structure: —O—]	CH_3	H	—	711
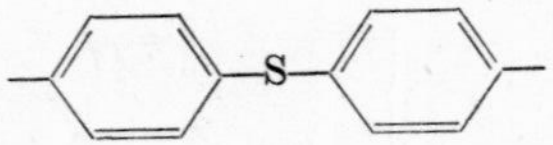 [structure: —S—]	CH_3	H	—	711
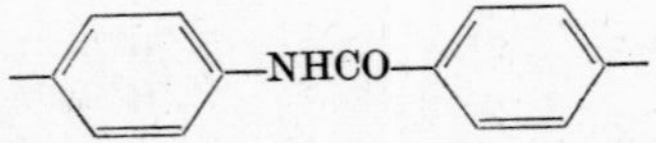 [structure: —NHCO—]	CH_3	H	—	209

 NHCONH	CH_3	H	—	656
 NHCONH; Cl, Cl	CH_3	H	—	656
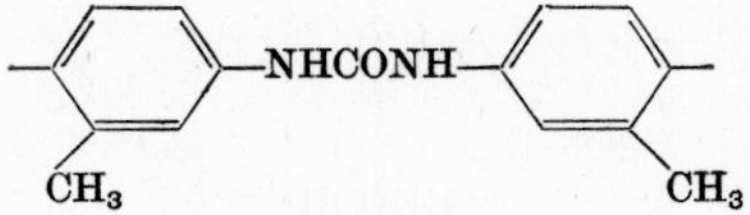 NHCONH; CH_3, CH_3	CH_3	H	—	656
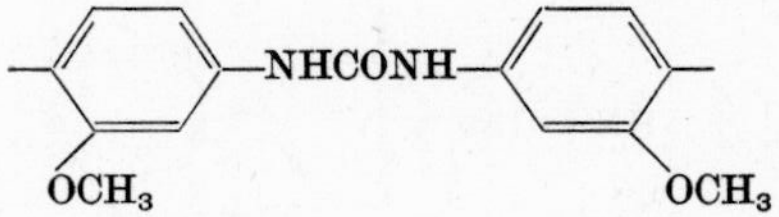 NHCONH; OCH_3, OCH_3	CH_3	H	—	656
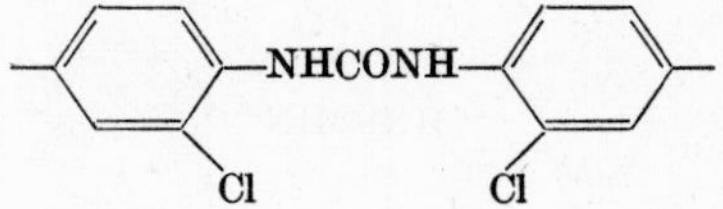 NHCONH; Cl, Cl	CH_3	H	—	656
 NHCONH; Br, Br	CH_3	H	—	656
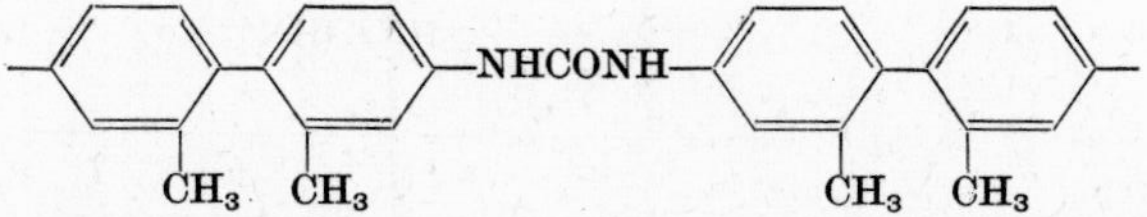 NHCONH; CH_3, CH_3, CH_3, CH_3	CH_3	H	—	656

(Table continued)

TABLE IX (*continued*)

R	R^1	R^2	M.p.	Reference
 —NHCSNH—	CH_3	H	—	656
 —NHCSNH—; Cl, Cl	CH_3	H	—	656
 —NHCSNH—; CH_3, CH_3	CH_3	H	—	656
 —NHCSNH—	CH_3	H	—	656
 —NHCONH—	C_2H_5	H	—	656
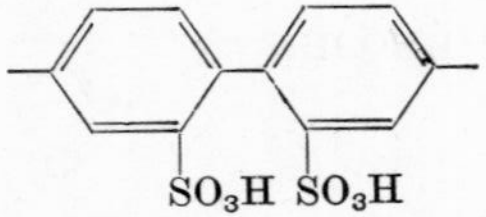 SO_3H SO_3H	HOOC	H	—	511
 —NHCONH—	HOOC	H	—	511
 —NHCONH—	HOOC	H	—	152

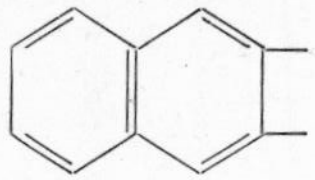	C_6H_5	H	245°	459
 NHCONH	C_6H_5	H	—	656
 NHCSNH	C_6H_5	H	—	656
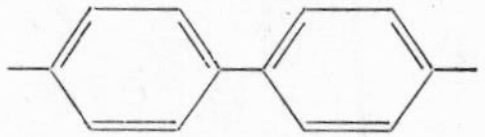	CH_3	$4\text{-}(C_2H_5)_2NC_6H_4N{=}$	—	494
CH_3 CH_3	CH_3	$4\text{-}(C_2H_5)_2NC_6H_4N{=}$	—	494
CH=CH	CH_3	$4\text{-}(C_2H_5)_2NC_6H_4N{=}$	—	494
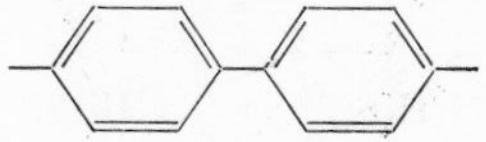	CH_3	$2\text{-}HO\text{-}4\text{-}(4\text{-}HO_3SC_6H_4NHCO)C_6H_4$	—	209
Cl Cl	CH_3	$2\text{-}HO\text{-}4\text{-}(4\text{-}HO_3SC_6H_4NHCO)C_6H_4$	—	209

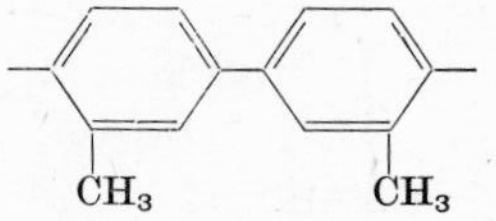

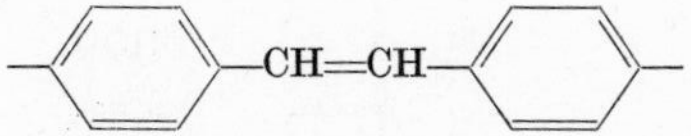

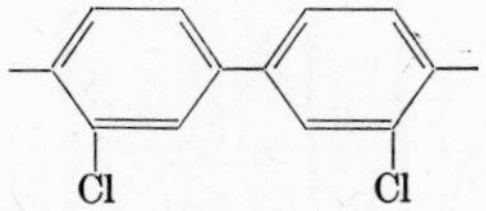

(*Table continued*)

TABLE IX (*continued*)

R	R^1	R^2	M.p.	Reference
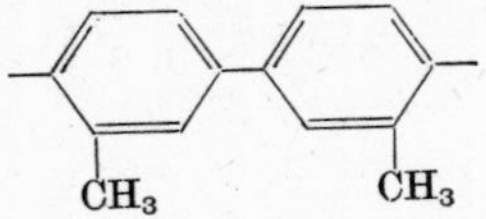 CH_3 CH_3	CH_3	2-HO-4-(4-$HO_3SC_6H_4NHCO)C_6H_4$	—	209
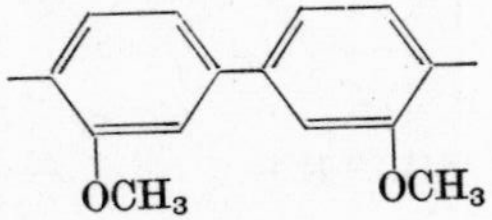 OCH_3 OCH_3	CH_3	2-HO-4-(4-$HO_3SC_6H_4NHCO)C_6H_4$	—	209
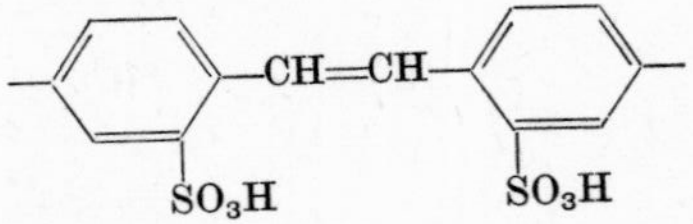 —CH=CH— SO_3H SO_3H	CH_3	2-HO-4-(4-$HO_3SC_6H_4NHCO)C_6H_4$	—	209
 —NHCO—	CH_3	2-HO-4-(4-$HO_3SC_6H_4NHCO)C_6H_4$	—	209
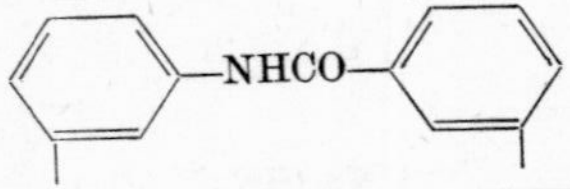 —NHCO—	CH_3	2-HO-4-(4-$HO_3SC_6H_4NHCO)C_6H_4$	—	209
 —NHCONH—	CH_3	2-HO-4-(4-$HO_3SC_6H_4NHCO)C_6H_4$	—	209
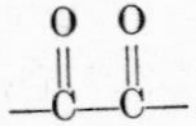 O O ‖ ‖ —C—C—	CH_3	$C_6H_5N{=}N$—	256°	255
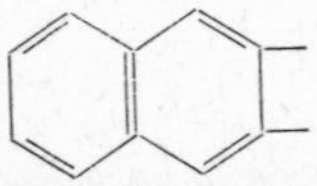	C_6H_5	NO	222°	459

TABLE X. Furlones

Compounds	M.p.	Reference
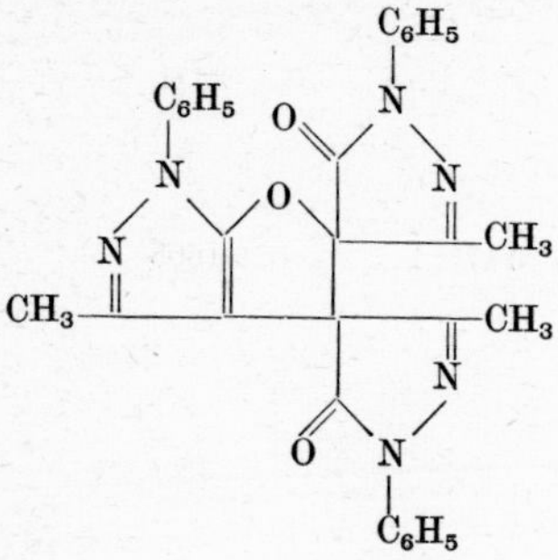 C_6H_5; C_6H_5, O, N; N, O, N; N, CH_3; CH_3, CH_3; N; O, N; C_6H_5	158°	1608, 1611
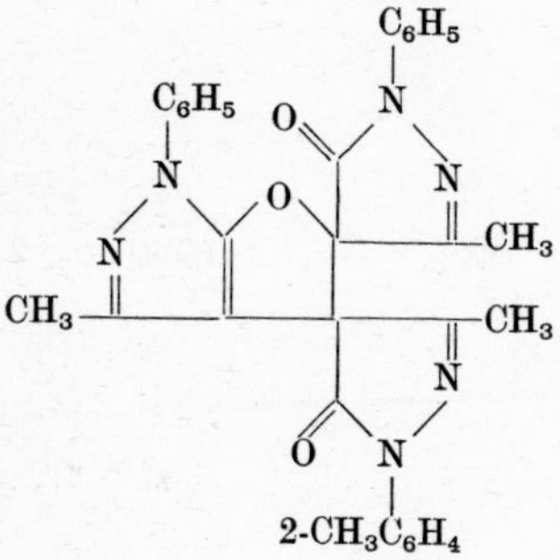 C_6H_5; C_6H_5, O, N; N, O, N; N, CH_3; CH_3, CH_3; N; O, N; 2-$CH_3C_6H_4$	151°	1608
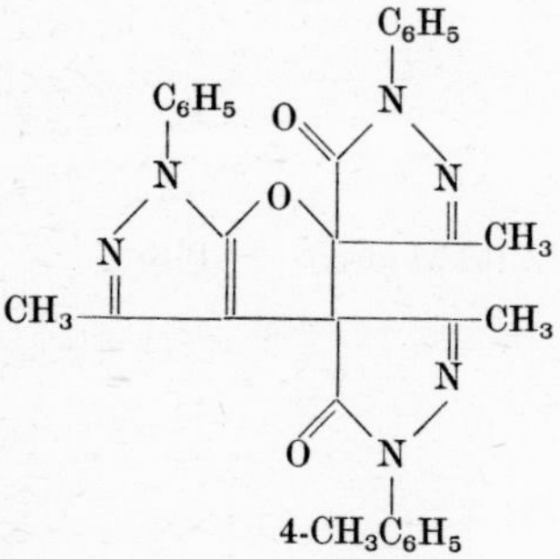 C_6H_5; C_6H_5, O, N; N, O, N; N, CH_3; CH_3, CH_3; N; O, N; 4-$CH_3C_6H_5$	134°	1608
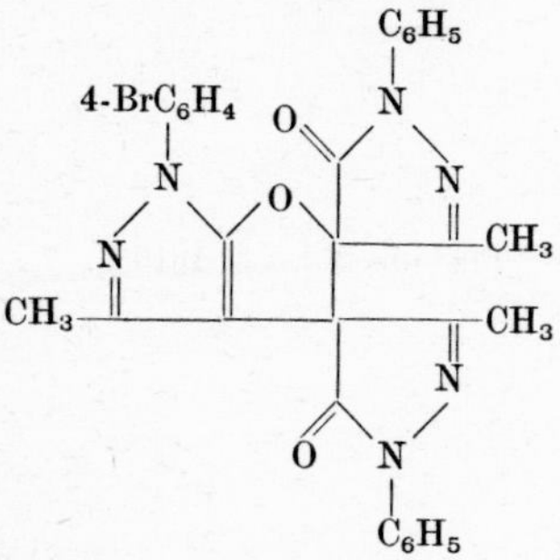 C_6H_5; 4-BrC_6H_4, O, N; N, O, N; N, CH_3; CH_3, CH_3; N; O, N; C_6H_5	161°	1608

(*Table continued*)

TABLE X (*continued*)

Compounds	M.p.	Reference
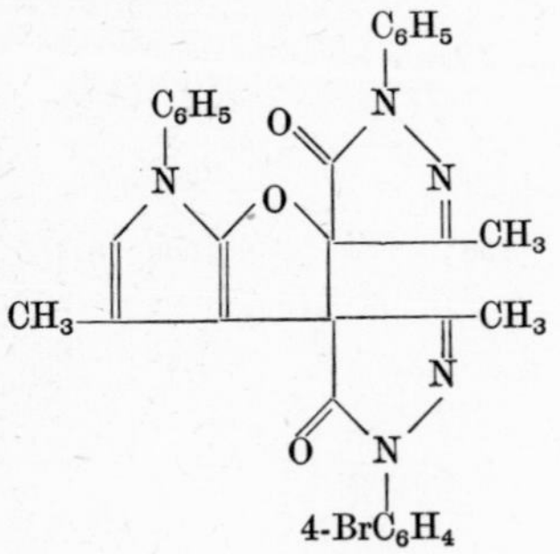 C_6H_5, C_6H_5, N, O, N, N, O, CH_3, CH_3, CH_3, N, O, N, 4-BrC_6H_4	147°	1608
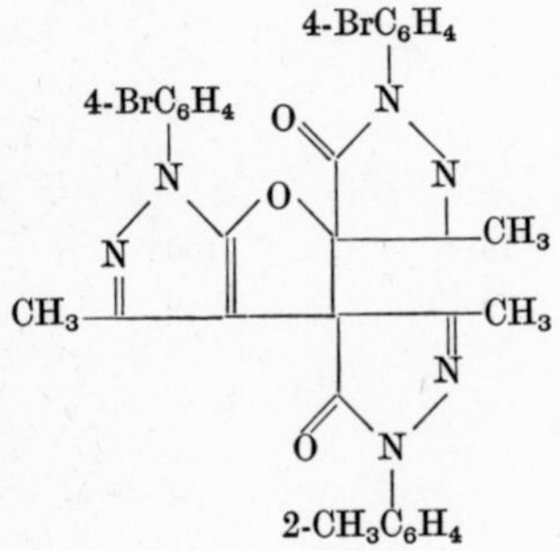 4-BrC_6H_4, 4-BrC_6H_4, N, O, N, N, O, N, CH_3, CH_3, CH_3, N, O, N, 2-$CH_3C_6H_4$	164°	1608
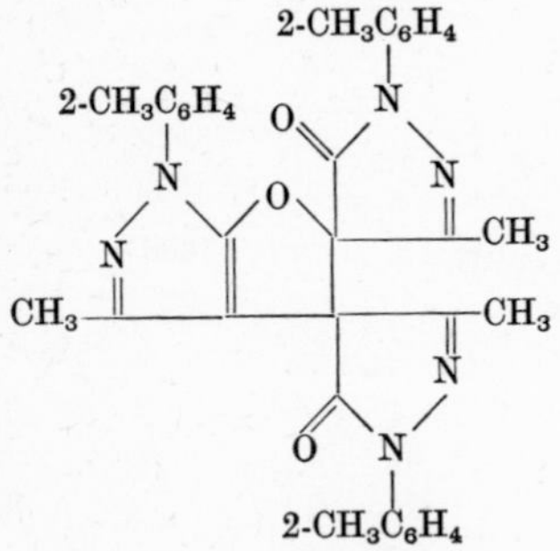 2-$CH_3C_6H_4$, 2-$CH_3C_6H_4$, N, O, N, N, O, N, CH_3, CH_3, CH_3, N, O, N, 2-$CH_3C_6H_4$	162.5° (dec.)	1610
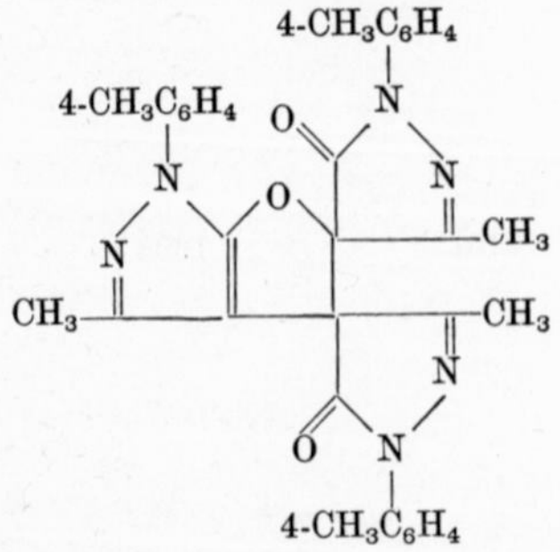 4-$CH_3C_6H_4$, 4-$CH_3C_6H_4$, N, O, N, N, O, N, CH_3, CH_3, CH_3, N, O, N, 4-$CH_3C_6H_4$	172° (dec.)	1610

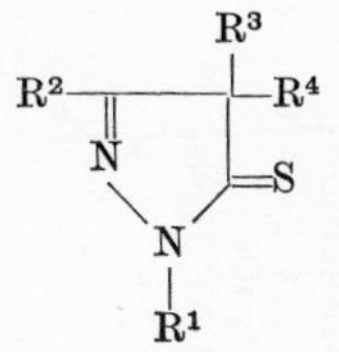

R³
R²—C—C—R⁴
N C=S
N
R¹

TABLE XI. 2-Pyrazolin-5-thiones

R^1	R^2	R^3	R^4	M.p.	Reference
H	CH_3	CH_3	CH_3	112°	759
H	CH_3	C_2H_5	C_2H_5	141°	759
C_6H_5	CH_3	H	H	109°	990, 1343
$4\text{-}CH_3C_6H_4$	CH_3	H	H	212°	990
$2,4\text{-}(NO_2)C_6H_3$	CH_3	H	H	179°	1207
C_6H_5	CH_3	CH_3	CH_3	—	785
C_6H_5	CH_3	C_2H_5	C_2H_5	80°	1343
C_6H_5	CH_3		$(CH_3)_2C{=}$	204°	990
$4\text{-}CH_3C_6H_4$	CH_3		$(CH_3)_2C{=}$	206°	990
C_6H_5	C_6H_5	H	H	163°	1003
C_6H_5	CH_3		$C_6H_5CH{=}$	183°	990
C_6H_5	CH_3		$C_6H_5C(CH_3){=}$	185°	990
$4\text{-}CH_3C_6H_4$	CH_3		$C_6H_5CH{=}$	212°	990
$4\text{-}CH_3C_6H_4$	CH_3		$C_6H_5C(CH_3){=}$	106°	990
C_6H_5	CH_3	C_6H_5CO	H	217°	977, 990
C_6H_5	CH_3	$C_6H_5N{=}N$	H	97°	990

TABLE XII. 5-Imino-2-pyrazolines

R^1	R^2	R^3	R^4	R^5	M.p.	Reference
H	H	H	H	H	b_{11}140°	819, 1266
H	H	H	H	C_2H_5OOC	153°	819
H	H	H	H	4-$H_2NC_6H_4SO_2$	235°	714
H	CH_3	H	H	H	94°	368, 1049
H	CH_3	H	H	C_2H_5OOC	158°	368, 1049
H	CH_3	H	H	4-$H_2NC_6H_4SO_2$	253°	368
H	C_5H_{11}	H	H	H	41°	1025, 1026
H	C_6H_{13}	H	H	H	32°	1025, 1026
H	C_9H_{19}	H	H	H	—	1065
H	H	CH_3	C_4H_9	H	172°	391
H	H	C_2H_5	C_2H_5	H	232°	391
$CH_3C(=CHCN)$	CH_3	H	H	H	—	1543
CH_3	H	C_2H_5	C_2H_5	H	b_{10}91°	391
H	H	C_6H_5	H	H	172°	1086
H	C_6H_5	H	H	H	125°	342, 344, 1025
H	C_6H_5	H	H	$CH_3C(=CHCOOC_2H_5)$	115°	299
H	C_6H_5	H	H	C_6H_5	166°	1652, 1656
H	C_6H_5	H	H	4-$CH_3C_6H_4$	157°	1656
H	C_6H_5	H	H	4-ClC_6H_4	174°	1655, 1656

H	C_6H_5	H	H	$3\text{-}BrC_6H_4$	205°	1656
H	C_6H_5	H	H	$4\text{-}BrC_6H_4$	176°	1654
H	C_6H_5	H	H	$4\text{-}IC_6H_4$	175°	1656
H	C_6H_5	H	H	$4\text{-}C_6H_5\text{—}C_6H_4$	219°	1656
H	C_6H_5	H	H	HCO	214°	301
H	C_6H_5	H	H	CH_3CO	—	301
H	C_6H_5	H	H	C_6H_5CO	190°	301
H	C_6H_5	H	H	C_2H_5OCO	160°	301
H	C_6H_5	H	H	C_2H_5OCOCO	164°	301
C_6H_5	H	H	H	C_6H_5	138°	1002
H	$4\text{-}CH_3C_6H_4$	H	H	H	143°	1542
H	$4\text{-}NO_2C_6H_4$	H	H	H	255°	342, 344
H	3-pyridyl (structural formula, N)	H	H	H	—	931
H	C_6H_5	CH_3	H	H	58°	299, 301
H	3-pyridyl (structural formula, N)	H	H	CH_3CO	308°	931
C_6H_5	CH_3	H	H	H	110°	322, 341, 838, 1010, 1043
C_6H_5	CH_3	H	H	C_2H_5	b315°	975
C_6H_5	CH_3	H	H	$C_6H_5CH_2$	$b_{12}228°$	975
C_6H_5	CH_3	H	H	C_6H_5	120°, 146°	826, 827, 1002

(*Table continued*)

TABLE XII (*continued*)

R¹	R²	R³	R⁴	R⁵	M.p.	Reference
C_6H_5	CH_3	H	H	2-$CH_3C_6H_4$	72°	1002
C_6H_5	CH_3	H	H	4-$CH_3C_6H_4$	109°	827, 1002
C_6H_5	CH_3	H	H	4-ClC_6H_4	139°	1002
C_6H_5	CH_3	H	H	4-BrC_6H_4	136°	1002
C_6H_5	CH_3	H	H	4-$HOOCC_6H_4$	140°	996
C_6H_5	CH_3	H	H	4-$C_2H_5OOCC_6H_4$	76°	996
C_6H_5	CH_3	H	H	3-$NO_2C_6H_4$	138°	1002
C_6H_5	CH_3	H	H	4-$NO_2C_6H_4$	153°	1002
C_6H_5	CH_3	H	H	1-$C_{10}H_7$	137°	828
C_6H_5	CH_3	H	H	HCO	135°	322, 996
C_6H_5	CH_3	H	H	CH_3CO	110°	996
C_6H_5	CH_3	H	H	C_6H_5CO	113°	996
C_6H_5	CH_3	H	H	$C_6H_5SO_2$	170°	996
C_6H_5	CH_3	H	H	4-$H_2NC_6H_4SO_2$	180°	325
C_6H_5	CH_3	H	H	4-$NO_2C_6H_4SO_2$	220°	325
C_6H_5	CH_3	H	H	H_2NOC	215°	996
C_6H_5	CH_3	H	H	C_6H_5HNOC	205°	996
C_6H_5	CH_3	H	H	C_6H_5HNSC	150°	996
C_6H_5	CH_3	H	H	CH_3 N N N=CH C_6H_5	—	322
C_6H_5	C_5H_{11}	H	H	H	b_{18}231°	1025, 1026
2-$CH_3C_6H_4$	CH_3	H	H	H	93°	996
2-$CH_3C_6H_4$	CH_3	H	H	C_6H_5	131°	1002
2-$CH_3C_6H_4$	CH_3	H	H	CH_3CO	157°	996
4-$CH_3C_6H_4$	CH_3	H	H	H	120°	996
4-$CH_3C_6H_4$	CH_3	H	H	C_6H_5	106°	1002
2-ClC_6H_4	CH_3	H	H	H	—	86

4-BrC_6H_4	CH_3	H	H	C_6H_5	106°	1002
X-$NO_2C_6H_4$	CH_3	H	H	H	98°	975
4-$H_2NO_2SC_6H_4$	CH_3	H	H	H	245°	324
2,5-$Cl_2C_6H_3$	CH_3	H	H	H	—	86
2,4-$(NH_2)_2C_6H_3$	CH_3	H	H	C_6H_5	184°	1207
2,4-$(NO_2)_2C_6H_3$	CH_3	H	H	H	204°	1207
2,4-$(NO_2)_2C_6H_3$	CH_3	H	H	$C_6H_5CH_2$	286°	1207
2,4-$(NO_2)_2C_6H_3$	CH_3	H	H	C_6H_5	190°	1207
2,4-$(NO_2)_2C_6H_3$	CH_3	H	H	4-$CH_3C_6H_4$	166°	1207
2,4-$(NO_2)_2C_6H_3$	CH_3	H	H	C_6H_5NH	216° (dec.)	1207
2-$C_{10}H_7$	CH_3	H	H	C_6H_5	122°	975
2-$C_{10}H_7$	CH_3	H	H	1-$C_{10}H_7$	145°	975
C_6H_5	C_6H_5	H	H	H	128°	129, 340, 342, 345
C_6H_5	H	C_6H_5	H	H	—	506
C_6H_5	C_6H_5	H	H	$CH_3C(=CHCOOC_2H_5)$—	125°	299
C_6H_5	C_6H_5	H	H	C_6H_5	153°	1652
C_6H_5	C_6H_5	H	H	CH_3CO	149°	1287
C_6H_5	C_6H_5	H	H	C_6H_5—C=N—N(C_6H_5)—C(=CH)—N=N (pyrazole ring)	217°	340
C_6H_5	4-$CH_3C_6H_4$	H	H	H	169°	1287
C_6H_5	4-$CH_3C_6H_4$	H	H	CH_3CO	—	1287
C_6H_5	4-$CH_3OC_6H_4$	H	H	H	188°	90, 129
C_6H_5	4-$C_2H_5OC_6H_4$	H	H	H	127°	1543
C_6H_5	4-$H_2NC_6H_4$	H	H	H	110°	340
C_6H_5	4-$CH_3COHNC_6H_4$	H	H	CH_3CO	235°	340
C_6H_5	2-ClC_6H_4	H	H	H	137°	1543

(*Table continued*)

TABLE XII (*continued*)

R[1]	R[2]	R[3]	R[4]	R[5]	M.p.	Reference
C_6H_5	3-ClC_6H_4	H	H	H	108°	1543
C_6H_5	4-ClC_6H_4	H	H	H	185°	1543
C_6H_5	H	4-ClC_6H_4	H	CH_3CO	219°	1562
C_6H_5	H	4-ClC_6H_4	H	C_6H_5CO	219°	1562
C_6H_5	4-$NO_2C_6H_4$	H	H	H	185°	340, 342
C_6H_5	4-$NO_2C_6H_4$	H	H	CH_3CO	218°	340
C_6H_5	[structure: 4-quinolyl]	H	H	H	—	127
C_6H_5	CH_3	CH_3	H	H	102°	975, 1011
C_6H_5	CH_3	CH_3	H	C_6H_5CO	196°	1011
C_6H_5	C_2H_5	CH_3	H	H	81°	132
C_6H_5	CH_3	C_2H_5	H	H	53°	1011
C_6H_5	CH_3	C_2H_5	H	C_6H_5CO	233°	1011
C_6H_5	CH_3	C_3H_7	H	H	55°	1011
C_6H_5	CH_3	C_3H_7	H	C_6H_5CO	150°	1011
C_6H_5	CH_3	$C_6H_5CH_2$	H	H	77°	975, 1011
C_6H_5	CH_3	$C_6H_5CH_2$	H	CH_3	120°	975
C_6H_5	CH_3	$C_6H_5CH_2$	H	C_6H_5CO	184°	975, 1011
C_6H_5	CH_3	$C_6H_5CH=$		C_6H_5	164°	1002
C_6H_5	CH_3	$C_6H_5CH=$		4-$CH_3C_6H_4$	163°	1002
C_6H_5	CH_3	4-$CH_3OC_6H_4CH=$		C_6H_5	295°	1002
C_6H_5	CH_3	4-$CH_3OC_6H_4CH=$		4-$CH_3C_6H_4$	184°	1002
C_6H_5	C_2H_5	4-ClC_6H_4	H	H	100°	918
C_6H_5	$C_6H_5OCH_2$	C_6H_5	H	H	120°	1562
C_6H_5	$C_6H_5OCH_2$	C_6H_5	H	CH_3CO	174°	1562

(*Table continued*)

TABLE XII (*continued*)

R^1	R^2	R^3	R^4	R^5	M.p.	Reference
C_6H_5	$C_6H_5OCH_2$	C_6H_5	H	C_6H_5CO	163°	1562
C_6H_5	C_6H_5	4-ClC_6H_4	H	H	149°	1563
2,4-$(NO_2)_2C_6H_3$	$C_6H_5CH_2$	C_6H_5	H	H	127°	310
2,4-$(NO_2)_2C_6H_3$	4-$CH_3C_6H_4CH_2$	C_6H_5	H	H	140°	310
2,4-$(NO_2)_2C_6H_3$	4-$CH_3OC_6H_4CH_2$	C_6H_5	H	H	114°	310
2,4-$(NO_2)_2C_6H_3$	4-$BrC_6H_4CH_2$	C_6H_5	H	H	155°	310
2,4-$(NO_2)_2C_6H_3$	C_6H_5	4-FC_6H_5	H	H	175°	310
2,4-$(NO_2)_2C_6H_3$	C_6H_5	4-ClC_6H_5	H	H	155°	310
CH_3	C_6H_5COO	H	H	C_6H_5CO	150°	594
H	CH_3COO	C_2H_5	C_2H_5	H	183°	391
H	CH_3COO	C_2H_5	C_2H_5	CH_3CO	202°	391
C_6H_5	C_6H_5COO	H	H	H	105°	1599
C_6H_5	C_6H_5COO	H	H	C_6H_5CO	193°	1599
C_6H_5	CH_3	4-$NO_2C_6H_4S$	H	H	170°	325
C_6H_5	CH_3	4-$NO_2C_6H_4S$	H	CH_3CO	201°	325
H	CH_3	H_2N	H	H	—	1044
C_6H_5	CH_3	H_2N	H	H	—	1043, 1044
C_6H_5	CH_3	H_2N	H	C_6H_5	140°	995, 1002
C_6H_5	CH_3	H_2N	H	4-$CH_3C_6H_4$	131°	1002
C_6H_5	CH_3	H_2N	H	3-NO_2-4-$CH_3C_6H_3$	97°	1002
C_6H_5	CH_3	$CH_3C{=}N$ (with $CH_2COOC_2H_5$ on C)	H	C_6H_5	127°	995
C_6H_5	CH_3	$C_6H_5CH{=}N$	H	C_6H_5	147°	995
C_6H_5	CH_3	4-$CH_3OC_6H_4CH{=}N$	H	C_6H_5	191°	995
C_6H_5	CH_3	C_6H_5CONH	H	C_6H_5	187°	995
C_6H_5	CH_3	H_2NOCHN	H	C_6H_5	201°	995
C_6H_5	CH_3	$C_6H_5NHOCHN$	H	H	220°	1002
C_6H_5	CH_3	$C_6H_5NHSCHN$	H	H	160°	1002

(*Table continued*)

TABLE XII (*continued*)

R^1	R^2	R^3	R^4	R^5	M.p.	Reference
H	4-$CH_3C_6H_4$	$C_6H_5N{=}N$	H	H	233°	1542
C_6H_5	CH_3	$C_6H_5N{=}N$	H	H	140°	975, 996
C_6H_5	CH_3	2-$CH_3OC_6H_4N{=}N$	H	H	93°	1039
C_6H_5	CH_3	2-$C_2H_5OC_6H_4N{=}N$	H	H	89°	1040
C_6H_5	CH_3	1-$C_{10}H_7N{=}N$	H	H	117°	996
2-$CH_3C_6H_4$	CH_3	$C_6H_5N{=}N$	H	H	118°	996
4-$HO_3SCH_2CH_2O_2SC_6H_4$	CH_3	2-$HOOCC_6H_4N{=}N$	H	H	—	651
C_6H_5	C_6H_5	3-C_6H_5-1-C_6H_5-pyrazol-4-yl–N=N (structure: C_6H_5–C=N–N(C_6H_5)–CH=C–N=N)	H	H	217°	1287
C_6H_5	4-$CH_3C_6H_4$	3-(4-$CH_3C_6H_4$)-1-C_6H_5-pyrazol-4-yl–N=N (structure: 4-$CH_3C_6H_4$–C=N–N(C_6H_5)–CH=C–N=N)	H	H	212°	1287
H	CH_3	Br	H	H	258°	1046
H	Cl	CH_3	C_4H_9	H	150°	391
H	Cl	C_2H_5	C_2H_5	H	161°	391
H	Cl	C_2H_5	C_2H_5	CH_3CO	182°	391
H	Br	CH_3	C_4H_9	H	144°	391
H	Br	C_2H_5	C_2H_5	H	165°	391
C_2H_5	Br	C_2H_5	C_2H_5	H	b_{11}102°	391
H	C_6H_5	Cl	H	2-Cl-4-BrC_6H_3	197°	1654
H	C_6H_5	Br	H	3-BrC_6H_4	178°	1656
H	C_6H_5	Br	H	2-Br-4-$CH_3C_6H_3$	181°	1656

H	C_6H_5	Br	H	2-Br-4-ClC_6H_3	198°	1655, 1656
H	C_6H_5	Br	H	2,4-$Br_2C_6H_3$	206° (dec.)	1652, 1654
H	C_6H_5	Br	H	2-Br-4-IC_6H_3	201°	1656
C_6H_5	CH_3	Cl	H	H	118°	975
C_6H_5	CH_3	Cl	H	CH_3CO	132°	975
C_6H_5	Cl_2CH	Cl	H	C_6H_5	138°	1201
C_6H_5	CH_3	Br	H	H	106°	975
C_6H_5	CH_3	Br	H	C_6H_5CO	172°	996
C_6H_5	CH_3	I	H	H	75°	975
2-$CH_3C_6H_4$	CH_3	Cl	H	H	114°	996
2-$CH_3C_6H_4$	CH_3	Br	H	H	134°	996
2-$CH_3C_6H_4$	CH_3	I	H	H	141°	996
4-$CH_3C_6H_4$	CH_3	Br	H	H	128°	996
4-BrC_6H_4	CH_3	Br	H	4-BrC_6H_4	131°	1002
X,Y-$Cl_2C_6H_3$	CH_3	Cl	H	H	—	975
CH_3C—(=CHCN)	CH_3	NO	H	H	167°	1543
H	C_6H_5	NO	H	H	270° (dec.)	301
H	C_6H_5	NO	H	CH_3CO	237°	301
H	C_6H_5	NO	H	C_6H_5CO	271°	301
H	C_6H_5	NO	H	C_6H_5OCOCO	240° (dec.)	301
C_6H_5	H	NO	H	C_6H_5	113°	1002
C_6H_5	CH_3	NO	H	H	168°, 199°	1002, 1010
C_6H_5	CH_3	NO	H	4-$CH_3C_6H_4$	117°	1002
2-$CH_3C_6H_4$	CH_3	NO	H	H	195°	996
4-$CH_3C_6H_4$	CH_3	NO	H	H	198°	996
C_6H_5	C_6H_5	NO	H	H	207°	340, 1153
C_6H_5	4-$CH_3C_6H_4$	NO	H	H	230°	1152, 1153
C_6H_5	4-$CH_3OC_6H_4$	NO	H	H	208°	1153
C_6H_5	4-$NO_2C_6H_4$	NO	H	H	—	340
H	H	NO_2	H	H	228°	1043
H	H	NO_2	H	CH_3CO	180°	1043
H	CH_3	NO_2	H	H	225°	1044, 1045

(Table continued)

TABLE XII (*continued*)

R^1	R^2	R^3	R^4	R^5	M.p.	Reference
H	CH_3	NO_2	H	C_2H_5OOC	200°	1049
H	C_6H_5	NO_2	H	2,4-$(NO_2)_2C_6H_3$	266° (dec.)	1652, 1654
H	C_6H_5	NO_2	H	2,4-$(NO_2)_2$-6-$CH_3C_6H_2$	245°	1656
H	N	NO_2	H	H	—	932
H	N	NO_2	H	CH_3CO	175°	932
C_6H_5	CH_3	NO_2	H	H	167°	1010, 1043, 1044
C_6H_5	CH_3	C_6H_5CO	H	H	153°	973, 977
C_6H_5	CH_3	C_6H_5CO	H	C_6H_5	171°	973
H	H	HOOC	H	H	—	1266
H	H	C_2H_5OOC	H	H	102°	1266
C_6H_5	HOOC	C_6H_5	H	H	—	506
C_6H_5	C_2H_5OOC	C_6H_5	H	H	—	506
H	$HOOCCH_2$	H_2NCO	H	H	—	1478
CH_3	$HOOCCH_2$	H_2NCO	H	H	—	1478
C_6H_5	$HOOCCH_2$	H_2NCO	H	H	—	1478
C_6H_5	CH_3	C_6H_5NHCO	H	C_6H_5	171°	826
C_6H_5	CH_3	C_6H_5NHCO	H	1-$C_{10}H_7$	168°	828
C_6H_5	CH_3	1-$C_{10}H_7NHCO$	H	1-$C_{10}H_7$	224°	828
C_6H_5	CH_3	C_6H_5NHCS	H	C_6H_5	224°	827
C_6H_5	CH_3	C_6H_5NHCS	H	1-$C_{10}H_7$	259°	828
H	H	NC	H	H	174°	1196
H	$NCCH_2$	NC	H	H	198°	1478
CH_3	$NCCH_2$	NC	H	H	—	1478

C_6H_5	C_6H_5	H_2NCO	H	H	186°	726
C_6H_5	C_6H_5	CH_3HNCO	H	H	153°	726
C_6H_5	C_6H_5	NC	H	H	168°	726
C_6H_5	$NCCH_2$	NC	H	H	—	1478
CH_3CO	C_6H_5	H	H	H	162°	1542
CH_3CO	C_6H_5	H	H	$CH_3C(=CHCOOC_2H_5)$	148°	299
CH_3CO	C_6H_5	H	H	CH_3CO	159°	301, 342, 344
CH_3CO	C_6H_5	H	H	C_2H_5OOCCO	144°	301
CH_3CO	$4\text{-}CH_3C_6H_4$	H	H	H	221°	1542
CH_3CO	$4\text{-}CH_3C_6H_4$	H	H	CH_3CO	163°	1542
CH_3CO	$4\text{-}NO_2C_6H_4$	H	H	CH_3CO	203°	344
C_6H_5CO	C_6H_5	H	H	CH_3CO	159°	301
C_6H_5CO	C_6H_5	H	H	C_6H_5CO	—	301
H_2NCO	C_6H_5	H	H	H	170°	343, 344
H_2NCO	$4\text{-}CH_3C_6H_4$	H	H	H	180°	1542
H_2NCO	$4\text{-}NO_2C_6H_4$	H	H	H	338°	343
H_2NCO	C_2H_5	$4\text{-}ClC_6H_4$	H	H	168°	918
C_6H_5NHCO	$4\text{-}CH_3C_6H_4$	H	H	H	173°	1542
C_6H_5NHCO	$4\text{-}CH_3C_6H_4$	H	H	CH_3CO	161°	1542
$C_6H_5N{=}C(OH)—$	$4\text{-}CH_3C_6H_4$	H	H	H	206°	1542
$C_6H_5N{=}C(OH)—$	$4\text{-}CH_3C_6H_4$	H	H	CH_3CO	184°	1542
C_6H_5NHCS	C_6H_5	H	H	H	187°	1542
C_6H_5NHCS	$4\text{-}CH_3C_6H_4$	H	H	H	196°	1542
C_6H_5	CH_3	Cl	Br	H	124°	996
C_6H_5	CH_3	Br	Br	H	125°	996
C_6H_5	HOOC	$4\text{-}NO_2C_6H_4SO_2$	H	H	174°	325
C_6H_5	HOOC	$4\text{-}NO_2C_6H_4SO_2$	H	CH_3CO	210°	325

(*Table continued*)

TABLE XII (*continued*)

R^1	R^2	R^3	R^4	R^5	M.p.	Reference
C_6H_5	H_5C_2OOC	$C_6H_5N{=}N$	H	H	105°	126
CH_3CO	CH_3COO	H	H	C_6H_5	—	1598
CH_3CO	CH_3COO	H	H	CH_3CO	131°	594
CH_3CO	Cl	C_2H_5	C_2H_5	CH_3CO	50°	391

TABLE XIII. *N,N′*-Bis(5-imino-2-pyrazolines)

R^1	R^2	R^3	R	M.p.	Reference
H	C_6H_5	H	—C(=O)—	310° (dec.)	301
H	C_6H_5	H	—C(=O)—C(=O)—	>310°	301
C_6H_5	CH_3	H	—C(=S)—	184°	996
C_6H_5	CH_3	H	—C(=O)—C(=O)—	—	322
CH_3CO	C_6H_5	H	—C(=O)—	243°	301
C_6H_5	CH_3	C_6H_5CO	none	—	973

TABLE XIV. 3-Pyrazolin-5-ones

Section A. Alkyl and Alicyclic Substituents

R^1	R^2	R^3	R^4	M.p.	Reference
H	CH_3	CH_3	H	174°	54, 788, 860, 1205
H	C_2H_5	CH_3	H	135°	1205
CH_3	CH_3	CH_3	H	40°	54, 788, 789, 985
	CH_3	CH_3	H	$b_3$161°	101
	CH_3	CH_3	H	66°	101, 103, 859
		CH_3	H	85°	101
C_2H_5	CH_3	CH_3	iso-C_3H_7	$b_{0.08}$97°	250
C_3H_7	CH_3	CH_3	iso-C_3H_7	$b_{0.12}$107°	250
iso-C_3H_7	CH_3	CH_3	iso-C_3H_7	$b_{0.07}$81°	250
C_4H_9	CH_3	CH_3	iso-C_3H_7	$b_{0.07}$98°	250
iso-C_4H_9	CH_3	CH_3	iso-C_3H_7	$b_{0.06}$90°	250

TABLE XIV (*continued*)

Section B. Alkyl and Aryl Substituents

R^1	R^2	R^3	R^4	M.p.	Reference
H	C_6H_5	H	H	155°	450, 858, 993, 1122, 1554, 1559
H	4-IC_6H_4	H	H	126°	446
C_6H_5	CH_3	H	H	117°	108
H	CH_3	C_6H_5	H	165°	54, 1205
H	C_6H_5	CH_3	H	166°	95, 247, 788, 826, 885, 888, 988, 1522, 1524, 1559, 1569
H	C_6H_5	H	CH_3	—	972, 1569
H	C_6H_5	C_5H_{11}	H	280°	1023, 1024
H	C_6H_5	C_6H_{13}	H	270°	1023, 1024
H	2-$CH_3C_6H_4$	CH_3	H	169°	988, 1524
H	4-$CH_3C_6H_4$	CH_3	H	196°	988
H	4-$CH_3C_6H_4$	H	CH_3	217°	446
H	4-BrC_6H_4	CH_3	H	227°	1001
H	4-BrC_6H_4	H	CH_3	245°	446
H	3-$NO_2C_6H_4$	CH_3	H	239°	1001
H	4-$NO_2C_6H_4$	CH_3	H	233°	885
H	4-$NO_2C_6H_4$	H	CH_3	266°	446
H	2,5-$(CH_3)_2C_6H_3$	CH_3	H	180°	679
H	2,5-$Cl_2C_6H_3$	CH_3	H	231°	885
H	1-$C_{10}H_7$	CH_3	H	240°	885
C_6H_5	C_6H_5	H	H	130°	370

(*Table continued*)

TABLE XIV, Section B (*continued*)

R^1	R^2	R^3	R^4	M.p.	Reference
H	C_6H_5	C_6H_5	H	256°	95, 808, 1023, 1024, 1042, 1071, 1333, 1522, 1524
H	2-$CH_3C_6H_4$	C_6H_5	H	207°	1524
H	C_6H_5	2-$CH_3OC_6H_4$	H	222°	670
[9-xanthenyl]	[9-xanthenyl]	H	H	—	457
C_6H_5	CH_3	CH_3	H	113°	781, 785, 801, 806, 807, 1173, 1174, 1198, 1508
CH_3	C_6H_5	CH_3	H	113°	95, 888, 1522
CH_3	CH_3	C_6H_5	H	108°	992
H	C_6H_5	CH_3	CH_3	256°	95, 984
C_6H_5	CH_3	C_2H_5	H	65°	1252
C_6H_5	CH_3	H	C_2H_5	121°	303
H	C_6H_5	CH_3	C_2H_5	172°	95, 984, 1522, 1524
C_6H_5	C_3H_7	CH_3	H	90°	1321
H	iso-C_3H_7	CH_3	C_6H_5	219°	250
C_6H_5	CH_3	[cyclopropyl]	H	115°	1477

C_6H_5	CH_3	$C_{15}H_{31}$	H	66°	636
C_6H_5	C_2H_5	C_2H_5	H	$b_{2.5}$178°	1252
C_6H_5	CH_3	CH_3	$HOCH_2CH_2$	115°	1171
C_6H_5	CH_3	CH_3	$HOOCCH_2$	186°	638
C_6H_5	CH_3	CH_3	$H_5C_2OOCCH_2$	—	638
C_6H_5	CH_3	CH_3	H_2NOCCH_2	147°	638
C_6H_5	CH_3	CH_3	$HOOCCHCH_2$ | NH_2	—	638
C_6H_5	CH_3	CH_3	$HOOCCHCH_2$ | $NHCOC_6H_5$	228°	638
C_6H_5	CH_3	CH_3	$H_5C_2OOCCHCH_2$ | NO_2	—	638
C_6H_5	CH_3	CH_3	$(H_3COOC)_2CCH_2$ | $NHCHO$	161°	638
C_6H_5	CH_3	CH_3	$(H_5C_2OOC)_2CCH_2$ | $NHCHO$	143°	638
C_6H_5	CH_3	CH_3	$(H_5C_2OOC)_2CCH_2$ | NO_2	—	638
$2\text{-}CH_3C_6H_4$	CH_3	CH_3	H	96°	806
CH_3	$2\text{-}CH_3C_6H_4$	CH_3	H	169°	988
H	$2\text{-}CH_3C_6H_4$	CH_3	C_2H_5	161.5°	1524
$3\text{-}CH_3C_6H_4$	CH_3	▷—	H	$b_{0.01}$201°	1477
$4\text{-}CH_3C_6H_4$	CH_3	CH_3	H	137°	806
CH_3	$4\text{-}CH_3C_6H_4$	CH_3	H	98°	988
$4\text{-}CH_3C_6H_4$	C_2H_5	CH_3	H	—	145
$4\text{-}CH_3C_6H_4$	CH_3	▷—	H	$b_{0.06}$185°	1477

(*Table continued*)

TABLE XIV, Section B (*continued*)

R^1	R^2	R^3	R^4	M.p.	Reference
4-$C_2H_5OC_6H_4$	CH_3	CH_3	H	81°	902
4-$C_2H_5OC_6H_4$	C_2H_5	CH_3	H	—	145
4-$C_3H_7OC_6H_4$	CH_3	CH_3	H	55°	1149
2-$H_2NC_6H_4$	CH_3	CH_3	H	165°	978
3-$H_2NC_6H_4$	CH_3	CH_3	H	148°	978
4-$H_2NC_6H_4$	CH_3	CH_3	H	210°	978
3-$(CH_3)_2NC_6H_4$	CH_3	CH_3	H	270° (dec., chloroplatinate)	978
4-$HO_3SCH_2NHC_6H_4$	CH_3	CH_3	H	—	541
3-$CH_3CONHC_6H_4$	CH_3	CH_3	H	167°	978
3-$C_6H_5CONHC_6H_4$	CH_3	CH_3	H	119°	978
3-$C_6H_5SO_2NHC_6H_4$	CH_3	CH_3	H	199°	978
4-$CH_3CONHC_6H_4$	CH_3	CH_3	H	221°	978
4-$C_6H_5CONHC_6H_4$	CH_3	CH_3	H	261°	978
4-$C_6H_5SO_2NHC_6H_4$	CH_3	CH_3	H	251°	978
4-(4-$H_2NC_6H_4SO_2NH$)C_6H_4	CH_3	CH_3	H	256°	674, 1290
4-(4-$CH_3CONHC_6H_4SO_2NH$)C_6H_4	CH_3	CH_3	H	—	674
4-$H_2NHNC_6H_4$	CH_3	CH_3	H	—	645
4-$H_2NC(=O)NHNHC_6H_4$	CH_3	CH_3	H	—	645
2-ClC_6H_4	CH_3	CH_3	H	113°	296
3-ClC_6H_4	CH_3	CH_3	H	89°	296
4-ClC_6H_4	CH_3	CH_3	H	126°	296
4-BrC_6H_4	CH_3	CH_3	H	—	540
CH_3	4-BrC_6H_4	CH_3	H	150°	1001
4-IC_6H_4	CH_3	CH_3	H	126°	446
2-$NO_2C_6H_4$	CH_3	CH_3	H	188°	978
3-$NO_2C_6H_4$	CH_3	CH_3	H	98°	978
4-$NO_2C_6H_4$	CH_3	CH_3	H	132°	978
4-$H_2NO_2SC_6H_4$	CH_3	CH_3	H	248°	1475, 1476
X-$H_2NO_2SC_6H_4$	CH_3	CH_3	H	239°	361

4-$H_2O_2AsC_6H_4$	CH_3	CH_3	H	—	546
2,5-$(CH_3)_2C_6H_3$	CH_3	CH_3	H	97.5°	679
2,4-$Cl_2C_6H_3$	CH_3	CH_3	H	143°	296
4-([methylcyclohexyl ring structure, CH_3])C_6H_4	CH_3	CH_3	H	87° (opt. act.)	141
4-([methylcyclohexyl ring structure, CH_3])C_6H_4	CH_3	CH_3	H	147° (racemic)	141
2-$C_{10}H_7$	CH_3	CH_3	H	129°	806
C_6H_5	$BrCH_2$	$BrCH_2$	H	175°	899
C_6H_5	C_6H_5	CH_3	H	130°	647, 789
C_6H_5	CH_3	C_6H_5	H	150°	818
[xanthen-9-yl structure]	[xanthen-9-yl structure]	H	CH_3	202°	457
H	C_6H_5	C_6H_5	CH_3	274°	1333
C_6H_5	CH_3	CH_3	CH_3	82°	95, 362, 809, 814, 1056, 1252

(Table continued)

TABLE XIV, Section B (*continued*)

R^1	R^2	R^3	R^4	M.p.	Reference
CH_3	C_6H_5	CH_3	CH_3	97°	95, 984
CH_3	CH_3	CH_3	C_6H_5	215°	250
C_6H_5	C_2H_5	CH_3	CH_3	$b_3$183°	1252
CH_3	C_6H_5	CH_3	C_2H_5	65°	95, 984
C_6H_5	CH_3	CH_3	C_3H_7	57°	1252, 1337
C_6H_5	CH_3	CH_3	iso-C_3H_7	101°	1252, 1337, 1522
C_6H_5	CH_3	CH_3	C_3H_5	52°	1252, 1337
C_6H_5	CH_3	CH_3	C_4H_9	44°	560, 1252
C_6H_5	CH_3	CH_3	sec.-C_4H_9	91°	1252
C_6H_5	CH_3	CH_3	iso-C_4H_9	56°	560, 1074, 1252
C_6H_5	CH_3	CH_3	iso-C_5H_{11}	61°	1252
C_6H_5	C_2H_5	CH_3	C_3H_7	$b_{1.5}$175°	1252
C_6H_5	C_2H_5	CH_3	iso-C_3H_7	88°	1252
C_6H_5	C_2H_5	CH_3	C_3H_5	$b_{1.5}$181°	1252
C_6H_5	C_2H_5	CH_3	C_4H_9	$b_3$194°	1252
C_6H_5	C_2H_5	CH_3	iso-C_4H_9	$b_3$187°	1252
C_6H_5	C_2H_5	CH_3	sec-C_4H_9	91°	1252
C_6H_5	C_2H_5	CH_3	iso-C_5H_{11}	$b_3$193°	1252
C_6H_5	C_3H_5	CH_3	iso-C_3H_7	84°	1447
C_6H_5	CH_3	$\triangleright$—	iso-C_3H_7	108°	1477
C_6H_5	CH_3	$BrCH_2$	CH_3	—	1320
C_6H_5	CH_3	CH_3	$CH_3C(=O)CH_2$	87°	113
C_6H_5	CH_3	CH_3	$CH_3C(=O)CH{=}CH$	161°	316

C_6H_5		CH_3	CH_3	$C_2H_5C(=O)CH{=}CH$	128°	316
C_6H_5		CH_3	CH_3	$O_2NCH{=}CH$	160°	696
C_6H_5		CH_3	CH_3	$HOOCCH{=}CH$	208° (dec.)	898
C_6H_5		CH_3	CH_3	$(H_5C_2OOC)_2C{=}CH$	135°	898
C_6H_5		CH_3	CH_3	$CH_3CH_2C(COOC_2H_5)_2CH_2$	115°	1320
C_6H_5		CH_3	CH_3	$H_5C_2OOCCH(NO_2)CHCH_2$	84° ($(C_2H_5)_2NH$ salt)	384
C_6H_5		CH_3	CH_3	$HON{=}C(CH_3)CH_2$	—	113
C_6H_5		CH_3	CH_3	$H_2NC(=O)NHN{=}C(CH_3)CH_2$	255° (dec.)	113
C_6H_5	CH_3	CH_3		$H_2NC(=S)NHN{=}C(CH_3)CH{=}CH$	228°	316
C_6H_5	CH_3	CH_3		$H_2NC(=S)HNN{=}C(C_6H_5)CH{=}CH$	254°	799
C_6H_5	$(CH_3)_2NCH_2CH_2$	CH_3		CH_3	$b_{0.9}$149°	249

(Table continued)

TABLE XIV, Section B (*continued*)

R^1	R^2	R^3	R^4	M.p.	Reference
C_6H_5	$(CH_3)_2NCH_2CH(CH_3)$	CH_3	CH_3	$b_{1.5}170°$	249
C_6H_5	$C_5H_{10}NCH_2CH_2$	CH_3	CH_3	$b_{0.3}158°$	249
C_6H_5	$C_5H_{10}NCH_2CH_2$	CH_3	C_2H_5	$b_{0.4}174°$	249
C_6H_5	$(CH_3)_2NCH_2CH_2$	CH_3	iso-C_3H_7	$b_{0.4}143°$	249
C_6H_5	$(CH_3)_2NCH_2CH(CH_3)$	CH_3	iso-C_3H_7	$b_{0.1}141°$	249
C_6H_5	$C_5H_{10}NCH_2CH_2$	CH_3	iso-C_3H_7	$b_{0.1}141°$	249
C_6H_5	CH_3	$BrCH_2$	iso-C_3H_7	—	1318
4-$H_2NC_6H_4$	CH_3	CH_3	CH_3	—	535
4-$(CH_3)_2NC_6H_4$	CH_3	CH_3	CH_3	140°, 212°	535, 1355, 1506
4-$HO_3SCH_2NHC_6H_4$	CH_3	CH_3	CH_3	—	541
4-$NO_2C_6H_4$	CH_3	CH_3	C_2H_5	129°	532
4-$NO_2C_6H_4$	CH_3	$BrCH_2$	C_2H_5	163°	532
C_6H_5	CH_3	$BrCH_2$	$BrCH_2$	175°	362

C_6H_5	CH_3	CH_3	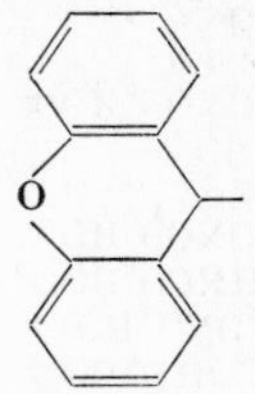	—	434

TABLE XIV (*continued*)

Section C. Alkyl, Aralkyl, Heterocyclicalkyl and Aryl Substituents

R^1	R^2	R^3	R^4	M.p.	Reference
H	$C_6H_5CH_2$	CH_3	H	224°	54
C_6H_5	$C_6H_5CH_2$	H	H	125°	1321
$C_6H_5CH_2$	CH_3	CH_3	H	84°	333
4-$CH_3C_6H_4CH_2$	CH_3	CH_3	H	78°	333
$C_6H_5CH_2CH_2$	CH_3	CH_3	H	102°	1566
C_6H_5	$C_6H_5CH_2$	CH_3	H	103°	1321
C_6H_5	CH_3	$C_6H_5CH_2$	H	105°	1320
C_6H_5	CH_3	H	$C_6H_5CH_2$	77.5°	1320
H	2-$C_{10}H_7$	CH_3	$C_6H_5CH_2$	202°	849
$C_6H_5CH_2CH_2$	CH_3	C_6H_5	H	—	1567

(*Table continued*)

TABLE XIV, Section C (*continued*)

R^1	R^2	R^3	R^4	M.p.	Reference
C_6H_5	CH_3	H	O / $CH=$ / O / CH_3 / CH_3	196°	897
C_6H_5	CH_3	H	O / $C=$ / H_3C / O / CH_3 / CH_3	258°	897
C_6H_5	CH_3	H	O / $-CH_2$	118°	378
$C_6H_5CH_2$	CH_3	CH_3	iso-C_3H_7	87°	250
C_6H_5	$C_6H_5CH_2$	CH_3	CH_3	128.5°	1321
C_6H_5	CH_3	CH_3	4-$HOC_6H_4CH_2$	204°	21, 553
C_6H_5	CH_3	CH_3	4-$H_2NC_6H_4CH_2$	140°	110, 1483
C_6H_5	CH_3	CH_3	4-$CH_3NHC_6H_4CH_2$	99°	110
C_6H_5	CH_3	CH_3	4-$(CH_3)_2NC_6H_4CH_2$	152°	110, 1483
C_6H_5	CH_3	CH_3	4-$CH_3CONHC_6H_4CH_2$	220°	110
C_6H_5	CH_3	CH_3	4-$CH_3CONC_6H_4CH_2$ (N–CH_3)	114°	110
C_6H_5	CH_3	CH_3	4-$CH_3CONC_6H_4CH_2$ (N–NO)	149°	110

C_6H_5	CH_3	CH_3	2,4-$(HO)_2C_6H_3CH_2$	155°	21
C_6H_5	CH_3	CH_3	3,4-$(HO)_2C_6H_3CH_2$	218°	21
C_6H_5	CH_3	CH_3	3-CH_3O-4-$HOC_6H_3CH_2$	165°	20
C_6H_5	CH_3	CH_3	3-CH_3O-4-$C_6H_5COOC_6H_3CH_2$	270°	20
C_6H_5	CH_3	CH_3	3-CH_3O-4-(α-[CH_3; CO_2H; CH_3CCH_3; COO^-])$C_6H_4CH_2$ 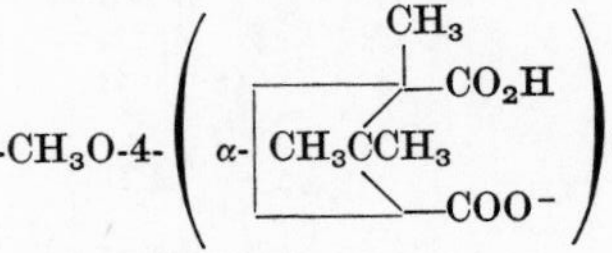	199°	20
C_6H_5	CH_3	CH_3	2-H_2N-5-$CH_3C_6H_3CH_2$	139°	110
C_6H_5	CH_3	CH_3	2-CH_3CONH-5-$CH_3C_6H_3CH_2$	171°	110
C_6H_5	CH_3	CH_3	2-CH_3-4-HO-5-iso-$C_3H_7C_6H_2CH_2$	191°	21
C_6H_5	CH_3	CH_3	$C_6H_5COCH{=}CH$	192°	107, 316
C_6H_5	$C_6H_5CH_2$	CH_3	$C_6H_5CH_2$	152°	700
C_6H_5	CH_3	CH_3	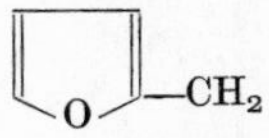 (O)—CH_2	89°	378
C_6H_5	CH_3	CH_3	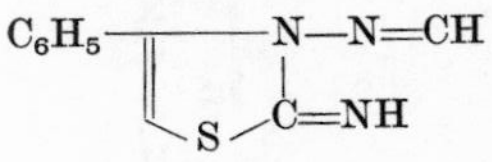 C_6H_5— N—N=CH; S; C=NH	195° (dec., HBr)	799
C_6H_5	CH_3	CH_3	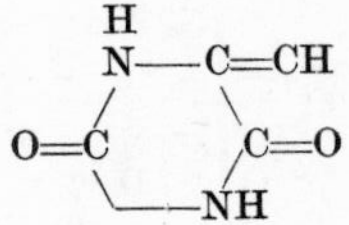 H; N—C=CH; O=C; C=O; NH	263°	696
C_6H_5	CH_3	CH_3	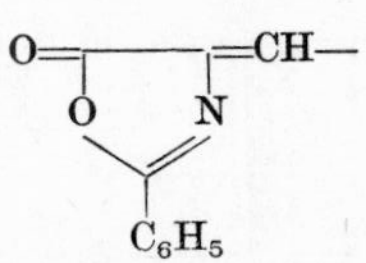 O= ; =CH—; O; N; C_6H_5	224° (dec.)	696

(Table continued)

TABLE XIV, Section C (*continued*)

R[1]	R[2]	R[3]	R[4]	M.p.	Reference
C_6H_5	CH_3	CH_3	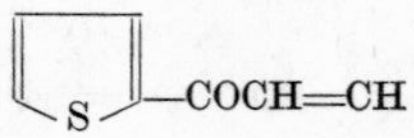 2-thienyl—COCH=CH	202°	316
C_6H_5	CH_3	CH_3	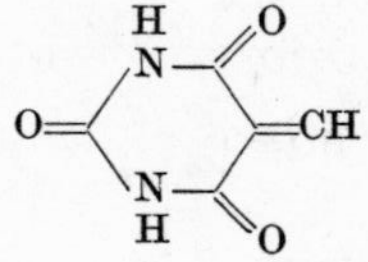 barbituric acid ring (N(H), N(H), three C=O) =CH	254°	890, 898
CH_3	C_6H_5	CH_3	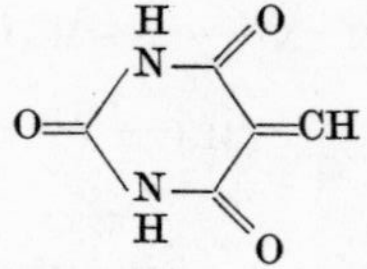 barbituric acid ring (N(H), N(H), three C=O) =CH	268°	1190
C_6H_5	CH_3	CH_3	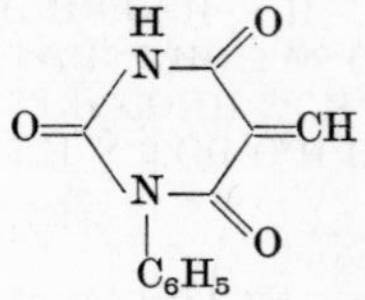 barbituric acid ring (N(H), N–C_6H_5, three C=O) =CH	190°	890, 898
CH_3	C_6H_5	CH_3	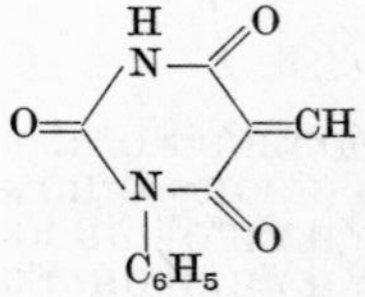 barbituric acid ring (N(H), N–C_6H_5, three C=O) =CH	276°	1190

C_6H_5	CH_3	CH_3	C_6H_5; N; O=; =CH; N; O; C_6H_5	280° (dec.)	890, 898
C_6H_5	CH_3	CH_3	H; N; O; S=; =CH; N; H; O	238° (dec.)	890, 898
C_6H_5	CH_3	C_6H_5	H; N; O; O=; =CH; N; H; O	274°	890, 898
C_6H_5	CH_3	CH_3	H; N; O; O=; CH_2—; iso-C_4H_9; N; H; O	251°	728
C_6H_5	CH_3	H; N; O; O=; CH_2—; C_2H_5; N; H; O	CH_3	> 250°	1320

(Table continued)

TABLE XIV, Section C (*continued*)

R^1	R^2	R^3	R^4	M.p.	Reference
C_6H_5	CH_3	CH_3	H N O; O=; —CH_2—; N H O	247° (dec.)	481
C_6H_5	CH_3	CH_3	H N O; O=; CH_2—; C_2H_5; N H O	270° (dec.)	481
C_6H_5	CH_3	CH_3	H N O; O=; CH_2—; iso-C_3H_7; N H O	274° (dec.)	481
C_6H_5	CH_3	CH_3	H N O; O=; CH_2—; C_3H_5; N H O	272° (dec.)	481

C_6H_5	CH_3	CH_3	(5-C_6H_5-hexahydropyrimidine-2,4,6-trion-5-yl)CH_2—	250° (dec.)	481
C_6H_5	CH_3	CH_3	(5-(2-oxocyclohexyl)CH_2-hexahydropyrimidine-2,4,6-trion-5-yl)CH_2—	220° (dec.)	481
4-$CH_3C_6H_4$	CH_3	CH_3	2-furyl-CH_2	90°	378
4-$C_2H_5OC_6H_4$	CH_3	CH_3	2-furyl-CH_2	—	378
C_6H_5	CH_3	CH_3	(5-iso-C_4H_9-hexahydropyrimidine-2,4,6-trion-5-yl)CH_2	251°	728
4-$H_2NC_6H_4$	CH_3	CH_3	2-furyl-CH_2	—	378

(*Table continued*)

TABLE XIV, Section C (*continued*)

R^1	R^2	R^3	R^4	M.p.	Reference
4-BrC_6H_4	CH_3	CH_3	O —CH_2	—	378
4-$NO_2C_6H_4$	CH_3	CH_3	O —CH_2	—	378
O, CH_3N, NCH_3, O, N, N, CH_3	CH_3	CH_3	H	251° (dec.)	1147
O, CH_3N, NCH_3, O, N, N, CH_3	CH_3	CH_3	CH_3	335° (dec.)	1147

TABLE XIV (*continued*)

Section D. Alkyl, Aryl and Heterocyclic Substituents

R^1	R^2	R^3	R^4	M.p.	Reference
C_6H_5	CH_3	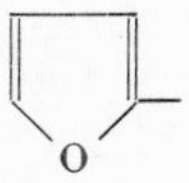 [furan ring, O]	H	—	1499
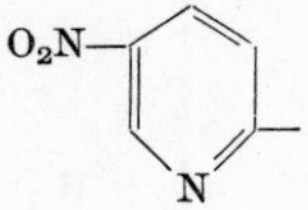 O_2N– [pyridine ring, N]	CH_3	CH_3	H	172°	1159
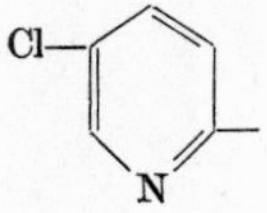 Cl– [pyridine ring, N]	CH_3	CH_3	H	135°	1159
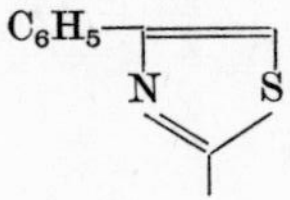 C_6H_5– [thiazole ring, N, S]	CH_3	CH_3	H	110°	94
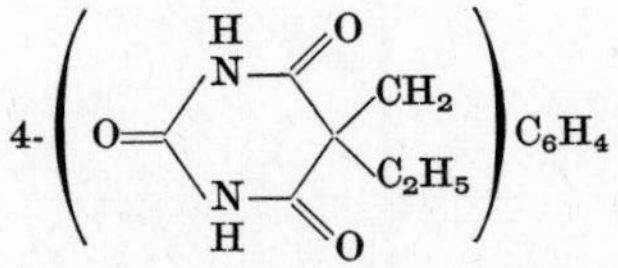 4-([pyrimidine-trione ring: O=, HN, NH, =O, =O; CH_2, C_2H_5])C_6H_4	CH_3	CH_3	H	300°	1160

(*Table continued*)

TABLE XIV, Section D (*continued*)

R[1]	R[2]	R[3]	R[4]	M.p.	Reference
C_6H_5	CH_3	H	COOH N	284°	903
C_6H_5	CH_3	CH_3	S N NH_2	235°	94
C_6H_5	CH_3	CH_3	S N CH_3	130°	94
C_6H_5	CH_3	CH_3	S N $NHNH_2$	152°	94
C_6H_5	CH_3	CH_3	S N $NHNHCOCH_3$	231°	94

C_6H_5	CH_3	CH_3	S, N (ring) —$NHN{=}C(CH_3)C_6H_5$ (as CH_3I)	216°	94
C_6H_5	CH_3	CH_3	N, N—C_6H_5 (ring) —Cl	203°	991
C_6H_5	CH_3	CH_3	N, N—C_6H_5 (ring) —I	—	991
C_6H_5	CH_3	CH_3	CH_3—, N, N—C_6H_5 (ring) —SCH_3	168°	991
C_6H_5	CH_3	CH_3	CH_3—, N, N—C_6H_5 (ring) —$N(CH_3)C_6H_5$	101°	991

(*Table continued*)

TABLE XIV, Section D (*continued*)

R^1	R^2	R^3	R^4	M.p.	Reference
C_6H_5	CH_3	CH_3	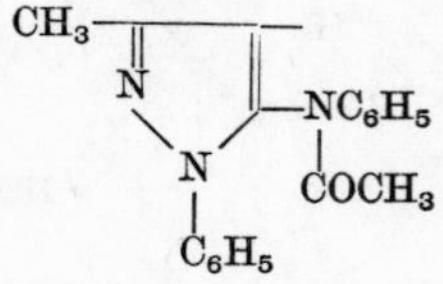 CH_3, N, N, NC_6H_5, $COCH_3$, C_6H_5	238°	991
C_6H_5	CH_3	CH_3	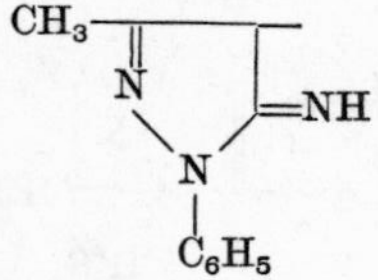 CH_3, N, N, =NH, C_6H_5	220°	991
C_6H_5	CH_3	CH_3	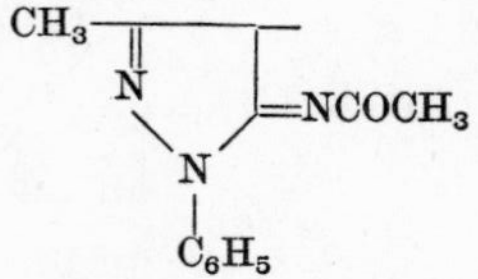 CH_3, N, N, $=NCOCH_3$, C_6H_5	237°	991
C_6H_5	CH_3	CH_3	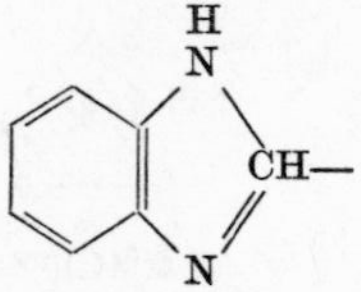 H, N, CH—, N	202°, 280°	799, 1190
C_6H_5	CH_3	CH_3	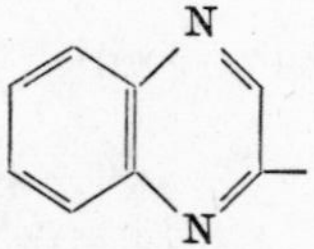 N, N	194°	799

C_6H_5	CH_3	CH_3	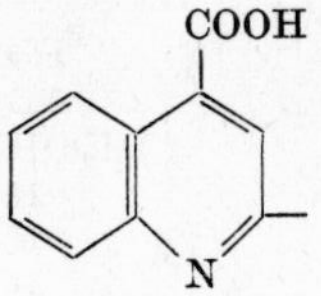 COOH, N	266°	903
C_6H_5	CH_3	CH_3	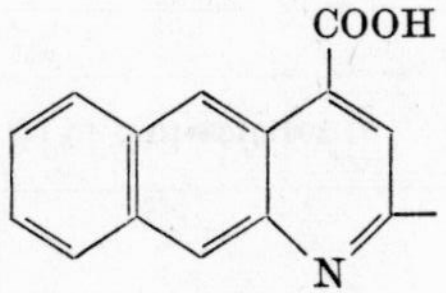 COOH, N	278° (dec.)	1190
C_6H_5	CH_3	CH_3	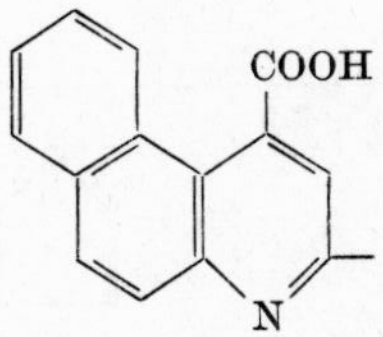 COOH, N	278°	903
CH_3	C_6H_5	CH_3	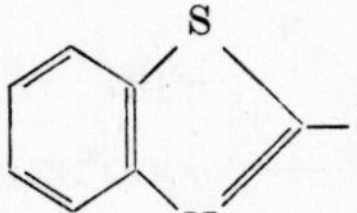 S, N	208°	829
C_6H_5	CH_3	CH_3	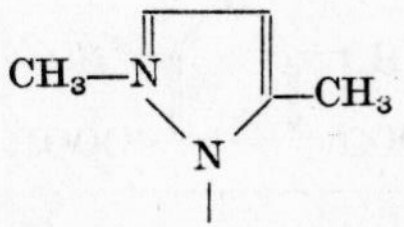 CH_3—N, N, CH_3	178°	452

(Table continued)

TABLE XIV, Section D (*continued*)

R¹	R²	R³	R⁴	M.p.	Reference
C_6H_5	CH_3	CH_3	HOOC— —COOH CH_3— —CH_3 N |	256°	452
C_6H_5	CH_3	CH_3	H_5C_2OOC— —$COOC_2H_5$ CH_3— —CH_3 N |	145°	452
C_6H_5	CH_3	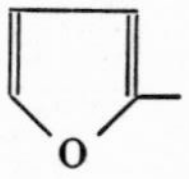 O	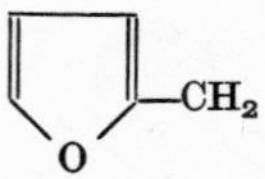 O —CH_2	144°	378

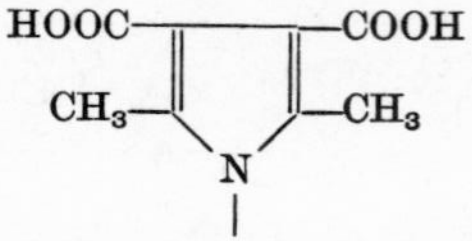

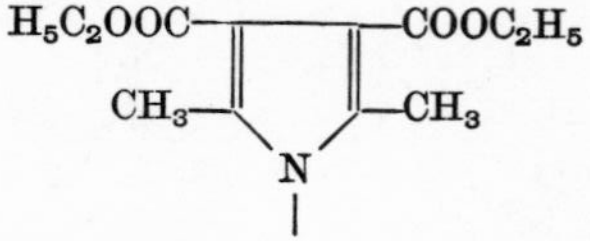

TABLE XIV (*continued*)

Section E. α-Hydroxy-, α-Acyloxy-, and α-Alkylthioalkyl, Alkyl and Aryl Substituents

R¹	R²	R³	R⁴	M.p.	Reference
C_6H_5	CH_3	$HOCH_2$	H	145	698
4-$H_2NC_6H_4$	CH_3	$HOCH_2$	H	223	532
4-$NO_2C_6H_4$	CH_3	$HOCH_2$	H	—	532
C_6H_5	CH_3	CH_3	$HOCH_2$	158	17
C_6H_5	CH_3	$HOCH_2$	CH_3	170	528
4-$H_2NC_6H_4$	CH_3	$HOCH_2$	CH_3	—	532

4-$(CH_3)_2NC_6H_4$	CH_3	$HOCH_2$	CH_3	186	532
4-$NCCH_2NHC_6H_4$	CH_3	$HOCH_2$	CH_3	—	532
4-$NCCH_2NC_6H_4$ (N–CH_3)	CH_3	$HOCH_2$	CH_3	—	532
4-$(HOOCCH_2)_2NC_6H_4$	CH_3	$HOCH_2$	CH_3	—	532
4-$H_2NC_6H_4$	CH_3	$HOCH_2$	C_2H_5	244	532
4-$(CH_3)_2NC_6H_4$	CH_3	$HOCH_2$	C_2H_5	183	532
4-$NO_2C_6H_4$	CH_3	$HOCH_2$	C_2H_5	169	532
C_6H_5	CH_3	CH_3	Cl_3CCH–OH	197	107, 196, 889, 895
CH_3	C_6H_5	CH_3	Cl_3CCH–OH	190	1190
CH_3	CH_3	C_6H_5	Cl_3CCH–OH	173	1190
C_6H_5	CH_3	C_2H_5	Cl_3CCH–OH	156°	901
4-$CH_3C_6H_4$	CH_3	CH_3	Cl_3CCH–OH	191°	889
4-$C_2H_5OC_6H_4$	CH_3	CH_3	Cl_3CCH–OH	146°	902
C_6H_5	CH_3	C_6H_5	Cl_3CCH–OH	188°	889, 902
C_6H_5	CH_3	CH_3	Br_3CCH–OH	188°	895
C_6H_5	CH_3	CH_3	$NCCH$–OH	—	107

(Table continued)

TABLE XIV, Section E (*continued*)

R^1	R^2	R^3	R^4	M.p.	Reference
C_6H_5	CH_3	CH_3	$CH_3CH(NH_2)CH(OH)$(HCl)	—	113
C_6H_5	CH_3	CH_3	$CH_3CH(NHCH_3)CH(OH)$(HCl)	163° (threo) 220° (erythro)	112, 113
C_6H_5	CH_3	CH_3	$CH_3CH(NHC_2H_5)CH(OH)$	123°	112
C_6H_5	CH_3	CH_3	$CH_3CH(NH$-iso-$C_3H_7)CH(OH)$	162°	112
C_6H_5	CH_3	CH_3	$CH_3CH(N(CH_3)_2)CH(OH)$	165°	112
C_6H_5	CH_3	CH_3	$C_6H_5CH(OH)$	173°	977

C_6H_5	CH_3	CH_3	(4-hydroxycoumarin-3-yl)–CH(OH)–	152°	800
C_6H_5	CH_3	CH_3	5-methyl-5-hydroxy-barbituric acid-5-yl (HN–CO–NH ring, OH)	240°	1194
CH_3	CH_3	C_6H_5	5-methyl-5-hydroxy-barbituric acid-5-yl (HN–CO–NH ring, OH)	227°	1194
C_6H_5	CH_3	$HOCH_2$	$HOCH_2$	164°	698
C_6H_5	CH_3	CH_3	CH_3COOCH_2	—	970
C_6H_5	CH_3	CH_3	4-$NO_2C_6H_4COOCH_2$	—	970
C_6H_5	CH_3	CH_3	2-$HOOCC_6H_4COOCH_2$	—	970
C_6H_5	CH_3	CH_3	$CH_3COOCH(CCl_3)$	154°	895
C_6H_5	CH_3	CH_3	$C_2H_5COOCH(CCl_3)$	141°	895

(Table continued)

TABLE XIV, Section E (*continued*)

R^1	R^2	R^3	R^4	M.p.	Reference
C_6H_5	CH_3	CH_3	$C_4H_9COOCH(CCl_3)$	136°	895
C_6H_5	CH_3	CH_3	iso-$C_4H_9COOCH(CCl_3)$	135°	895
C_6H_5	CH_3	CH_3	$C_6H_5COOCH(CCl_3)$	214°	895
C_6H_5	CH_3	CH_3	4-$NO_2C_6H_5COOCH(CCl_3)$	160°	895
C_6H_5	CH_3	CH_3	3-$HO_3SC_6H_5COOCH(CCl_3)$	230°	895
C_6H_5	CH_3	CH_3	$CH_3COOCH(CBr_3)$	138°	895
C_6H_5	CH_3	CH_3	$C_6H_5COOCH(CBr_3)$	170°	895
C_6H_5	CH_3	CH_3	$C_6H_5NHCOOCH_2$	271.5°	402
C_6H_5	CH_3	CH_3	$C_2H_5SCH_2$	97°	1127
C_6H_5	CH_3	CH_3	$C_3H_7SCH_2$	64°	1127
C_6H_5	CH_3	CH_3	$C_4H_7SCH_2$	53°	1127
C_6H_5	CH_3	CH_3	$C_6H_5CH_2SCH_2$	100°	1127
C_6H_5	CH_3	CH_3	$C_6H_5SCH_2$	102°	1127

TABLE XIV (*continued*)

Section F. α-Amino-, α-Imino-, α-Oximino-, α-Amido- and α-Hydrazinoalkyl, Alkyl and Aryl Substituents

R¹	R²	R³	R⁴	M.p.	Reference
C_6H_5	CH_3	CH_3NHCH_2	H	70°	697
C_6H_5	CH_3	$(CH_3)_2NCH_2$	H	83°	697
C_6H_5	CH_3	CH_3	H_2NCH_2	—	901
C_6H_5	CH_3	CH_3	$CH_3NHCH_2(HNO_3)$	168°	107
C_6H_5	CH_3	CH_3	$C_2H_5NHCH_2$	—	107
C_6H_5	CH_3	CH_3	cyclohexyl—$NHCH_2$	88°	107
C_6H_5	CH_3	$CH_3CHNHCH_2$ | $CH_2C_6H_5$	iso-C_3H_7	65°	1319
C_6H_5	CH_3	CH_3	$C_6H_5NHCH_2$	171°, 143°	110, 111, 1483
C_6H_5	CH_3	CH_3	4-$CH_3C_6H_5NHCH_2$	140°	110
C_6H_5	CH_3	CH_3	CH_3NHCH | C_2H_5	105°	112
C_6H_5	CH_3	CH_3	C_6H_5NHCH | C_6H_5	185°	1094
C_6H_5	CH_3	CH_3	$(CH_3)_2NCH_2$	93°	945
CH_3	C_6H_5	CH_3	$(CH_3)_2NCH_2$	66°	945
C_6H_5	CH_3	CH_3	$(C_2H_5)_2NCH_2$	68°	945
C_6H_5	CH_3	$C_6H_5CH_2CHNCH_2$ | | CH_3 CH_3	iso-C_3H_7	132°	1318

(*Table continued*)

10+C.H.C. 20

TABLE XIV, Section F (*continued*)

R^1	R^2	R^3	R^4	M.p.	Reference
C_6H_5	CH_3	CH_3	$NCH_2CH_2NCH_2$ (with ring structures)	oil	111
C_6H_5	CH_3	CH_3	$(C_6H_5CH_2)_2NCH_2$	131°	910
C_6H_5	CH_3	CH_3	NCH_2 (ring structure)	100°	637
C_6H_5	CH_3	CH_3	N—CH_2 (ring structure)	153°	945
C_6H_5	CH_3	CH_3	$C_6H_5COCH_2CH_2N(CH_3)CH_2$	86°	944
C_6H_5	CH_3	CH_3	—$N(OH)CH_2$ (ring structure)	132°	1482
C_6H_5	CH_3	CH_3	$C_6H_5CONHCH_2$	140°	1014

C_6H_5	CH_3	CH_3	$H_2NCONCH_2$ | CH_3	167°	107
C_6H_5	CH_3	CH_3	$H_2NCONCH_2$ | C_2H_5	165°	107
C_6H_5	CH_3	CH_3	CH_3CONCH_2 | C_6H_5	128°	110, 1483
C_6H_5	CH_3	CH_3	C_6H_5NHCH | SO_3Na	170°	202, 891
C_6H_5	CH_3	CH_3	4-$H_2NO_2SC_6H_4NHCH$ | SO_3Na	—	202, 891, 894
4-$C_2H_5OC_6H_4$	CH_3	CH_3	4-$C_2H_5OC_6H_4NHCH$ | SO_3Na	150° (dec.)	202, 891
C_6H_5	CH_3	C_6H_5	C_6H_5NHCH | SO_3Na	120° (dec.)	202, 891
C_6H_5	CH_3	CH_3	$C_2H_5N{=}CH$	—	107
C_6H_5	CH_3	CH_3	$CH_3N{=}CH$	—	107
C_6H_5	CH_3	CH_3	C_6H_{11}—$N{=}CH$	148°	107, 891
C_6H_5	CH_3	CH_3	$C_6H_5N{=}CH$	152°	107, 202, 891, 897
C_6H_5	CH_3	CH_3	2-$CH_3C_6H_4N{=}CH$	192°	891
C_6H_5	CH_3	CH_3	4-$C_2H_5OC_6H_4N{=}CH$	163°	891
C_6H_5	CH_3	CH_3	2-$H_2NC_6H_4N{=}CH$	215°	1190
C_6H_5	CH_3	CH_3	4-$OHCC_6H_4N{=}CH$	232°	891

(*Table continued*)

TABLE XIV, Section F (*continued*)

R^1	R^2	R^3	R^4	M.p.	Reference
C_6H_5	CH_3	CH_3	$4\text{-}H_2NO_2SC_6H_4N{=}CH$	—	202
C_6H_5	CH_3	CH_3	$3\text{-}HO\text{-}4\text{-}HOOCC_6H_4N{=}CH$	190°	891
C_6H_5	CH_3	CH_3	$1\text{-}C_{10}H_7N{=}CH$	97°	891
CH_3	C_6H_5	CH_3	$4\text{-}C_2H_5OC_6H_4NH{=}CH$	135°	1190
$4\text{-}C_2H_5OC_6H_4$	CH_3	CH_3	$4\text{-}C_2H_5OC_6H_4N{=}CH$	161°	1186
C_6H_5	CH_3	C_6H_5	$C_6H_5N{=}CH$	140°	202, 891, 902
C_6H_5	CH_3	C_6H_5	$C_6H_5N{=}CH$	—	1183
C_6H_5	CH_3	CH_3	$HON{=}CH$	220°	196, 201, 889, 1092, 1181
CH_3	C_6H_5	CH_3	$HON{=}CH$	221°	1190
C_6H_5	CH_3	CH_3	$HON{=}C(C_6H_5)$	197°	977
$4\text{-}C_2H_5OC_6H_4$	CH_3	CH_3	$HON{=}CH$	210°	902, 1186
C_6H_5	CH_3	C_6H_5	$HON{=}CH$	239°	201, 1183
C_6H_5	CH_3	$C_6H_5NHN{=}CH$	H	227°	698
C_6H_5	CH_3	CH_3	$H_2NN{=}C(CH_2Cl)$	211°	799
C_6H_5	CH_3	CH_3	$H_2NN{=}C(C_6H_5)$	215°	977
C_6H_5	CH_3	CH_3	$C_6H_5NHN{=}CH$	225°, 236°, 255°	196, 201, 889, 1181, 1182
CH_3	C_6H_5	CH_3	$C_6H_5NHN{=}CH$	230°	1190
C_6H_5	CH_3	CH_3	$4\text{-}NO_2C_6H_4NHN{=}CH$	272°	201, 1181
C_6H_5	CH_3	CH_3	$2,4\text{-}(NO_2)_2C_6H_3NHN{=}CH$	260°	201
C_6H_5	CH_3	CH_3	$C_6H_5NHN{=}C(C_6H_5)$	160°	977

C_6H_5	CH_3	CH_3	3-C_5H_4N–CONHN=CH	263°	696
C_6H_5	CH_3	CH_3	4-C_5H_4N–CONHN=CH	270°	412
4-$C_2H_5OC_6H_4$	CH_3	CH_3	$C_6H_5NHN{=}CH$	260°	1186
4-$C_2H_5OC_6H_4$	CH_3	CH_3	4-$C_2H_5OC_6H_4NHN{=}CH$	—	1186
C_6H_5	CH_3	CH_3	$C_6H_5CH{=}CHCHNN{=}C(CH_2Cl)$	160°	799
C_6H_5	CH_3	CH_3	3-CH_3O-4-$HOC_6H_3CH{=}NN{=}C(CH_2Cl)$	235°	799
C_6H_5	CH_3	CH_3	2-$HOC_6H_4CH{=}NN{=}C(CH_2Cl)$	164°	799
C_6H_5	CH_3	CH_3	$C_6H_5C(CH_3){=}NN{=}C(CH_2Cl)$	104°	799
C_6H_5	CH_3	$C_6H_5NHN{=}CH$	$C_6H_5NHN{=}CH$	216° (dec.)	698
C_6H_5	CH_3	CH_3	$H_2NCONHN{=}CH$	204°, 223°, 245°	201, 204, 892, 1181
4-$C_2H_5OC_6H_4$	CH_3	CH_3	$H_2NCONHN{=}CH$	256°	1186
C_6H_5	CH_3	C_6H_5	$H_2NCONHN{=}CH$	210°, 256°	201, 1180
C_6H_5	CH_3	CH_3	$H_2NCSNHN{=}CH$	226°, 246°	510, 616, 799, 900
CH_3	C_6H_5	CH_3	$H_2NCSNHN{=}CH$	238° (dec.)	1190
C_6H_5	CH_3	CH_3	$C_2H_5NHCSNHN{=}CH$	246°	900
C_6H_5	CH_3	CH_3	$C_6H_5NHCSNHN{=}CH$	215°	900
4-$C_2H_5OC_6H_4$	CH_3	CH_3	$H_2NCSNHN{=}CH$	233°	900
C_6H_5	CH_3	C_6H_5	$H_2NCSNHN{=}CH$	233°	900

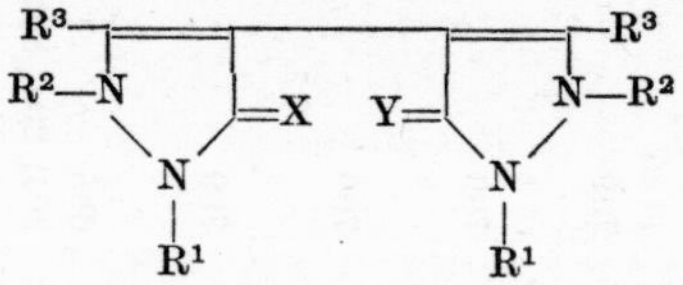

TABLE XV. 4,4′-Bis(3-pyrazolin-5-ones) Linked by a Single Bond

R^1	R^2	R^3	X	Y	M.p.	Reference
C_6H_5	CH_3	CH_3	O	O	254°	785, 807, 809, 991
C_6H_5	CH_3	CH_3	S	S	237°	785, 991
C_6H_5	CH_3	CH_3	Se	Se	270°	986
C_6H_5	CH_3	CH_3	NH	HN	250°	991
C_6H_5	CH_3	CH_3	O	S	225°	991
C_6H_5	CH_3	CH_3	O	HN	259°	991
C_6H_5	CH_3	CH_3	O	C_6H_5N	215°	991
C_6H_5	C_2H_5	CH_3	O	O	240°	807
C_6H_5	C_6H_5CO	CH_3	O	O	203°	1056

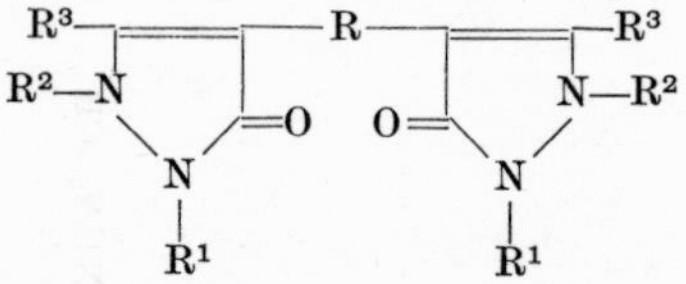

TABLE XVI. 4,4′Bis(3-pyrazolin-5-ones) Linked by Carbon or Heteroatoms

R	R^1	R^2	R^3	M.p.	Reference
CH_2	C_6H_5	CH_3	H	180°	902
$CH_3CH_2CH<$	C_6H_5	C_6H_5	H	192°	1042
CH_2	C_6H_5	CH_3	CH_3	155°, 178°	19, 740, 910, 1192, 1483
$HOOCCH<$	C_6H_5	CH_3	CH_3	239°	107, 896
$H_3COOCH<$	C_6H_5	CH_3	CH_3	204°	107
$C_2H_5OOCH<$	C_6H_5	CH_3	CH_3	92°	107
$CH{=}CH\overset{O}{\overset{\|}{C}}CH{=}CH$	C_6H_5	CH_3	CH_3	270°	316
$(CH_3)_2CHCH_2CH<$	C_6H_5	CH_3	CH_3	160°	409
$C_6H_5CH<$	H	C_6H_5	CH_3	270°	988
$4\text{-}CH_3OC_6H_4CH<$	H	C_6H_5	CH_3	287°	988
$C_6H_5CH<$	H	$4\text{-}CH_3C_6H_4$	CH_3	278°	988
$4\text{-}CH_3OC_6H_4CH<$	H	$4\text{-}CH_3C_6H_4$	CH_3	270°	988

(*Table continued*)

TABLE XVI (*continued*)

R	R^1	R^2	R^3	M.p.	Reference
$C_6H_5CH<$	C_6H_5	CH_3	CH_3	201°	807, 809, 1133
$C_6H_5CH<$	CH_3	CH_3	C_6H_5	213°	992
$2\text{-}HOC_6H_4CH<$	C_6H_5	CH_3	CH_3	193°	21
$2\text{-}CH_3OC_6H_4CH<$	C_6H_5	CH_3	CH_3	216°	568
$3\text{-}CH_3OC_6H_4CH<$	C_6H_5	CH_3	CH_3	186°	569
$4\text{-}(CH_3)_2NC_6H_4CH<$	C_6H_5	CH_3	CH_3	—	1133
$2\text{-}ClC_6H_4CH<$	C_6H_5	CH_3	CH_3	260°	568
$4\text{-}ClC_6H_4CH<$	C_6H_5	CH_3	CH_3	169°	566
$2\text{-}NO_2C_6H_4CH<$	C_6H_5	CH_3	CH_3	214°	566, 568
$3\text{-}NO_2C_6H_4CH<$	C_6H_5	CH_3	CH_3	214°	566
$4\text{-}NO_2C_6H_4CH<$	C_6H_5	CH_3	CH_3	232°	566
$2\text{-}HO_3SC_6H_4CH<$	C_6H_5	CH_3	CH_3	288° (dec.)	568
$4\text{-}HO_3SC_6H_4CH<$	C_6H_5	CH_3	CH_3	300° (dec.)	568
$3\text{-}CH_3\text{-}4\text{-}HOC_6H_3CH<$	C_6H_5	CH_3	CH_3	119°	21
$3\text{-}CH_3O\text{-}4\text{-}HOC_6H_3CH<$	C_6H_5	CH_3	CH_3	146°	566
$3,4\text{-}(CH_3O)_2C_6H_3CH<$	C_6H_5	CH_3	CH_3	200°	569
$1\text{-}C_{10}H_7CH<$	C_6H_5	CH_3	CH_3	254°	566
C_6H_5COH	C_6H_5	CH_3	CH_3	172°	569
$3\text{-}CH_3OC_6H_4COH$	C_6H_5	CH_3	CH_3	111° (picrate)	569
$4\text{-}(CH_3)_2NC_6H_4COH$	C_6H_5	CH_3	CH_3	135°	569
$2\text{-}ClC_6H_4COH$	C_6H_5	CH_3	CH_3	109° (picrate)	568
$4\text{-}ClC_6H_4COH$	C_6H_5	CH_3	CH_3	137°	566
$2\text{-}NO_2C_6H_4COH$	C_6H_5	CH_3	CH_3	130° (picrate)	568
$3\text{-}NO_2C_6H_4COH$	C_6H_5	CH_3	CH_3	148° (picrate)	569
$4\text{-}NO_2C_6H_4COH$	C_6H_5	CH_3	CH_3	180°	566, 569
$2\text{-}HO_3SC_6H_4COH$	C_6H_5	CH_3	CH_3	—	568
$4\text{-}HO_3SC_6H_4COH$	C_6H_5	CH_3	CH_3	—	568
$3,4\text{-}(CH_3O)_2C_6H_3COH$	C_6H_5	CH_3	CH_3	118° (picrate)	569
$1\text{-}C_{10}H_7COH$	C_6H_5	CH_3	CH_3	235° (picrate)	566, 569
C=O	C_6H_5	CH_3	CH_3	246°	740
O ‖ —CCH=CH—	C_6H_5	CH_3	H	256°	902
CH₃ O │ ‖ —C=CHC—	C_6H_5	CH_3	H	256°	901
H │ N—C=O O=C C< N—C=O │ H	C_6H_5	CH_3	CH_3	269° (dec.)	481

(*Table continued*)

TABLE XVI (*continued*)

R	R^1	R^2	R^3	M.p.	Reference
H N O O= N O C_3H_5	C_6H_5	CH_3	CH_3	221°	481
—$COOCH_2CO$—	C_6H_5	CH_3	CH_3	256°	740, 741
O_2N NO_2 —O— —O—	C_6H_5	CH_3	CH_3	243°	744
—S—S—	C_6H_5	CH_3	CH_3	256°	8, 742, 848
—S—S—	C_6H_5	C_2H_5	CH_3	199°	848
—S—Hg—S—	C_6H_5	CH_3	CH_3	—	848
—S—Hg—S—	C_6H_5	C_2H_5	CH_3	230°	848
—Se—	C_6H_5	CH_3	CH_3	240°	545, 850
Se ← Se<	C_6H_5	CH_3	CH_3	215°	850
Cl_2Se<	C_6H_5	CH_3	CH_3	225°	850
CONHN=CH	C_6H_5	CH_3	CH_3	232°	696
CH_2NCH_2 CH_3	C_6H_5	CH_3	CH_3	111°	945
CH_2NCH_2 C_2H_5	C_6H_5	CH_3	CH_3	143°	945
CH_2NCH_2 C_3H_5	C_6H_5	CH_3	CH_3	163°	945
CH_2NCH_2 $CH_2COOC_2H_5$	C_6H_5	CH_3	CH_3	174°	945
CH_2NCH_2	C_6H_5	CH_3	CH_3	217°	945
CH_2NCH_2 $CH_2COC_6H_5$	C_6H_5	CH_3	CH_3	93°	945
CH_2—N— —CH_2 CH_3	C_6H_5	CH_3	CH_3	163°	1483

(*Table continued*)

TABLE XVI (*continued*)

R	R^1	R^2	R^3	M.p.	Reference
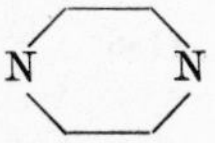 N N (ring)	C_6H_5	CH_3	CH_3	262°	927
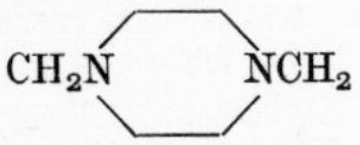 CH_2N NCH_2 (ring)	C_6H_5	CH_3	CH_3	248°	945
$SO_2NHCH_2CH_2NHSO_2$	C_6H_5	CH_3	CH_3	275°	745
N=N	H	4-BrC_6H_4	CH_3	175°	1001
N=N	H	C_6H_5	CH_3	160°	984
N=N	C_6H_5	CH_3	CH_3	165°	456
N=NC(=NNHC(=NH)NHN=)C(…)N=N, with C_6H_5 on each C: N=NC=NNHC(NH)NHN=CN=N / C_6H_5 C_6H_5	C_6H_5	CH_3	CH_3	154°	1284
CH=N	C_6H_5	CH_3	CH_3	224°	891
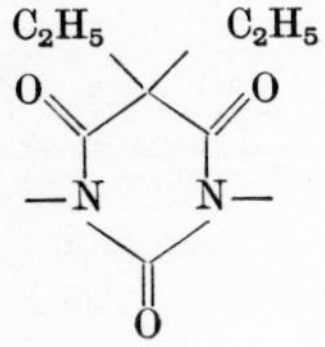 C_2H_5 C_2H_5 / O=C–C–C=O / –N N– / C=O (ring)	C_6H_5	CH_3	CH_3	312°	589

TABLE XVII. Miscellaneous Bis(3-pyrazolin-5-ones) and Bis(5-imino-3-pyrazolines)

Structure	M.p.	Reference
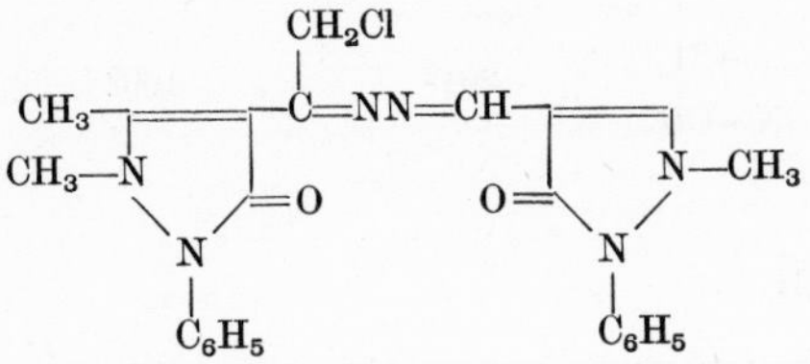 CH_3–C=C–C(CH_2Cl)=NN=CH–C=C–N–CH_3; CH_3–N, C=O, N–C_6H_5 (left ring); O=C, N–C_6H_5 (right ring)	226°	799
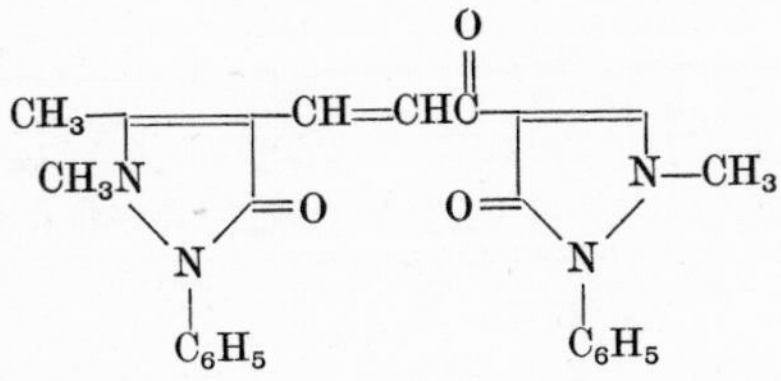 CH_3–C=C–CH=CHC(=O)–C=C–N–CH_3; CH_3N, C=O, N–C_6H_5 (left ring); O=C, N–C_6H_5 (right ring)	258° (hydrate)	108, 696

(*Table continued*)

TABLE XVII (*continued*)

Structure	M.p.	Reference
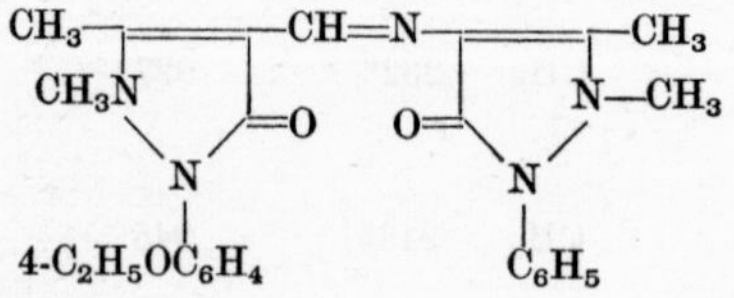 CH_3 —CH=N— CH_3 CH_3N N—CH_3 O O N N 4-$C_2H_5OC_6H_4$ C_6H_5	220°	891, 1186
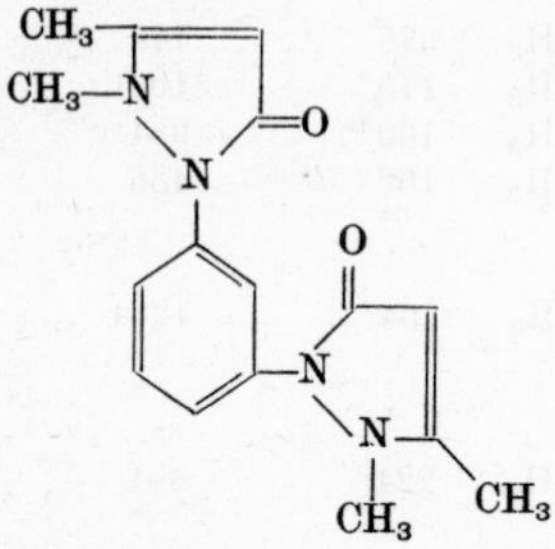 CH_3 CH_3—N O N O N N CH_3 CH_3	177°	116
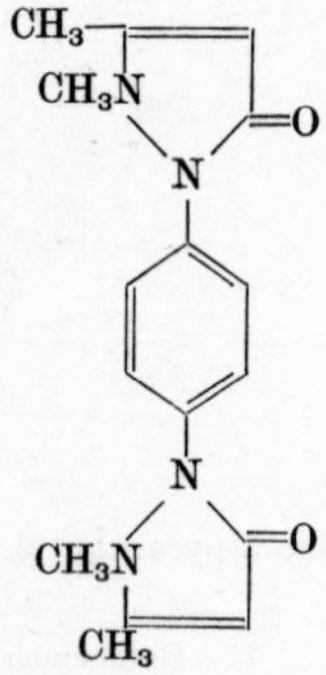 CH_3 CH_3N O N N CH_3N O CH_3	300°	116
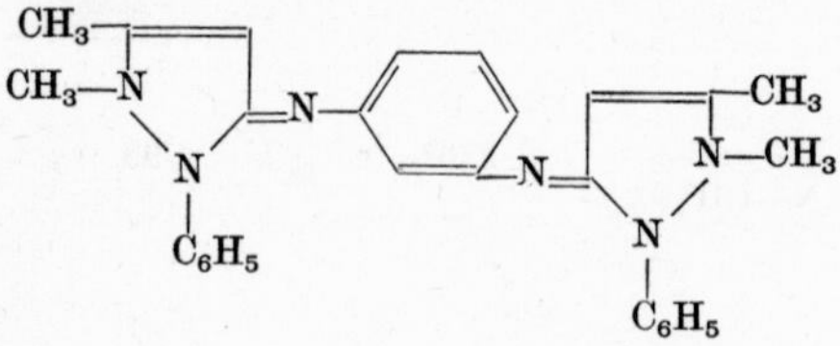 CH_3 CH_3—N =N— CH_3 N —N= N—CH_3 C_6H_5 N C_6H_5	204°	1002

R³, R⁴, R²—N, X, N, R¹

TABLE XVIII. 3-Pyrazolin-5-thiones and -5-selenones

R^1	R^2	R^3	R^4	M.p.	Reference
X=S					
H	C_6H_5– (ring: N, N–H)	C_6H_5	H	169°	1653
CH_3	CH_3	CH_3	H	147°	789, 985
C_6H_5	CH_3	CH_3	H	182°	785, 844, 845
CH_3	C_6H_5	CH_3	H	136°	988
CH_3	CH_3	C_6H_5	H	178°	992
CH_3	2-$CH_3C_6H_4$	CH_3	H	133°	988
CH_3	4-$CH_3C_6H_4$	CH_3	H	223°	988
2-$H_2NC_6H_4$	CH_3	CH_3	H	172°	978
3-$H_2NC_6H_4$	CH_3	CH_3	H	199°	978
4-$H_2NC_6H_4$	CH_3	CH_3	H	255°	978
4-$CH_3CONHC_6H_4$	CH_3	CH_3	H	271°	978
4-$C_6H_5CONHC_6H_4$	CH_3	CH_3	H	265°	978
CH_3	3-$H_2NC_6H_4$	CH_3	H	97°	1001
CH_3	4-BrC_6H_4	CH_3	H	236°	1001
2-$NO_2C_6H_4$	CH_3	CH_3	H	190°	978
3-$NO_2C_6H_4$	CH_3	CH_3	H	204°	978
CH_3	3-$NO_2C_6H_4$	CH_3	H	242°	1001

(Table continued)

TABLE XVIII (*continued*)

R^1	R^2	R^3	R^4	M.p.	Reference
$4\text{-}NO_2C_6H_4$	CH_3	CH_3	H	240°	978
C_6H_5	C_6H_5	CH_3	H	185°	789
CH_3	C_6H_5	C_6H_5	H	185°	1001
$3\text{-}NO_2C_6H_4$	CH_3	C_6H_5	H	106°	1003
CH_3	$3\text{-}NO_2C_6H_4$	C_6H_5	H	112°	1001
CH_3	C_6H_5	CH_3	CH_3	103°	984
CH_3	C_6H_5	CH_3	C_2H_5	126	984
C_6H_5	CH_3	CH_3	$(CH_3)_2N$	—	986, 1000
CH_3	C_6H_5	Cl	H	123°	981
C_6H_5	CH_3	CH_3	Cl	188.5°	795
CH_3	C_6H_5	Cl	Br	173°	981
$4\text{-}NO_2C_6H_4$	CH_3	CH_3	NO_2	240°	978
X=Se					
CH_3	C_6H_5	CH_3	H	168°	988
CH_3	CH_3	C_6H_5	H	198°	992

R³—C=C—R⁴; R²N, N(R¹), =NR⁵ (5-imino-3-pyrazoline ring)

TABLE XIX. 5-Imino-3-pyrazolines

R^1	R^2	R^3	R^4	R^5	M.p.	Reference
H	C_6H_5	H	H	H	93°	398

H	C_6H_5	H	H	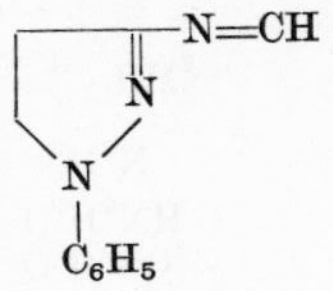 —N=CH, N, N, C_6H_5	—	398
H	3-$CH_3C_6H_4$	H	H	H	100°	398
H	4-$CH_3OC_6H_4$	H	H	H	124°	398
H	4-ClC_6H_4	H	H	H	108°	398
H	4-BrC_6H_4	H	H	H	176°	398
H	C_6H_5	CH_3	H	H	112°	398
H	C_6H_5	CH_3	H	C_6H_5	146°	826
H	C_6H_5	CH_3	H	4-$CH_3C_6H_4$	116°	826
C_6H_5	CH_3	H	H	C_6H_5	128°	1002
C_6H_5	C_2H_5	H	H	C_6H_5	155°	1002
C_6H_5	C_3H_7	H	H	C_6H_5	124°	1002
H	C_6H_5	C_5H_{11}	H	H	b_{18} 231°	1025
H	C_6H_5	C_6H_5	H	H	135°	398, 1025
H	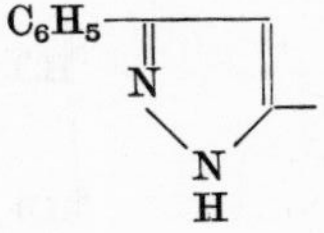 C_6H_5—, N, N, H	C_6H_5	H	C_6H_5NH	234°	1653
CH_3	CH_3	CH_3	H	H	—	985
C_6H_5	CH_3	CH_3	H	H	63°, 211°	975, 1352
C_6H_5	CH_3	CH_3	H	CH_3	131°	1352
C_6H_5	CH_3	CH_3	H	C_2H_5	—	1352
C_6H_5	CH_3	CH_3	H	$C_6H_5CH_2$	oil	975
C_6H_5	CH_3	CH_3	H	C_6H_5	79°	827, 975
C_6H_5	CH_3	CH_3	H	2-$CH_3C_6H_4$	69°	1002
C_6H_5	CH_3	CH_3	H	4-$CH_3C_6H_4$	106°	1002
C_6H_5	CH_3	CH_3	H	3-$H_2NC_6H_4$	45°	1002
C_6H_5	CH_3	CH_3	H	3-$CH_3COHNC_6H_4$	212°	1002

(Table continued)

TABLE XIX (*continued*)

R^1	R^2	R^3	R^4	R^5	M.p.	Reference
C_6H_5	CH_3	CH_3	H	3-$C_6H_5COHNC_6H_4$	172°	1002
C_6H_5	CH_3	CH_3	H	4-$H_2NC_6H_4$	112°	1002
C_6H_5	CH_3	CH_3	H	4-$CH_3HNC_6H_4$	143°	1002
C_6H_5	CH_3	CH_3	H	4-$(CH_3)_2NC_6H_4$	120°	1002
C_6H_5	CH_3	CH_3	H	4-$CH_3COHNC_6H_4$	196°	1002
C_6H_5	CH_3	CH_3	H	4-$CH_3NC_6H_4$ | $COCH_3$	142°	1002
C_6H_5	CH_3	CH_3	H	4-$CH_3NC_6H_4$ | NO	169°	1002
C_6H_5	CH_3	CH_3	H	4-$C_2H_5NC_6H_4$ | NO	—	1002
C_6H_5	CH_3	CH_3	H	4-ClC_6H_4	78°	1002
C_6H_5	CH_3	CH_3	H	3-BrC_6H_4	205°	1002
C_6H_5	CH_3	CH_3	H	4-BrC_6H_4	81°	1002
C_6H_5	CH_3	CH_3	H	3-$NO_2C_6H_4$	114°	1002
C_6H_5	CH_3	CH_3	H	4-$NO_2C_6H_4$	129°	1002
C_6H_5	CH_3	CH_3	H	4-$HOOCC_6H_4$	150°	996
C_6H_5	CH_3	CH_3	H	4-$CH_3OOCC_6H_4$	155°	996
C_6H_5	CH_3	CH_3	H	3-NO_2-4-$CH_3C_6H_4$	100°	1002
C_6H_5	CH_3	CH_3	H	3,4-$Cl_2C_6H_4$	—	1002
C_6H_5	CH_3	CH_3	H	1-$C_{10}H_7$	161°	975
C_6H_5	CH_3	CH_3	H	2-$C_{10}H_7$	70°	975
C_6H_5	CH_3	CH_3	H	C_6H_5CO	176°	1352
C_6H_5	CH_3	CH_3	H	$C_6H_5SO_2$	211°	1352
C_6H_5	CH_3	CH_3	H	C_6H_5NH	oil	983
C_6H_5	CH_3	CH_3	H	$_6H_5N$ | CH_3	128°	983

C_6H_5	CH_3	CH_3	H	$C_6H_5N(C_2H_5)$	78°	983
CH_3	C_6H_5	CH_3	H	H	—	1352
C_6H_5	C_2H_5	CH_3	H	H	170°	975
C_6H_5	C_2H_5	CH_3	H	$C_6H_5SO_2$	173°	975
2-$CH_3C_6H_4$	CH_3	CH_3	H	H	35°	996
2-$CH_3C_6H_4$	CH_3	CH_3	H	C_6H_5	129°	1002
2-$CH_3C_6H_4$	CH_3	CH_3	H	C_6H_5CO	186°	996
2-$CH_3C_6H_4$	CH_3	CH_3	H	$C_6H_5SO_2$	179°	996
4-$CH_3C_6H_4$	CH_3	CH_3	H	H	177°	996
4-$CH_3C_6H_4$	CH_3	CH_3	H	C_6H_5	106°	1002
4-$CH_3C_6H_4$	CH_3	CH_3	H	$C_6H_5SO_2$	203°	996
4-ClC_6H_4	CH_3	CH_3	H	C_6H_5	96°	1002
4-BrC_6H_4	CH_3	CH_3	H	C_6H_5	119°	1002
2-$C_{10}H_7$	CH_3	CH_3	H	C_6H_5	182°	975
2-$C_{10}H_7$	CH_3	CH_3	H	2-$C_{10}H_7$	122°	975
C_6H_5	CH_3	CH_3	CH_3	H	—	1352
C_6H_5	CH_3	CH_3	CH_3	CH_3	—	1352
C_6H_5	CH_3	CH_3	$C_6H_5CH_2$	H	148°	975
C_6H_5	CH_3	CH_3	$C_6H_5CH_2$	CH_3	—	975
C_6H_5	CH_3	CH_3	$C_6H_5CH_2$	C_6H_5CO	124°	975
C_6H_5	CH_3	CH_3	$C_6H_5CH_2$	$C_6H_5SO_2$	141°	975
2-$CH_3C_6H_4$	CH_3	CH_3	$C_6H_5N{=}N$	H	188°	996
4-$CH_3C_6H_4$	CH_3	CH_3	$C_6H_5N{=}N$	H	191°	996
C_6H_5	CH_3	CH_3	Br	4-$CH_3OOCC_6H_4$	170°	996
C_6H_5	CH_3	CH_3	C_6H_5CO	H	155°	977
C_6H_5	CH_3	CH_3	C_6H_5CO	C_6H_5	159°	977
C_6H_5	CH_3	CH_3	$C_6H_5C({=}NNHC_6H_5)$—	C_6H_5	178°	977
H	C_6H_5	CH_3	C_6H_5HNCS	C_6H_5	224°	826
C_6H_5	CH_3	CH_3	C_6H_5HNCO	C_6H_5	215°	826
H	CH_3CO	CH_3COO	H	CH_3CO	202°	594
C_6H_5	CH_3CO	CH_3COO	H	CH_3CO	83°	1599

TABLE XX. 2-Pyrazolin-5-ones. Hydroxy and Mercapto Derivatives

R^1	R^2	R^3	R^4	M.p.	Reference
H	CH_3	H	OH	205°	262
H	CH_3	CH_3	OH	96°	1526
H	CH_3	C_2H_5	OH	128°	1526
H	CH_3	C_3H_7	OH	117°	1526
H	CH_3	C_3H_5 (allyl)	OH	103°	1526
H	CH_3	C_4H_9	OH	101°	1526
H	CH_3	C_6H_{11}	OH	140°	1526
C_6H_5	CH_3	H	OH	190°, 225°	99, 372, 1491
H	CH_3	$C_6H_5CH_2$	OH	143°	1526
H	C_6H_5	$C_6H_5CH_2$	OH	185°	1526
CH_3	CH_3	C_2H_5	OH	39°	1525, 1526
CH_3	CH_3	C_6H_5	OH	126°	1527
CH_3	CH_3	$C_6H_5CH_2$	OH	143°, 155°	1525, 1526
C_6H_5	CH_3	CH_3	OH	105°, 113°	1525, 1526, 1528
C_6H_5	CH_3	C_2H_5	OH	117°, 130°	1525, 1526, 1528
C_6H_5	CH_3	C_3H_7	OH	116°	1525, 1526
C_6H_5	CH_3	iso-C_3H_7	OH	115°	1525
C_6H_5	CH_3	C_4H_9	OH	95°	1525, 1526
C_6H_5	CH_3	$C_6H_5CH_2$	OH	145°	1525, 1526
C_6H_5	CH_3	C_6H_{11}	OH	110°	1525

C_6H_5	CH_3O	CH_3	CH_3	70°	994
C_6H_5	CH_3O	C_2H_5	C_2H_5	94°	41, 317
H	C_2H_5O	H	H	177°	1143
C_6H_5	C_2H_5O	H	H	116.5°	598
4-$NO_2C_6H_4$	C_2H_5O	H	H	151°	1143
4-$H_2NO_2SC_6H_4$	C_2H_5O	H	H	197°	598, 1143
benzothiazol-2-yl	C_2H_5O	H	H	200°	1143
benzoxazol-2-yl	C_2H_5O	H	H	152°	1143
C_6H_5	C_4H_9O	H	H	59°	1143
benzothiazol-2-yl	C_4H_9O	H	H	59°	1143
6-[4-(t-C_4H_9)C_6H_4O]benzothiazol-2-yl	C_4H_9O	H	H	185°	1143
C_6H_5	CH_3	4-$NO_2C_6H_4COO$	H	162°	783
H	CH_3COO	C_6H_5	C_2H_5	159.5°	1234
C_6H_5	CH_3	$C_6H_5CH_2COO$	H	—	320
C_6H_5	C_6H_5COO	CH_3	CH_3	80°	998
C_6H_5	CH_3COO	C_2H_5	C_2H_5	97°	317
C_6H_5	C_6H_5COO	C_2H_5	C_2H_5	110°	317
C_6H_5	$(CH_3)_2NCOO$	H	H	115°	200

(Table continued)

TABLE XX (*continued*)

R^1	R^2	R^3	R^4	M.p.	Reference
C_6H_5	C_6H_5	OH	H	200°	1243
C_6H_5	C_6H_5	C_6H_5COO	H		1243
C_6H_5	C_6H_5	OH	OH	82°	1243
C_6H_5	C_6H_5	OH	C_2H_5O	165°	1243
C_6H_5	C_6H_5	OH	NaO_3S	—	1243
H	CH_3	OC_2H_5 N —S— NH_2	H	226° (dec.)	1474
C_6H_5	CH_3	$4\text{-}CH_3C_6H_4S$	H	212°	28
C_6H_5	CH_3	$2\text{-}NH_2C_6H_4S$	H	181°	28
C_6H_5	CH_3	$4\text{-}NH_2C_6H_4S$	H	217°	28
C_6H_5	CH_3	$4\text{-}ClC_6H_4S$	H	205°	28
C_6H_5	CH_3	$4\text{-}BrC_6H_4S$	H	221°	28
C_6H_5	CH_3	$2,4\text{-}Cl_2C_6H_3S$	H	225°	28
C_6H_5	CH_3	$2\text{-}NO_2C_6H_4S$	H	207°	28
C_6H_5	CH_3	$4\text{-}NO_2C_6H_4S$	H	236°	27
$4\text{-}NO_2C_6H_4$	CH_3	OH	OH	185°	690
$4\text{-}NO_2C_6H_4$	CH_3	OH	CH_3O	192°	690

R³—C=C—R⁴ / R²—N, C=O / N / R¹

TABLE XXI. 3-Pyrazolin-5-ones. Alkoxy, Aryloxy, Acyloxy, and Alkylthio Substituents

R^1	R^2	R^3	R^4	M.p.	Reference
H	C_6H_5	CH_3O	H	92°	41
C_6H_5	C_6H_5	$(CH_3)_2NC(=O)O$	H	188°	200
C_6H_5	C_6H_5	(pyridine ring, N)—COO	H	314°	1048
C_6H_5	C_6H_5	(quinoline ring, N)—COO	H	337°	1048
C_6H_5	CH_3	CH_3	CH_3O	75°	820
C_6H_5	CH_3	CH_3	C_2H_5O	60°	820
C_6H_5	CH_3	CH_3	C_6H_5COO	139°	820
C_6H_5	CH_3	CH_3	$2\text{-}NO_2\text{-}5\text{-}ClC_6H_3O$	176°	744
C_6H_5	CH_3	CH_3	$2,4\text{-}(NO_2)_2C_6H_3O$	174°	744
C_6H_5	CH_3	CH_3	$2\text{-}CH_3OOC\text{-}4\text{-}NO_2C_6H_3O$	191°	744
C_6H_5	CH_3	CH_3	$2\text{-}HOOC\text{-}4\text{-}NO_2C_6H_3O$	250°	744
C_6H_5	CH_3	CH_3	$2\text{-}C_2H_5OOC\text{-}4\text{-}NO_2C_6H_3O$	171°	744
C_6H_5	CH_3	CH_3	$2,4\text{-}(NO_2)_2\text{-}5\text{-}ClC_6H_2O$	205°	744
C_6H_5	CH_3	CH_3	$2,4\text{-}(NO_2)_2\text{-}5\text{-}CH_3OC_6H_2O$	195	744
C_6H_5	CH_3	CH_3	$2,4\text{-}(NO_2)_2\text{-}5\text{-}H_2NC_6H_2O$	267° (dec.)	744
C_6H_5	CH_3	CH_3	$2,4\text{-}(NO_2)_2\text{-}5\text{-}C_6H_5NHC_6H_2O$	240°	744
C_6H_5	CH_3	CH_3	$2,4\text{-}(NO_2)_2\text{-}5\text{-}(2\text{-}C_2H_5OC_6H_2NH)C_6H_2O$	246°	744
C_6H_5	CH_3	CH_3	$2,4,6\text{-}(NO_2)_3C_6H_2O$	150°	744
C_6H_5	CH_3	CH_3	(benzothiazole ring, S, N)—O	142°	744
C_6H_5	CH_3	CH_3	O_2N—(pyridine ring, N)—O—	126°	744

(*Table continued*)

TABLE XXI *(continued)*

R^1	R^2	R^3	R^4	M.p.	Reference
C_6H_5	CH_3	CH_3	4-$H_2NC_6H_4COO$	194°	783
C_6H_5	CH_3	CH_3	4-$O_2NC_6H_4COO$	143°	783
C_6H_5	C_6H_5	CH_3	CH_3O	—	887
C_6H_5	C_6H_5	$(CH_3)_2NCOO$	C_4H_9	135°	200
C_6H_5	CH_3	CH_3	CH_2S— (naphthalene ring) —OH	201°	1127
C_6H_5	CH_3	CH_3	CH_2S— (naphthalene ring) —$OCOCH_3$	133°	1127
C_6H_5	CH_3	C_6H_5	CH_3O	155°	1243
C_6H_5	CH_3	C_6H_5	C_6H_5COO	—	1243

TABLE XXII. 2-Pyrazolin-5-ones. Amino, Imino, Hydrazino, Azo, and Related Derivatives

R^1	R^2	R^3	R^4	M.p.	Reference
H	CH_3	H	NH_2	247° (dec., HCl salt)	480
CH_3	CH_3	CH_3	NH_2	225° (HCl salt)	478
H	CH_3	$4\text{-}(C_2H_5)_2NC_6H_4N{=}$		202°	519
H	CH_3	$2\text{-}CH_3\text{-}4\text{-}(C_2H_5)_2NC_6H_3N{=}$		195°	244
CH_3	CH_3	CH_3	$4\text{-}CH_3OC_6H_4CH{=}N$	202°	478
CH_3	CH_3	CH_3	$3,4\text{-}(OCH_2O)C_6H_3CH{=}N$	245°	478
CH_3	CH_3	CH_3	$4\text{-}NO_2C_6H_4CH{=}N$	257°	478
H	H	H	C_6H_5CONH	200°	59, 319
H	H	H	$C_6H_5CON(CH_3)$—	237°	318
H	H	H	$C_6H_5CH_2CONH$	215°, 222°	243, 1027
H	2-benzothiazolyl-$N(C_6H_5)$—	H	H	165°	705
H	$C_2H_5OOCCH_2$	$C_2H_5ON{=}$		116°	866
$C_6H_5CH_2$	CH_3	$AgO_2N{=}$		—	333

(*Table continued*)

TABLE XXII *(continued)*

R¹	R²	R³	R⁴	M.p.	Reference
$C_6H_5CH_2$	CH_3		$(C_6H_5NH)_2N=$ | OAg	—	333
H	$2\text{-}HOC_6H_4CH{=}N$		$2\text{-}HOC_6H_4CH=$	>245°	1083
H	C_6H_5	H	NH_2	—	1560
H	C_6H_5	H	$C_6H_5CH{=}N$	152°	1560
C_6H_5	H		$4\text{-}(C_2H_5)_2NC_6H_4N=$	165°	519
C_6H_5	H		$2\text{-}CH_3\text{-}4\text{-}(C_2H_5)_2NC_6H_3N=$	134°	244
C_6H_5	H	H	$C_6H_5NHN{=}CHCHN—$ | CH₃ (on N) | $COOC_2H_5$ (on CH)	224°	1537
H	C_6H_5		$C_2H_5ON=$	153°	1560
H	C_6H_5		$CH_3COON=$	82°	1560
H	C_6H_5		$C_6H_5COON=$	142°	1560
C_6H_5	H	H	C_6H_5CONH	198°	319
C_6H_5	H	H	$C_6H_5CH_2CONH$	173°	1102
C_6H_5	$C_6H_5CON—$ | C_2H_5	H	H	111°	595
H	C_6H_5		$4\text{-}(C_2H_5)_2NC_6H_5N=$	192°	519
H	C_6H_5		$2\text{-}CH_3\text{-}4\text{-}(C_2H_5)_2NC_6H_3N=$	209°	244
C_6H_5	CH_3	H	NH_2	—	809, 996
C_6H_5	CH_3	H	$HOOCCH_2NH—$	—	525
C_6H_5	CH_3	H	C_2H_5OOCNH	—	525
C_6H_5	CH_3	H	C_6H_5CONH	183°	52
C_6H_5	CH_3	H	N_2	—	1144
C_6H_5	CH_3	H	C_6H_5NH	198°	1107
C_6H_5	CH_3		$4\text{-}(CH_3)_2NC_6H_4N=$	158°, 187°	519, 1242
C_6H_5	CH_3		$4\text{-}(C_2H_5N)C_6H_4N=$ | CH_3	102°	519

C_6H_5	CH_3		$4\text{-}(C_2H_5)_2NC_6H_4N{=}$		117°	494, 519
C_6H_5	CH_3		$4\text{-}(C_4H_9)_2NC_6H_4N{=}$		90°	519
C_6H_5	CH_3		$4\text{-}(HOCH_2CH_2N)C_6H_4N{=}$ C_2H_5		45°	519
C_6H_5	CH_3		CH_3 CH_3 $4\text{-}(NCCHN)C_6H_4N{=}$		190°	1244
C_6H_5	CH_3		CH_3 CH_3 $4\text{-}(H_2NOCCHN)C_6H_4N{=}$		159°	1244
C_6H_5	CH_3		$4\text{-}CH_3\text{-}2\text{-}(C_2H_5)_2NC_6H_3N{=}$		124°	1538
C_6H_5	CH_3		$2\text{-}CH_3\text{-}4\text{-}(C_2H_5)_2NC_6H_3N{=}$		129°	244, 519, 1255
C_6H_5	CH_3	H		$C_6H_5CH{=}N$	186°	809
C_6H_5	CH_3	H		$2\text{-}NO_2C_6H_5CH{=}N$	198°	633
C_6H_5	CH_3	H		$C_6H_5CH{=}CHCH{=}N$	192°	633
C_6H_5	CH_3		N= N C_2H_5		185°	1072
C_6H_5	CH_3		CH_3 CH_3 =CHN= N CH_3		185° (dec.)	240

(Table continued)

TABLE XXII (*continued*)

R^1	R^2	R^3	R^4	M.p.	Reference
C_6H_5	CH_3		O; N; C_2H_5; =CHN=	214° (dec.)	240
C_6H_5	CH_3		S; N; CH_3; =CHN=	237° (dec.)	240
C_6H_5	CH_3		S; N; C_2H_5; =CHN=	256° (dec.)	240
C_6H_5	CH_3		CHN=; C_2H_5—N; S	279° (dec.)	240

C_6H_5	CH_3		3-ethylbenzoxazol-2-ylidene $=CHN=$ (benzoxazoline ring: O, N–C_2H_5)		220° (dec.)	240
C_6H_5	CH_3		4-methyl-3-ethylthiazol-2-ylidene $=CHN=$ (ring: S, N–C_2H_5, CH_3)		186° (dec.)	240
C_6H_5	CH_3		3-ethylbenzoselenazol-2-ylidene $=CHN=$ (ring: Se, N–C_2H_5)		225° (dec.)	240
C_6H_5	CH_3		$C_6H_5N(CH_3)$—$N=$		—	52
C_6H_5	CH_3	H		C_6H_5CONH	183°	52
C_6H_5	CH_3	H		iso-C_4H_9CONH	—	536
C_6H_5	CH_3	H		$(CH_3)_2CCHBrCONH$	—	536
CH_3	C_6H_5	H		NH_2	>175° (HCl salt)	992
CH_3	C_6H_5		4-$(C_2H_5)_2NC_6H_4N=$		96°	519
CH_3	C_6H_5	H		2-$HOC_6H_4CH{=}N$	230° (dec.)	992
CH_3	C_6H_5	H		4-$CH_3OC_6H_4CH{=}N$	220° (dec.)	992
CH_3	C_6H_5	H		4-$NO_2C_6H_4CH{=}N$	250° (dec.)	992

(Table continued)

TABLE XXII (*continued*)

R^1	R^2	R^3	R^4	M.p.	Reference
CH_3	C_6H_5	H	O —CH=N	180°	992
C_6H_5	t-C_4H_9		2-CH_3-4-$(C_2H_5)_2NC_6H_3N=$	131°	244
C_6H_5	$C_{15}H_{31}$		2-CH_3-4-$(C_2H_5)_2NC_6H_3N=$	44°	244
C_6H_5	$HOCH_2$	H	NH_2	201° (HCl)	397
C_6H_5	$H_5C_2OOCH_2$		2-CH_3-4-$(C_2H_5)_2NC_6H_3N=$	96°	244
3-$CH_3C_6H_4$	CH_3		CH_3 CH_3 =CHN= N CH_3	203° (dec.)	240
4-$CH_3C_6H_4$	CH_3		CH_3 CH_3 =CHN= N CH_3	246° (dec.)	240
3-$NH_2C_6H_4$	CH_3		$(C_2H_5)_2N$—$C_6H_4N=$	—	494
4-$NH_2C_6H_4$	CH_3		$(C_2H_5)_2N$—$C_6H_4N=$	144°	494, 519
4-$NH_2C_6H_4$	CH_3		2-CH_3-4-$(C_2H_5)_2NC_6H_3N=$	189°	244
2-ClC_6H_4	CH_3		2-CH_3-4-$(C_2H_5)_2NC_6H_3N=$	148°	244
4-ClC_6H_4	CH_3		2-CH_3-4-$(C_2H_5)_2NC_6H_3N=$	169°	244
3-BrC_6H_4	CH_3		4-$(C_2H_5)_2NC_6H_4N=$	118°	519

4-BrC_6H_4	CH_3		4-$(C_2H_5)_2NC_6H_4N$=	139°	519
4-$NO_2C_6H_4$	CH_3		4-$(C_2H_5)_2NC_6H_4N$=	163°	519
4-$NO_2C_6H_4$	CH_3		2-CH_3-4-$(C_2H_5)_2NC_6H_3N$=	189°	244
4-$HOOCC_6H_4$	CH_3		2-CH_3-4-$(C_2H_5)_2NC_6H_3N$=	243°	244
3-$HOOCC_6H_4$	$C_{17}H_{35}$		4-$(C_2H_5)_2NC_6H_4N$=	73°	519
4-$HOOCC_6H_4$	$C_{17}H_{35}$		4-$(C_2H_5)_2NC_6H_4N$=	135°	519
4-NCC_6H_4	CH_3		2-CH_3-4-$(C_2H_5)_2NC_6H_3N$=	201°	244
3-$HO_3SC_6H_4$	CH_3		4-$(C_2H_5)_2NC_6H_4N$=	280°	519
4-$KO_3SC_6H_4$	CH_3		4-$(C_2H_5)_2NC_6H_4N$=	—	494
3-$HO_3SC_6H_4$	$C_{17}H_{35}$		4-$(C_2H_5)_2NC_6H_4N$=	180°	519
4-$HO_3SC_6H_4$	$C_{17}H_{35}$		4-$(C_2H_5)_2NC_6H_4N$=	150°	519
4-$NH_2O_2SC_6H_4$	CH_3		4-$(C_2H_5)_2NC_6H_4N$=	213°	519
4-$NH_2O_2SC_6H_4$	CH_3	H	4-$(C_2H_5)NC_6H_4NH$	215°	695
4-$NH_2O_2SC_6H_4$	CH_3		2-CH_3-4-$(C_2H_5)_2NC_6H_3N$=	229° (dec.)	244
2,4-$Cl_2C_6H_3$	CH_3		2-CH_3-4-$(C_2H_5)_2NC_6H_3N$=	141°	244
2,4-$(NO_2)_2C_6H_3$	CH_3	H	CH_3CONH	201°	11
3-HO_3S-4-$(C_6H_4O)C_6H_3$	$C_{17}H_{35}$		4-$(C_2H_5)_2NC_6H_4N$=	100°	519
2,4,6-$Cl_3C_6H_2$	CH_3		2-CH_3-4-$(C_2H_5)_2NC_6H_3N$=	176°	244
1-$C_{10}H_7$	CH_3		4-$(C_2H_5)_2NC_6H_4N$=	—	494
N	CH_3		2-CH_3-4-$(C_2H_5)_2NC_6H_3N$=	200°	244
N	CH_3		2-CH_3-4-$(C_2H_5)_2NC_6H_3N$=	153°	244
S, N	CH_3		4-$(C_2H_5)_2NC_6H_4N$=	218°	519

(Table continued)

TABLE XXII (*continued*)

R^1	R^3	R^3	R^4	M.p.	Reference
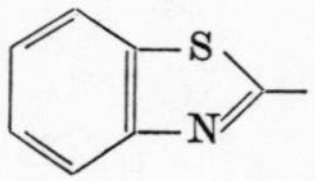 S N	CH_3		$2\text{-}CH_3\text{-}4\text{-}(C_2H_5)_2NC_6H_4N=$	204°	244
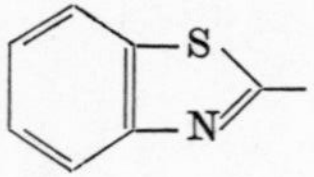 S N	CH_3		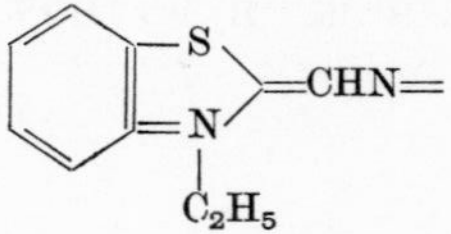 S N =CHN= C_2H_5	> 300°	240
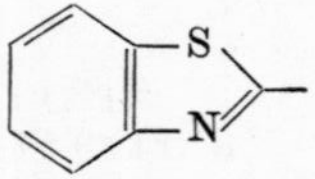 S N	CH_3		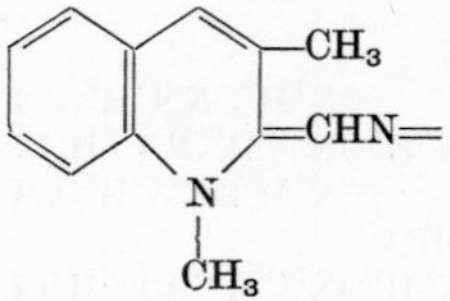 CH_3 =CHN= N CH_3	278° (dec.)	240
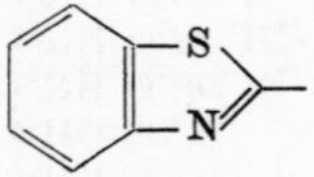 S N	CH_3		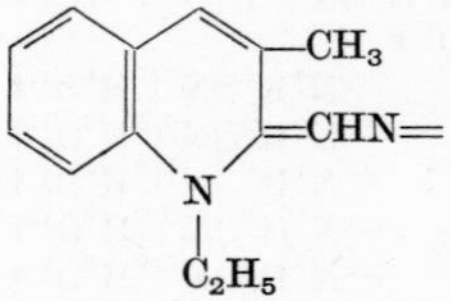 CH_3 =CHN= N C_2H_5	270° (dec.)	240
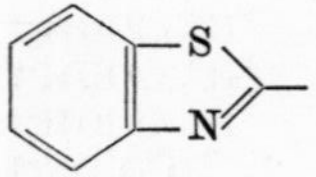 S N	CH_3		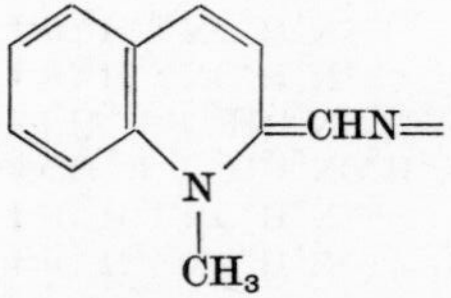 =CHN= N CH_3	> 300°	240

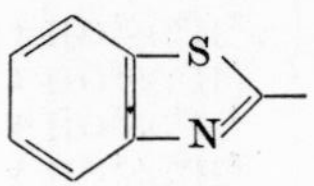 S N	CH_3	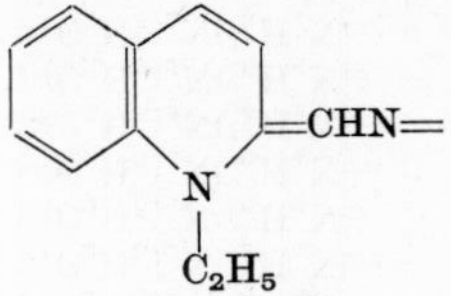 =CHN= N C_2H_5	> 300°	240
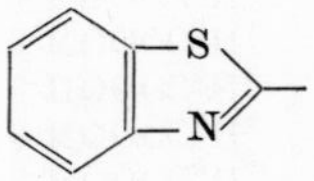 S N	CH_3	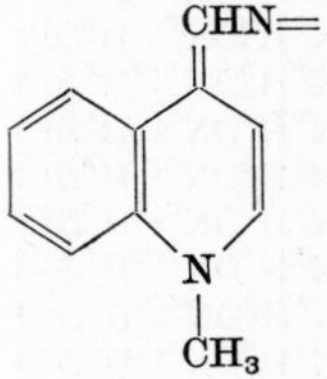 CHN= N CH_3	303° (dec.)	240
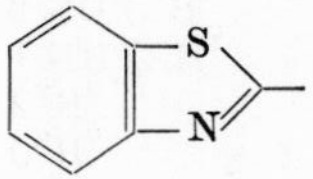 S N	CH_3	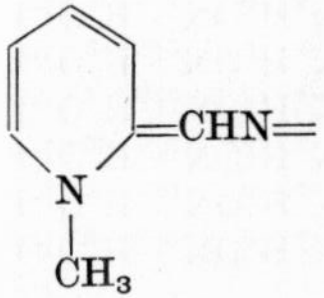 =CHN= N CH_3	303° (dec.)	240
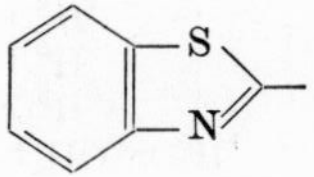 S N	CH_3	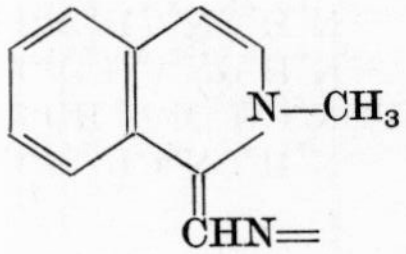 N—CH_3 CHN=	261° (dec.)	240
C_6H_5	CH_3	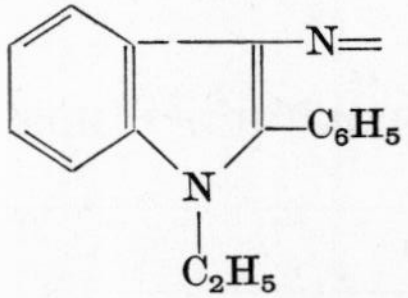 N= C_6H_5 N C_2H_5	207°	943

(Table continued)

TABLE XXII *(continued)*

R^1	R^2	R^3	R^4	M.p.	Reference
C_6H_5	2-furyl		$2\text{-}CH_3\text{-}4\text{-}(C_2H_5)_2NC_6H_3N{=}$	191°	244
$4\text{-}HO_3SC_6H_4$	$4\text{-}NO_2C_6H_4CH_2$		$4\text{-}(C_2H_5)_2NC_6H_4N{=}$	> 350°	519
C_6H_5	C_6H_5		$2\text{-}CH_3\text{-}4\text{-}(C_2H_5)_2NC_6H_3N{=}$	166°	244
C_6H_5	C_6H_5		$4\text{-}(C_2H_5)_2NC_6H_4N{=}$	136°	519
C_6H_5	$2\text{-}CH_3C_6H_4$		$4\text{-}(C_2H_5)_2NC_6H_4N{=}$	129°	519
C_6H_5	$2\text{-}HOC_6H_4$	H	CH_3CONH	172°	670
C_6H_5	$3\text{-}NH_2C_6H_4$		$4\text{-}(C_2H_5)_2NC_6H_4N{=}$	169°	519
C_6H_5	$4\text{-}NH_2C_6H_4$		$4\text{-}(C_2H_5)_2NC_6H_4N{=}$	163°	519
C_6H_5	$3\text{-}NO_2C_6H_4$		$4\text{-}(C_2H_5)_2NC_6H_4N{=}$	170°	519
C_6H_5	$4\text{-}NO_2C_6H_4$		$4\text{-}(C_2H_5)_2NC_6H_4N{=}$	168°	519
$4\text{-}NH_2C_6H_4$	C_6H_5		$4\text{-}(C_2H_5)_2NC_6H_4N{=}$	—	494
$3\text{-}NO_2C_6H_4$	$4\text{-}NO_2C_6H_4$		$4\text{-}(C_2H_5)_2NC_6H_4N{=}$	—	494
$4\text{-}NO_2C_6H_4$	C_6H_5		$4\text{-}(C_2H_5)_2NC_6H_4N{=}$	—	494
$3\text{-}HOOCC_6H_4$	$3\text{-}C_{17}H_{35}CONHC_6H_4$		$4\text{-}(C_2H_5)_2NC_6H_4N{=}$	145°	519
$3\text{-}HOOCC_6H_4$	$4\text{-}C_{17}H_{35}CONHC_6H_4$		$4\text{-}(C_2H_5)_2NC_6H_4N{=}$	213°	519
$3\text{-}HOOCC_6H_4$	$3\text{-}NO_2C_6H_4$		$4\text{-}(C_2H_5)_2NC_6H_4N{=}$	254°	519
$3\text{-}HOOCC_6H_4$	$4\text{-}NO_2C_6H_4$		$4\text{-}(C_2H_5)_2NC_6H_4N{=}$	> 350°	519
$3\text{-}KOOCC_6H_4$	$4\text{-}NO_2C_6H_4$		$4\text{-}(C_2H_5)_2NC_6H_4N{=}$	—	494
$4\text{-}KOOCC_6H_4$	C_6H_5		$4\text{-}(C_2H_5)_2NC_6H_4N{=}$	—	494
$4\text{-}KOOCC_6H_4$	$4\text{-}NO_2C_6H_4$		$4\text{-}(C_2H_5)_2NC_6H_4N{=}$	—	494
$3\text{-}HO_3SC_6H_4$	$3\text{-}C_{17}H_{35}CONHC_6H_4$		$4\text{-}(C_2H_5)_2NC_6H_4N{=}$	193°	519
$3\text{-}HO_3SC_6H_4$	$4\text{-}C_{17}H_{35}CONHC_6H_4$		$4\text{-}(C_2H_5)_2NC_6H_4N{=}$	> 350°	519
$3\text{-}HO_3SC_6H_4$	$3\text{-}NO_2C_6H_4$		$4\text{-}(C_2H_5)_2NC_6H_4N{=}$	245°	519
$4\text{-}HO_3SC_6H_4$	C_6H_5		$4\text{-}(C_2H_5)_2NC_6H_4N{=}$	219°	519
$4\text{-}HO_3SC_6H_4$	$3\text{-}NH_2C_6H_4$		$4\text{-}(C_2H_5)_2NC_6H_4N{=}$	> 350°	519
$4\text{-}HO_3SC_6H_4$	$4\text{-}NH_2C_6H_4$		$4\text{-}(C_2H_5)_2NC_6H_4N{=}$	> 300°	519
$4\text{-}HO_3SC_6H_4$	$3\text{-}C_{17}H_{35}CONHC_6H_4$		$4\text{-}(C_2H_5)_2NC_6H_4N{=}$	224°	519

$4\text{-}HO_3SC_6H_4$	$4\text{-}C_{17}H_{35}CONHC_6H_4$		$4\text{-}(C_2H_5)_2NC_6H_4N{=}$		>350°	519
$4\text{-}HO_3SC_6H_4$	$3\text{-}NO_2C_6H_4$		$4\text{-}(C_2H_5)_2NC_6H_4N{=}$		275°	519
$4\text{-}HO_3SC_6H_4$	$4\text{-}NO_2C_6H_4$		$4\text{-}(C_2H_5)_2NC_6H_4N{=}$		>250°	519
$4\text{-}NH_2O_2SC_6H_4$	C_6H_5	H		$4\text{-}(C_2H_5)_2NC_6H_4NH$	225°	695
$2\text{-}C_{10}H_7$	C_6H_5		$4\text{-}(C_2H_5)_2NC_6H_4N{=}$		—	494
$2\text{-}C_{10}H_7$	$4\text{-}NO_2C_6H_4$		$4\text{-}(C_2H_5)_2NC_6H_4N{=}$		—	494
C_6H_5	CH_3	CH_3		$(CH_3)_2N$	96°	938
C_6H_5	$C_6H_5CH{=}N$		$4\text{-}(C_2H_5)_2NC_6H_4N{=}$		152°	519
C_6H_5	CH_3	CH_3OOCCH_2NH		CH_3OOCNH	—	525
CH_3CO	CH_3		$4\text{-}(C_2H_5)_2NC_6H_4N{=}$		119°	519
CH_3CO	C_6H_5		$4\text{-}(C_2H_5)_2NC_6H_4N{=}$		113°	519

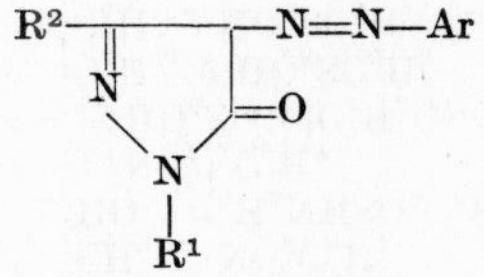

TABLE XXIII. 4-Arylazo-2-pyrazolin-5-ones

Section A. Alkyl and Aralkyl Substituents

R^1	R^2	Ar	M.p.	Reference
H	H	C_6H_5	196°	813
H	H	$4\text{-}CH_3C_6H_4$	223° (dec.)	813, 1548, 1553
H	H	$2\text{-}Cl\text{-}4\text{-}H_5C_2NHSO_2\text{-}6\text{-}NO_2C_6H_2$	—	963
H	CH_3	C_6H_5	197°	255, 257, 262, 263, 264, 1553

(Table continued)

TABLE XXIII, Section A (*continued*)

R^1	R^2	Ar	M.p.	Reference
H	CH_3	$2\text{-}CH_3C_6H_5$	223°	263, 264
H	CH_3	$3\text{-}CH_3C_6H_4$	190°	262, 263, 264
H	CH_3	$4\text{-}CH_3C_6H_4$	234°	263, 264
H	CH_3	$4\text{-}NO_2C_6H_4$	267° (dec.)	262, 263
H	CH_3	$2\text{-}HOOCC_6H_4$	>280°	263, 264
H	CH_3	$2\text{-}H_2O_3AsC_6H_4$	268°	314
H	CH_3	$3\text{-}H_2O_3AsC_6H_4$	>250°	314
H	CH_3	$4\text{-}H_2O_3AsC_6H_4$	>250°	314
H	CH_3	$2\text{-}CH_3\text{-}X\text{-}NO_2C_6H_3$	223° (dec.)	260
H	CH_3	$3\text{-}CH_3\text{-}4\text{-}NO_2C_6H_3$	—	262
H	CH_3	$4\text{-}CH_3\text{-}X\text{-}NO_2C_6H_3$	235°	260
H	CH_3	$2\text{-}HO\text{-}5\text{-}C_6H_5NHSO_2C_6H_3$	—	1457
H	CH_3	$2,4\text{-}(NO_2)_2C_6H_3$	277°	263
H	CH_3	$2\text{-}(2\text{-}HO_3S\text{-}4\text{-}ClC_6H_3O)\text{-}5\text{-}ClC_6H_3$	—	582
H	CH_3	$4\text{-}C_6H_{11}\text{-}2\text{-}HO_3SC_6H_3$	—	582
H	CH_3	$4\text{-}C_6H_5\text{-}2\text{-}HO_3SC_6H_3$	—	582
H	CH_3	$2\text{-}NO_2\text{-}4\text{-}C_2H_5NHSO_2C_6H_3$	—	963
H	CH_3	$2\text{-}NO_2\text{-}4\text{-}H_2O_3AsC_6H_3$	>250°	314
H	CH_3	$2\text{-}HO\text{-}3\text{-}Cl\text{-}5\text{-}NO_2C_6H_2$	—	865
H	CH_3	$2\text{-}HO\text{-}4\text{-}NO_2\text{-}5\text{-}ClC_6H_2$	—	865
H	CH_3	$1\text{-}C_{10}H_7$	247°	263, 264
H	CH_3	$2\text{-}C_{10}H_7$	238°	263, 264
H	CH_3	[anthraquinonyl structure]	—	1251
H	$H_5C_2OOCCH_2$	$4\text{-}CH_3C_6H_4$	172°	866

H	CH_3	C_6H_5	188°	1560
(This is 3,4-dimethyl-4-phenylazo-2-pyrazolin-5-one)				
C_4H_9	CH_3	2-NO_2-4-$CH_3C_6H_3$	—	206
C_4H_9	CH_3	2-HO-4-$NH_2O_2SC_6H_3$	—	206
C_4H_9	CH_3	2-HO-4-$CH_3NHO_2SC_6H_3$	—	228, 1681
C_4H_9	CH_3	2-HO-3-HO_3S-5-$NO_2C_6H_2$	—	206
C_4H_9	CH_3	2-HO-4-$NO_2C_6H_3$	—	253
C_4H_9	CH_3	2-HO-5-$CH_3O_2SC_6H_3$	—	253
C_4H_9	CH_3	2-HO-4-$H_2NO_2SC_6H_3$	—	253
C_4H_9	CH_3	2-HO-5-$H_2NO_2SC_6H_3$	—	253
C_5H_{11}	CH_3	2-HO-4-$H_2NO_2SC_6H_3$	—	253
C_5H_{11}	CH_3	2-HO-5-$H_2NO_2SC_6H_3$	—	253
C_6H_{13}	CH_3	2-HO-5-$H_2NO_2SC_6H_3$	—	253, 1463
C_8H_{17}	CH_3	2-HO-5-$H_2NO_2SC_6H_3$	—	253, 1459
C_8H_{17}	CH_3	2-HO-4-H_2NO_2S-6-$NO_2C_6H_2$	—	253
C_8H_{17}	CH_3	2-HO-3-NO_2-5-$H_2NO_2SC_6H_2$	—	253, 1463
$C_{12}H_{25}$	CH_3	4-$HO_3SC_6H_4$	—	206
$C_{12}H_{25}$	CH_3	2,5-$(HO_3S)_2C_6H_3$	—	206
$C_{12}H_{25}$	CH_3	4,8-$(HO_3S)_2$-2-$C_{10}H_5$	—	206
$C_2H_5OCH_2CH_2OOCCH_2CH_2$	CH_3	2-$CH_3C_6H_4$	83°	1118
$C_4H_9OCH_2CH_2OOCCH_2CH_2$	CH_3	2-$CH_3C_6H_4$	—	1118
$HOOCCH_2CH_2$	CH_3	2-$NO_2C_6H_4$	—	1118
$C_2H_5OOCCH_2CH_2$	CH_3	2-$NO_2C_6H_4$	112°	1118
iso-$C_3H_7OOCCH_2CH_2$	CH_3	2-$NO_2C_6H_4$	101°	1118
$C_4H_9OOCCH_2CH_2$	CH_3	2-$CH_3C_6H_4$	59°	1118
$C_4H_9OOCCH_2CH_2$	CH_3	2-$NO_2C_6H_4$	96°	1118
iso-$C_4H_9OOCCH_2CH_2$	CH_3	2-$NO_2C_6H_4$	85°	1118
iso-$C_7H_{15}OOCCH_2CH_2$	CH_3	2-$NO_2C_6H_4$	70°	1118
$CH_3CHOOCCH_2CH_2$ (with iso-C_5H_{11} attached to the CH)	CH_3	2-$NO_2C_6H_4$	112°	1118
iso-$C_8H_{17}OOCCH_2CH_2$	CH_3	2-$NO_2C_6H_4$	54°	1118
$HOCH_2CH_2OOCCH_2CH_2$	CH_3	2-$NO_2C_6H_4$	92°	1118
$C_2H_5OCH_2CH_2OOCCH_2CH_2$	CH_3	2-$NO_2C_6H_4$	120°	1118

(Table continued)

TABLE XXIII, Section A (*continued*)

R^1	R^2	Ar	M.p.	Reference
$C_4H_9OCH_2CH_2OOCCH_2CH_2$	CH_3	$2\text{-}NO_2C_6H_4$	60°	1118
$HOCH_2CH_2OCH_2CH_2OOCCH_2CH_2$	CH_3	$2\text{-}NO_2C_6H_4$	107°	1118
$CH_3CH(OH)CH_2OOCCH_2CH_2$	CH_3	$2\text{-}NO_2C_6H_4$	115°	1118
$HOCH_2CH(Cl)CH_2OOCCH_2CH_2$	CH_3	$2\text{-}NO_2C_6H_4$	135°	1118
(cyclohexene ring)$-OOCCH_2CH_2$, ring CH_3	CH_3	$2\text{-}NO_2C_6H_4$	97°	1118
(cyclohexane ring)$-OOCCH_2CH_2$, ring CH_3	CH_3	$2\text{-}NO_2C_6H_4$	122°	1118
$t\text{-}C_4H_9-$(cyclohexane ring)$-OOCCH_2CH_2$	CH_3	$2\text{-}NO_2C_6H_4$	150°	1118
(cyclohexane ring)$-OOCCH_2CH_2$, ring OH	CH_3	$2\text{-}NO_2C_6H_4$	125°	1118
(tetrahydrofuran ring, O)$-CH_2OOCCH_2CH_2$	CH_3	$2\text{-}NO_2C_6H_4$	110°	1118

$CNCH_2CH_2$	CH_3	$2\text{-}NO_2C_6H_4$	—	1118
$HOOCCH$ | CH_3	CH_3	$2\text{-}NO_2C_6H_4$	—	1118
C_4H_9OOCCH | CH_3	CH_3	$2\text{-}NO_2C_6H_4$	80°	1118
$C_4H_9OOCCH_2CH_2$	CH_3	$2\text{-}CH_3\text{-}3\text{—}ClC_6H_3$	59°	1118
$C_4H_9OOCCH_2CH_2$	CH_3	$2\text{-}NO_2\text{-}4\text{-}Cl\text{—}C_6H_3$	132°	1118
$C_6H_5CH_2$	CH_3	$4\text{-}CH_3C_6H_4$	123°	333

TABLE XXIII (*continued*)

Section B. Alkyl, Aryl, and Heterocyclic Substituents

R^1	R^2	Ar	M.p.	Reference
C_6H_5	H	C_6H_5	150°	283, 352
H	C_6H_5	C_6H_5	208°	992, 1552, 1553
C_6H_5	H	$4\text{-}CH_3C_6H_4$	149°	1550
H	C_6H_5	$2\text{-}CH_3C_6H_4$	179°	1552
H	C_6H_5	$4\text{-}CH_3C_6H_4$	185°	1552
H	C_6H_5	$1\text{-}C_{10}H_7$	216°	1552
H	C_6H_5	$2\text{-}C_{10}H_7$	250°	1552
C_6H_5	H	$4\text{-}ClC_6H_4$	—	782
C_6H_5	H	$3\text{-}NO_2C_6H_4$	—	782
C_6H_5	H	$4\text{-}NO_2C_6H_4$	—	782

(*Table continued*)

TABLE XXIII, Section B (*continued*)

R^1	R^2	Ar	M.p.	Reference
C_6H_5	H	4-$HO_3SC_6H_4$	—	782
C_6H_5	H	2-NO_2-4-$CH_3C_6H_3$	—	782
C_6H_5	H	2-NO_2-4-(t-C_6H_9)C_6H_3	—	782
C_6H_5	H	2-HO-5-$HO_3SC_6H_3$	—	782
C_6H_5	H	2-HOOC-4-$HO_3SC_6H_3$	—	782
C_6H_5	H	2-HOOC-5-$HO_3SC_6H_3$	—	782
C_6H_5	H	2-HO-3-HO_3S-5-ClC_6H_2	—	782
C_6H_5	H	2-HO-3-NO_2-5-$HO_3SC_6H_2$	—	782
C_6H_5	H	2-HO-3-HO_3S-5-$NO_2C_6H_2$	—	782
C_6H_5	H	1-$C_{10}H_7$	—	782
C_6H_5	H	2-$C_{10}H_7$	—	782
C_6H_5	H	6-HO_3S-2-$C_{10}H_6$	—	782
C_6H_5	H	2-HO-6-HO_3S-1-$C_{10}H_5$	—	782
C_6H_5	H	5,7-$(HO_3S)_2$-2-$C_{10}H_5$	—	782
C_6H_5	H	3,6-$(NaO_3S)_2$-2-$C_{10}H_5$	—	782
C_6H_5	H	2-HO-4-HO_3S-6-NO_2-1-$C_{10}H_4$	—	782
4-$NO_2C_6H_4$	H	2-HO-3-HO_3S-5-ClC_6H_2	—	782
4-$HO_3SC_6H_4$	H	2-HOC_6H_4	—	782
4-$HO_3SC_6H_4$	H	4-$NO_2C_6H_4$	—	782
4-$HO_3SC_6H_4$	H	2-$HOOCC_6H_4$	—	782
4-$HO_3SC_6H_4$	H	4-$HO_3SC_6H_4$	—	782
4-$HO_3SC_6H_4$	H	2-HO-5-ClC_6H_3	—	782
4-$HO_3SC_6H_4$	H	2-HO-5-$NO_2C_6H_3$	—	782
4-$HO_3SC_6H_4$	H	2-HO-5-$HO_3SC_6H_3$	—	782
4-$HO_3SC_6H_4$	H	2-HOOC-4-$HO_3SC_6H_3$	—	782
4-$HO_3SC_6H_4$	H	2-HO-3-HO_3S-5-ClC_6H_2	—	782
4-$HO_3SC_6H_4$	H	2-HO-3-HO_3S-5-$NO_2C_6H_2$	—	782
4-$HO_3SC_6H_4$	H	2-HO-4-HO_3S-1-$C_{10}H_5$	—	782
4-$HO_3SC_6H_4$	H	1-HO-4-HO_3S-2-$C_{10}H_5$	—	782
4-$HO_3SC_6H_4$	H	2-HO-4-HO_3S-6-NO_2-1-$C_{10}H_4$	—	782
2,4,5-$Cl_3C_6H_2$	H	2,4,5-$Cl_3C_6H_2$	308° (dec.)	285

C_6H_5	CH_3	C_6H_5	155°	52, 99, 255, 257, 258, 262, 372, 591, 809, 1096, 1185, 1351, 1513
CH_3	C_6H_5	C_6H_5	158°	992
C_6H_5	CH_3	2-$CH_3C_6H_4$	185°	263, 278, 327
C_6H_5	CH_3	3-$CH_3C_6H_4$	116°, 141°, 167°	263, 278, 327
C_6H_5	CH_3	4-$CH_3C_6H_4$	137°	263, 327
C_6H_5	CH_3	2-$CH_3OC_6H_4$	109°, 168°	278, 327
C_6H_5	CH_3	4-$CH_3OC_6H_4$	136°	278, 327, 1255
C_6H_5	CH_3	2-$C_2H_5OC_6H_4$	150°	278, 1040
C_6H_5	CH_3	4-$C_2H_5OC_6H_4$	159°	278
C_6H_5	CH_3	4-$HC{\equiv}CCH_2OC_6H_4$	—	1172
C_6H_5	CH_3	2-$C_6H_5OC_6H_4$	89°	327, 1040
C_6H_5	CH_3	4-$C_6H_5OC_6H_4$	136°	327
C_6H_5	CH_3	4-$CH_3CONHC_6H_4$	139°	327
C_6H_5	CH_3	4-$C_6H_5CONHC_6H_4$	139°	327
C_6H_5	CH_3	4-(4-$CH_3OC_6H_4$)N(SO_3H)—C_6H_4	—	178
C_6H_5	CH_3	4-($C_6H_5CH_2CH_2NHCONH$)C_6H_4	235°	468
C_6H_5	CH_3	4-[2,4-$(NO_2)C_6H_3NH$]C_6H_4	283°	1302
C_6H_5	CH_3	4-(Cl^- $CH_3N^+(CH_3){=}C(N(CH_3)CH_3)SCH_2CON(C_6H_{11})$—)$C_6H_4$	—	724
C_6H_5	CH_3	2-ClC_6H_4	195°	268, 278
C_6H_5	CH_3	3-ClC_6H_4	144°	278

(Table continued)

TABLE XXIII, Section B (*continued*)

R^1	R^2	Ar	M.p.	Reference
C_6H_5	CH_3	$4\text{-}ClC_6H_4$	140°	278, 327
C_6H_5	CH_3	$4\text{-}BrC_6H_4$	151°	278, 327
C_6H_5	CH_3	$2\text{-}NO_2C_6H_4$	209°	278, 327
C_6H_5	CH_3	$3\text{-}NO_2C_6H_4$	183°	278, 327
C_6H_5	CH_3	$4\text{-}NO_2C_6H_4$	198°	263, 278, 732
C_6H_5	CH_3	$4\text{-}CH_3COC_6H_4$	136°	327
C_6H_5	CH_3	$4\text{-}CH_3C(=NOH)C_6H_4$	187°	327
C_6H_5	CH_3	$4\text{-}CH_3C(=NNHC_6H_5)C_6H_4$	148°	327
C_6H_5	CH_3	$4\text{-}CH_3C(=NNHCONH_2)C_6H_4$	260°	327
C_6H_5	CH_3	$2\text{-}(C_6H_5SO_2NHOC)C_6H_4$	—	864
C_6H_5	CH_3	$4\text{-}(4\text{-}NO_2C_6H_4SO_2)C_6H_4$	240°	1677
C_6H_5	CH_3	$3\text{-}NaO_3SC_6H_4$	—	280
C_6H_5	CH_3	$4\text{-}NaO_3SC_6H_4$	—	280
C_6H_5	CH_3	$4\text{-}ClO_2SC_6H_4$	150°	1591
C_6H_5	CH_3	$4\text{-}H_2NO_2SC_6H_4$	247°	1591
C_6H_5	CH_3	$4\text{-}CH_3NHO_2SC_6H_4$	192°	1591
C_6H_5	CH_3	$4\text{-}(C_2H_5)_2NO_2SC_6H_4$	154°	1591
C_6H_5	CH_3	$4\text{-}C_6H_5NHO_2SC_6H_4$	243°	1591
C_6H_5	CH_3	4-([ring]NO_2S)C_6H_4	—	1591
C_6H_5	CH_3	$4\text{-}(4\text{-}H_2N\text{—}C_6H_4\text{—}SO_2NHSO_2)C_6H_4$	255°	1591

C_6H_5	CH_3	2-$(C_6H_5CONHO_2S)C_6H_4$	—	864
C_6H_5	CH_3	2,4-$(CH_3)_2C_6H_3$	159°	327
C_6H_5	CH_3	2,5-$(CH_3)_2C_6H_3$	131°	327
C_6H_5	CH_3	3-CH_3-4-$NaO_3SC_6H_3$	—	280
C_6H_5	CH_3	2-HO-5-$NO_2C_6H_3$	—	1462
C_6H_5	CH_3	2-HO-4-$CH_3O_2SC_6H_3$	—	1461
C_6H_5	CH_3	2-HO-5-$CH_3O_2SC_6H_3$	—	211, 1446, 1461
C_6H_5	CH_3	2-HO-5-$C_2H_5O_2SC_6H_3$	—	211
C_6H_5	CH_3	2-HO-5-$C_3H_7O_2SC_6H_3$	—	219
C_6H_5	CH_3	2-HO-4-$CH_2{=}CHO_2SC_6H_3$	—	650
C_6H_5	CH_3	2-HO-5-$C_6H_5CH_2O_2SC_6H_3$	—	225
C_6H_5	CH_3	2-HO-4-$HOCH_2CH_2O_2SC_6H_3$	—	650
C_6H_5	CH_3	2-HO-5-$HOCH_2CH_2O_2SC_6H_3$	—	648
C_6H_5	CH_3	2-HO-5-$HO_3SOCH_2CH_2O_2SC_6H_3$	—	649
C_6H_5	CH_3	2-HO-4-$H_2NO_2SC_6H_3$	—	374
C_6H_5	CH_3	2-HO-5-$H_2NO_2SC_6H_3$	—	211
C_6H_5	CH_3	2-HO-4-$CH_3HNO_2SC_6H_3$	—	228, 1681
C_6H_5	CH_3	2,5-$Cl_2C_6H_3$	224°	278
C_6H_5	CH_3	3-NaO_3S-4-ClC_6H_3	—	280
C_6H_5	CH_3	2-NO_2-4-ClC_6H_3	295°	278
C_6H_5	CH_3	2-Cl-5-(2,4,5-$Cl_3C_6H_4O_2SNHO_2S)C_6H_3$	—	180
C_6H_5	CH_3	2-CH_3-4-ClC_6H_3	214°	278
C_6H_5	CH_3	2-CH_3-5-ClC_6H_3	177°	278
C_6H_5	CH_3	2,4-$(NO_2)_2C_6H_3$	> 300°	263
C_6H_5	CH_3	2-HOOC-4-$NO_2C_6H_3$	285°	263
C_6H_5	CH_3	2-HOOC-5-$CH_3NHO_2SC_6H_3$	—	1462
C_6H_5	CH_3	2-HOOC-4-(2-$HOOCC_6H_4O_3S)C_6H_3$	—	203
C_6H_5	CH_3	2-NaOOC-5-ClC_6H_3	—	625
C_6H_5	CH_3	2-$Ca_{1/2}OOC$-5-ClC_6H_3	—	625
C_6H_5	CH_3	2-$Sr_{1/2}OOC$-5-ClC_6H_3	—	625
C_6H_5	CH_3	2-Cl-5-(4-$ClC_6H_4O_2SNHO_2S)C_6H_3$	—	180
C_6H_5	CH_3	2-HO-5-$(H_2NO_2SCH_2CH_2NSO_2)C_6H_3$	—	142
		$\vert$ CH_3		

(*Table continued*)

TABLE XXIII, Section B (*continued*)

R^1	R^2	Ar	M.p.	Reference
C_6H_5	CH_3	3,4-$(CH_3)_2$-2-$HO_3SC_6H_2$	—	523
C_6H_5	CH_3	3-NO_2-4-CH_3-5-$HO_3SC_6H_2$	—	123
C_6H_5	CH_3	2-HO-4-HS-5-ClC_6H_2	—	879
C_6H_5	CH_3	2-HO-4-NO_2-5-$CH_3O_2SC_6H_2$	—	1445
C_6H_5	CH_3	2-HO-3-HO_3S-5-ClC_6H_2	—	1444
C_6H_5	CH_3	2-HO-3-H_2NO_2S-5-$NO_2C_6H_2$	—	214
C_6H_5	CH_3	2,5-$(C_2H_5O)_2$-4-$C_6H_5CONHC_6H_2$	254°	885
C_6H_5	CH_3	2-C_6H_5COO-3-HO_3S-5-$NO_2C_6H_2$	—	442
C_6H_5	CH_3	2-C_6H_5COO-3-HO_3S-5-ClC_6H_2	—	442
C_6H_5	CH_3	2-C_6H_5COO-3-HOOC-4-$HO_3SC_6H_2$	—	442
C_6H_5	CH_3	2-(4-$NO_2C_6H_5COO$)-3-HO_3S-5-$NO_2C_6H_2$	—	442
C_6H_5	CH_3	2-HO-3-HO_3S-5-[2,2,4-$(CH_3)_3C_5H_8$]C_6H_2	—	1386
C_6H_5	CH_3	2-HO-3,6-Cl_2-5-HO_3SC_6H	—	276
C_6H_5	CH_3	2-HO-3,5-Cl_2-4-HSC_6H	—	879
C_6H_5	CH_3	1-$C_{10}H_7$	202°	263, 278, 327
C_6H_5	CH_3	2-$C_{10}H_7$	186°	263, 278, 327
C_6H_5	CH_3	2-NO_2-1-$C_{10}H_6$	138°	327
C_6H_5	CH_3	4-NO_2-1-$C_{10}H_6$	125°	327
C_6H_5	CH_3	1-NaO_3S-2-$C_{10}H_6$	—	280
C_6H_5	CH_3	2-C_3H_7COO-4-HO_3S-1-$C_{10}H_5$	—	442
C_6H_5	CH_3	2-C_6H_5COO-4-$HO_3SC_{10}H_5$	—	442
C_6H_5	CH_3	2-HO-4-HO_3S-6-CH_3O-1-$C_{10}H_5$	—	189, 1616
C_6H_5	CH_3	2-HO-4-HO_3S-1-$C_{10}H_5$	—	441, 1618
C_6H_5	CH_3	2-C_6H_5COO-4-HO_3S-6-NO_2-1-$C_{10}H_4$	—	442
C_6H_5	CH_3	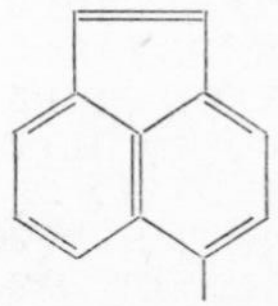	146°	327

11*

C_6H_5	CH_3	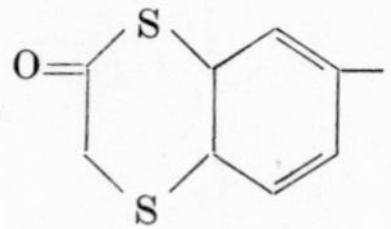	272°	936
C_6H_5	CH_3	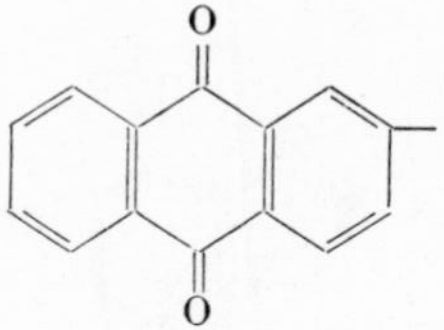	247°	1009
C_6H_5	CH_3	1-C_6H_5-3-CH_3-4-pyrazolyl	220° (dec.)	995
C_6H_5	CH_3	1-C_6H_5-5-Cl-4-pyrazolyl	143°	974
C_6H_5	CH_3	4-[2,5-$(CH_3)_2$-3,4-$(H_5C_2OOC)_2$-1-pyrollyl]C_6H_4	154°	261
C_6H_5	CH_3	5-Tetrazolyl	201°	256
C_6H_5	CH_3	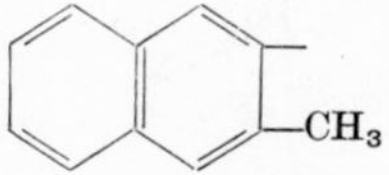	228° (dec.)	1629
C_6H_5	CH_3	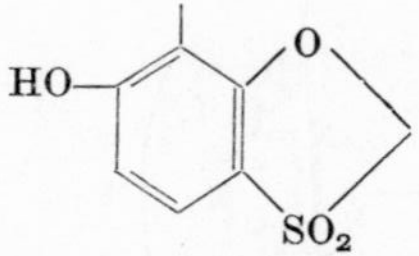	—	375
C_6H_5	CH_3	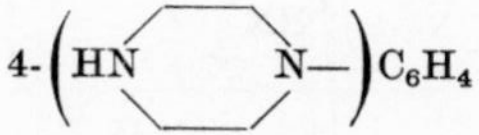 4-(HN N—)C_6H_4	—	834, 1146

(Table continued)

TABLE XXIII, Section B (*continued*)

R^1	R^2	Ar	M.p.	Reference
C_6H_5	CH_3	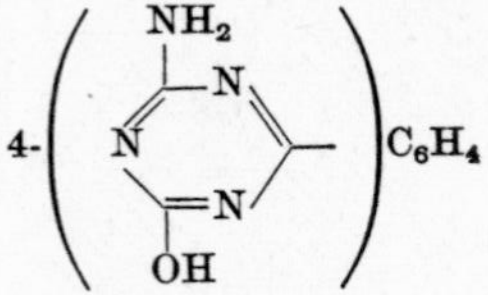 4-(NH_2, N, N, N, OH triazine ring)C_6H_4	—	1493
C_6H_5	CH_3	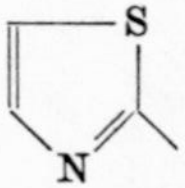 (S, N ring)	160°	281
C_6H_5	CH_3	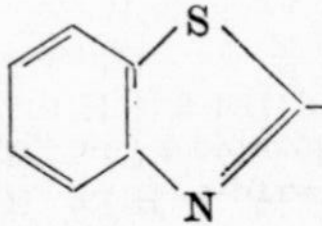 (S, N fused ring)	205°	281
C_6H_5	CH_3	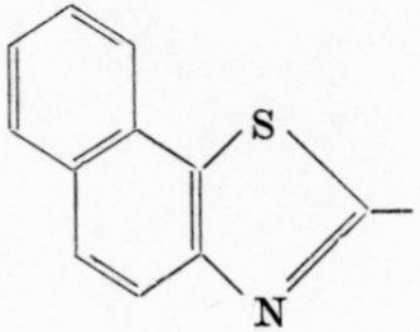 (S, N fused ring)	215°	281
C_6H_5	CH_3	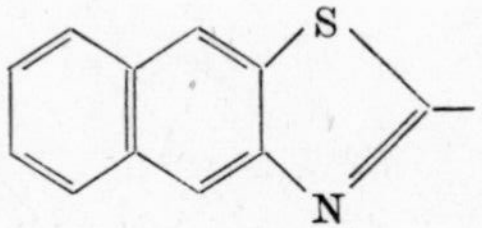 (S, N fused ring)	248°	281

C_6H_5	C_3H_7	C_6H_5	133°	1535
C_6H_5	C_4H_9	C_6H_5	119°	1576
C_6H_5	$C_{15}H_{31}$	4-$CH_3CONHC_6H_4$	—	403
C_6H_5	3-$HOCH_2$	C_6H_5	155°	397
C_6H_5	3-CH_3COOCH_2	C_6H_5	131°	397
C_6H_5	3-$HOCH_2$	4-ClC_6H_4	186°	397
C_6H_5	3-$HOCH_2CH(OH)CH(OH)$—	C_6H_5	210°	627
$HOOCCH_2CH_2$	C_6H_5	2-CH_3-3-ClC_6H_5	—	1118
$H_9C_4OOCCH_2CH_2$	C_6H_5	2-CH_3-3-ClC_6H_3	73°	1118
2-$CH_3C_6H_4$	CH_3	2-$NaOOCCH_2CH_2COOCH_2CH_2SO_2C_6H_4$	—	1398
2-$CH_3C_6H_4$	CH_3	2-$NaOOCCH{=}CHCOOCH_2CH_2SO_2C_6H_4$	—	1398
2-$CH_3C_6H_4$	CH_3	$HO_3SOCH_2CH_2SO_2C_6H_4$	—	1398
2-$CH_3C_6H_4$	$HOCH_2$	2-$CH_3C_6H_4$	149°	397
2-$CH_3C_6H_4$	CH_3	2-HOOC-4-$[(CH_3)_2CHNHSO_2]C_6H_3$	—	1462
2-$CH_3C_6H_4$	CH_3	2-HOOC-4-$C_4H_9NHSO_2C_6H_3$	—	1462
2-$CH_3C_6H_4$	CH_3	2-HOOC-4-$C_6H_5NHSO_2C_6H_3$	—	1462
4-$CH_3C_6H_4$	CH_3	4-$CH_3C_6H_4$	216°	987
4-$CH_3C_6H_4$	CH_3	2-NaOOC-5-ClC_6H_3	—	625
4-$CH_3C_6H_4$	CH_3	2-$Ca_{1/2}$OOC-5-ClC_6H_3	—	625
4-$CH_3C_6H_4$	CH_3	2-$Sr_{1/2}$OOC-5-ClC_6H_3	—	625
4-$CH_3C_6H_4$	CH_3	3-(4-$ClC_6H_4SO_2NHSO_2)C_6H_4$	—	180
4-$CH_3C_6H_4$	CH_3	2-HOOC-4-$CH_3NHSO_2C_6H_3$	—	1458, 1462
4-t-$C_4H_9C_6H_4$	CH_3	2-HO-5-$NO_2C_6H_3$	—	1383
4-$CH_3OC_6H_4$	$H_5C_2OOCCH{=}CHCH{=}CH$	2,4-$(NO_2)_2C_6H_3$	258°	125
4-(t-$C_4H_9C_6H_4O)C_6H_4$	CH_3	4-HOC_6H_4	185°	403, 575
4-(4-$ClC_6H_4O)C_6H_4$	CH_3	2-HO-3-NO_2-5-$HO_3SC_6H_2$	—	79
3-$NH_2C_6H_4$	CH_3	3-ClC_6H_4	—	878
3-$NH_2C_6H_4$	CH_3	2-CH_3-4-ClC_6H_3	—	878
3-$NH_2C_6H_4$	CH_3	2-CH_3O-5-ClC_6H_3	—	877, 878
3-$NH_2C_6H_4$	CH_3	2-F_3C-4-ClC_6H_3	—	878
3-$NH_2C_6H_4$	CH_3	1-$C_{10}H_7$	—	878
4-$NH_2C_6H_4$	CH_3	2-HO-5-(4-$HO_3SC_6H_4NHCO)C_6H_3$	—	209
4-$NH_2C_6H_4$	CH_3	3-ClC_6H_4	—	878

(*Table continued*)

TABLE XXIII, Section B (*continued*)

R^1	R^2	Ar	M.p.	Reference
$4-NH_2C_6H_4$	CH_3	$2-HOOC-4-HO_3SC_6H_3$	—	226
$3-C_6H_5SO_2NHC_6H_5$	CH_3	$4-HO_3S-2-C_{10}H_6$	—	467
$4-(4-HOOCC_6H_4SO_2NH)C_6H_4$	CH_3	$2,3,5-Cl_3-6-HOOCC_6H$	—	160
$3-(2-HO-1-C_{10}H_6CONH)C_6H_4$	CH_3	$2-CH_3O-5-ClC_6H_3$	262°	877
$3-(2-HO-1-C_{10}H_6CONH)C_6H_4$	CH_3	$2-CH_3O-4-ClC_6H_3$	277°	877
$3-(2-HO-1-C_{10}H_6CONH)C_6H_4$	CH_3	$2-CH_3-4-ClC_6H_3$	260°	877
$4-(2-HO-1-C_{10}H_6CONH)C_6H_4$	CH_3	$2-CH_3-4-ClC_6H_3$	283°	877
$3-(2-HO-1-C_{10}H_6CONH)C_6H_4$	CH_3	$2-CF_3-4-ClC_6H_3$	262°	877
$4-(2-HO-1-C_{10}H_6CONH)C_6H_4$	CH_3	$3-ClC_6H_4$	260°	877
$3-(2-HO-1-C_{10}H_6CONH)C_6H_4$	CH_3	$1-C_{10}H_7$	226°	877
$4-CH_3OC_6H_4$	CH_3	$2-HO-5-ClC_6H_3$	—	1456
$4-CH_3OC_6H_4$	CH_3	$2-HO-4-H_2NO_2SC_6H_3$	—	1456
$4-C_2H_5OC_6H_4$	CH_3	$2-HO-4-H_2NO_2SC_6H_3$	—	1456
$4-C_2H_5OC_6H_4$	CH_3	$2-HO-5-H_2NO_2SC_6H_3$	—	1456
$2-ClC_6H_4$	CH_3	$2-ClC_6H_4$	212°	296
$2-ClC_6H_4$	CH_3	$4-HOOCCH_2CH_2COOCH_2CH_2SO_2C_6H_4$	—	1034
$2-ClC_6H_4$	CH_3	$4-NaOOCCH_2CH_2COOCH_2CH_2SO_2C_6H_4$	—	1398
$2-ClC_6H_4$	CH_3	$4-NaOOCH{=}CHCOOCH_2CH_2SO_2C_6H_4$	—	1398
$2-ClC_6H_4$	CH_3	$4-HO_3SOCH_2CH_2SO_2C_6H_4$	—	1398
$2-ClC_6H_4$	CH_3	$2-HO-5-H_5C_2SO_2C_6H_3$	—	1455
$2-ClC_6H_4$	CH_3	$2-C_6H_5COO-4-HO_3S-1-C_{10}C_5$	—	442
$2-ClC_6H_4$	$HOCH_2$	$2-ClC_6H_4$	203° (dec.)	397
$3-ClC_6H_4$	CH_3	$2-H_{21}C_{10}OOCC_6H_4$	—	217
$3-ClC_6H_4$	CH_3	$2-(3,4-Cl_2C_6H_3SO_2NHSO_2)C_6H_4$	—	180
$3-ClC_6H_4$	CH_3	$2-(2,4,5-Cl_3C_6H_2SO_2NHSO_2)C_6H_4$	—	180
$3-ClC_6H_4$	CH_3	$2-(4-ClC_6H_4SO_2NHSO_2)-5-ClC_6H_3$	—	180
$3-ClC_6H_4$	CH_3	$2-(1-C_{10}H_7SO_2NHSO_2)C_6H_4$	—	180
$3-ClC_6H_4$	CH_3	$2-(2-C_{10}H_7SO_2NHSO_2)C_6H_4$	—	180
$3-ClC_6H_4$	CH_3	$2-(2-CH_3-5-iso-C_3H_7C_6H_3SO_2NHSO_2)C_6H_4$	—	180
$3-ClC_6H_4$	CH_3	$2-(5-CH_3-2-iso-C_3H_7C_6H_3SO_2NHSO_2)C_6H_4$	—	180
$3-ClC_6H_4$	CH_3	$2-(5,6,7,8-H_4-1-C_{10}H_7SO_2NHSO_2)C_6H_4$	—	180

$3\text{-ClC}_6\text{H}_4$	CH_3	$2\text{-(5,6,7,8-H}_4\text{-2-C}_{10}\text{H}_7\text{SO}_2\text{NHSO}_2\text{)C}_6\text{H}_4$	—	180
$3\text{-ClC}_6\text{H}_4$	CH_3	$3\text{-(1-C}_{10}\text{H}_7\text{SO}_2\text{NHSO}_2\text{)-4-CH}_3\text{C}_6\text{H}_3$	—	180
$3\text{-ClC}_6\text{H}_4$	CH_3	$3\text{-(2,4-Cl}_2\text{C}_6\text{H}_3\text{SO}_2\text{NHSO}_2\text{)-4-CH}_3\text{C}_6\text{H}_3$	—	180
$3\text{-ClC}_6\text{H}_4$	CH_3	$3\text{-(2,5-Cl}_2\text{C}_6\text{H}_3\text{SO}_2\text{NHSO}_2\text{)C}_6\text{H}_4$	—	180
$3\text{-ClC}_6\text{H}_4$	CH_3	$2\text{-(C}_6\text{H}_5\text{SO}_2\text{NHSO}_2\text{)-5-ClC}_6\text{H}_3$	—	180
$3\text{-ClC}_6\text{H}_4$	CH_3	$2\text{-(2,5-Cl}_2\text{C}_6\text{H}_3\text{SO}_2\text{NHSO}_2\text{)-5-ClC}_6\text{H}_3$	—	180
$3\text{-ClC}_6\text{H}_4$	CH_3	$3\text{-(2,4,5-Cl}_3\text{C}_6\text{H}_2\text{SO}_2\text{NHSO}_2\text{)C}_6\text{H}_4$	—	180
$3\text{-ClC}_6\text{H}_4$	CH_3	$3\text{-(4,5-Cl}_2\text{C}_6\text{H}_3\text{SO}_2\text{NHSO}_2\text{)-4-ClC}_6\text{H}_3$	—	180
$3\text{-ClC}_6\text{H}_4$	CH_3	$2\text{-(2,4-Cl}_2\text{C}_6\text{H}_3\text{SO}_2\text{NHSO}_2\text{)-5-ClC}_6\text{H}_3$	—	180
$3\text{-ClC}_6\text{H}_4$	CH_3	$3\text{-(5,6,7,8-H}_4\text{-1-C}_{10}\text{H}_7\text{SO}_2\text{NHSO}_2\text{)C}_6\text{H}_4$	—	180
$3\text{-ClC}_6\text{H}_4$	CH_3	$3\text{-(5,6,7,8-H}_4\text{-2-C}_{10}\text{H}_7\text{SO}_2\text{NHSO}_2\text{)C}_6\text{H}_4$	—	180
$3\text{-ClC}_6\text{H}_4$	CH_3	$2\text{-(5,6,7,8-H}_4\text{-1-C}_{10}\text{H}_7\text{SO}_2\text{NHSO}_2\text{)-5-ClC}_6\text{H}_3$	—	180
$3\text{-ClC}_6\text{H}_4$	CH_3	$2\text{-(5,6,7,8-H}_4\text{-2-C}_{10}\text{H}_7\text{SO}_2\text{NHSO}_2\text{)-5-ClC}_6\text{H}_3$	—	180
$3\text{-ClC}_6\text{H}_4$	CH_3	$2\text{-(3,4-Cl}_2\text{C}_6\text{H}_3\text{SO}_2\text{NHSO}_2\text{)-5-ClC}_6\text{H}_3$	—	180
$3\text{-ClC}_6\text{H}_4$	CH_3	$2\text{-(1-C}_{10}\text{H}_7\text{SO}_2\text{NHSO}_2\text{)-5-ClC}_6\text{H}_3$	—	180
$3\text{-ClC}_6\text{H}_4$	CH_3	$2\text{-(4-ClC}_6\text{H}_4\text{SO}_2\text{NHSO}_2\text{)-5-ClC}_6\text{H}_3$	—	180
$3\text{-ClC}_6\text{H}_4$	CH_3	$2\text{-(4-BrC}_6\text{H}_4\text{SO}_2\text{NHSO}_2\text{)-5-ClC}_6\text{H}_3$	—	180
$3\text{-ClC}_6\text{H}_4$	CH_3	$2\text{-(4-CH}_3\text{OC}_6\text{H}_4\text{SO}_2\text{NHSO}_2\text{)-5-ClC}_6\text{H}_3$	—	180
$3\text{-ClC}_6\text{H}_4$	CH_3	$2\text{-(4-CH}_3\text{CONHC}_6\text{H}_4\text{SO}_2\text{NHSO}_2\text{)-5-ClC}_6\text{H}_3$	—	180
$3\text{-ClC}_6\text{H}_4$	CH_3	$3\text{-(C}_6\text{H}_5\text{CH}_2\text{SO}_2\text{NHSO}_2\text{)C}_6\text{H}_4$	—	180
$3\text{-ClC}_6\text{H}_4$	CH_3	$3\text{-(4-ClC}_6\text{H}_4\text{CH}_2\text{SO}_2\text{NHSO}_2\text{)C}_6\text{H}_4$	—	180
$3\text{-ClC}_6\text{H}_4$	CH_3	$3\text{-(4-BrC}_6\text{H}_4\text{CH}_2\text{SO}_2\text{NHSO}_2\text{)C}_6\text{H}_4$	—	180
$3\text{-ClC}_6\text{H}_4$	CH_3	$2\text{-(3,4-Cl}_2\text{C}_6\text{H}_3\text{SO}_2\text{NHSO}_2\text{)-5-(4-ClC}_6\text{H}_5\text{O)C}_6\text{H}_3$	—	180
$3\text{-ClC}_6\text{H}_4$	CH_3	$2\text{-(3,4-Cl}_2\text{C}_6\text{H}_3\text{SO}_2\text{NHSO}_2\text{)-5-(4-C}_6\text{H}_5\text{O)C}_6\text{H}_3$	—	180
$3\text{-ClC}_6\text{H}_4$	CH_3	$2\text{-(4-ClC}_6\text{H}_4\text{SO}_2\text{NHSO}_2\text{)-5-(2-CH}_3\text{OC}_6\text{H}_4\text{O)C}_6\text{H}_3$	—	180
$3\text{-ClC}_6\text{H}_4$	CH_3	$4\text{-(4-ClC}_6\text{H}_4\text{SO}_2\text{NHSO}_2\text{)C}_6\text{H}_4$	—	180
$3\text{-ClC}_6\text{H}_4$	CH_3	$4\text{-(C}_6\text{H}_5\text{CH}_2\text{SO}_2\text{NHSO}_2\text{)C}_6\text{H}_4$	—	180
$3\text{-ClC}_6\text{H}_4$	CH_3	$2,4\text{-Cl}_2\text{C}_6\text{H}_3$	190°	296
$3\text{-ClC}_6\text{H}_4$	CH_3	$2\text{-HOOC-4-H}_2\text{NO}_2\text{SC}_6\text{H}_3$	—	208
$3\text{-ClC}_6\text{H}_4$	CH_3	$2\text{-HO-5-CH}_3\text{SO}_2\text{C}_6\text{H}_3$	—	211, 1446
$3\text{-ClC}_6\text{H}_4$	CH_3	$2\text{-HO-4-CH}_2\text{=CHO}_2\text{SC}_6\text{H}_3$	—	650
$3\text{-ClC}_6\text{H}_4$	CH_3	$2\text{-HO-5-NO}_2\text{C}_6\text{H}_3$	—	211
$3\text{-ClC}_6\text{H}_4$	CH_3	$2\text{-HO-4-HOCH}_2\text{CH}_2\text{NHO}_2\text{SC}_6\text{H}_3$	—	211
$3\text{-ClC}_6\text{H}_4$	CH_3	$2\text{-HO-5-CH}_3\text{NHO}_2\text{SC}_6\text{H}_3$	—	1460, 1461

(Table continued)

TABLE XXIII, Section B (*continued*)

R^1	R^2	Ar	M.p.	Reference
3-ClC_6H_4	CH_3	2-HO-4-$(C_2H_5)_2NO_2SC_6H_3$	—	211
3-ClC_6H_4	CH_3	2-HO-3-CH_3CONH-5-$CH_3O_2SC_6H_2$	—	211
3-ClC_6H_4	CH_3	2-HO-5-$C_2H_5O_2SC_6H_3$	—	219
3-ClC_6H_4	CH_3	2-HO-5-$ClCH_2O_2SC_6H_3$	—	223
3-ClC_6H_4	CH_3	2-HOOC-5-$ClCH_2O_2SC_6H_3$	—	223
3-ClC_6H_4	CH_3	2-HO-4-NO_2-5-$CH_3SO_2C_6H_2$	—	1445
3-ClC_6H_4	CH_3	2-HO-3-NO_2-5-$ClCH_2O_2SC_6H_2$	—	223
4-ClC_6H_4	CH_3	4-ClC_6H_4	232°	296
4-ClC_6H_4	CH_3	2-HO-5-$CH_3HNO_2SC_6H_3$	—	225, 1460, 1681
4-ClC_6H_4	CH_3	2-HO-4-$CH_3HNO_2SC_6H_3$	—	228
4-ClC_6H_4	CH_3	2-HO-5-$CH_3O_2SC_6H_3$	—	254
4-BrC_6H_4	CH_3	4-BrC_6H_4	229°	446
4-BrC_6H_4	CH_3	2-(2-CH_3-5-iso-$C_3H_7C_6H_3SO_2NHSO_2)C_6H_4$	—	180
4-BrC_6H_4	CH_3	2-(5-CH_3-2-iso-$C_3H_7C_6H_3SO_2NHSO_2)C_6H_4$	—	180
4-BrC_6H_4	CH_3	2-(1-$C_{10}H_7SO_2NHSO_2)C_6H_4$	—	180
4-BrC_6H_4	CH_3	2-(2-$C_{10}H_7SO_2NHSO_2)C_6H_4$	—	180
4-BrC_6H_4	CH_3	2-(5,6,7,8-H_4-1-$C_{10}H_7SO_2NHSO_2)C_6H_4$	—	180
4-BrC_6H_4	CH_3	2-(5,6,7,8-H_4-2-$C_{10}H_7SO_2NHSO_2)C_6H_4$	—	180
4-BrC_6H_4	$H_5C_2OOCHC{=}CH$	2,4-$(NO_2)C_6H_3$	237°	125
4-BrC_6H_4	$H_5C_2OOCHC{=}CHCH{=}CH$	2,4-$(NO_2)C_6H_3$	264°	125
3-$NO_2C_6H_4$	CH_3	2-HO-5-ClC_6H_3	—	1456
3-$NO_2C_6H_4$	CH_3	2-HO-5-$H_2NO_2SC_6H_3$	—	1453, 1456
4-$NO_2C_6H_4$	CH_3	C_6H_5	242°	690, 732
4-$NO_2C_6H_4$	CH_3	2-ClC_6H_4	—	268
4-$NO_2C_6H_4$	CH_3	4-$NO_2C_6H_4$	297°	732
4-$NO_2C_6H_4$	CH_3	2,5-$Cl_2C_6H_3$	259°	591
4-$NO_2C_6H_4$	CH_3	2-HO-5-ClC_6H_3	—	1456
4-$NO_2C_6H_4$	CH_3	2-HO-4-$H_2NO_2SC_6H_3$	—	1456
4-$NO_2C_6H_4$	CH_3	2-Cl-5-(3,4-$Cl_2C_6H_3SO_2NHSO_2)C_6H_3$	—	180
2-$HOOCC_6H_4$	CH_3	C_6H_5	205°	1004

3-HOOCC$_6$H$_4$	CH$_3$	C$_6$H$_5$	245°	980
4-HOOCC$_6$H$_4$	CH$_3$	C$_6$H$_5$	277°	980
4-HOOCC$_6$H$_4$	CH$_3$	4-H$_2$NO$_2$SC$_6$H$_4$	291°	356
4-CH$_3$O$_2$SC$_6$H$_4$	CH$_3$	2-HO-5-NO$_2$C$_6$H$_3$	—	1461
3-CH$_2$═CHO$_2$SC$_6$H$_4$	CH$_3$	4-HO$_3$SC$_6$H$_4$	—	651
4-CH$_2$═CHO$_2$SC$_6$H$_4$	CH$_3$	2-HO$_3$SC$_6$H$_4$	—	651
4-CH$_2$═CHO$_2$SC$_6$H$_4$	CH$_3$	2-CH$_3$O-5-HO$_3$SOCH$_2$CH$_2$O$_2$SC$_6$H$_4$	—	651
4-HOCH$_2$CH$_2$O$_2$SC$_6$H$_4$	CH$_3$	2-HOOCC$_6$H$_4$	—	651
4-HOCH$_2$CH$_2$O$_2$SC$_6$H$_4$	CH$_3$	2-HO-4-HOCH$_2$CH$_2$O$_2$SC$_6$H$_3$	—	648
4-HOCH$_2$CH$_2$O$_2$SC$_6$H$_4$	CH$_3$	2-HO-3,5-(NO$_2$)$_2$C$_6$H$_2$	—	651
4-HO$_3$SOCH$_2$CH$_2$O$_2$SC$_6$H$_4$	CH$_3$	2-HOOCC$_6$H$_4$	—	651
4-HO$_3$SOCH$_2$CH$_2$O$_2$SC$_6$H$_4$	CH$_3$	2-HO-3,5-(NO$_2$)$_2$C$_6$H$_2$	—	651
2-HO$_3$SC$_6$H$_4$	CH$_3$	C$_6$H$_5$	—	1293
3-HO$_3$SC$_6$H$_4$	CH$_3$	2-HO-5-CH$_3$COC$_6$H$_3$	—	1619
3-HO$_3$SC$_6$H$_4$	CH$_3$	2-(C$_6$H$_5$SO$_2$HNOC)C$_6$H$_4$	—	864
3-HO$_3$SC$_6$H$_4$	CH$_3$	2-(C$_6$H$_5$COHNO$_2$S)C$_6$H$_4$	—	864
3-HO$_3$SC$_6$H$_4$	CH$_3$	3-(C$_6$H$_5$COHNO$_2$S)C$_6$H$_4$	—	864
3-HO$_3$SC$_6$H$_4$	CH$_3$	2-HO-5-CH$_3$NHO$_2$SC$_6$H$_3$	—	1460
3-HO$_3$SC$_6$H$_4$	CH$_3$	2-HOOC-4-(4-*t*-C$_6$H$_{11}$C$_6$H$_4$O$_3$S)C$_6$H$_3$	—	203
3-HO$_3$SC$_6$H$_4$	CH$_3$	2-HO-4-HO$_3$S-6-CH$_3$O-1-C$_{10}$H$_4$	—	189
3-HO$_3$SC$_6$H$_4$	CH$_3$	2-CH$_3$O-4-HO$_3$S-6-CH$_3$O-1-C$_{10}$H$_4$	—	189
3-HO$_3$SC$_6$H$_4$	CH$_3$	2,6-(CH$_3$O)$_2$-4-HO$_3$S-1-C$_{10}$H$_4$	—	1616
3-H$_2$NO$_2$SC$_6$H$_4$	CH$_3$	2-Cl-5-(3,4-Cl$_2$C$_6$H$_3$SO$_2$NHSO$_2$)C$_6$H$_3$	—	180
3-H$_2$NO$_2$SC$_6$H$_4$	CH$_3$	2-HOOC-4-C$_6$H$_5$NHO$_2$SC$_6$H$_3$	—	195, 1617
3-H$_2$NO$_2$SC$_6$H$_4$	CH$_3$	2-HOOC-4-iso-C$_3$H$_7$NHO$_2$SC$_6$H$_3$	—	195
3-H$_2$NO$_2$SC$_6$H$_4$	CH$_3$	2-HO-3-Cl-5-NO$_2$C$_6$H$_2$	—	207
3-H$_2$NO$_2$SC$_6$H$_4$	CH$_3$	2-HO-5-ClC$_6$H$_3$	—	1680
3-H$_2$NO$_2$SC$_6$H$_4$	CH$_3$	2-HO-3-Cl-5-NO$_2$C$_6$H$_2$	—	1680
3-H$_2$NO$_2$SC$_6$H$_4$	CH$_3$	2-HO-4-NO$_2$C$_6$H$_3$	—	1444
3-H$_2$NO$_2$SC$_6$H$_4$	CH$_3$	2-HOOC-4-C$_6$H$_5$NO$_2$SC$_6$H$_3$ │ CH$_3$	—	1617
3-H$_2$NO$_2$SC$_6$H$_4$	CH$_3$	2-HOOC-4-C$_6$H$_5$NHO$_2$SC$_6$H$_4$	—	1617
3-C$_6$H$_5$NHO$_2$SC$_6$H$_4$	CH$_3$	2-HO-4-NO$_2$C$_6$H$_3$	—	1444

(Table continued)

TABLE XXIII, Section B (*continued*)

R^1	R^2	Ar	M.p.	Reference
$4\text{-}HO_3SC_6H_4$	CH_3	$2\text{-}HOOCC_6H_4$	—	217, 935
$4\text{-}HO_3SC_6H_4$	CH_3	$4\text{-}H_2NO_2SC_6H_4$	> 320°	356
$4\text{-}HO_3SC_6H_4$	CH_3	$3\text{-}C_{17}H_{35}CONHSO_2C_6H_4$	—	173
$4\text{-}HO_3SC_6H_4$	CH_3	$2\text{-}C_8H_{17}OOCC_6H_4$	—	217
$4\text{-}HO_3SC_6H_4$	CH_3	$3\text{-}C_{12}H_{25}NHSO_2C_6H_4$	—	1620
$4\text{-}HO_3SC_6H_4$	CH_3	$2\text{-}HO\text{-}5\text{-}NO_2C_6H_3$	—	475
$4\text{-}HO_3SC_6H_4$	CH_3	$3\text{-}C_{12}H_{14}NHSO_2\text{-}4\text{-}CH_3C_6H_3$	—	1620
$4\text{-}HO_3SC_6H_4$	CH_3	$2\text{-}HOOC\text{-}4\text{-}H_2NC_6H_3$	—	746
$4\text{-}HO_3SC_6H_4$	CH_3	$2\text{-}HO_3S\text{-}4,5\text{-}(CH_3)_2C_6H_2$	—	523
$4\text{-}HO_3SC_6H_4$	CH_3	$2\text{-}HO\text{-}3\text{-}NO_2\text{-}5\text{-}(t\text{-}C_5H_{11})C_6H_2$	—	1392
$4\text{-}HO_3SC_6H_4$	CH_3	$2\text{-}HO\text{-}3\text{-}Cl\text{-}5\text{-}NO_2C_6H_2$	—	1421
$4\text{-}HO_3SC_6H_4$	CH_3	$2\text{-}C_6H_5COO\text{-}3\text{-}Cl\text{-}5\text{-}NO_2C_6H_2$	—	442
$4\text{-}HO_3SC_6H_4$	CH_3	$2\text{-}HO\text{-}1\text{-}C_{10}H_6$	—	1059
$4\text{-}HO_3SC_6H_4$	CH_3	$2\text{-}HO\text{-}4\text{-}HO_3S\text{-}6\text{-}CH_3O\text{-}1\text{-}C_{10}H_4$	—	1616
$4\text{-}HO_3SC_6H_4$	CH_3	$2\text{-}HO\text{-}3,6\text{-}(HO_3S)_2\text{-}1\text{-}C_{10}H_4$	—	1060
$4\text{-}HO_3SC_6H_4$	CH_3	$2\text{-}NH_2\text{-}3,6\text{-}(HO_3S)_2\text{-}1\text{-}C_{10}H_4$	—	1060
$4\text{-}NaO_3SC_6H_4$	CH_3	$2\text{-}C_2H_5OC_6H_4COCH(CN)\text{—}$	—	1062
$4\text{-}NaO_3SC_6H_4$	CH_3	C_6H_5	—	279, 913, 914
$4\text{-}NaO_3SC_6H_4$	CH_3	$2\text{-}NO_2C_6H_4$	—	279
$4\text{-}NaO_3SC_6H_4$	CH_3	$4\text{-}NO_2C_6H_4$	—	279
$4\text{-}NaO_3SC_6H_4$	CH_3	$2\text{-}CH_3\text{-}4\text{-}ClC_6H_3$	—	279
$4\text{-}NaO_3SC_6H_4$	CH_3	$2\text{-}CH_3\text{-}5\text{-}ClC_6H_3$	—	279
$4\text{-}NaO_3SC_6H_4$	CH_3	$2,5\text{-}Cl_2C_6H_3$	—	279
$4\text{-}NAO_3SC_6H_4$	CH_3	$2,3\text{-}(NH_2)_2\text{-}5\text{-}CH_3C_6H_2$	—	1062
$4\text{-}H_2NO_2SC_6H_4$	CH_3	$4\text{-}CH_3OC_6H_4$	270°	324
$4\text{-}H_2NO_2SC_6H_4$	CH_3	$4\text{-}C_2H_5OC_6H_4$	260°	324
$4\text{-}H_2NO_2SC_6H_4$	CH_3	$4\text{-}HOOCC_6H_4$	320°	324
$4\text{-}H_2NO_2SC_6H_4$	CH_3	$4\text{-}HO_3SC_6H_4$	—	324
$4\text{-}H_2NO_2SC_6H_4$	CH_3	$4\text{-}H_2NO_2SC_6H_4$	301°	324, 356

$4\text{-}H_2NO_2SC_6H_4$	CH_3	CH_3— N	211°	1629
$2\text{-}(2\text{-}HOOCC_6H_4CO)C_6H_4$	CH_3	$2\text{-}HOOCC_6H_4$	—	160
$2\text{-}CH_3\text{-}4\text{-}HO_3SOCH_2CH_2C_6H_4$	CH_3	$2\text{-}F_3C\text{-}4\text{-}ClC_6H_4$	—	651
$4\text{-}CH_3\text{-}3\text{-}(CH_3)_2NO_2SC_6H_3$	CH_3	$2\text{-}HO\text{-}5\text{-}CH_3NHO_2SC_6H_3$	—	1460
$2\text{-}CH_3O\text{-}5\text{-}CH_2{=}CHO_2SC_6H_3$	CH_3	$2\text{-}HO_3S\text{-}4\text{-}ClC_6H_3$	—	651
$2\text{-}CH_3O\text{-}5\text{-}HOCH_2CH_2O_2SC_6H_3$	CH_3	$2\text{-}ClC_6H_4$	—	651
$2,4\text{-}Cl_2C_6H_3$	CH_3	C_6H_5	137°	296
$2,5\text{-}Cl_2C_6H_3$	CH_3	$2,4\text{-}(CH_3)_2C_6H_3$	—	1438
$2,5\text{-}Cl_2C_6H_3$	CH_3	$2\text{-}Cl\text{-}5\text{-}(C_6H_5SO_2NHSO_2)C_6H_3$	—	180
$3,4\text{-}Cl_2C_6H_3$	CH_3	$2\text{-}HO\text{-}5\text{-}HO_3SC_6H_3$	—	80
$3,4\text{-}Cl_2C_6H_3$	CH_3	$2\text{-}(2\text{-}CH_3\text{-}5\text{-}iso\text{-}C_3H_7C_6H_3SO_2NHSO_2)C_6H_4$	—	180
$3,4\text{-}Cl_2C_6H_3$	CH_3	$2\text{-}(5\text{-}CH_3\text{-}2\text{-}iso\text{-}C_3H_7C_6H_3SO_2NHSO_2)C_6H_3$	—	180
$3,4\text{-}Cl_2C_6H_3$	CH_3	$2\text{-}HOOC\text{-}4\text{-}H_2NO_2SC_6H_3$	—	208
$3,4\text{-}Cl_2C_6H_3$	CH_3	$2\text{-}HOOC\text{-}4\text{-}(2\text{-}HOC_2H_4NHO_2S)C_6H_3$	—	208
$3,4\text{-}Cl_2C_6H_3$	CH_3	$2\text{-}HO\text{-}3\text{-}NO_2\text{-}5\text{-}HO_3SC_6H_2$	—	80
$3,4\text{-}Cl_2C_6H_3$	CH_3	$2\text{-}HO\text{-}3\text{-}HO_3S\text{-}5\text{-}CH_3C_6H_2$	—	80
$3,4\text{-}Cl_2C_6H_3$	CH_3	$3\text{-}(4\text{-}CH_3C_6H_4SO_2NHSO_2)C_6H_4$	—	180
$3,4\text{-}Cl_2C_6H_3$	CH_3	$3\text{-}[X,Y\text{-}(CH_3)_2C_6H_3SO_2NHSO_2]C_6H_4$	—	180
$3,4\text{-}Cl_2C_6H_3$	CH_3	$3\text{-}(4\text{-}CH_3C_6H_4SO_2NHSO_2)\text{-}4\text{-}CH_3C_6H_3$	—	180
$3,4\text{-}Cl_2C_6H_3$	CH_3	$2\text{-}CH_3\text{-}5\text{-}(4\text{-}CH_3C_6H_4SO_2NHSO_2)C_6H_3$	—	180
$3,4\text{-}Cl_2C_6H_3$	CH_3	$2\text{-}Cl\text{-}5\text{-}(4\text{-}CH_3C_6H_4SO_2NHSO_2)C_6H_3$	—	180
$3,4\text{-}Cl_2C_6H_3$	CH_3	$2\text{-}CH_3\text{-}5\text{-}(C_6H_5SO_2NHSO_2)C_6H_3$	—	180
$3,4\text{-}Cl_2C_6H_3$	CH_3	$2\text{-}(1\text{-}C_{10}H_7SO_2NHSO_2)C_6H_4$	—	180
$3,4\text{-}Cl_2C_6H_3$	CH_3	$2\text{-}(2\text{-}C_{10}H_7SO_2NHSO_2)C_6H_4$	—	180
$3,4\text{-}Cl_2C_6H_3$	CH_3	$2\text{-}(5,6,7,8\text{-}H_4\text{-}1\text{-}C_{10}H_6SO_2NHSO_2)C_6H_4$	—	180
$3,4\text{-}Cl_2C_6H_3$	CH_3	$2\text{-}(5,6,7,8\text{-}H_4\text{-}2\text{-}C_{10}H_8SO_2NHSO_2)C_6H_4$	—	180
$2\text{-}Cl\text{-}5\text{-}HOCH_2CH_2O_2SC_6H_3$	CH_3	C_6H_5	—	651
$2\text{-}CH_3\text{-}4\text{-}HO_3SC_6H_3$	CH_3	$2\text{-}HO_3S\text{-}4,5\text{-}(CH_3)_2C_6H_3$	—	523
$3\text{-}HO_3S\text{-}4\text{-}(2\text{-}HO_3S\text{-}4\text{-}H_2NC_6H_3\text{-}CH{=}CH)C_6H_3$	CH_3	$2\text{-}HOOC\text{-}4\text{-}C_6H_5CONHC_6H_3$	—	176

(*Table continued*)

TABLE XXIII, Section B (*continued*)

R^1	R^2	Ar	M.p.	Reference
3-HOOC-4-HOC_6H_3	CH_3	2-HO_3S-4-(4-$H_2NC_6H_5$)C_6H_5	—	1361
3-HOOC-4-$C_6H_5OC_6H_3$	CH_3	2-HOOC-6-ClC_6H_3	—	160
2-Cl-5-$HO_3SC_6H_3$	CH_3	3-$CF_3C_6H_4$	—	1486
2-Cl-5-$HO_3SC_6H_3$	CH_3	2-$C_{10}H_{21}OOCC_6H_4$	—	217
2-Cl-5-$HO_3SC_6H_3$	CH_3	2-HO-4-$NH_2C_6H_3$	—	176
2-Cl-5-$HO_3SC_6H_3$	CH_3	2-HOOC-4-$NH_2C_6H_3$	—	176
2-Cl-5-$HO_3SC_6H_3$	CH_3	3-$C_{12}H_{25}CONHSO_2$-4-$CH_3C_6H_3$	—	173
2-Cl-5-$HO_3SC_6H_3$	CH_3	2-CF_3-4-ClC_6H_3	—	1486
2-Cl-5-$HO_3SC_6H_3$	CH_3	2-CH_3O-5-$C_{12}H_{25}NHSO_2C_6H_4$	—	1620
4-Cl-2-$HO_3SC_6H_3$	CH_3	3-$C_{17}H_{35}CONHSO_2C_6H_4$	—	173
2,4-$(NO_2)_2C_6H_3$	CH_3	C_6H_5	216°	263
2,5-$(HO_3S)_2C_6H_3$	CH_3	2-CH_3O-5-$C_{12}H_{25}NHSO_2C_6H_3$	—	1620
2-(3-HOOC-4-$HOC_6H_3SO_2$)-5-$HO_3SC_6H_3$	CH_3	3-$CF_3C_6H_4$	—	1486
2-Cl-4-$HO_3SC_6H_3$	CH_3	3-$CH_2{=}CHSO_2C_6H_4$	—	652
2-CH_3-3-$C_{17}H_{35}$CONH-5-$HO_3SC_6H_2$	CH_3	4-$(C_2H_5)_2NC_6H_4$	—	1331
2-CH_3-4-$CH_2{=}CHO_2S$-6-ClC_6H_2	CH_3	2-$HO_3SC_6H_4$	—	651
2,3-Cl_2-4-$HO_3SC_6H_2$	CH_3	4-$HO_3SC_6H_4$	—	913
2,5-Cl_2-4-$HO_3SC_6H_2$	CH_3	4-$HO_3SC_6H_4$	—	40
2,5-Cl_2-4-$HO_3SC_6H_2$	CH_3	3-$C_{17}H_{35}CONHSO_2C_6H_4$	—	173
2,5-Cl_2-4-$HO_3SC_6H_2$	CH_3	3-$C_{15}H_{31}CONHSO_2C_6H_4$	—	173
2,5-Cl_2-4-$HO_3SC_6H_2$	CH_3	3-$C_{17}H_{35}CONHSO_2$-4-$CH_3OC_6H_3$	—	173
2-CH_3-4-HO_3S-6-ClC_6H_2	CH_3	3-$CF_3C_6H_4$	—	1486
2,3,6-Cl_3-5-HO_3SC_6H	CH_3	3-$CF_3C_6H_4$	—	1486
2-$C_6H_5C_6H_4$	CH_3	2-$HOOCC_6H_4$	—	1382
2-$C_6H_5C_6H_4$	CH_3	2-HOOC-4(or 5)-$HO_3SC_6H_3$	—	1382
2-$C_6H_5C_6H_4$	CH_3	2(or 6)-HO-3-HO_3S-5-$NO_2C_6H_2$	—	1382
2-C_6H_5-4-$HO_3SC_6H_3$	CH_3	2-$HOOCC_6H_4$	—	1382
2-C_6H_5-4-$HO_3SC_6H_3$	CH_3	2-HO-4(or 5)-$NO_2C_6H_3$	—	1382
2-$C_{10}H_7$	CH_3	2-Cl-5-(4-$ClC_6H_4SO_2NHSO_2$)C_6H_3	—	180

2-$C_{10}H_7$	CH_3	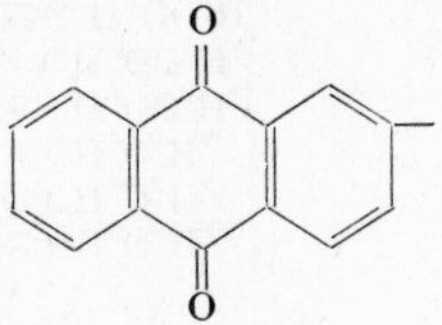	—	1251
6-HO_3S-2-$C_{10}H_6$	CH_3	2-$C_{10}H_{21}OOCC_6H_4$	—	217
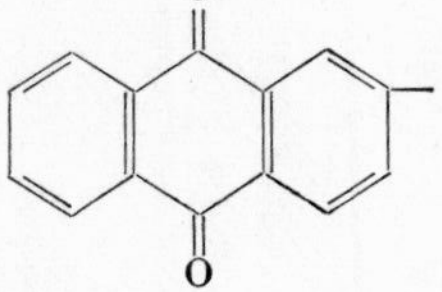	CH_3	C_6H_5	—	1251
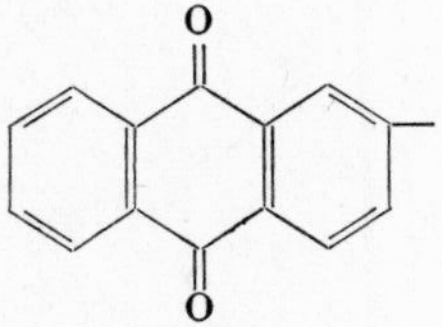	CH_3	1-$C_{10}H_7$	—	1251
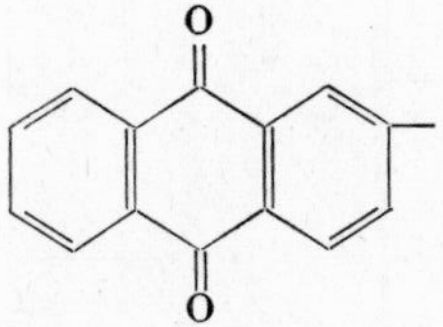	CH_3	2-$C_{10}H_7$	—	1251

(Table continued)

TABLE XXIII, Section B (*continued*)

R^1	R^2	Ar	M.p.	Reference
[structure]	CH_3	[structure]	—	1251
[structure]	CH_3	C_6H_5	237°	413
[structure]	CH_3	4-$NaO_3SC_6H_4$	—	413
C_6H_5	C_6H_5	C_6H_5	173°	129, 278, 372, 818, 1003, 1514, 1552, 1573
C_6H_5	C_6H_5	2-$CH_3C_6H_4$	183°, 226°	278, 1552
C_6H_5	C_6H_5	3-$CH_3C_6H_4$	179°	278
C_6H_5	C_6H_5	4-$CH_3C_6H_4$	193°, 242°	278, 1552
C_6H_5	C_6H_5	2-$CH_3OC_6H_4$	209°	278
C_6H_5	C_6H_5	4-$CH_3OC_6H_4$	167°	278
C_6H_5	C_6H_5	2-$C_2H_5OC_6H_4$	206°	278

C_6H_5	C_6H_5	$4\text{-}C_2H_5OC_6H_4$	177°	278
C_6H_5	C_6H_5	$4\text{-}H_2NC_6H_4$	208°	259
C_6H_5	C_6H_5	$4\text{-}CH_3CONHC_6H_4$	—	259
C_6H_5	C_6H_5	$2\text{-}ClC_6H_4$	177°	278
C_6H_5	C_6H_5	$3\text{-}ClC_6H_4$	193°	278
C_6H_5	C_6H_5	$4\text{-}ClC_6H_4$	216°	278
C_6H_5	C_6H_5	$4\text{-}BrC_6H_4$	231°	278
C_6H_5	C_6H_5	$2\text{-}NO_2C_6H_4$	204°	278
C_6H_5	C_6H_5	$3\text{-}NO_2C_6H_4$	203°	278
C_6H_5	C_6H_5	$4\text{-}NO_2C_6H_4$	245°	278
C_6H_5	C_6H_5	$4\text{-}CH_3COCH(COOC_2H_5)\text{—}N{=}NC_6H_4$	195°	259
C_6H_5	C_6H_5	$4\text{-}C_6H_5COCH(COOC_2H_5)N{=}NC_6H_4$	203°	259
C_6H_5	C_6H_5	$3\text{-}NaO_3SC_6H_4$	—	280
C_6H_5	C_6H_5	$4\text{-}NaO_3SC_6H_4$	—	280
C_6H_5	C_6H_5	$2\text{-}CH_3\text{-}4\text{-}ClC_6H_3$	204°	278
C_6H_5	C_6H_5	$2\text{-}CH_3\text{-}5\text{-}ClC_6H_3$	220°	278
C_6H_5	C_6H_5	$3\text{-}CH_3\text{-}4\text{-}NaO_3SC_6H_3$	—	280
C_6H_5	C_6H_5	$2,5\text{-}Cl_2C_6H_3$	206°	278
C_6H_5	C_6H_5	$2\text{-}NO_2\text{-}4\text{-}ClC_6H_3$	244°	278
C_6H_5	C_6H_5	$3\text{-}NaO_3S\text{-}4\text{-}ClC_6H_3$	—	280
C_6H_5	C_6H_5	$2\text{-}Cl\text{-}5\text{-}(4\text{-}ClC_6H_4SO_2NHSO_2)C_6H_3$	—	180
C_6H_5	C_6H_5	$1\text{-}C_{10}H_7$	238°, 196°	278, 1552
C_6H_5	C_6H_5	$2\text{-}C_{10}H_7$	175°, 225°	278, 1552
C_6H_5	C_6H_5	$1\text{-}NaO_3S\text{-}2\text{-}C_{10}H_6$	—	280
C_6H_5	C_6H_5	S N	176°	281

(*Table continued*)

TABLE XXIII, Section B (*continued*)

R^1	R^2	Ar	M.p.	Reference
C_6H_5	C_6H_5	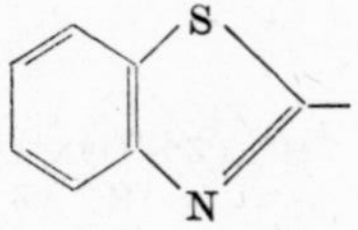	212°	281
C_6H_5	C_6H_5	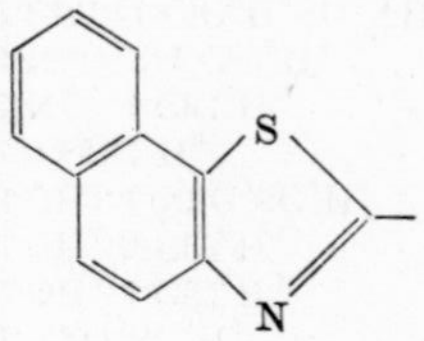	271°	281
C_6H_5	C_6H_5	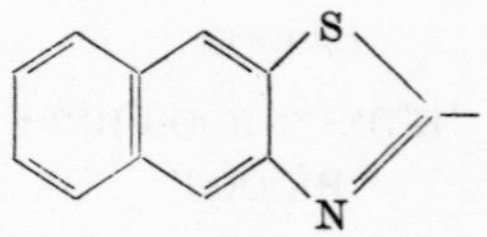	265°	281
C_6H_5	$3\text{-}CH_3C_6H_4$	C_6H_5	141°	1145
C_6H_5	$2\text{-}HOC_6H_4$	C_6H_5	189°	670
C_6H_5	$2\text{-}HOC_6H_4$	$4\text{-}CH_3C_6H_5$	205°	670
C_6H_5	$2\text{-}HOC_6H_4$	$4\text{-}NO_2C_6H_4$	285°	670
C_6H_5	$2\text{-}CH_3OC_6H_4$	C_6H_5	139°, 149°	670, 1581
C_6H_5	$2\text{-}CH_3OC_6H_4$	$4\text{-}NO_2C_6H_4$	267°	1581
C_6H_5	$3\text{-}CH_3OC_6H_4$	C_6H_5	137°	1581
C_6H_5	$3\text{-}CH_3OC_6H_4$	$4\text{-}NO_2C_6H_4$	235°	1581
C_6H_5	$4\text{-}CH_3OC_6H_4$	C_6H_5	177°	129, 1581
C_6H_5	$4\text{-}CH_3OC_6H_4$	$4\text{-}NO_2C_6H_4$	213°	1581

C_6H_5	2-ClC_6H_4	C_6H_5	—	1580
C_6H_5	3-ClC_6H_4	C_6H_5	—	1580
C_6H_5	4-ClC_6H_4	C_6H_5	—	1580
3-ClC_6H_4	C_6H_5	2-Cl-5-(4-$ClC_6H_4SO_2NHSO_2$)C_6H_3	—	180
3-$NO_2C_6H_4$	C_6H_5	C_6H_5	179°	1003
4-$NO_2C_6H_4$	C_6H_5	4-$NO_2C_6H_4$	290°	1574
4-$NO_2C_6H_4$	2-$CH_3OC_6H_4$	C_6H_5	200°	1581
4-$NO_2C_6H_4$	4-$CH_3OC_6H_4$	C_6H_5	239°	1581
2-$HOOCC_6H_4$	C_6H_5	C_6H_5	225°	1004
2-$HOOCC_6H_4$	C_6H_5	4-$CH_3C_6H_4$	194°	1004
4-$NaO_3SC_6H_4$	C_6H_5	C_6H_5	—	279
4-$NaO_3SC_6H_4$	C_6H_5	2-$NO_2C_6H_4$	—	279
4-$NaO_3SC_6H_4$	C_6H_5	4-$NO_2C_6H_4$	—	279
4-$NaO_3SC_6H_4$	C_6H_5	2-CH_3-4-ClC_6H_3	—	279
4-$NaO_3SC_6H_4$	C_6H_5	2-CH_3-5-ClC_6H_3	—	279
4-$NaO_3SC_6H_4$	C_6H_5	2,5-$Cl_2C_6H_3$	—	279
2-$C_6H_5C_6H_4$	C_6H_5	2-HO-3-NO_2-5-$HO_3SC_6H_2$	—	77
4-$C_6H_5C_6H_4$	C_6H_5	2-HO-3-Cl-5-$HO_3SC_6H_2$	—	77
4-$C_6H_5C_6H_4$	C_6H_5	2-HO-3-NO_2-5-$HO_3SC_6H_2$	—	77
C_6H_5	2-C_4H_3O	C_6H_5	165°	278, 1499
C_6H_5	2-C_4H_3O	2-$CH_3C_6H_4$	195°	278
C_6H_5	2-C_4H_3O	3-$CH_3C_6H_4$	187°	278
C_6H_5	2-C_4H_3O	4-$CH_3C_6H_4$	190°	278
C_6H_5	2-C_4H_3O	2-$CH_3OC_6H_4$	193°	278
C_6H_5	2-C_4H_3O	4-$CH_3OC_6H_4$	154°	278
C_6H_5	2-C_4H_3O	2-$C_2H_5OC_6H_4$	196°	278
C_6H_5	2-C_4H_3O	4-$C_2H_5OC_6H_4$	173°	278
C_6H_5	2-C_4H_3O	2-ClC_6H_4	200°	278
C_6H_5	2-C_4H_3O	3-ClC_6H_4	201°	278
C_6H_5	2-C_4H_3O	4-ClC_6H_4	227°	278
C_6H_5	2-C_4H_3O	4-BrC_6H_4	231°	278
C_6H_5	2-C_4H_3O	2-$NO_2C_6H_4$	223°	278
C_6H_5	2-C_4H_3O	3-$NO_2C_6H_4$	193°	278
C_6H_5	2-C_4H_3O	4-$NO_2C_6H_4$	260°	278

(*Table continued*)

TABLE XXIII, Section B (*continued*)

R^1	R^2	Ar	M.p.	Reference
C_6H_5	2-C_4H_3O	3-$NaO_3SC_6H_4$	—	280
C_6H_5	2-C_4H_3O	4-$NaO_3SC_6H_4$	—	280
C_6H_5	2-C_4H_3O	2-CH_3-4-ClC_6H_3	217°	278
C_6H_5	2-C_4H_3O	2-CH_3-5-ClC_6H_3	214°	278
C_6H_5	2-C_4H_3O	3-CH_3-4-$NaO_3SC_6H_3$	—	280
C_6H_5	2-C_4H_3O	2,5-$Cl_2C_6H_3$	231°	278
C_6H_5	2-C_4H_3O	2-NO_2-4-ClC_6H_3	266°	278
C_6H_5	2-C_4H_3O	3-NaO_3S-4-ClC_6H_3	—	280
C_6H_5	2-C_4H_3O	1-$C_{10}H_7$	161°	278
C_6H_5	2-C_4H_3O	2-$C_{10}H_7$	202°	278, 1499
C_6H_5	2-C_4H_3O	1-NaO_3S-2-$C_{10}H_6$	—	280
C_6H_5	2-C_4H_3O	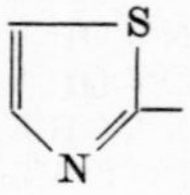	198°	281
C_6H_5	2-C_4H_3O	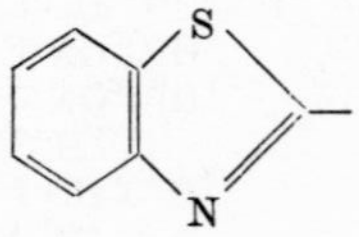	228°	281
C_6H_5	2-C_4H_3O	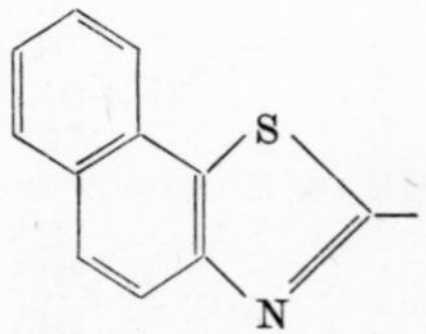	261°	281

C_6H_5	2-C_4H_3O	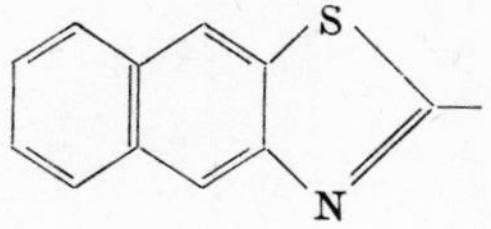 S, N	287°	281
4-$NaO_3SC_6H_4$	2-C_4H_3O	C_6H_5	—	279
4-$NaO_3SC_6H_4$	2-C_4H_3O	2-$NO_2C_6H_4$	—	279
4-$NaO_3SC_6H_4$	2-C_4H_3O	4-$NO_2C_6H_4$	—	279
4-$NaO_3SC_6H_4$	2-C_4H_3O	2-CH_3-4-ClC_6H_3	—	279
4-$NaO_3SC_6H_4$	2-C_4H_3O	2-CH_3-5-ClC_6H_3	—	279
4-$NaO_3SC_6H_4$	2-C_4H_3O	2,5-$Cl_2C_6H_3$	—	279
3-$HO_3SC_6H_4$	CH_3	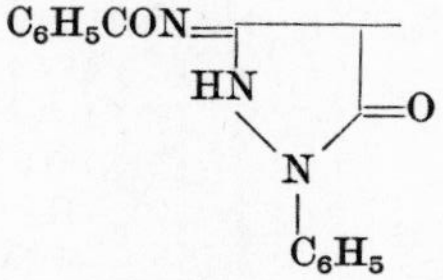 $C_6H_5CON=$ HN, N, =O, C_6H_5	180°	593
4-$HO_3SC_6H_4$	CH_3	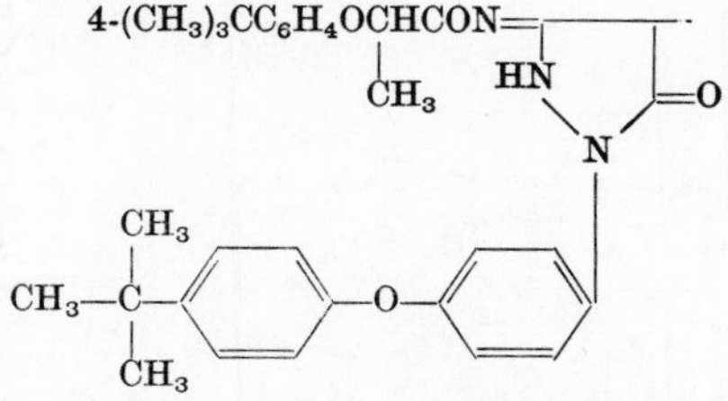 4-$(CH_3)_3CC_6H_4OCHCON=$ CH_3, HN, N, =O; CH_3–C(CH_3)(CH_3)–, O	184°	593

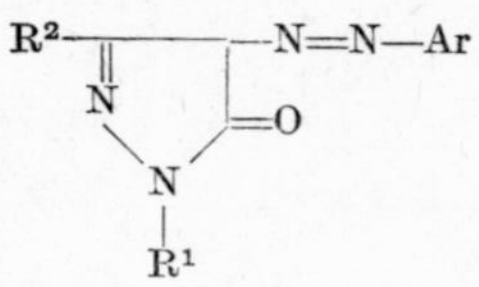

TABLE XXIII

Section C. Arylazo Substituted with Functional Groups

R^1	R^2	Ar	M.p.	Reference
C_6H_5	CH_3CO	C_6H_5	182° (dec.)	768, 770
H	HOOC	C_6H_5	> 250°	449, 1545
H	HOOC	$3\text{-}CH_3C_6H_4$	—	449
H	HOOC	$2\text{-}HOOCC_6H_4$	227°	1552
C_6H_5	HOOC	C_6H_5	230°	292, 1082
C_6H_5	HOOC	$4\text{-}BrC_6H_4$	—	292
$2\text{-}CH_3C_6H_4$	HOOC	$2\text{-}CH_3C_6H_4$	229° (dec.)	293
$4\text{-}CH_3C_6H_4$	HOOC	$4\text{-}CH_3C_6H_4$	233° (dec.)	293
$3\text{-}H_2NC_6H_4$	HOOC	$4\text{-}[3\text{-}HO_3S\text{-}4\text{-}(4\text{-}HO_3SC_6H_4N{=}N)C_6H_4NHCO]C_6H_4$	—	215
$3\text{-}ClC_6H_4$	HOOC	$2\text{-}HO\text{-}3\text{-}NO_2\text{-}5\text{-}C_6H_{11}C_6H_2$	—	873
$3\text{-}ClC_6H_4$	HOOC	$2\text{-}HO\text{-}3\text{-}NO_2\text{-}5\text{-}t\text{-}C_5H_{11}C_6H_2$	—	873
$3\text{-}ClC_6H_4$	HOOC	$2\text{-}HO\text{-}3\text{-}NO_2\text{-}5\text{-}C_8H_7C_6H_2$	—	873
$4\text{-}ClC_6H_4$	HOOC	$4\text{-}ClC_6H_4$	254° (dec.)	291
$4\text{-}BrC_6H_4$	HOOC	$4\text{-}BrC_6H_4$	260° (dec.)	291
$3\text{-}NO_2C_6H_4$	HOOC	$2\text{-}HO\text{-}3,6\text{-}Cl_2\text{-}4\text{-}HO_3SC_6H$	—	276
$2\text{-}HO_3SC_6H_4$	HOOC	$2\text{-}HO_3SC_6H_4$	—	1079
$4\text{-}HO_3SC_6H_4$	HOOC	$4\text{-}(4\text{-}NO_2C_6H_4SO_2)C_6H_4$	—	571
$4\text{-}HO_3SC_6H_4$	HOOC	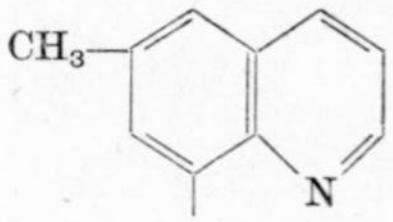 CH_3 … N	323° (dec.)	1629

4-$H_2NO_2SC_6H_4$	HOOC	4-$H_2NO_2SC_6H_4$	—	1628, 1662
2-CH_3-4-$HO_3SC_6H_3$	HOOC	2-HO_3S-4,5-$(CH_3)_2C_6H_2$	—	523
2,4-$Cl_2C_6H_3$	HOOC	2,4-$Cl_2C_6H_4$	252° (dec.)	291
3,4-$Cl_2C_6H_3$	HOOC	2-HO-3-NO_2-5-$C_6H_{11}C_6H_2$	—	873
3,4-$Cl_2C_6H_3$	HOOC	2-HO-3-NO_2-5-*t*-$C_5H_{11}C_6H_2$	—	873
3,6-$Cl_2C_6H_3$	HOOC	2-HO-3-NO_2-5-*t*-$C_5H_{11}C_6H_2$	—	873
3,6-$Cl_2C_6H_3$	HOOC	2-HO-3-NO_2-5-$C_8H_{17}C_6H_2$	—	873
2,4-$Br_2C_6H_3$	HOOC	2,4-$Br_2C_6H_3$	248°	291
2-CH_3-4-HO_3S-6-ClC_6H_2	HOOC	3-$CF_3C_6H_4$	—	1486
4-$NaO_3SC_6H_4$	NaOOC	4-$NaO_3SC_6H_4$	—	768, 770, 1066
5-HO-7-NaO_3S-2-$C_{10}H_5$	NaOOC	5-HO-7-NaO_3S-2-$C_{10}H_5$	—	71
H	H_3COOC	C_6H_5	209°	1549
H	H_3COOC	2-NO_2-4-$CH_3OC_6H_3$	243°	369
H	H_3COOC	2-NO_2-4-$C_2H_5OC_6H_3$	244°	369
H	H_3COOC	2-NO_2-4-ClC_6H_3	225°	369
H	H_3COOC	2-NO_2-4-$CH_3COC_6H_3$	254°	369
H	H_3COOC	2-NO_2-4-$C_4H_9NHO_2SC_6H_3$	230°	369
4-BrC_6H_4	H_3COOC	4-BrC_6H_4	213°	291
2,4-$Br_2C_6H_3$	H_3COOC	2,4-$Br_2C_6H_3$	233°	291
H	C_2H_5OOC	2-$HOOCC_6H_4$	255°	1552
H	C_2H_5OOC	C_6H_5	241°	1544, 1545
H	C_2H_5OOC	2-$NO_2C_6H_4$	256°	369
H	C_2H_5OOC	2-NO_2-4-$F_3CC_6H_3$	185°	369
H	C_2H_5OOC	2-NO_2-4-$CH_3OC_6H_3$	246°	369
H	C_2H_5OOC	2-NO_2-4-ClC_6H_3	228°	369
H	C_2H_5OOC	2-NO_2-4-$C_2H_5OOCC_6H_3$	205°	369
H	C_2H_5OOC	2-NO_2-4-$HOCH_2CH_2NHCOC_6H_3$	154°	369
H	C_2H_5OOC	2-NO_2-4-$CH_3OCH_2CH_2NHCOC_6H_3$	226°	369
H	C_2H_5OOC	2-NO_2-4-$C_2H_5NHSO_2C_6H_3$	251°	369
H	C_2H_5OOC	2-NO_2-4-$C_4H_9NHSO_2C_6H_3$	230°	369
H	C_2H_5OOC	2-NO_2-4-$SCNC_6H_3$	—	1357
CH_3	C_2H_5OOC	4-$CH_3OC_6H_4$	125°	594
C_6H_5	C_2H_5OOC	C_6H_5	152°	37, 44, 1240
2-$CH_3C_6H_4$	C_2H_5OOC	2-$CH_3C_6H_4$	145°	293, 445

(*Table continued*)

TABLE XXIII, Section C (*continued*)

R^1	R^2	Ar	M.p.	Reference
$3\text{-}CH_3C_6H_4$	C_2H_5OOC	$3\text{-}CH_3C_6H_4$	146°	445
$4\text{-}CH_3C_6H_4$	C_2H_5OOC	$4\text{-}CH_3C_6H_4$	143°	293, 445
$2\text{-}CH_3OC_6H_4$	C_2H_5OOC	$2\text{-}CH_3OC_6H_4$	177°	1661
$2\text{-}C_2H_5OC_6H_4$	C_2H_5OOC	$2\text{-}C_2H_5OC_6H_4$	152°	1661
$2\text{-}H_2NC_6H_4$	C_2H_5OOC	$2\text{-}H_2NC_6H_4$	195°	444
$3\text{-}H_2NC_6H_4$	C_2H_5OOC	$3\text{-}H_2NC_6H_4$	146°	444
$3\text{-}H_2NC_6H_4$	C_2H_5OOC	$2\text{-}CH_3\text{-}4\text{-}ClC_6H_3$	—	878
$4\text{-}H_2NC_6H_4$	C_2H_5OOC	$4\text{-}H_2NC_6H_4$	143°	444
$4\text{-}C_6H_5N{=}NC_6H_4$	C_2H_5OOC	$4\text{-}C_6H_5N{=}NC_6H_4$	198°	770
$3\text{-}(3\text{-}HO\text{-}2\text{-}C_{10}H_6CONH)C_6H_2$	C_2H_5OOC	$2\text{-}CH_3\text{-}4\text{-}ClC_6H_3$	228°	877
$2\text{-}ClC_6H_4$	C_2H_5OOC	$2\text{-}ClC_6H_4$	179°	1661
$3\text{-}ClC_6H_4$	C_2H_5OOC	$2\text{-}Cl\text{-}5\text{-}(2,4,5\text{-}Cl_3C_6H_2SO_2NHSO_2)C_6H_3$	—	180
$4\text{-}ClC_6H_4$	C_2H_5OOC	$4\text{-}ClC_6H_4$	190°	291, 1661
$3\text{-}BrC_6H_4$	C_2H_5OOC	$3\text{-}BrC_6H_4$	160°	1661
$4\text{-}BrC_6H_4$	C_2H_5OOC	$4\text{-}BrC_6H_4$	260°	291
$4\text{-}NO_2C_6H_4$	C_2H_5OOC	$4\text{-}NO_2C_6H_4$	246°, 260°	444, 770
$4\text{-}HOOCC_6H_4$	C_2H_5OOC	$4\text{-}HOOCC_6H_4$	224° (dec.)	768, 770
$3\text{-}C_2H_5OOCC_6H_4$	C_2H_5OOC	$3\text{-}C_2H_5OOCC_6H_4$	132°	1661
$4\text{-}(2\text{-}C_{10}H_7OCO)C_6H_4$	C_2H_5OOC	$4\text{-}(2\text{-}C_{10}H_7OCO)C_6H_4$	228°	1661
$4\text{-}HO_3SC_6H_4$	C_2H_5OOC	$4\text{-}HO_3SC_6H_4$	—	444
$4\text{-}HOCH_2CH_2SO_2C_6H_4$	C_2H_5OOC	C_6H_5	—	651
$3\text{-}H_2NO_2SC_6H_4$	C_2H_5OOC	$2\text{-}HO\text{-}3\text{-}NO_2\text{-}5\text{-}t\text{-}C_5H_{11}C_6H_2$	—	874
$3\text{-}H_2NO_2SC_6H_4$	C_2H_5OOC	$2\text{-}HO\text{-}3\text{-}NO_2\text{-}5\text{-}t\text{-}C_5H_{11}C_6H_2$	—	1450
$3\text{-}HOCH_2CH_2NHSO_2C_6H_4$	C_2H_5OOC	$2\text{-}HO\text{-}3\text{-}NO_2\text{-}5\text{-}t\text{-}C_5H_{11}C_6H_2$	—	1450
$2,4\text{-}(CH_3)_2C_6H_3$	C_2H_5OOC	$2,4\text{-}(CH_3)_2C_6H_3$	165°	1661
$2\text{-}CH_3\text{-}4\text{-}NO_2C_6H_3$	C_2H_5OOC	$2\text{-}CH_3\text{-}4\text{-}NO_2C_6H_3$	158°	1661
$2,5\text{-}Cl_2C_6H_3$	C_2H_5OOC	$2,5\text{-}Cl_2C_6H_3$	213°	285
$2,4\text{-}Br_2C_6H_3$	C_2H_5OOC	$2,4\text{-}Br_2C_6H_3$	229°	291
$3\text{-}H_2NO_2S\text{-}5\text{-}ClC_6H_3$	C_2H_5OOC	$2\text{-}HO\text{-}3\text{-}NO_2\text{-}5\text{-}t\text{-}C_5H_{11}C_6H_2$	—	874
$1\text{-}C_{10}H_7$	C_2H_5OOC	$1\text{-}C_{10}H_7$	170° (dec.)	768, 770
$2\text{-}C_{10}H_7$	C_2H_5OOC	$2\text{-}C_{10}H_7$	216° (dec.)	768, 770

$1\text{-}NaO_3S\text{-}2\text{-}C_{10}H_6$	C_2H_5OOC	$1\text{-}NaO_3S\text{-}2\text{-}C_{10}H_6$	200° (dec.)	768, 770
$4,8\text{-}(HO_3S)_2\text{-}2\text{-}C_{10}H_6$	C_2H_5OOC	$4,8\text{-}(HO_3S)_2\text{-}2\text{-}C_{10}H_6$	260°	770
$2,4\text{-}Br_2C_6H_3$	C_4H_9OOC	$2,4\text{-}Br_2C_6H_3$	175°	291
H	H_2NOC	$2\text{-}NO_2\text{-}4\text{-}ClC_6H_3$	218°	369
H	C_4H_9NHOC	$2\text{-}HO\text{-}5\text{-}C_6H_5SC_6H_3$	—	225
C_6H_5	H_2NOC	$2\text{-}HO\text{-}4\text{-}(C_6H_5NHSO_2)C_6H_3$	—	1218
C_6H_5	H_2NOC	$2\text{-}HO\text{-}3\text{-}(C_6H_5NHSO_2)\text{-}5\text{-}ClC_6H_2$	—	1218
C_6H_5	H_2NOC	$2\text{-}HO\text{-}4\text{-}(C_6H_5NHSO_2)\text{-}6\text{-}CH_3C_6H_2$	—	1218
$2\text{-}CH_3OC_6H_4$	H_2NOC	$2\text{-}HO\text{-}5\text{-}(C_6H_5NHSO_2)C_6H_3$	—	1218
$3\text{-}ClC_6H_5$	H_2NOC	$2\text{-}Cl\text{-}5\text{-}(2,4,5\text{-}Cl_3C_6H_2NHSO_2)C_6H_3$	—	180
$3\text{-}H_2NO_2SC_6H_4$	H_2NOC	$2\text{-}HO\text{-}3\text{-}NO_2\text{-}5\text{-}t\text{-}C_5H_{11}C_6H_2$	—	1450
$2\text{-}Cl\text{-}5\text{-}H_2NO_2SC_6H_3$	H_2NOC	$2\text{-}HO\text{-}3\text{-}NO_2\text{-}4\text{-}t\text{-}C_4H_9C_6H_2$	—	874
$3\text{-}H_2NO_2S\text{-}4\text{-}ClC_6H_3$	H_2NOC	$2\text{-}HO\text{-}3\text{-}NO_2\text{-}5\text{-}t\text{-}C_5H_{11}C_6H_2$	—	874
H	C_4H_9HNOC	$2\text{-}HO\text{-}3\text{-}HO_3S\text{-}5\text{-}ClC_6H_2$	—	1464
$3\text{-}H_2NO_2SC_6H_4$	CH_3NHOC	$2\text{-}HO\text{-}3\text{-}NO_2\text{-}5\text{-}t\text{-}C_5H_{11}C_6H_2$	—	1450
$3\text{-}HOCH_2CH_2NHO_2SC_6H_4$	CH_3NHOC	$2\text{-}HO\text{-}3\text{-}NO_2\text{-}5\text{-}t\text{-}C_5H_{11}C_6H_2$	—	1450
$3\text{-}H_2NO_2SC_6H_4$	$HOCH_2CH_2NHOC$	$2\text{-}HO\text{-}3\text{-}NO_2\text{-}5\text{-}t\text{-}C_5H_{11}C_6H_2$	—	1450
CH_3	H_2NHNOC	$4\text{-}CH_3OC_6H_4$	212°	594
CH_3	ONC	$4\text{-}CH_3OC_6H_4$	253°	594
C_6H_5	CN	C_6H_5	152° (dec.), 189°	126, 768
$4\text{-}BrC_6H_4$	CN	C_6H_5	203°	126
CH_3	N_3OC	$4\text{-}CH_3OC_6H_4$	120° (exp.)	594
CH_3CO	C_6H_5	C_6H_5	199°	1560
C_6H_5CO	CH_3	$2\text{-}CH_3C_6H_4$	209°	264
C_6H_5CO	CH_3	$3\text{-}CH_3C_6H_4$	171°	264
C_6H_5CO	CH_3	$1\text{-}C_{10}H_7$	212°	264
C_6H_5CO	CH_3	$2\text{-}C_{10}H_7$	224°	264
H_2NCO	CH_3	C_6H_5	—	355
H_2NCS	CH_3	C_6H_5	217°	355

TABLE XXIV. 3-Pyrazolin-5-ones. Imino, Amino, Amido, Azo, Aminoazo, and Hydrazido Substituents

R^1	R^2	R^3	R^4	M.p.	Reference
H	CH_3	CH_3	$(CH_3)_2N$	—	860
C_6H_5	CH_3	$C_6H_5CH_2NCH_2CH_2N(CH_3)_2$	H	216°	1052
H	C_6H_5	CH_3	$C_6H_5CH{=}N$	248°	984
H	C_6H_5	CH_3	$4\text{-}CH_3OC_6H_4CH{=}N$	245°	984
H	C_6H_5	CH_3	$C_6H_5CH{=}CHCH{=}N$	232°	984
H	$4\text{-}CH_3C_6H_4$	CH_3	$CH_3C(COOH){=}N$	303°	984
H	$4\text{-}CH_3C_6H_4$	CH_3	$C_6H_5CH{=}N$	233°	984
H	$4\text{-}CH_3C_6H_4$	CH_3	$4\text{-}CH_3OC_6H_4CH{=}N$	235°	984
H	$4\text{-}CH_3C_6H_4$	CH_3	$C_6H_5CH{=}CHCH{=}N$	217°	984
H	$4\text{-}CH_3C_6H_4$	CH_3	$C_6H_5C(CH_3){=}N$	302°	984
H	$4\text{-}CH_3C_6H_4$	CH_3	$(C_6H_5)_2C{=}N$	305°	984
H	$4\text{-}BrC_6H_4$	CH_3	$(CH_3)_2N$	190°	1001

H	4-BrC_6H_4	CH_3	$C_6H_5CH{=}N$	249°	1001
H	4-BrC_6H_4	CH_3	4-$CH_3OC_6H_4CH{=}N$	303°	1001
H	4-BrC_6H_4	CH_3	4-$(CH_3)_2NC_6H_4CH{=}N$	330°	1001
H	4-BrC_6H_4	CH_3	3-$NO_2C_6H_4CH{=}N$	274°	1001
H	4-BrC_6H_4	CH_3	$H_5C_2OOCCH_2C(CH_3){=}N$	199°	1001
H	4-BrC_6H_4	CH_3	$OS{=}N$	168°	1001
cyclopentyl	CH_3	CH_3	$(CH_3)_2N$	b_3 160°	101
cyclohexyl	CH_3	CH_3	$HO_3SCH_2N(CH_3)$	153° (dec.)	105
$C_6H_5CH_2$	CH_3	CH_3	$(CH_3)_2N$	74°	860
C_6H_5	CH_3	CH_3	$CH_2{=}N$	—	134, 172
C_6H_5	CH_3	CH_3	$(CH_3)_2N$	106°	133, 144, 150, 172, 371, 463, 525, 527, 550, 551, 554, 603, 661, 691, 781, 915, 938, 941, 1198, 1256, 1356
CH_3	C_6H_5	CH_3	$(CH_3)_2N$	74°	984
CH_3	CH_3	C_6H_5	$(CH_3)_2N$	118°	992
CH_3	CH_3	C_6H_5	$(C_2H_5)_2N$	oil	992
C_6H_5	CH_3	CH_3	iso-$C_3H_7N(CH_3)$	102°	431
C_6H_5	CH_3	CH_3	$(C_6H_5CH_2)_2N$	101°	130, 743
C_6H_5	CH_3	CH_3	$(4\text{-}ClC_6H_4CH_2)_2N$	105°	130

(Table continued)

TABLE XXIV (*continued*)

R^1	R^2	R^3	R^4	M.p.	Reference
C_6H_5	CH_3	CH_3	—N—CH_3	84°	101
C_6H_5	CH_3	CH_3	( )$_2$N	94°	101
C_6H_5	CH_3	CH_3	$CH_3C{=}N$ (with $COOC_2H_5$ on C)	158°	821
C_6H_5	CH_3	CH_3	$C_6H_5CH{=}N$	173°	821, 940, 1592
CH_3	CH_3	C_6H_5	$C_6H_5CH{=}N$	151°	992
C_6H_5	CH_3	CH_3	2-$HOC_6H_4CH{=}N$	198°	430, 954
CH_3	CH_3	C_6H_5	2-$HOC_6H_4CH{=}N$	173°	992
CH_3	CH_3	C_6H_5	4-$CH_3OC_6H_4CH{=}N$	177°	992
C_6H_5	CH_3	CH_3	3-$NO_2C_6H_4CH{=}N$	213°	821
C_6H_5	CH_3	CH_3	2,3-$(OCH_2O)C_6H_3CH{=}N$	230°	430
CH_3	CH_3	C_6H_5	4-$NO_2C_6H_4CH{=}N$	155°	992
C_6H_5	CH_3	CH_3	$C_6H_5CH{=}CHCH{=}N$	157°	430, 821
CH_3	CH_3	C_6H_5	$C_6H_5CH{=}CHCH{=}N$	151°	992
C_6H_5	CH_3	CH_3	O —$CH{=}N$	206°	1184
C_6H_5	CH_3	CH_3	CH_3, O= ={=}N	—	426

C_6H_5	CH_3	CH_3	$O{=}C_{10}H_5(OH){=}N$	227° (dec.)	1217
CH_3	CH_3	C_6H_5	$C_6H_5C(CH_3){=}N$	167°	992
C_6H_5	CH_3	CH_3	$(HOCH_2CH_2)_2N$	—	460
C_6H_5	CH_3	CH_3	$(HOCH_2CH_2CH_2)_2N$	—	460
C_6H_5	CH_3	CH_3	$(HOCH_2CH_2CH_2CH_2)_2N$	—	460
C_6H_5	CH_3	CH_3	$(CH_3)_2NCH_2CH_2N(CH_2C_6H_5)$	213° (HCl)	111, 1298
C_6H_5	CH_3	CH_3	$(C_2H_5)_2NCH_2CH_2N(CH_2C_6H_5)$	oil	111
C_6H_5	CH_3	CH_3	$C_5H_{10}NCH_2CH_2N(CH_2C_6H_5)$	182° (HCl)	111
C_6H_5	CH_3	CH_3	$HOOCCH_2N(CH_3)$	—	524
C_6H_5	CH_3	CH_3	$NCCH_2N(CH_3)$	75°	524
C_6H_5	CH_3	CH_3	$H_2NCOCH_2N(CH_3)$	153°	524
CH_3	CH_3	C_6H_5	$H_5C_2OOCCH_2C(CH_3){=}N$	141°	992

(*Table continued*)

TABLE XXIV (*continued*)

R^1	R^2	R^3	R^4	M.p.	Reference
C_6H_5	CH_3	CH_3	$HO_2SCH_2N-CH_3$	131° (dec.)	105
C_6H_5	CH_3	CH_3	$HO_3SCH_2N-CH(CH_3)(CH_3)$	—	104
C_6H_5	CH_3	CH_3	$HO_3SCH_2N-CH(CH_3)_2$	—	104
C_6H_5	CH_3	CH_3	HO_2SCH_2N-s-C_4H_9	166° (dec.)	104
C_6H_5	CH_3	CH_3	HO_3SCH_2N-s-C_4H_9	—	104
C_6H_5	CH_3	CH_3	HO_2SCH_2N-iso-C_4H_9	170°	104
C_6H_5	CH_3	CH_3	$HO_3SCH_2N-CH_2C_6H_5$	133° (dec.)	105
C_6H_5	CH_3	CH_3	$[H_2N{=}C_6H_4{=}N]^+ Cl^-$	—	417
C_6H_5	CH_3	CH_3	$[H_2N{=}C_6H_3(NH_2){=}N]^+ Cl^-$	—	417

C_6H_5	CH_3	CH_3	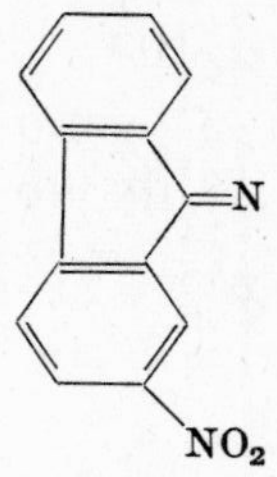 =N; NO_2	153°	270
C_6H_5	CH_3	CH_3	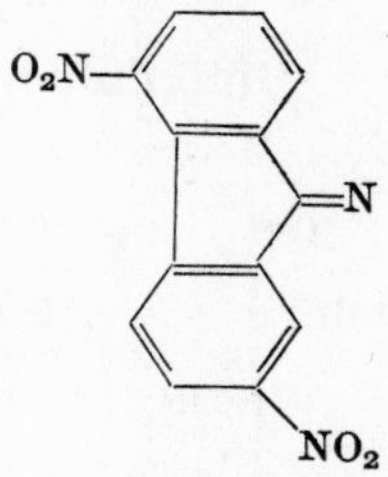 O_2N; =N; NO_2	280°	270
C_6H_5	CH_3	CH_3	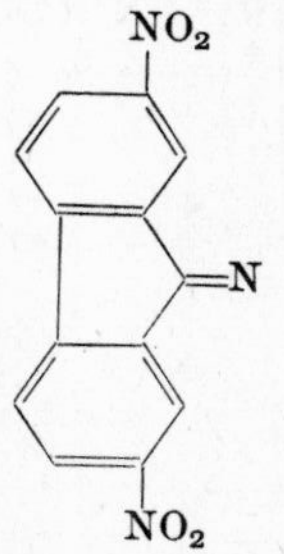 NO_2; =N; NO_2	280°	270

(Table continued)

TABLE XXIV (*continued*)

R^1	R^2	R^3	R^4	M.p.	Reference
C_6H_5	CH_3	CH_3	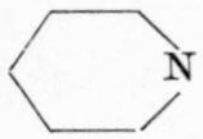 N	144°	927
C_6H_5	CH_3	CH_3	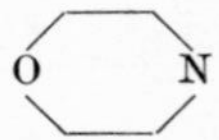 O N	157°	927
C_6H_5	CH_3	CH_3	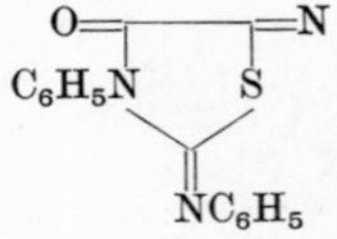 O= =N C_6H_5N S NC_6H_5	148°	7
C_6H_5	CH_3	CH_3	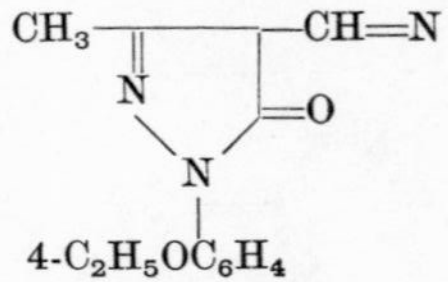 CH_3 —CH=N N =O N $4\text{-}C_2H_5OC_6H_4$	196°	1186
C_6H_5	CH_3	CH_3	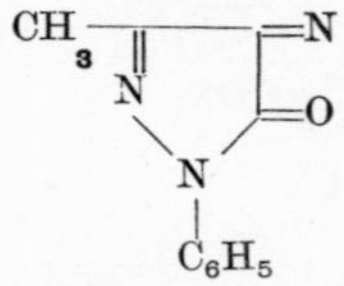 CH_3 =N N =O N C_6H_5	175°	424
C_6H_5	CH_3	CH_3	OHCNH	189°	821
C_6H_5	CH_3	CH_3	OHCN CH_3	106°	618

C_6H_5	CH_3	CH_3	CH_3CONH	197°	821
C_6H_5	CH_3	CH_3	$CH_3CON(CH_3)$	152°	618
C_6H_5	CH_3	CH_3	iso-$C_4H_9CON(CH_3)$	—	537
C_6H_5	CH_3	CH_3	$CH_3CH(Br)CON(CH_3)$	128°	1471
C_6H_5	CH_3	CH_3	$CH_3CH(NHCH_3)CON(CH_3)$	162°	1471
C_6H_5	CH_3	CH_3	$CH_3CH(N(CH_3)_2)CON(CH_3)$	181°	1471
C_6H_5	CH_3	CH_3	H_2NCONH	245°	821
C_6H_5	CH_3	CH_3	C_2H_5OOCNH	206°	821
C_6H_5	CH_3	CH_3	$H_2NC(=S)N(CH_3)$	115° (dec.)	1297
C_6H_5	C_2H_5	CH_3	$(CH_3)_2N$	107°	548
C_6H_5	CH_3	$\triangleright$—	$(CH_3)_2N$	94°	1477

(Table continued)

TABLE XXIV *(continued)*

R^1	R^2	R^3	R^4	M.p.	Reference
$4\text{-}C_3H_7OC_6H_5$	CH_3	CH_3	$(CH_3)_2N$	82°	1149
$4\text{-}C_3H_7OC_6H_5$	CH_3	CH_3	$C_6H_5CH{=}N$	139°	1149
C_6H_5	CH_3	$C_6H_5CH_2$	$(CH_3)_2N$	111°	1320
$4\text{-}H_2O_3AsC_6H_4$	CH_3	CH_3	$3\text{-HO-}4\text{-}H_2O_3AsC_6H_3CH{=}N{-}$	—	1365
H	C_6H_5	CH_3	ClN_2	120°	984
H	$4\text{-}BrC_6H_4$	CH_3	ClN_2	—	1001
C_6H_5	CH_3	CH_3	ClN_2	—	426, 1353
CH_3	CH_3	C_6H_5	ClN_2	—	992
H	C_6H_5	$C_6H_5N{=}N$	CH_3	99°	972
H	C_6H_5	CH_3	$2,5\text{-}(C_2H_5O)_2\text{-}4\text{-}C_6H_5CONHC_6H_2N{=}N$	236°	885
H	C_6H_5	CH_3	$2\text{-HO-}1\text{-}C_{10}H_6N{=}N$	215°	984
H	C_6H_5	CH_3	$3,6\text{-}(HO_3S)_2\text{-}2\text{-HO-}1\text{-}C_{10}H_4N{=}N$	—	1060
H	C_6H_5	CH_3	$3,6\text{-}(HO_3S)_2\text{-}2\text{-}NH_2\text{-}1\text{-}C_{10}H_4N{=}N$	—	1060
H	$4\text{-}BrC_6H_4$	CH_3	$2\text{-HO-}1\text{-}C_{10}H_6N{=}N$	253°	1001
H	$2\text{-}HOOCC_6H_4$	CH_3	$C_6H_5N{=}N$	210°	1004
H	C_6H_5	$2\text{-}HOC_6H_4$	$C_6H_5N{=}N$	189°	670
H	C_6H_5	$2\text{-}HOC_6H_4$	$4\text{-}CH_3C_6H_4N{=}N$	205°	670
C_6H_5	CH_3	CH_3	$H_5C_2O_2CCHN{=}N$ | $COCH_3$	174°	426, 1017
C_6H_5	CH_3	CH_3	$(CH_3CO)_2CHN{=}N$	181°	1017
C_6H_5	CH_3	CH_3	$(CH_3CO)_2CN{=}N$ | CH_3	199°	1017
C_6H_5	CH_3	CH_3	$C_6H_5COCHN{=}N$ | $COCH_3$	142°	1018
C_6H_5	CH_3	CH_3	$C_6H_5N{=}N$	174°	999
C_6H_5	CH_3	CH_3	$3\text{-HOOC-}4\text{-}HOC_6H_3N{=}N$	256°	1323

C_6H_5	CH_3	CH_3	$2\text{-}H_2N\text{-}5\text{-}H_2NO_2SC_6H_3N{=}N$	159° (dec.)	1105
C_6H_5	CH_3	CH_3	$2\text{-}HO\text{-}1\text{-}C_{10}H_6N{=}N$	246° (dec.)	426, 817
CH_3	CH_3	C_6H_5	$2\text{-}HO\text{-}1\text{-}C_{10}H_6N{=}N$	—	992
C_6H_5	CH_3	CH_3	$2\text{-}H_2N\text{-}1\text{-}C_{10}H_6N{=}N$	235°	1017, 1018
C_6H_5	CH_3	CH_3	$2\text{-}H_2N\text{-}6\text{-}HO_3S\text{-}1\text{-}C_{10}H_5N{=}N$	—	1018
C_6H_5	CH_3	CH_3	CH_3, N=N, N, =O, N, C_6H_5	200° (dec.)	426
C_6H_5	CH_3	CH_3	CH_3, N=N, N, =O, N, C_6H_4, $4\text{-}(4\text{-}t\text{-}C_4H_9C_6H_4O)$	—	403
C_6H_5	CH_3	H_2NOC	$2\text{-}HO\text{-}4\text{-}(C_6H_5NHSO_2)C_6H_3N{=}N$	—	1218
C_6H_5	CH_3	CH_3	N_3	74°	456
C_6H_5	CH_3	CH_3	$(CH_3)_2NN{=}N$	110°	527, 1353
C_6H_5	CH_3	CH_3	$(C_2H_5)_2NN{=}N$	111°	1353
C_6H_5	CH_3	CH_3	$C_6H_5NHN{=}N$	136°	821

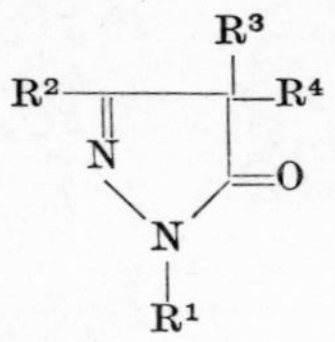

TABLE XXV. 2-Pyrazolin-5-ones. Halogen Substituted

R^1	R^2	R^3	R^4	M.p.	Reference
H	CH_3	Br	H	182°	1028, 1029
Br	CH_3	H	H	78°	1309
CH_3	CH_3	Br	H	170° (HBr salt)	1309
H	CH_3	Br	Br	132°	355, 1028, 1029
$C_6H_5CH_2$	CH_3	Cl	Cl	59°	333
$C_6H_5CH_2$	CH_3	Br	Br	81°	333
C_6H_5	Cl	H	H	143°	981, 994
H	C_6H_5	Br	Br	198°	1028, 1560
H	2-HOC_6H_4	Br	Br	178°	353
H	3-$NO_2C_6H_4$	Br	H	188°	335
C_6H_5	CH_3	Cl	H	153°	1513, 1514
C_6H_5	CH_3	Br	H	128°	809, 816, 1056, 1307, 1605
C_6H_5	CH_3	I	H	—	1605
C_6H_5	CH_3	Cl	Cl	65°	809, 816, 1605
C_6H_5	CH_3	Br	Br	80°	809, 816, 1605
C_6H_5	CH_3	I	I	—	1605
2-$CH_3C_6H_4$	CH_3	Br	H	116°	351
4-BrC_6H_4	CH_3	Br	H	171°	1513
2-$HOOCC_6H_4$	CH_3	Br	H	202°	1004
3-$HOOCC_6H_4$	CH_3	Cl	Cl	116°	980
4-$HO_3SC_6H_4$	CH_3	Br	H	—	1309
C_6H_5	CH_3	CH_3	Cl	68°	1522, 1528, 1605
C_6H_5	CH_3	CH_3	Br	83°	1605

C_6H_5	CH_3	CH_3	I	70°	1605
C_6H_5	Cl	CH_3	CH_3	b_{22}170°	994, 998
$2\text{-}HOOCC_6H_4$	C_6H_5	Cl	H	210°	1004
$2\text{-}CH_3C_6H_4$	C_6H_5	Br	H	110°	351
C_6H_5	Cl	$C_6H_5CH{=}$		108°	994
CH_3CO	CH_3	Br	H	160°	1309
H_2NOC	CH_3	Br	Br	225°	355
H_2NSC	CH_3	Br	H	220°	355
H_2NSC	CH_3	Br	Br	250°	355
H_2NOC	C_6H_5	Br	Br	144°	357
H_2NSC	C_6H_5	Br	Br	130° (dec.)	357
C_6H_5	Cl	NO	H	146°	994

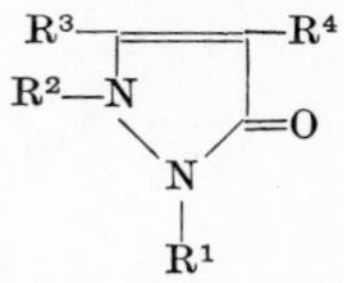

TABLE XXVI. 3-Pyrazolin-5-ones. Halogen and Halogen Combined with Carboxylic Acid and Derivatives

R^1	R^2	R^3	R^4	M.p.	Reference
H	CH_3	CH_3	Br	218°	1205
H	C_2H_5	CH_3	Br	39°	1205
C_6H_5	CH_3	Cl	H	67°	981
CH_3	C_6H_5	Cl	H	117°	981
H	C_6H_5	CH_3	Cl	261°	988
H	C_6H_5	CH_3	Br	241° (dec.)	988
H	$4\text{-}BrC_6H_4$	CH_3	Cl	220°	1001

(Table continued)

TABLE XXVI (*continued*)

R^1	R^2	R^3	R^4	M.p.	Reference
H	4-BrC_6H_4	CH_3	Br	231°	1001
H	4-BrC_6H_4	CH_3	I	207° (dec.)	1001
H	3-$NO_2C_6H_4$	CH_3	Cl	253°	1001
H	3-$NO_2C_6H_4$	CH_3	Br	245°	1001
H	3-$NO_2C_6H_4$	CH_3	I	221°	1001
C_6H_5	CH_3	CH_3	Cl	126°	795, 907, 908,
C_6H_5	CH_3	CH_3	Br	115°	362, 793, 794, 809, 1297, 1320, 1491, 1605
CH_3	C_6H_5	CH_3	Br	—	888
CH_3	CH_3	C_6H_5	Br	179°	992
C_6H_5	CH_3	CH_3	I	—	1155
C_6H_5	CH_3	$C_6H_5CH_2$	Br	116°	1320
3-$CH_3CONHC_6H_4$	CH_3	CH_3	Br	217°	978
4-$CH_3CONHC_6H_4$	CH_3	CH_3	Br	240°	978
4-$C_6H_5CONHC_6H_4$	CH_3	CH_3	Br	237°	978
4-$C_6H_5SO_2NHC_6H_4$	CH_3	CH_3	Br	235°	978
4-BrC_6H_5	CH_3	CH_3	I	163°	540, 1354
4-IC_6H_4	CH_3	CH_3	Br	—	540
3-$NO_2C_6H_4$	CH_3	CH_3	Br	184°	978
4-$NO_2C_6H_4$	CH_3	CH_3	Br	173°	978
CH_3	3-$NO_2C_6H_4$	CH_3	Br	200°	1001
C_6H_5	CH_3	$HOCH_2$	Br	181°	362, 697, 698
C_6H_5	CH_3	CH_3NHCH_2	Br	224° (dec.)	697
C_6H_5	CH_3	$(CH_3)_2NCH_2$	Br	143°	697
C_6H_5	CH_3	$BrCH_2$	Br	135°	362, 697, 698, 899
H	C_6H_5	Cl	Cl	249°	1201
CH_3	C_6H_5	Cl	Br	112°	981
C_6H_5	CH_3	HOOC	Br	186°	697, 698
C_6H_5	CH_3	CH_3OOC	Br	128°	697, 698
C_6H_5	CH_3	H_2NHNOC	Br	192°	697
C_6H_5	CH_3	N_3OC	Br	104° (exp.)	167

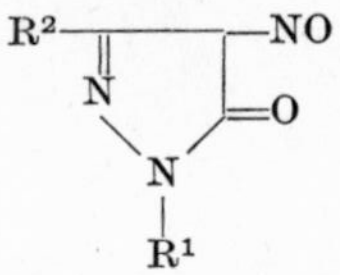

TABLE XXVII. 2-Pyrazolin-5-ones. 4-Nitroso Derivatives

R^1	R^2	M.p.	Reference
H	H	87°	1544, 1546, 1549, 1550
H	CH_3	237°, 232° (dec.)	258, 355, 406, 478, 480, 676, 1553
H	CH_3 (also 4-CH_3)	214°	1560
NO	CH_3 (no 4-NO group)	135°	262
H	$H_5C_2OOCCH_2$	114°	866
H	N_3COCH_2	97°	866
H	$C_6H_5NHCOCH_2$	165°	866
$C_6H_5CH_2$	CH_3	157° (dec.)	333
4-$CH_3C_6H_5CH_2$	CH_3	154° (dec.)	333
C_6H_5	H	160° (dec.)	306
H	C_6H_5	188°	406, 1028, 1552, 1553
H	4-$CH_3C_6H_4$	191°	1125
H	3-$NO_2C_6H_4$	217°	335
C_6H_5	CH_3	158°	240, 676, 809, 816
CH_3	C_6H_5	162°	992
C_6H_5	C_4H_9	131°	1536
C_6H_5	$C_6H_5CH_2$	172°	1534
2,4-$(CH_3)_2C_6H_3CH_2$	C_6H_5	128°	334
3-$CH_3C_6H_4$	CH_3	162°	240
4-$CH_3C_6H_4$	CH_3	180°	240
2-ClC_6H_4	CH_3	174°	296

(*Table continued*)

TABLE XXVII (*continued*)

R^1	R^2	M.p.	Reference
3-ClC_6H_4	CH_3	173°	296
4-ClC_6H_4	CH_3	180°	296, 676
4-IC_6H_4	CH_3	189°	446
4-$NO_2C_6H_4$	CH_3	215°	9
2-$HOOCC_6H_4$	CH_3	200°	1004
3-$HOOCC_6H_4$	CH_3	242°	980
4-$HOOCC_6H_4$	CH_3	253°	980
4-(2-C_5H_4N-NHO_2S)C_6H_4	CH_3	237°	25
2-CH_3-4-IC_6H_3	CH_3	181°	446
3,4-(OCH_2O)C_6H_3	CH_3	161°	334
2,4-$Cl_2C_6H_3$	CH_3	166°	296
3-$HO_3SC_6H_4$	C_8H_{17}	> 250°	593
C_6H_5	C_6H_5	199°	9, 676, 818, 1125, 1153, 1552
C_6H_5	4-$CH_3C_6H_4$	202°	1125, 1152
C_6H_5	3-$CH_3OC_6H_4$	157°	1581
C_6H_5	4-$CH_3OC_6H_4$	244°	1581
4-$CH_3C_6H_4$	C_6H_5	241°	1125
2-$HOOCC_6H_4$	C_6H_5	213°	1004
3,4-(OCH_2O)C_6H_3	C_6H_5	162°	334
H	3-C_5H_4N	253°	269

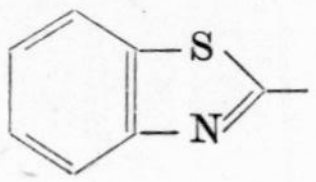 S, N (benzothiazol-2-yl)	CH_3	274°	240, 413
C_6H_5	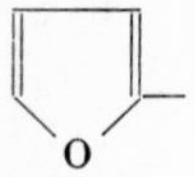 O (2-furyl)	183°	1499
C_6H_5	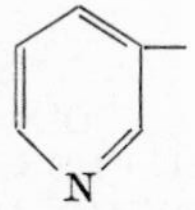 N (3-pyridyl)	229°	269
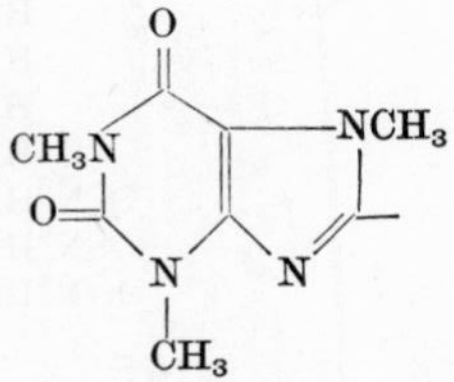 O, CH_3N, O, N, CH_3, NCH₃, N	CH_3	248° (dec.)	1147
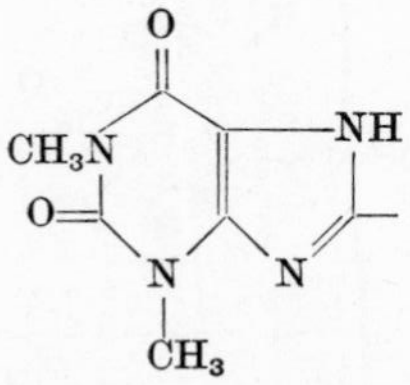 O, CH_3N, O, N, CH_3, NH, N	CH_3	310° (dec.)	1147

(*Table continued*)

TABLE XXVII (*continued*)

R^1	R^2	M.p.	Reference
O, CH_3N, N—CH_3, O=, N, N, H	CH_3	285° (dec.)	1147
H_2NOC	CH_3	210°	355
H_2NSC	CH_3	180°	355
H_2NSC	C_6H_6	174°	357
H	HOOC	215° (dec.)	1544, 1545
H	H_3COOC	199°	1549
H	H_5C_2OOC	182°	1545
H	H_2NOC	240°	337
H	C_6H_5HNOC	211° (dec.)	337
H	$4\text{-}CH_3C_6H_4HNOC$	222°	337
H	N_3OC	100° (exp.)	337

TABLE XXVIII. 3-Pyrazolin-5-ones. Nitroso and Nitro Substituted Derivatives

R^1	R^2	R^3	R^4	M.p.	Reference
H	NO	CH_3	H	—	1029
H	C_6H_5	NO	CH_3	159°	972
H	C_6H_5	CH_3	NO	159°	984
H	4-$CH_3C_6H_4$	CH_3	NO	167°	984
H	4-BrC_6H_4	CH_3	NO	185°	1001
cyclohexyl	CH_3	CH_3	NO	—	103
$C_6H_5CH_2$	CH_3	CH_3	NO	oil	333
C_6H_5	CH_3	CH_3	NO	200° (exp.)	99, 461, 603, 781, 807, 809, 845, 854, 1174, 1175, 1257
CH_3	C_6H_5	CH_3	NO	155° (exp.)	888
CH_3	CH_3	C_6H_5	NO	—	992
C_6H_5	CH_3	cyclopropyl	NO	195°	1477
C_6H_5	CH_3	2-furyl	NO	185°	1499

(*Table continued*)

TABLE XXVIII (*continued*)

R^1	R^2	R^3	R^4	M.p.	Reference
C_6H_5	C_6H_5	CH_3	NO	—	647
4-$CH_3C_6H_4$	C_2H_5	CH_3	NO	—	145
4-$C_2H_5OC_6H_4$	CH_3	CH_3	NO	—	541
4-$C_2H_5OC_6H_4$	C_2H_5	CH_3	NO	—	145
4-$C_3H_7OC_6H_4$	CH_3	CH_3	NO	163° (dec.)	1149
4-$CH_3CONHC_6H_4$	CH_3	CH_3	NO	237°	978
4-$C_6H_5CONHC_6H_4$	CH_3	CH_3	NO	214°	978
4-$C_6H_5SO_2NHC_6H_4$	CH_3	CH_3	NO	211°	978
3-$NO_2C_6H_4$	CH_3	CH_3	NO	188°	978
3-$NO_2C_6H_4$	CH_3	C_6H_5	NO	225° (dec.)	1003
4-$NO_2C_6H_4$	CH_3	CH_3	NO	188°	978
4-$H_2O_2AsC_6H_4$	CH_3	CH_3	NO	—	546
H	CH_3	CH_3	NO_2	217°	860
H	C_6H_5	CH_3	NO_2	222°	984
H	4-$CH_3C_6H_4$	CH_3	NO_2	190°	984
H	4-BrC_6H_4	CH_3	NO_2	211°	1001
H	C_6H_5	2-$CH_3OC_6H_4$	NO_2	164°	670
$C_6H_5CH_2$	CH_3	CH_3	NO_2	161°	333
C_6H_5	CH_3	CH_3	NO_2	273°	807, 809, 1491
CH_3	C_6H_5	CH_3	NO_2	210°	888
CH_3	CH_3	C_6H_5	NO_2	143° (dec.)	992
C_6H_5	CH_3	$C_6H_5CH_2$	NO_2	193°	1320
CH_3	4-BrC_6H_4	CH_3	NO_2	221°	1001
2-$NO_2C_6H_4$	CH_3	CH_3	NO_2	244°	978
3-$NO_2C_6H_4$	CH_3	CH_3	NO_2	203° (dec.)	978
CH_3	3-$NO_2C_6H_4$	CH_3	NO_2	271° (exp.)	1001
4-$NO_2C_6H_4$	CH_3	CH_3	NO_2	276°	978

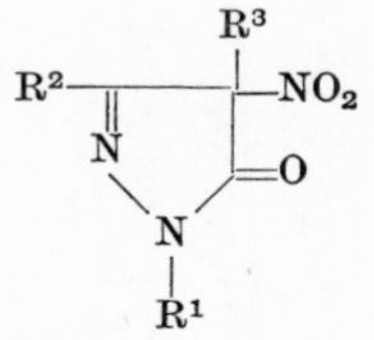

TABLE XXIX. 2-Pyrazolin-5-ones. 4-Nitro Derivatives

R^1	R^2	R^3	M.p.	Reference
H	H	H	136°	653
H	CH_3	H	276°	9, 61, 478, 480
CH_3	CH_3	CH_3	127°	478
$C_6H_5CH_2$	CH_3	H	144° (dec.)	333
C_6H_5	CH_3	H	129° (dec.)	9, 809, 1607
C_6H_5	CH_3	K	250°	1642
4-$NO_2C_6H_4$	CH_3	H	—	672
3-Br-4-$NO_2C_6H_3$	CH_3	H	128°	1683
2-$HOOCC_6H_4$	C_6H_5	H	288° (dec.)	1004
C_6H_5	CH_3	Br	84° (dec.)	1642
4-BrC_6H_4	CH_3	Br	85° (dec.)	1642
4-$NO_2C_6H_4$	CH_3	NO_2	—	690
H_5C_2OOC	CH_3	H	172°	61
H_7C_3OOC	CH_3	H	157°	61

TABLE XXX. 2-Pyrazolin-5-ones. Aldehydes and Ketones

R^1	R^2	R^3	R^4	M.p.	Reference
H	HCO	H	H	—	1546
H	H	CH_3CO	H	225°	1295
H	CH_3	C_6H_5CO	H	261°, 280° (dec.)	947, 1193
H	C_6H_5	HCO	H	215° (dec.)	1188
C_6H_5	CH_3CO	H	H	180°	767
C_6H_5	H	CH_3CO	H	191°	1295
H	C_6H_5	CH_3CO	H	204°	1188
C_6H_5	$H_5C_2OOCCH_2CO$	H	H	182°	837
3-$CH_3C_6H_4$	$H_5C_2OOCCH_2CO$	H	H	178°	837
4-$CH_3C_6H_4$	$H_5C_2OOCCH_2CO$	H	H	184°	837
4-$CH_3OC_6H_4$	$H_5C_2OOCCH_2CO$	H	H	189°	837
3-ClC_6H_4	$H_5C_2OOCCH_2CO$	H	H	180°	837
4-ClC_6H_4	$H_5C_2OOCCH_2CO$	H	H	109°	837
3-$NO_2C_6H_4$	$H_5C_2OOCCH_2CO$	H	H	183°	837
4-$NO_2C_6H_4$	$H_5C_2OOCCH_2CO$	H	H	227°	837
4-$HO_3SC_6H_4$	$H_5C_2OOCCH_2CO$	H	H	—	837
C_6H_5	CH_3	HCO	H	173°	586, 824, 1089, 1092, 1093
C_6H_5	CH_3	CH_3CO	H	66°	591, 1192
C_6H_5	CH_3	C_2H_5CO	H	68°	1193
C_6H_5	CH_3	C_3H_7CO	H	35°	1193
C_6H_5	CH_3	$C_6H_5CH_2CH_2CO$	H	131°	1532, 1533
C_6H_5	CH_3	$(CH_3)_2NCH_2CH_2CO$	H	220°	1098

C_6H_5	CH_3	$(C_2H_5)_2NCH_2CH_2CO$	H	212°	1098
C_6H_5	CH_3	NCH_2CH_2CO	H	220°	1098
C_6H_5	CH_3	HOOCCO	H	236° (dec.)	1641
C_6H_5	CH_3	C_2H_5OOCCO	H	81°	1641
C_6H_5	CH_3	C_6H_5CO	H	86°, 102°, 118°	973, 977, 1056
C_6H_5	CH_3	$4\text{-}NO_2C_6H_4CO$	H	203°	110
C_6H_5	CH_3	$2\text{-}HOOCC_6H_4CO$	H	—	1202
C_6H_5	$C_{17}H_{35}$	$C_{17}H_{35}CO$	H	44°	1124
C_6H_5	$C_{21}H_{43}$	$C_{19}H_{39}CO$	H	52°	1124
C_6H_5	$C_{16}H_{33}CO$	$4\text{-}HOC_6H_4CH{=}$		148°	315
$4\text{-}CH_3C_6H_4$	CH_3	HCO	H	166°	107
$4\text{-}CH_3C_6H_4$	CH_3	HOOCCO	H	218°	1641
$4\text{-}CH_3C_6H_4$	CH_3	H_5C_2OOCCO	H	108°	1641
$4\text{-}H_5C_2OC_6H_4$	CH_3	HCO	H	152°	1186
$4\text{-}H_5C_2OC_6H_4$	CH_3	CH_3CO	H	114°	1193
$4\text{-}NO_2C_6H_4$	CH_3	CH_3CO	H	198°	591
$4\text{-}NO_2C_6H_4$	$C_{16}H_{33}CO$	$4\text{-}HOC_6H_4CH{=}$		197°	315
$4\text{-}HO_3SC_6H_4$	$C_{16}H_{33}CO$	$4\text{-}HOC_6H_4CH{=}$		222°	315
$2,4\text{-}(NO_2)_2C_6H_3$	$C_6H_5CH_2CH_2$	CH_6CO	H	178°	124
	CH_3	CH_3CO	H	237°	1009
C_6H_5	C_6H_5	HCO	H	149°	1185
C_6H_5	C_6H_5	H_5C_2OOCCO	H	108°	1641

TABLE XXXI. 3-Pyrazolin-5-ones. Acyl Substituents on Carbon

R^1	R^2	R^3	R^4	M.p.	Reference
H	C_6H_5	H	CH_3CO	191°	1295
C_6H_5	CH_3	HCO	H	119°	698
C_6H_5	CH_3	H	CH_3CO	216°	108, 109, 331, 696, 901, 902, 1097
C_6H_5	CH_3	H	C_2H_5CO	169°	901
C_6H_5	CH_3	H	HOOCCO	205°	108
C_6H_5	CH_3	H	$C_6H_5CH{=}CHCO$	190°, 234° (dec.)	696, 902
C_6H_5	CH_3	CH_3	HCO	161°	196, 201, 204, 889, 892, 893, 896, 897, 1092, 1093, 1097, 1181, 1634
CH_3	C_6H_5	CH_3	HCO	138°	1190
CH_3	CH_3	C_6H_5	HCO	155°	1190
C_6H_5	CH_3	CH_3	CH_3CO	156°	799
C_6H_5	CH_3	CH_3	C_2H_5CO	146°	112, 740
C_6H_5	CH_3	CH_3	C_3H_7CO	113°, 148°	88, 737
C_6H_5	CH_3	CH_3	C_4H_9CO	104°	737
C_6H_5	CH_3	CH_3	iso-C_4H_9CO	103°	88
C_6H_5	CH_3	CH_3	$C_5H_{11}CO$	94°	737
C_6H_5	CH_3	CH_3	$(C_2H_5)_2CHCO$	133°	735, 740
C_6H_5	CH_3	CH_3	$HOCH_2CO$	121°	362, 740
C_6H_5	CH_3	CH_3	CH_3COOCH_2CO	173°	88, 740
C_6H_5	CH_3	CH_3	2-$HOC_6H_5COOCH_2CO$	196°	740
C_6H_5	CH_3	CH_3	CH_3CHCO | CH_3COO	148°	112

C_6H_5	CH_3	CH_3	$CH_3CH_2CH(OCOCH_3)CO$ (CH₃CH₂CHCO with CH₃COO on CH)	141°	88
C_6H_5	CH_3	CH_3	H_2NCH_2CO	139°	88
C_6H_5	CH_3	CH_3	CH_3NHCH_2CO	242°	740
C_6H_5	CH_3	CH_3	$C_2H_5NHCH_2CO$	177°	740
C_6H_5	CH_3	CH_3	$(C_2H_5)_2NCH_2CO$	—	371
C_6H_5	CH_3	CH_3	(piperidino)NCH_2CO	125°	88
C_6H_5	CH_3	CH_3	$C_6H_5CH_2NHCH_2CO$	222°	740
C_6H_5	CH_3	CH_3	$C_6H_5NHCH_2CO$	152°	740
C_6H_5	CH_3	CH_3	$4\text{-}C_2H_5OC_6H_4NHCH_2CO$	185°	740
C_6H_5	CH_3	CH_3	$CH_3CH(NH_2)CO$	315°	23, 88
C_6H_5	CH_3	CH_3	CH_3COCO	224°	112
C_6H_5	CH_3	CH_3	$CH_3CH(NHC_2H_5)CO$	221°	112
C_6H_5	CH_3	CH_3	$CH_3CH(NH\text{-iso-}C_3H_7)CO$	238°	112
C_6H_5	CH_3	CH_3	$CH_3CH(N(CH_3)_2)CO$	203°	112
C_6H_5	CH_3	CH_3	$H_2NCH_2CH_2CO$	162°	23
C_6H_5	CH_3	CH_3	$CH_3CH(NHCH_3)CO$	130°	23, 112

(Table continued)

TABLE XXXI (*continued*)

R^1	R^2	R^3	R^4	M.p.	Reference
C_6H_5	CH_3	CH_3	$CH_3CH(N\text{-piperidino})CO$	125°	88
C_6H_5	CH_3	CH_3	$ClCH_2CO$	170°	88, 737, 799
C_6H_5	CH_3	CH_3	$BrCH_2CO$	135°	362
C_6H_5	CH_3	CH_3	ICH_2CO	140°	88
C_6H_5	CH_3	CH_3	Cl_3CCO	181°	88
C_6H_5	CH_3	CH_3	$CH_3CHBrCO$	145°	88, 112
C_6H_5	CH_3	CH_3	$C_2H_5CHBrCO$	127°	88
C_6H_5	CH_3	CH_3	$(CH_3)_2C(Br)CO$	152°	88
C_6H_5	CH_3	CH_3	$(CH_3)_2CHCH(Br)CO$	129°	88
C_6H_5	CH_3	CH_3	$CNCH_2CO$	156°	740
C_6H_5	CH_3	CH_3	$HOOCCO$	206°	108
C_6H_5	CH_3	CH_3	C_6H_5CO	149°	737, 740
C_6H_5	CH_3	CH_3	$4\text{-}C_2H_5OC_6H_4CO$	194°	740
C_6H_5	CH_3	CH_3	$2\text{-}H_2NC_6H_4CO$	144°	740
C_6H_5	CH_3	CH_3	$4\text{-}H_2NC_6H_4CO$	260°	88, 740
C_6H_5	CH_3	CH_3	$4\text{-}(CH_3)_2NC_6H_4CO$	217°	740
C_6H_5	CH_3	CH_3	$4\text{-}CH_3CONHC_6H_4CO$	216°	740
C_6H_5	CH_3	CH_3	$4\text{-}H_2NCONHC_6H_4CO$	223°	740
C_6H_5	CH_3	CH_3	$4\text{-}C_6H_5NHCONHC_6H_4CO$	210°	740
C_6H_5	CH_3	CH_3	$2\text{-}NO_2C_6H_4CO$	172°	740
C_6H_5	CH_3	CH_3	$4\text{-}NO_2C_6H_4CO$	165°, 209°	88, 110, 740

C_6H_5	CH_3	CH_3	[structure: CO, N, C_6H_5]	198°	740
C_6H_5	CH_3	C_2H_5	HCO	78°	901
C_6H_5	C_2H_5	CH_3	$ClCH_2CO$	132°	737
C_6H_5	CH_3	CH_3S	CH_3CO	113°	89
C_6H_5	CH_3	C_6H_5	HCO	158°	107, 196, 201, 889, 902, 1097, 1180
C_6H_5	CH_3	HCO	HCO	216°	698
4-$CH_3C_6H_4$	CH_3	CH_3	HCO	166°	196, 889
4-$C_2H_5OC_6H_4$	CH_3	CH_3	HCO	—	1097
CH_3	4-$C_2H_5OC_6H_4$	CH_3	HCO	146°	902

[Structure: 2-pyrazolin-5-one ring with substituents R¹ (N1), R² (C3), R³ and R⁴ (C4), =O (C5)]

TABLE XXXII. 2-Pyrazolin-5-one-(3 or 4)-carboxylic Acids

R¹	R²	R³	R⁴	M.p.	Reference
H	HOOC	H	H	> 260°	337, 1229, 1544, 1547

(Table continued)

TABLE XXXII (*continued*)

R^1	R^2	R^3	R^4	M.p.	Reference
H	H	HOOC	H	—	1228
H	HOOC	$C_{14}H_{29}$	H	206°	43
H	HOOC	$C_6H_5CH=$		—	1546
C_6H_5	HOOC	H	H	241°	626, 767, 837, 1304, 1635
C_6H_5	H	HOOC	H	91° (dec.)	306, 1230
4-$CH_3C_6H_4$	HOOC	H	H	188°	167, 1162, 1304
4-$CH_3OC_6H_4$	HOOC	H	H	250°	87
3-$H_2NC_6H_4$	HOOC	H	H	—	152, 347
3-ClC_6H_4	HOOC	H	H	—	873
4-$NO_2C_6H_4$	HOOC	H	H	233°	624
4-$HO_3SC_6H_4$	HOOC	H	H	—	1162
4-$H_2NO_2SC_6H_4$	HOOC	H	H	260° (dec.)	1628
3,4-$Cl_2C_6H_3$	HOOC	H	H	—	873
3,6-$Cl_2C_6H_3$	HOOC	H	H	—	873
2,4,6-$Br_3C_6H_2$	HOOC	H	H	—	312
2-HO_3S-4,5-$Cl_2C_6H_2$	HOOC	H	H	—	518
1-$C_{10}H_7$	HOOC	H	H	264° (dec.)	767
2-$C_{10}H_7$	HOOC	H	H	264° (dec.)	767
2-(C_6H_5)-C_6H_4	HOOC	H	H	—	1379
C_6H_5	CH_3	HOOC	H	189°	24
C_6H_5	HOOC	s-C_4H_9	H	96°	167
4-$CH_3C_6H_4$	CH_3	HOOC	H	187°	107
4-$CH_3C_6H_4$	HOOC	iso-C_3H_7	H	110°	167
C_6H_5	HOOC	$C_6H_5CH_2$	H	196°, 233°	167, 498
C_6H_5	HOOC	C_6H_5	H	144°	167, 506
C_6H_5	HOOC	CH= , —OH			948

H	CH_3OOC	H	H	226	1549
H	CH_3OOC	$C_6H_5CH_2$		>250°	1549
C_6H_5	CH_3OOC	H	H	196°	767
4-$CH_3OOCC_6H_4$	CH_3OOC	H	H	241° (dec.)	1274
4-$HO_3SC_6H_4$	CH_3OOC	H	H	—	153
C_6H_5	CH_3OOC	CH_3	H	191°	1064
H	C_2H_5OOC	H	H	178°	2, 337, 358, 1220, 1229, 1357, 1544, 1547
H	H	C_2H_5OOC	H	180°	604, 1228, 1231, 1232, 1233
CH_3	C_2H_5OOC	H	H	148°	594
H	CH_3	C_2H_5OOC	H	195°	1081
H	H	CH_3	C_2H_5OOC	—	1232
H	C_2H_5OOC	C_7H_{15}	H	151°	43
H	C_2H_5OOC	$C_{10}H_{21}$	H	142°	43
H	C_2H_5OOC	$C_{12}H_{25}$	H	130°	43
H	C_2H_5OOC	$C_{14}H_{29}$	H	130°	43
H	C_2H_5OOC	$C_{16}H_{33}$	H	123°	43
H	C_2H_5OOC	$C_2H_5OOCCH_2$	H	156°	962
H	C_2H_5OOC	$C_6H_5CH=$		>250°	1545
CH_3	C_2H_5OOC	CH_3	H	150°	499
C_6H_5	C_2H_5OOC	H	H	180°	366, 767, 1082, 1339, 1595
C_6H_5	H	C_2H_5OOC	H	116°	306, 1230, 1231, 1556
H	C_2H_5OOC	C_6H_5	H	233°	43
4-$NO_2C_6H_5$	C_2H_5OOC	H	H	288°	767
4-$HOOCC_6H_5$	C_2H_5OOC	H	H	197°	767
4-$HO_3SC_6H_4$	C_2H_5OOC	H	H	—	153
2-$KO_3SC_6H_4$	C_2H_5OOC	H	H	—	414
4-$H_2NO_2SC_6H_4$	C_2H_5OOC	H	H	197°	767, 1628
2-CH_3-6-Cl-4-$HO_3SC_6H_2$	C_2H_5OOC	H	H	—	153

(*Table continued*)

TABLE XXXII (*continued*)

R^1	R^2	R^3	R^4	M.p.	Reference
4-(4-$CH_3CONHC_6H_4$)C_6H_4	C_2H_5OOC	H	H	—	163
C_6H_5	CH_3	C_2H_5OOC	H	121°	810, 1008
C_6H_5	C_2H_5OOC	CH_3	H	151°	37, 499
C_6H_5	H	C_2H_5OOC	CH_3	—	1232
C_6H_5	C_2H_5OOC	C_2H_5	H	199°	499
C_6H_5	C_2H_5OOC	iso-C_3H_7	H	100°	1339
C_6H_5	$HOOCCH_2CH_2$	C_2H_5OOC	H	—	1222
C_6H_5	$C_2H_5OOCCH_2CH_2$	C_2H_5OOC	H	61°	418
C_6H_5	$CH_3OOCCH{=}CH$	C_2H_5OOC	H	147°	419
C_6H_5	$C_2H_5CH(CN)COCH_2CH_2$	C_2H_5OOC	H	106°	1223
C_6H_5	C_2H_5OOC	$C_6H_5CH_2$	H	194°	498
C_6H_5	C_2H_5OOC	$(C_6H_5)_2CH$	H	148°	1639
C_6H_5	$C_6H_4(CO)_2NCH_2$	C_2H_5OOC	H	215°	138
C_6H_5	4-NC-1-C_6H_5-pyrazolin-3-yl-CH_2CH_2 (ring: NC—C—C(=N—N(C_6H_5)—CH_2)—CH_2CH_2)	C_2H_5OOC	H	167°	1223

C_6H_5	C_2H_5OOC—C—CCH_2CH_2 (ring: C=O, N—C_6H_5, =N)	C_2H_5OOC	H	—	1223
$4\text{-}NO_2C_6H_4$	$C_2H_5OCH_2$	C_2H_5OOC	H	135°	532
C_6H_5	CH_3	C_2H_5OOC	CH_3	176°	563
C_6H_5	C_2H_5OOC	C_6H_5	H	142°	506
C_6H_5	$(C_2H_5)_2NCH_2CH_2OOC$	H	H	200° (2HCl)	574
H	H	$C_2H_5S_2C$	H	184°	89
H	CH_3	$C_2H_5S_2C$	H	186°	89
C_6H_5	CH_3	$C_2H_5S_2C$	H	81°	89
H	H_2NOC	H	H	219°	1549
H	C_4H_9HNOC	H	H	246°	225°
CH_3	H_2NOC	H	H	> 230°	594
H	CH_3	H_2NOC	H	255°	1193
C_6H_5	H_2NOC	H	H	233°	194, 1595
C_6H_5	CH_3NHOC	H	H	—	194
$2\text{-}CH_3OC_6H_4$	H_2NOC	H	H	—	194
C_6H_5	$2\text{-}ClC_6H_4NHOC$	H	H	82°	767
C_6H_5	CH_3	H_2NOC	H	223°	924, 1193
$4\text{-}C_2H_5OC_6H_4$	CH_3	H_2NOC	H	140°	1193
C_6H_5	C_6H_5	H_2NOC	H	227°	924
H	$H_2NHNOOC$	H	H	196°, 238°, 253°	282, 337, 443, 1544, 1545, 1547
H	$C_2H_5OOCCH_2C(CH_3){=}NHNOC$	H	H	182° (dec.)	337
H	$C_6H_5CH{=}NHNOC$	H	H	252°	337, 1545
H	$C_6H_5CONHNHOC$	H	H	269° (dec.)	337
CH_3	H_2NHNOC	H	H	253° (HCl)	594

(Table continued)

TABLE XXXII (*continued*)

R^1	R^2	R^3	R^4	M.p.	Reference
C_6H_5	H_2NHNOC	H	H	235°	1595
C_6H_5	H_2NHNOC	CH_3	H	179°	499
C_6H_5	H_2NHNOC	C_2H_5	H	144°	499
C_6H_5	H_2NHNOC	$C_6H_5CH_2$	H	—	498
C_6H_5	H_2NHNOC	C_6H_5	H	213°	506
CH_3	N_3OC	H	H	113° (def.)	594
C_6H_5	N_3OC	H	H		1595
C_6H_5	N_3OC	$C_6H_5CH_2$	H	134° (def.)	498
C_6H_5	N_3OC	C_6H_5	H		506
H	CH_3	CN	H	281°	924
C_6H_5	CH_3	CN	H	>316°, 218°	24, 924, 925
C_6H_5	$C_6H_5CH_2$	CN	H	173°	1310
4-$C_2H_5OC_6H_4$	CH_3	CN	H	198°	1186
C_6H_5	$C_6H_5CH_2$	CN	C_2H_5	167°	1310
C_6H_5	C_6H_5	CN	H	232°	924
C_6H_5	ClOC	$C_6H_5CH_2$	H	liquid	498
CH_3	C_6H_5	CN	H	225°	1190

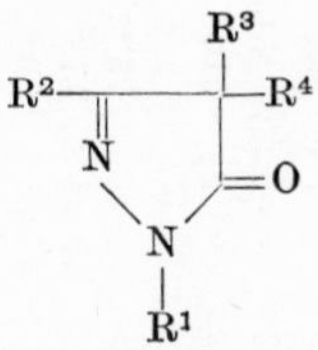

TABLE XXXIII. 2-Pyrazolin-5-ones. Carboxyl Derivatives Combined with Other Functional Substituents

R^1	R^2	R^3	R^4	M.p.	Reference
H	$C_6H_5CH{=}N$	HOOC	H	>280°	557
H	HOOC	NO	H	215° (dec.)	1545
C_6H_5	HOOC	NO	H	—	1635
C_6H_5	HOOC	H_2N	H	225°	292
4-$HO_3SC_6H_4$	HOOC	H_2N	H	—	35
C_6H_5	HOOC	CH_3CONH	H	216°	292
H	H_3COOC	NO	H	—	1549
H	C_2H_5OOC	C_6H_5O	H	213°	677
H	C_2H_5OOC	C_6H_5S	H	213°	677
H	C_2H_5OOC	NO	H	182°	1545
H_2NOC	C_2H_5OOC	$HOOCCH_2CH_2$	H	170°	1222
H_2NOC	C_2H_5OOC	CN	H	—	366
C_6H_5	C_2H_5OOC	C_6H_5CONH	H	195°	292
C_6H_5	C_2H_5OOC	C_6H_5S	H	183.5°	677
C_6H_5	C_2H_5OOC	4-$(C_2H_5)_2NC_6H_4N{=}$		150°	519
C_6H_5	C_2H_5OOC	2-CH_3-4-$(C_2H_5)_2NC_6H_3N{=}$		161°	244
C_6H_5CO	C_2H_5OOC	$C_6H_5CH_2$	H	217°	497
C_6H_5	H_2NOC	2-CH_3-4-$(C_2H_5)_2NC_6H_3N{=}$		210° (dec.)	244
H	H_2NHNOC	$H_2NN{=}$		178°	1549
CH_3	H_2NHNOC	NO	H	112° (exp.)	594
C_6H_5CO	H_2NHNOC	$C_6H_5CH_2$	H	203°	497
C_6H_5CO	N_3OC	$C_6H_5CH_2$	H	135° (def.)	497
H	$C_6H_5CONHNHCO$	C_6H_5CO	H	214°	337

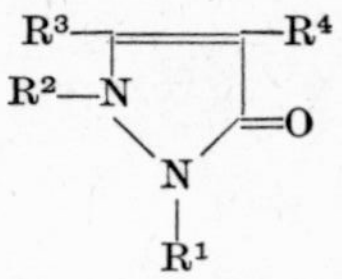

TABLE XXXIV. 3-Pyrazolin-5-ones. Carboxylic Acids and Thiocarboxylic Acids and Derivatives

R^1	R^2	R^3	R^4	M.p.	Reference
H	C_6H_5	H	HOOC	216° (dec.)	993
C_6H_5	CH_3	HOOC	H	198°	108
C_6H_5	CH_3	H	HOOC	220°	108
C_6H_5	C_6H_5	HOOC	H	205° (dec.)	370
C_6H_5	CH_3	CH_3	HOOC	214°	17, 107, 741, 896
C_6H_5	CH_3	HOOC	C_2H_5	72°	167
C_6H_5	C_2H_5	CH_3	HOOC	178°	741
C_6H_5	CH_3	HOOC	iso-C_3H_7	73°	167
C_6H_5	CH_3	HOOC	$C_6H_5CH_2$	110°	167
C_6H_5	CH_3	C_6H_5	HOOC	186°	107, 196
C_6H_5	CH_3	HOOC	C_6H_5	107°	167
4-$CH_3C_6H_4$	CH_3	CH_3	HOOC	187°	196
C_6H_5	CH_3	CH_3	HSOC	189°	107, 109
C_6H_5	CH_3	CH_3	HSSC	189° (dec.)	109, 831
C_6H_5	CH_3	CH_3OOC	H	121°	698
C_6H_5	C_6H_5	CH_3OOC	H	138°	370
C_6H_5	CH_3	CH_3	CH_3OOC	154°	18, 741
C_6H_5	CH_3	CH_3	CH_3S_2C	187°	109
H	C_6H_5	H	C_2H_5OOC	oil	993
CH_3	CH_3	H	C_2H_5OOC	—	1228

C_6H_5	CH_3	H	C_2H_5OOC	71°	1230
C_6H_5	C_6H_5	C_2H_5OOC	H	—	370
C_6H_5	CH_3	CH_3	C_2H_5OOC	152°	107, 741
C_6H_5	CH_3	C_2H_5OOC	CH_3	96°	167
C_6H_5	CH_3	C_2H_5OOC	iso-C_3H_7	73°	1339
4-$CH_3C_6H_4$	CH_3	C_2H_5OOC	iso-C_3H_7	101°	167
C_6H_5	CH_3	CH_3	iso-C_4H_9OOC	111°	741
C_6H_5	CH_3	CH_3	iso-$C_5H_{11}OOC$	99°	741
C_6H_5	CH_3	CH_3	$ClCH_2CH_2OOC$	144°	741
C_6H_5	CH_3	CH_3	$NCCH_2CH_2OOC$	230° (dec.)	741
C_6H_5	CH_3	CH_3	$H_2NCH_2CH_2OOC$	>260°	741
C_6H_5	CH_3	CH_3	$CH_3NHCH_2CH_2OOC$	208°	741
C_6H_5	CH_3	CH_3	$(CH_3)_2NCH_2CH_2OOC$	202° (dec.)	741
C_6H_5	CH_3	CH_3	$C_6H_5NHCH_2CH_2OOC$	242° (dec.)	741
C_6H_5	CH_3	CH_3	4-$C_2H_5OC_6H_4NHCH_2CH_2OOC$	186°	741
C_6H_5	CH_3	CH_3	4-$C_2H_5OOCC_6H_4NHCH_2CH_2OOC$	175°	741
C_6H_5	CH_3	CH_3	$(C_6H_5)_2NCH_2CH_2OOC$	134°	741
C_6H_5	CH_3	CH_3	4-$C_2H_5OC_6H_4NHCH(CH_3)OOC$	160°	741
C_6H_5	CH_3	CH_3	$H_2NC(=O)NHCH_2CH_2OOC$	130°	741
C_6H_5	CH_3	CH_3	$C_6H_5CH_2OOC$	126°	741
C_6H_5	CH_3	CH_3	C_6H_5OOC	198°	741
C_6H_5	CH_3	CH_3	2-$CH_3OC_6H_4OOC$	163°	741
C_6H_5	CH_3	CH_3	2-$CH_3OOCC_6H_4OOC$	138°	741
C_6H_5	CH_3	CH_3	2-$C_6H_5OOCC_6H_4OOC$	179°	741
C_6H_5	CH_3	CH_3	1-$C_{10}H_7OOC$	175°	741
C_6H_5	CH_3	CH_3	2-$C_{10}H_7OOC$	186°	741

(Table continued)

TABLE XXXIV (*continued*)

R^1	R^2	R^3	R^4	M.p.	Reference
C_6H_5	CH_3	CH_3	—OOC, N	217°	741
C_6H_5	CH_3	CH_3	CH_3—, —$COCH_2OOC$, CH_3N, N, C_6H_5	256°	741
C_6H_5	CH_3	CH_3	CH_3O, N, CH—, OOC, CH_2, CH_2, N, —CH=CH_2	265°	741
H	C_6H_5	CH_3	C_2H_5SSC	114°	89
C_6H_5	CH_3	CH_3	C_2H_5SSC	178°	89, 831
CH_3	C_6H_5	CH_3	C_2H_5SSC	161°	829
C_6H_5	CH_3	H_2NOC	H	197°	167, 697, 1339
C_6H_5	CH_3	C_6H_5NHOC	C_6H_5	291°	167
H	C_6H_5	CH_3	C_6H_5NHOC	258°	826
H	C_6H_5	CH_3	1-$C_{10}H_7NHOC$	231°	826
C_6H_5	CH_3	CH_3	H_2NOC	246°	741, 831, 925
C_6H_5	CH_3	CH_3	CH_3NHOC	207°	741
C_6H_5	CH_3	CH_3	$(CH_3)_2NOC$	211°	741
C_6H_5	CH_3	CH_3	$(C_2H_5)_2NOC$	106°	23, 107, 741
C_6H_5	CH_3	CH_3	$H_2NCH_2CH_2NHOC$	234°	741
C_6H_5	CH_3	CH_3	$C_2H_5O_2CCH_2NHOC$	—	741

C_6H_5	CH_3	CH_3	$CH_3CONHCONHOC$	249°	741
C_6H_5	CH_3	CH_3	$(C_2H_5)_2C(Br)OCNHOCNHOC$	182°	741
C_6H_5	CH_3	CH_3	$H_2NCONHOC$	250°	741
C_6H_5	CH_3	CH_3	$(CH_3)_2CH_2CH(Br)OCNHOCNHOC$	—	741
C_6H_5	CH_3	CH_3	$C_6H_5CH_2NHOC$	141°	741
C_6H_5	CH_3	CH_3	C_6H_5NHOC	250°	741
C_6H_5	CH_3	CH_3	$4\text{-}CH_3C_6H_4NHOC$	208°	741
C_6H_5	CH_3	CH_3	$4\text{-}C_2H_5OC_6H_4NHOC$	186°	741
C_6H_5	CH_3	CH_3	$4\text{-}H_2NC_6H_4NHOC$	370° (dec.)	741
C_6H_5	CH_3	CH_3	$4\text{-}CH_3CONHC_6H_4NHOC$	260°	741
C_6H_5	CH_3	CH_3	$3\text{-}NO_2C_6H_4NHOC$	245°	741
C_6H_5	CH_6	CH_3	$4\text{-}NO_2C_6H_4NHOC$	230°	741
C_6H_5	CH_3	CH_3	$2\text{-}HOOCC_6H_4NHOC$	228°	741
C_6H_4	CH_3	CH_3	$4\text{-}C_2H_5O_2CC_6H_4NHOC$	194°	741
C_6H_5	CH_3	CH_3	$4\text{-iso-}C_4H_9O_2CC_6H_4NHOC$	203°	741
C_6H_5	CH_3	CH_3	$4\text{-}H_2NO_2SC_6H_4NHOC$	261°	741
C_6H_5	CH_3	CH_3	$4\text{-}(CH_3)_2NO_2SC_6H_4NHOC$	26°	741
C_6H_5	CH_3	CH_3	$4\text{-}(C_2H_5)_2NO_2SC_6H_4NHOC$	174°	741
C_6H_5	CH_3	CH_3	$4\text{-}(4\text{-}H_2NC_6H_4)C_6H_4NHOC$	304°	741
C_6H_5	CH_3	CH_3	$2,4\text{-}(CH_3)_2C_6H_3NHOC$	172°	741
C_6H_5	CH_3	CH_3	$1\text{-}C_{10}H_7NHOC$	210°	741
C_6H_5	CH_3	CH_3	$2\text{-}C_{10}H_7NHOC$	230°	741
C_6H_5	CH_3	CH_3	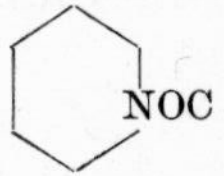 (piperidine ring) NOC	169°	741
C_6H_5	CH_3	CH_3	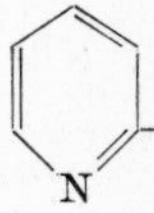 (2-pyridyl ring, N) –NHOC	197°	741

(*Table continued*)

TABLE XXXIV (*continued*)

R^1	R^2	R^3	R^4	M.p.	Reference
C_6H_5	CH_3	CH_3	H_2N–[pyridine ring, N]–NHOC	298°	741
C_6H_5	CH_3	CH_3	CH_3–, CH_3–N, N–C_6H_5, =O [pyrazolone ring]–NHOC	246°	741
C_6H_5	CH_3	CH_3	$(C_6H_5)_2NOC$	208°	741
C_6H_5	CH_3	CH_3	[benzene ring](CO)(CO)NOC	186° (dec.)	741
CH_3	C_6H_5	CH_3	H_2NOC	215°	830
CH_3	C_6H_5	CH_3	C_6H_5NHOC	164°	829
CH_3	C_6H_5	CH_3	$3\text{-}NO_2C_6H_5NHOC$	—	829
C_6H_5	CH_3	H_2NOC	iso-C_3H_7	130°	1339
CH_3	C_6H_5	CH_3	$1\text{-}C_{10}H_7NHOC$	185°	829
H	C_6H_5	CH_3	C_6H_5NHSC	238°	826
C_6H_5	CH_3	CH_3	C_6H_5NHSC	184°, 199°	826, 831
C_6H_5	CH_3	CH_3	$C_6H_5N{=}C$(–SH)	148°, 200°	826, 831
CH_3	C_6H_5	CH_3	H_2NSC	186°	830

CH_3	C_6H_5	CH_3	$HN{=}C(SH)$	197°	830
CH_3	C_6H_5	CH_3	C_6H_5HNSC	152°	830
CH_3	C_6H_5	CH_3	$C_6H_5N{=}C(SH)$	206°	829
CH_3	C_6H_5	CH_3	$1\text{-}C_{10}H_7N{=}C(SH)$	195°	829
CH_3	CH_3	H_2NHNOC	H	204°	167
C_6H_5	CH_3	H_2NHNOC	H	233°, 147°	167, 698, 1387
C_6H_5	CH_3	$CH_2O_2C_6H_3\text{—}CH{=}NHNOC$	H	247°	698
C_6H_5	CH_3	$C_6H_5SO_2NHNHOC$	H	229° (dec.)	698
C_6H_5	C_2H_5	H_2NHNOC	H	171°	167
C_6H_5	CH_3	CH_3	H_2NHNOC	200°, 270°	696, 892, 1634
C_6H_5	CH_3	H_2NHNOC	CH_3	158°	167
C_6H_5	CH_3	CH_3	$C_6H_5SO_2NHNHOC$	262°	892, 204, 1634
C_6H_5	CH_3	H_2NHNOC	C_2H_5	175°	167
C_6H_5	CH_3	H_2NHNOC	iso-C_3H_7	113°	167, 1387
C_6H_5	CH_3	H_2NHNOC	s-C_4H_9	145°	167
C_6H_5	CH_3	H_2NHNOC	$C_6H_5CH_2$	191°	167
C_6H_5	CH_3	H_2NHNOC	C_6H_5	75° (C_2H_5OH)	167
C_6H_5	CH_3	H_2NHNOC	Br	183°	167

Table continued)

TABLE XXXIV (*continued*)

R^1	R^2	R^3	R^4	M.p.	Reference
4-$CH_3C_6H_4$	CH_3	H_2NHNOC	iso-C_3H_7	96°	167
CH_3	C_6H_5	CH_3	H_2NHNSC	166°	830
CH_3	C_6H_5	CH_3	$C_6H_5HNHNSC$	186°	830
CH_3	C_6H_5	CH_3	$H_2NN{=}C(SH)$	165°	830
CH_3	CH_3	N_3OC	H	110° (exp.)	167
C_6H_5	CH_3	N_3OC	H	95° (dec.)	167, 1387
C_6H_5	C_2H_5	N_3OC	H	117° (dec.)	167
C_6H_5	CH_3	N_3OC	iso-C_3H_7	88° (dec.)	167, 1387
C_6H_5	CH_3	N_3OC	s-C_4H_9	90° (dec.)	167
C_6H_5	CH_3	N_3OC	$C_6H_5CH_2$	110° (exp.)	167
C_6H_5	CH_3	N_3OC	C_6H_5	97° (dec.)	167
4-$CH_3C_6H_4$	CH_3	N_3OC	iso-C_3H_7	92° (dec.)	167
C_6H_5	CH_3	CH_3	CN	224°	741, 925, 1181
C_6H_5	CH_3	C_6H_5	CN	188°	1183
4-$C_2H_5OC_6H_4$	CH_3	CH_3	CN	186°	1180
C_6H_5	CH_3	CH_3	ClOC	171°	18, 107, 741
C_6H_5	CH_3	CH_3	NCOC	174°	741
C_6H_5	CH_3	CH_3	CH_3COOOC	154°	741
C_6H_5	CH_3	CH_3	$(C_2H_5)_2CHCOOOC$	218° (dec.)	741
C_6H_5	CH_3	CH_3	$ClCH_2COOOC$	122°	23
C_6H_5	CH_3	CH_3	C_6H_5COOOC	185°	741
C_6H_5	CH_3	CH_3	$C_6H_5SO_3OC$	103°	741
C_6H_5	CH_3	CH_3	4-$CH_3C_6H_4SO_3OC$	102°	741

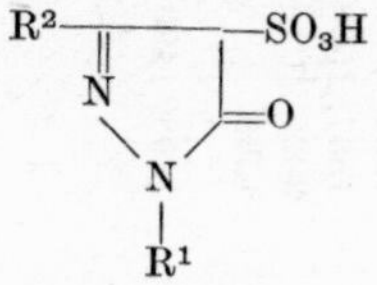

TABLE XXXV. 2-Pyrazolin-5-ones. Sulfonic Acids

R^1	R^2	M.p.	Reference
H	CH_3	—	1671
C_6H_5	CH_3	218°	684, 685, 738, 745, 1671, 1672
3-$H_2NC_6H_4$	CH_3	—	1674
4-$H_2NC_6H_4$	CH_3	—	1671, 1672, 1674
3-$NO_2C_6H_4$	CH_3	—	1674
4-$NO_2C_6H_4$	CH_3	—	1671
4-$HO_3SC_6H_4$	CH_3	—	684, 685
3-$NO_2C_6H_4$	HOOC	—	1671

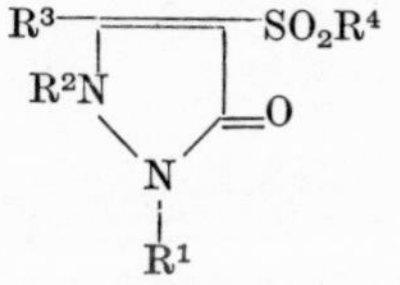

TABLE XXXVI. 3-Pyrazolin-5-ones. Sulfonic Acids

R^1	R^2	R^3	R^4	M.p.	Reference
C_6H_5	CH_3	CH_3	HO	276° (dec.)	738, 745, 1249
C_6H_5	C_2H_5	CH_3	HO	—	738
C_6H_5	CH_3	CH_3	Cl	191°	745, 1248, 1249
C_6H_5	CH_3	CH_3	H_2N	228°	745, 1248, 1249
C_6H_5	CH_3	CH_3	CH_3HN	193°	745, 1248
C_6H_5	CH_3	CH_3	$(C_2H_5)_2N$	153°	745, 1248
C_6H_5	CH_3	CH_3	C_6H_5NH	203°	745
C_6H_5	CH_3	CH_3	4-$C_2H_5OC_6H_4NH$	93°	745
C_6H_5	CH_3	CH_3	4-$H_2NO_2SC_6H_4NH$	213°	1248
C_6H_5	CH_3	CH_3	C_6H_5CONH	242°	745
C_6H_5	CH_3	CH_3	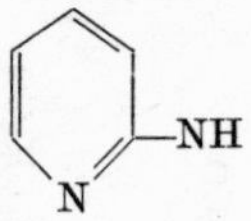 N —NH	244° (dec.)	745, 1249

TABLE XXXVII. 2-Pyrazolin-5-ones. Acyl and Carboxyl Derivatives and Sulfonyl Substituents on N–1

R^1	R^2	R^3	R^4	M.p.	Reference
CH_3CO	$C_2H_5OOCCH_2$	H	H	116°	866
CH_3CO	CH_3	CH_3	H	126°	1531
CH_3CO	CH_3	CH_3	CH_3	168°	1557, 1560
CH_3CO	CH_3	$C_6H_5CH_2$	H	128°	302
CH_3CO	C_6H_5	H	H	127°	1598
CH_3CO	2-furyl	H	H	153°	1498, 1499
$C_6H_5CH_2CO$	CH_3	H	H	134°	6
C_6H_5CO	CH_3	H	H	—	6
2-C_6H_5-quinolin-3-yl-CO	CH_3	H	H	237°	718
6-CH_3-2-C_6H_5-quinolin-4-yl-CO	CH_3	H	H	> 300°	719

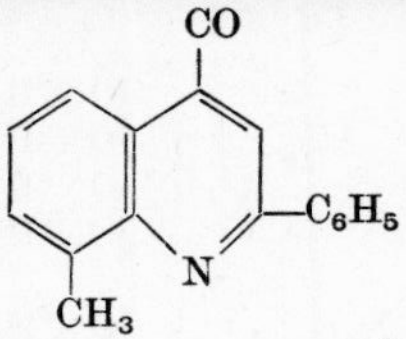 CO, C_6H_5, N, CH_3	CH_3	H	H	—	719
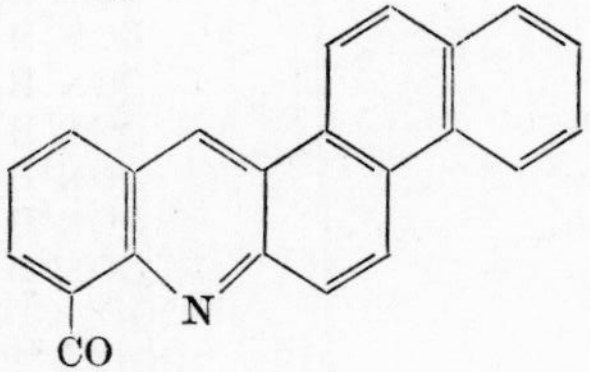 N, CO	CH_3	H	H	—	720
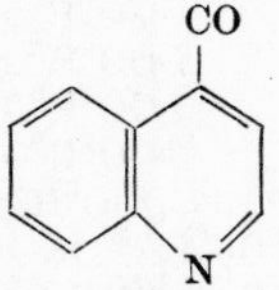 CO, N	C_6H_5	H	H	—	1050
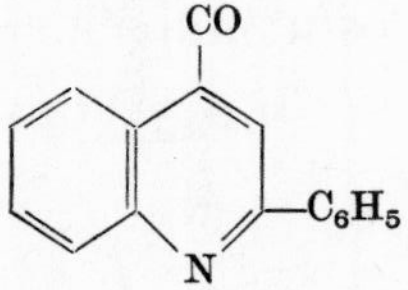 CO, C_6H_5, N	C_6H_5	H	H	190°	1050
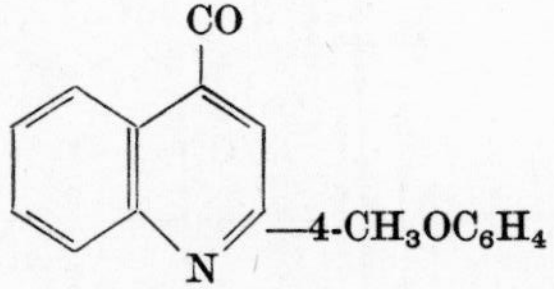 CO, 4-$CH_3OC_6H_4$, N	C_6H_5	H	H	183°	1050

(Table continued)

TABLE XXXVII (*continued*)

R^1	R^2	R^3	R^4	M.p.	Reference
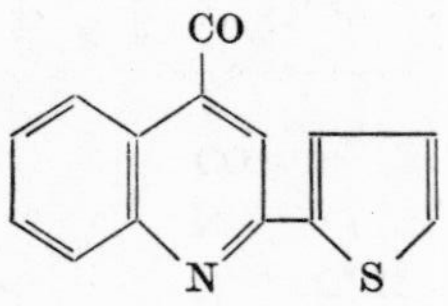	C_6H_5	H	H	182°	1050
4-$H_2NC_6H_4SO_2$	CH_3	H	H	152°, 166°	716, 1197, 1199
4-$CH_3CONHC_6H_4SO_2$	CH_3	H	H	167°	356
4-$CH_3OOCNHC_6H_4SO_2$	CH_3	H	H	158°	1199
4-$NO_2C_6H_4SO_2$	CH_3	H	H	—	1627
CH_3OOC	CH_3	C_2H_5	H	—	61
C_6H_5OOC	CH_3	H	H	203°	61
C_2H_5OOC	CH_3	CH_3	H	184°	61
C_2H_5OOC	CH_3	C_2H_5	H	170°	61
C_3H_7OOC	CH_3	H	H	120°	61
C_3H_7OOC	CH_3	CH_3	H	149°	61
C_3H_7OOC	CH_3	C_2H_5	H	126°	61
H_2NOC	CH_3	H	H	170°, 192°	61, 275, 355
H_2NOC	iso-C_4H_9	H	H	165°	97
H_2NOC	H	$HOOCCH_2$	H	185°	275
H_2NOC	$HOOCCH_2CH_2$	H	H	195° (dec.)	1221
H_2NOC	$CH_3OOCCH_2CH_2$	H	H	172°	1221
H_2NOC	CH_3	CH_3	H	180°, 194°	61, 358, 692
H_2NOC	CH_3	C_2H_5	H	168°	61, 358, 1012
H_2NOC	C_3H_7	C_2H_5	H	145°	1013
H_2NOC	CH_3	iso-C_5H_{11}	H	157°	65
H_2NOC	CH_3	2-$CH_3C_4H_9$	H	156°	65
H_2NOC	C_6H_5	H	H	179°	357

13*

H_2NOC	C_6H_5	C_2H_5	H	181°	1012
H_2NOC	iso-C_3H_7	C_6H_5	H	318°	1640
H_2NOC	C_6H_5	$C_6H_5CH_2CH_2$	H	131°	1345
H_2NOC	2-Pyrrolyl (N–H)	H	H	192°	1067
C_6H_5NHOC	CH_3	H	H	237°	643
C_6H_5NHOC	2-Furyl	H	H	192°	1498, 1500
C_6H_5NHOC	2-Furyl	$C_6H_5CH=$		> 300°	1498, 1500
4-$CH_3C_6H_4NHOC$	CH_3	H	H	234°	643
4-(1-$C_{10}H_7$)NHOC	CH_3	H	H	195°	643
$H_2NC(=NH)$ (HNO_3 salt)	CH_3	H	H	235° (dec.)	359, 1568
$H_2NC(=NH)$ (HNO_3 salt)	CH_3	CH_3	H	202°	359
$H_2NC(=NH)$ (HNO_3 salt)	CH_3	C_2H_5	H	262°	359
$H_2NC(=NH)$ (HNO_3 salt)	CH_3	C_3H_7	H	260°	359

(Table continued)

TABLE XXXVII (*continued*)

R^1	R^2	R^3	R^4	M.p.	Reference
$H_2NC(=NH)$ (HNO_3 salt)	CH_3	CH_3	CH_3	151°	359
$H_2NC(=NH)$ (HNO_3 salt)	CH_3	C_2H_5OOC	H	290°	359
$H_2NC(=NH)$	C_6H_5	H	H	102°	359, 1568
$H_2NC(=NH)$	CH_3	$C_6H_5CH=$		210° (dec.)	1296
$C_2H_5OOCCH_2C(CH_3)=NC(=NH)$	CH_3	H	H	180° (dec.)	1568
$C_2H_5OOCCH_2C(C_6H_5)=NC(=NH)$	CH_3	H	H	185°	1568
$C_6H_5NHC(=NC_6H_5)$	CH_3	H	H	198°	359
$4\text{-}CH_3C_6H_4C(=N\text{-}4\text{-}CH_3C_6H_4)$	CH_3	H	H	210°	359
$2\text{-}C_{10}H_7NHC(=N\text{-}2\text{-}C_{10}H_7)$	CH_3	H	H	290°	359
$C_6H_5NHC(=NC_6H_5)$	C_6H_5	H	H	206°	359

$4\text{-}CH_3C_6H_4NHC(=N\text{-}4\text{-}CH_3C_6H_4)$	C_6H_5	H	H	249°	359
$2\text{-}C_{10}H_7NHC(=N\text{-}2\text{-}C_{10}H_7)$	C_6H_5	H	H	180°	359
$C_2H_5OOCCH_2C(CH_3)=NNHCO$	CH_3	H	H	230° (dec.)	1037, 1632
H_2NCS	CH_3	H	H	180°	355, 358, 421
H_2NCS	C_6H_5	H	H	161°	357
CH_3NHCS	CH_3	H	H	84°	357
C_2H_5NHCS	C_6H_5	H	H	179°	357
$C_2H_5OOCCH=C(CH_3)NHCS$	CH_3	H	H	175°	355
C_6H_5NHCS	CH_3	H	H	117°	357
C_6H_5NHCS	C_6H_5	H	H	127°	357
$4\text{-}CH_3C_6H_4NHCS$	CH_3	H	H	121°	357
$4\text{-}CH_3C_6H_4NHCS$	C_6H_5	H	H	106°	357
$C_6H_5NHNHCS$	CH_3	H	H	—	602

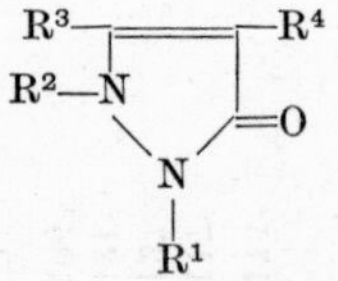

R[3]—R[4]
R[2]—N
=O
N
R[1]

TABLE XXXVIII. 3-Pyrazolin-5-ones. Acyl Substituents on Nitrogen

R[1]	R[2]	R[3]	R[4]	M.p.	Reference
H	CH_3CO	C_6H_5	H	144°	1598
H	4-H_2N——SO_2 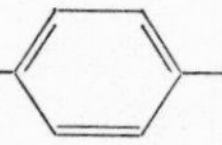	CH_3	H	169°	356
H	4-CH_3CONH——SO_2 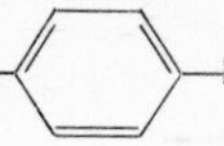	CH_3	H	195°	356
C_6H_5	C_6H_5CO	CH_3	H	75°	1056
C_6H_5	C_6H_5NHCO	CH_3	H	142°	643
C_6H_5	CH_3CO	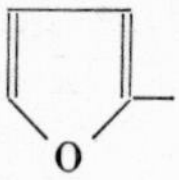 O	H	69°	1499
CH_3CO	CH_3CO	CH_3	H	54°	729
CH_3CO	CH_3CO	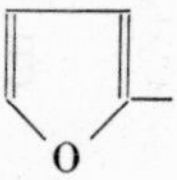 O	H	102°	1498, 1499
C_6H_5	C_6H_5CO	CH_3	CH_3	99°	1056
C_6H_5	C_6H_5CO	CH_3	Br	82.5°	1056
CH_3CO	$C_6H_5N{=}N$	CH_3	CH_3	—	1531
CH_3CO	CH_3CO	CH_3	CH_3	44°, 56°	1531, 1557
CH_3CO	CH_3CO	CH_3	C_2H_5	57°	729
CH_3CO	CH_3CO	CH_3	C_3H_7	40°	729
CH_3CO	CH_3CO	CH_3	$C_6H_5CH_2$	69°	729
C_6H_5	C_6H_5CO	CH_3	C_6H_5CO	157°	973, 1056

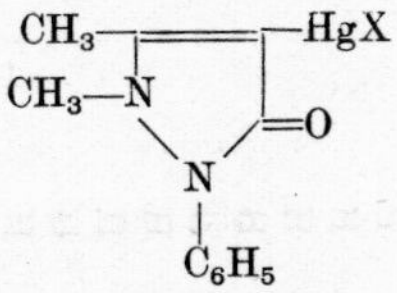

$$
\begin{array}{l}
CH_3\text{—C}=\text{C—HgX} \\
CH_3\text{—N} \quad \text{C}=O \\
\quad\quad \text{N} \\
\quad\quad | \\
\quad\quad C_6H_5
\end{array}
$$

TABLE XXXIX. Mercurated 3-Pyrazolin-5-ones

X	M.p.	Reference
Cl	95°	1155
Br	130°	1155
I	—	1155
OH	—	1155
CH_3COO	—	1155

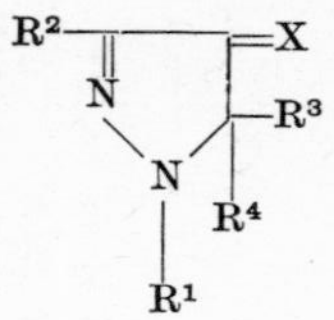

TABLE XL. 2-Pyrazolin-4-ones and 4-Imino-2-pyrazolines

X=O

R^1	R^2	R^3	R^4	M.p.	Reference
H	H	H	H	118°	1644
CH_3	H	H	H	—	1644
H	$(CH_3)_2CHCH_2CH_2$	H	H	185°	92
H	$C_6H_5CH_2$	H	H	157°	92
C_6H_5	H	H	H	—	425
H	HOOC	H	H	208°	425, 1644
H	H	HOOC	H	204°	92
C_6H_5	H	$C_6H_5N{=}N$	H	122°	1644
C_6H_5	H	NO	H	190°	1644
$2\text{-}NO_2C_6H_4$	C_6H_5CO	H	H	121°	288
$4\text{-}NO_2C_6H_4$	C_6H_5CO	H	H	211°	288
H	$(CH_3)_2CHCH_2CH_2$	HOOC	H	186°	92
H	$C_6H_5CH_2$	HOOC	H	183°	92
C_6H_5	HOOC	H	H	153°	425, 1644
H	$(CH_3)_2CHCH_2CH_2$	C_2H_5OOC	H	115°	92
H	$C_6H_5CH_2$	C_2H_5OOC	H	169°	92
H	C_6H_5	C_2H_5OOC	H	162°	92
C_6H_5	C_2H_5OOC	H	H	84°	1644
$2\text{-}NO_2C_6H_4$	C_2H_5OOC	H	H	153°	286
$4\text{-}NO_2C_6H_4$	C_2H_5OOC	H	H	220°	286
$4\text{-}H_2O_3AsC_6H_4$	C_2H_5OOC	H	H	—	1292
$2\text{-}CH_3\text{-}4\text{-}NO_2C_6H_3$	C_2H_5OOC	H	H	177°	290

2-CH_3-5-$NO_2C_6H_3$	C_2H_5OOC	H	H	114°	290
3,5-$Cl_2C_6H_3$	C_2H_5OOC	H	H	154°	295
3,5-$Br_2C_6H_3$	C_2H_5OOC	H	H	154°	295
2-Br-4-$NO_2C_6H_3$	C_2H_5OOC	H	H	189°	286
2,4-$(NO_2)_2C_6H_3$	C_2H_5OOC	H	H	150°	289
2-CH_3-6-$NO_2C_6H_3$	C_2H_5OOC	H	H	99°	290
2-NO_2-4-$CH_3C_6H_3$	C_2H_5OOC	H	H	119°	290
3-NO_2-4-$CH_3C_6H_3$	C_2H_5OOC	H	H	182°	290
2-CH_3-4-Br-6-$NO_2C_6H_2$	C_2H_5OOC	H	H	162°	290
2-CH_3-4-NO_2-6-BrC_6H_2	C_2H_5OOC	H	H	183°	290
2-NO_2-4-CH_3-6-BrC_6H_2	C_2H_5OOC	H	H	165°	290
2,6-Br_2-3-NO_2-4-CH_3C_6H	C_2H_5OOC	H	H	184°	290
2,4,6-$Cl_3C_6H_2$	C_2H_5OOC	H	H	158°	294
2,4,6-$Br_3C_6H_2$	C_2H_5OOC	H	H	160°	294
2,4-Cl_2-4-$NO_2C_6H_2$	C_2H_5OOC	H	H	—	287
2,6-Br_2-4-$NO_2C_6H_2$	C_2H_5OOC	H	H	170°	286
C_6H_5	(pyrazole ring: N, N–C_6H_5)—OOC	H	H	177°	1644
H	CH_3OOC	CH_3OOC	H	232°	92
H	C_2H_5OOC	C_2H_5OOC	H	151°	92
2-$NO_2C_6H_4$	C_6H_5CO	Cl	H	120°	288
4-$NO_2C_6H_4$	C_6H_5CO	Cl	H	177°	288
C_6H_5	HOOC	$C_6H_5N{=}N$	H	209° (dec.)	1644
2-$NO_2C_6H_4$	C_2H_5OOC	Cl	H	142°	287
3-$NO_2C_6H_4$	C_2H_5OOC	Cl	H	109°	287
4-$NO_2C_6H_4$	C_2H_5OOC	Cl	H	146°	287
4-$NO_2C_6H_4$	C_2H_5OOC	H	H (4-NOH)	222°	287
2-CH_3-4-$NO_2C_6H_3$	C_2H_5OOC	Cl	H	181°	290
2-CH_3-5-$NO_2C_6H_3$	C_2H_5OOC	Cl	H	101°	290

(*Table continued*)

TABLE XL (*continued*)

R^1	R^2	R^3	R^4	M.p.	Reference
$2\text{-}CH_3\text{-}6\text{-}NO_2C_6H_3$	C_2H_5OOC	Cl	H	135°	290
$3\text{-}NO_2\text{-}4\text{-}CH_3C_6H_3$	C_2H_5OOC	Cl	H	128°	290
$2\text{-}Cl\text{-}4\text{-}NO_2C_6H_3$	C_2H_5OOC	Cl	H	191°	287
$2\text{-}CH_3\text{-}4\text{-}Br\text{-}6\text{-}NO_2C_6H_2$	C_2H_5OOC	Cl	H	164°	290
$2\text{-}CH_3\text{-}4\text{-}NO_2\text{-}6\text{-}BrC_6H_2$	C_2H_5OOC	Cl	H	202°	290
$2\text{-}NO_2\text{-}4\text{-}CH_3\text{-}6\text{-}BrC_6H_2$	C_2H_5OOC	Cl	H	168°	290
$2,4,6\text{-}Cl_3C_6H_2$	C_2H_5OOC	Cl	H	178°, 195°	294
$2,6\text{-}Cl_2\text{-}4\text{-}NO_2C_6H_2$	C_2H_5OOC	Cl	H	200°	287
$2\text{-}CH_3\text{-}4,6\text{-}Br_2\text{-}5\text{-}NO_2C_6H$	C_2H_5OOC	Cl	H	165°	290
$2,6\text{-}Br_2\text{-}3\text{-}NO_2\text{-}4\text{-}CH_3C_6H$	C_2H_5OOC	Cl	H	169°	290
$2\text{-}NO_2C_6H_4$	C_2H_5OOC	Br	H	161°	286
$3\text{-}NO_2C_6H_4$	C_2H_5OOC	Br	H	167°	286
$4\text{-}NO_2C_6H_4$	C_2H_5OOC	Br	H	163°	286
$4\text{-}H_2O_3AsC_6H_4$	C_2H_5OOC	Br	H	—	1292
$2\text{-}CH_3\text{-}5\text{-}NO_2C_6H_3$	C_2H_5OOC	Br	H	133°	290
$2\text{-}CH_3\text{-}6\text{-}NO_2C_6H_3$	C_2H_5OOC	Br	H	146°	290
$3\text{-}NO_2\text{-}4\text{-}CH_3C_6H_3$	C_2H_5OOC	Br	H	143°	290
$3,5\text{-}Cl_2C_6H_3$	C_2H_5OOC	Br	H	156°	295
$2\text{-}Br\text{-}4\text{-}NO_2C_6H_3$	C_2H_5OOC	Br	H	218°	286
$2,4,6\text{-}Cl_3C_6H_2$	C_2H_5OOC	Br	H	190°	294
$2,4,6\text{-}Br_3C_6H_2$	C_2H_5OOC	Br	H	208°	294
$2,6\text{-}Br_2\text{-}4\text{-}NO_2C_6H_2$	C_2H_5OOC	Br	H	209°	286
C_6H_5	HOOC	NO	H	190°	1644
$2\text{-}NO_2C_6H_4$	C_2H_5CO	Cl	Cl	166°	288
$4\text{-}NO_2C_6H_4$	C_6H_5CO	Cl	Cl	145°	288
$2\text{-}NO_2C_6H_4$	C_2H_5OOC	Cl	Cl	98°	287
$3\text{-}NO_2C_6H_4$	C_2H_5OOC	Cl	Cl	135°	287
$4\text{-}NO_2C_6H_4$	C_2H_5OOC	Cl	Cl	—	287
$2\text{-}CH_3\text{-}4\text{-}NO_2C_6H_3$	C_2H_5OOC	Cl	Cl	124°	290
$2\text{-}Cl\text{-}4\text{-}NO_2C_6H_3$	C_2H_5OOC	Cl	Cl	131°	287

TABLE XL (*continued*)

$X=NR^5$

R^1	R^2	R^3	R^4	R^5	M.p.	Reference
H	H	H	H	H	80°, 195°	92, 368, 819
H	H	H	H	C_6H_5CO	173°	1646
H	H	H	H	$4\text{-}H_2NC_6H_4SO_2$	185°	368, 1157
H	CH_3	H	H	H	97°	368, 680
H	CH_3	H	H	C_6H_5CO	205°	1045
H	CH_3	H	H	$4\text{-}H_2NC_6H_4SO_2$	176°	368
C_6H_5	H	H	H	H	104°	671
H	3-pyridyl	H	H	H	—	1529
H	3-pyridyl	H	H	$4\text{-}H_2NC_6H_4SO_2$	210° (H_2O)	1529
H	3-pyridyl	H	H	$4\text{-}CH_3CONHC_6H_4SO_2$	234°	1529
H	CH_3	CH_3	H	H	—	680, 1015, 1019
H	CH_3	CH_3	H	C_6H_5CO	290° (dec.)	1019

(*Table continued*)

TABLE XL *(continued)*

$X=NR^5$

R^1	R^2	R^3	R^4	R^5	M.p.	Reference
H	CH_3	CH_3	H	4-$H_2NC_6H_4SO_2$	233°	1157
C_6H_5	CH_3	H	H	H	88°	995
C_6H_5	CH_3	H	H	4-$H_2NC_6H_4$	188°	995
C_6H_5	CH_3	H	H	4-$CH_3CONHC_6H_4$	239°	995
C_6H_5	CH_3	H	H	HCO	81°	995
C_6H_5	CH_3	H	H	CH_3CO	120°	995
C_6H_5	CH_3	H	H	H_2NCO	198°	995
C_6H_5	CH_3	H	H	C_6H_5NHCO	193°	995
C_6H_5	CH_3	H	H	C_6H_5NHCS	173°	995
CH_3	CH_3	CH_3	H	H	102°	812
C_6H_5	CH_3	CH_3	H	H	38°	1043
C_6H_5	CH_3	CH_3	H	CH_3CO	130°	1043
C_6H_5	CH_3	CH_3	H	C_6H_5CO	153°	1165
H	CH_3	Cl	H	H	182°	1045
H	CH_3	Br	H	CH_3CO	185°	1045
C_6H_5	CH_3	Cl	H	H	227°	974, 995
C_6H_5	CH_3	Cl	H	HCO	137°	974
C_6H_5	CH_3	Cl	H	CH_3CO	123°	974
C_6H_5	CH_3	Cl	H	C_6H_5CO	148°	974
C_6H_5	CH_3	Cl	H	$C_6H_5SO_2$	154°	974
C_6H_5	CH_3	Cl	H	H_2NCO	230°	974
C_6H_5	CH_3	Cl	H	C_6H_5NHCO	216°	974
C_6H_5	CH_3	Cl	H	C_6H_5NHCS	182°	974
H	H	HOOC	H	H	212°	92, 1210
H	CH_3	HOOC	H	H	208°	1049
H	C_2H_5OOC	C_2H_5OOC	H	H	144°	92
CH_3CO	C_6H_5	CH_3	H	CH_3CO	186°	1044
CH_3CO	CH_3	Cl	H	CH_3CO	176°	1045

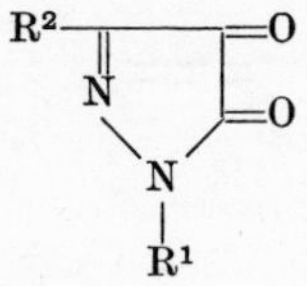

TABLE XLI. 2-Pyrazolin-4,5-diones

R^1	R^2	M.p.	Reference
C_6H_5	CH_3	118°	52, 424, 809, 1242
4-BrC_6H_4	CH_3	171°	1642
4-$NO_2C_6H_4$	CH_3	185°	690
4-$CH_3OC_6H_4$	$C_2H_5OOCCH{=}CHCH{=}CH$	164°	125
4-BrC_6H_4	$C_2H_5OOCCH{=}CH$	91°	125
4-BrC_6H_4	$C_2H_5OOCCH{=}CHCH{=}CH$	159°	125
C_6H_5	C_6H_5	—	1243

TABLE XLII. 3-Pyrazolidinones

Section A. All Substituents Except Mercury

R^1	R^2	R^3	R^4	R^5	R^6	M.p.	Reference
H	H	H	H	H	H	b_{760} 132°	1209, 1550
H	H	CH_3	H	H	H	b_{12} 162°	911, 1209
C_6H_5	H	H	H	H	H	120°	57, 396, 750, 756, 758, 1122, 1177, 1550, 1630
H	C_6H_5	H	H	H	H	78°	1351, 1491
H	H	H	H	C_6H_5	H	101°	581, 1028
2-$CH_3C_6H_4$	H	H	H	H	H	195°	1177
3-$CH_3C_6H_4$	H	H	H	H	H	178°	1177
4-$CH_3C_6H_4$	H	H	H	H	H	163°	396, 750, 756, 758, 1177, 1631
4-$CH_3OC_6H_4$	H	H	H	H	H	146°	758
4-ClC_6H_4	H	H	H	H	H	117°	396, 750, 756, 758
4-$NO_2C_6H_4$	H	H	H	H	H	212°	1177
H	H	H	H	3-$NO_2C_6H_4$	H	139°	335, 581
4-NCC_6H_4	H	H	H	H	H	195°	1177
4-$HOCH_2CH_2C_6H_4$	H	H	H	H	H	109°	1177, 1630

4-$CH_3SO_2NHCH_2CH_2C_6H_4$	H	H	H	H	H	142°	1177
S N	H	H	H	H	H	215°	1177
C_6H_5	H	CH_3	H	H	H	135°	396, 701, 758, 762, 1569
C_6H_5	H	H	H	CH_3	H	127°	758, 762, 888
H	C_6H_5	CH_3	H	H	H	110°	911, 1569
H	C_6H_5	H	H	CH_3	H	84°	68, 816, 1569
H	4-$CH_3C_6H_4$	H	H	CH_3	H	—	68
4-ClC_6H_4	H	CH_3	H	H	H	117°	758
H	3-$HO_3SC_6H_4$	H	H	CH_3	H	—	1388
4-$HOCH_2CH_2C_6H_4$	H	CH_3	H	H	H	—	1631
H	2-Cl-3-$HO_3SC_6H_3$	H	H	CH_3	H	—	1388
H	2-$C_{10}H_7$	H	H	CH_3	H	107°	849
C_6H_5	H	H	H	C_6H_5	H	159°	396, 758, 762, 1327
$C_6H_5CH_2$	H	H	H	C_6H_5	H	114°	581
NO	H	CH_3	H	H	H	116°	911
NO	H	H	H	CH_3	H	131° (dec.), 173°	479, 1028, 1029
NO	H	H	H	C_6H_5	H	127° (dec.)	1028
NO	H	H	H	2-HOC_6H_4	H	126°	353
NO	H	H	H	3-$NO_2C_6H_4$	H	108°	335
H	H	C_6H_5CONH	H	C_6H_5	H	228°	319, 1342
C_6H_5	CH_3	H	H	CH_3	H	160°	888
C_6H_5	H	CH_3	CH_3	H	H	164°	15, 701
C_6H_5	H	H	H	CH_3	CH_3	166°	758, 762
CH_3	C_6H_5	H	H	CH_3	H	107°	26, 816, 1491, 1592
2-$CH_3C_6H_4$	H	CH_3	CH_3	H	H	143°	15, 1630

(Table continued)

TABLE XLII, Section A (*continued*)

R^1	R^2	R^3	R^4	R^5	R^6	M.p.	Reference
3-$CH_3C_6H_4$	H	CH_3	CH_3	H	H	105°	15
4-$CH_3C_6H_4$	H	CH_3	CH_3	H	H	105°	15, 1176, 1630
4-HOC_6H_4	H	CH_3	CH_3	H	H	—	15
4-$HOCH_2CH_2C_6H_4$	H	CH_3	CH_3	H	H	140°	15, 1176, 1630
4-$CH_3COOCH_2CH_2C_6H_4$	H	CH_3	CH_3	H	H	81.5°	15
4-ClC_6H_4	H	CH_3	C_2H_5	H	H	—	15
4-$H_2NC_6H_4$	H	CH_3	C_3H_7	H	H	—	15
4-$CH_3OC_6H_4$	H	C_2H_5	C_2H_5	H	H	—	15
4-$CH_3CONHC_6H_4$	H	C_2H_5	C_2H_5	H	H	—	15
2-(7-$HOC_{10}H_6$)	H	CH_3	C_3H_7	H	H	—	15
C_6H_5	C_6H_5	H	H	CH_3	H	—	647
C_6H_5	H	CH_3	H	C_6H_5	H	164°	1327
C_6H_5	H	H	H	C_6H_5	C_6H_5	170°	1327
H	4-$H_2NC_6H_4$	H_2N	H	CH_3	H	—	12
H	3-$HO_3SC_6H_4$	H_2N	H	CH_3	H	—	12
H	4-(4-$H_2NC_6H_4$)C_6H_4	H_2N	H	CH_3	H	—	12
H	H	C_6H_5CONH	H	CH_3	CH_3	106°	319
NO	H	C_6H_5CONH	H	C_6H_5	H	107° (dec.)	1342
NO	C_6H_5	H	H	CH_3	H	54°	1491
NO	C_2H_5	H	H	CH_3	H	83°	1029
NO	C_2H_5	H	H	3-$NO_2C_6H_4$	H	168°	335
C_6H_5	CH_3CO	H	H	CH_3	H	79°	888
CH_3CO	C_6H_5	H	CH_3	H	H	61°	1569
H	C_6H_5	H	H	CH_3	HOOC	139°	446
H	4-$CH_3C_6H_4$	H	H	CH_3	HOOC	148°	446
H	C_6H_5	H	H	CH_3	$C_6H_5NHNHCO$	144°	446
H	4-$CH_3C_6H_4$	H	H	CH_3	4-$BrC_6H_5NHNHCO$	204°	446
C_6H_5	H	CH_3	H	C_6H_5	CH_3	220°	1327
H	C_6H_5	HO	H	CH_3	CH_3	182°	156, 1260, 1261
CH_3	C_6H_5	HO	H	CH_3	CH_3	109°	1261

C_6H_5	C_6H_5	HO	H	HO	H	160°	1501
C_6H_5	C_6H_5	H	H	CH_3	HOOC	122° (dec.)	647
C_6H_5	C_6H_5	H	H	CH_3	H_3COOC	130°	647
H	C_6H_5	NO	H	CH_3	HOOC	—	446
H	$4\text{-}CH_3C_6H_5$	NO	H	CH_3	HOOC	—	446
CH_3	C_6H_5	HO	Br	CH_3	Br	218°	820

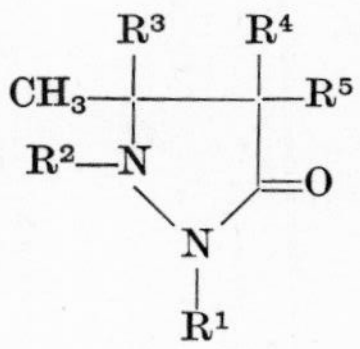

TABLE XLII (*continued*)

Section B. Mercury Substituents

R^1	R^2	R^3	R^4	R^5	M.p.	Reference
$X,Y\text{-}(CH_3COOHg)_2C_6H_3$	CH_3	CH_3COOHg	CH_3O	CH_3COOHg	200° (dec.)	1275
$X,Y\text{-}(ClHg)_2C_6H_3$	CH_3	ClHg	CH_3O	H	—	1275
$X,Y\text{-}(CH_3COOHg)_2C_6H_3$	CH_3	CH_3OOHg	C_2H_5O	CH_3COOHg	—	1275
$X,Y\text{-}(ClHg)_2C_6H_3$	CH_3	ClHg	C_2H_5O	H	—	1275
$X,Y\text{-}(CH_3COO)_2C_6H_3$	C_2H_5	CH_3COOHg	CH_3O	CH_3COOHg	> 200° (dec.)	1275

(*Table continued*)

TABLE XLII, Section B (*continued*)

R^1	R^2	R^3	R^4	R^5	M.p.	Reference
X,Y-$(ClHg)_2C_6H_3$	C_2H_5	ClHg	CH_3O	H	—	1275
4-CH_3-X,Y-$(CH_3COO)_2C_6H_2$	CH_3	CH_3COOHg	CH_3O	CH_3COOHg	—	1275
2-CH_3-X,Y-$(CH_3COO)_2C_6H_2$	C_2H_5	CH_3COOHg	CH_3O	CH_3COOHg	—	1275
2-CH_3-X,Y-$(ClHg)_2C_6H_2$	C_2H_5	ClHg	CH_3O	H	—	1275
X-$CH_3COOHgC_6H_4$	H	CH_3COOHg	CH_3O	CH_3COOHg	167°	1275
X-$ClHgC_6H_4$	H	ClHg	CH_3O	H	—	1275
X,Y-$(CH_3COOHg)_2C_6H_3$	H	CH_3COOHg	CH_3O	CH_3COOHg	225°	1275
X,Y-$(CH_3COOHg)_2C_6H_3$	CH_3	CH_3COOHg	HO	Br	225° (dec.)	1275
X,Y-$(CH_3COOHg)_2C_6H_3$	CH_3	CH_3COOHg	HO	CH_3	237° (dec.)	1275
X,Y-$(ClHg)_2C_6H_3$	CH_3	ClHg	HO	CH_3	245° (dec.)	1275

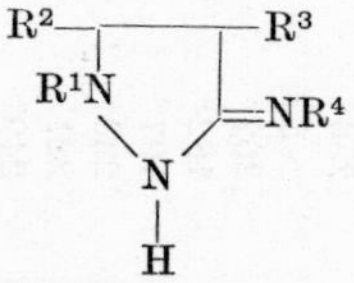

$$
\begin{array}{c}
R^2-\!\!\!-\!\!\!-\!\!\!-R^3 \\
R^1N \quad\quad =NR^4 \\
\diagdown\; N \;\diagup \\
| \\
H
\end{array}
$$

TABLE XLIII. 3-Iminopyrazolidines

R^1	R^2	R^3	R^4	M.p.	Reference
H	H	H	H	196° (HCl)	757
C_6H_5	H	H	H	167°	396, 757, 1122
$2\text{-}CH_3C_6H_4$	H	H	H	74°	396, 757
$3\text{-}CH_3C_6H_4$	H	H	H	110°	396, 757
$4\text{-}CH_3C_6H_4$	H	H	H	143°	396, 757
$4\text{-}CH_3OC_6H_4$	H	H	H	179°	757
$4\text{-}C_2H_5OC_6H_4$	H	H	H	192°	760
$4\text{-}CH_3CONHC_6H_4$	H	H	H	204°	757
$4\text{-}(4\text{-}CH_3C_6H_4S)C_6H_4$	H	H	H	123°	760
$3\text{-}ClC_6H_4$	H	H	H	142°	760
$4\text{-}ClC_6H_4$	H	H	H	132°	396, 760
$4\text{-}BrC_6H_4$	H	H	H	121°	760
$2,5\text{-}(CH_3)_2C_6H_3$	H	CH_3	H	99°	760
C_6H_5	H	CH_3	H	82°	396, 757
C_6H_5	CH_3	H	H	106°	396, 757
C_6H_5	CH_3	CH_3	H	172°	760
$3\text{-}CH_3C_6H_4$	C_6H_5	H	H	152°	396, 757
$4\text{-}CH_3C_6H_4$	C_6H_5	H	H	195°	396, 757
$4\text{-}ClC_6H_4$	C_6H_5	H	H	129°	396, 760
C_6H_5	H	H	C_2H_5	74°	396
C_6H_5	H	H	CH_3CO	192°	396
C_6H_5	H	H	C_6H_5NHSC	196°	396
H	H_2N	H_2N	H	—	336
H	C_2H_5OOCHN	C_2H_5OOCHN	C_2H_5OOC	—	336

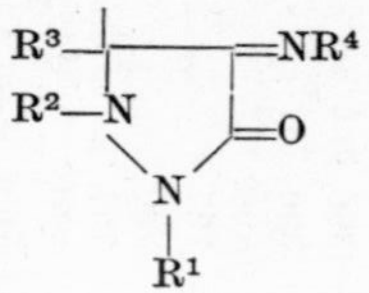

TABLE XLIV. 4-Imino-3-pyrazolidinones

R^1	R^2	R^3	R^4	M.p.	Reference
H	C_6H_5	CH_3	H	—	1168
H	4-BrC_6H_4	CH_3	H	238°	1001
H	4-BrC_6H_4	CH_3	HCO	240°	1001
H	4-BrC_6H_4	CH_3	CH_3CO	259°	1001
H	4-BrC_6H_4	CH_3	H_2NCO	> 350°	1001
H	4-BrC_6H_4	H	C_6H_5NHCS	262°	1001
H	C_6H_5	CH_3	H	182°	984
H	C_6H_5	CH_3	HCO	197°	984
H	C_6H_5	CH_3	CH_3CO	233°	984
H	C_6H_5	CH_3	C_6H_5NHCS	221°	984
H	4-$CH_3C_6H_4$	CH_3	H	249°	984
H	4-$CH_3C_6H_4$	CH_3	CH_3CO	244°	984
H	4-$CH_3C_6H_4$	CH_3	C_6H_5NHCS	220°	984
H	3-$NO_2C_6H_4$	CH_3	H	155°	1001
H	3-$NO_2C_6H_4$	CH_3	CH_3CO	199°	1001
H	C_6H_5	2-HOC_6H_4	H	255°	670
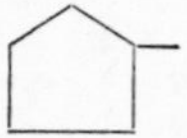	CH_3	CH_3	H	b_4 178°	101
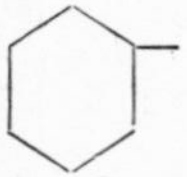	CH_3	CH_3	CH_3	102°	101

		CH_3	$H \cdot HCl$	205°	101
		CH_3	CH_3	—	101
C_6H_5	CH_3	CH_3	H	108°	99, 426, 461, 527, 617, 1174, 1175, 1491
C_6H_5	CH_3	CH_3	CH_3	63°	172, 431, 537, 940, 1303
C_6H_5	CH_3	CH_3	C_2H_5	61°	1303
C_6H_5	CH_3	CH_3	C_3H_7	82°	1303
C_6H_5	CH_3	CH_3	iso-C_3H_7	80°	164, 431, 1303
C_6H_5	CH_3	CH_3	iso-C_4H_9	67°	1303
C_6H_5	CH_3	CH_3	s-C_4H_9	78°	104, 431, 1303
C_6H_5	CH_3	CH_3	iso-C_5H_{11}	53.5°	1303
C_6H_5	CH_3	CH_3	$(C_2H_5)_2CH$	61°	1303
C_6H_5	CH_3	CH_3	$(iso\text{-}C_3H_7)_2CH$	100°	1303
C_6H_5	CH_3	CH_3	$C_6H_{11}CH(CH_3)$	37°	1303
C_6H_5	CH_3	CH_3	—CH_2	44°	1303
C_6H_5	CH_3	CH_3		159°	1303

(*Table continued*)

TABLE XLIV *(continued)*

R^1	R^2	R^3	R^4	M.p.	Reference
C_6H_5	CH_3	CH_3	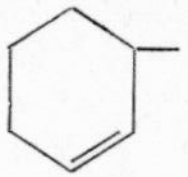	93°	101
C_6H_5	CH_3	CH_3	$C_6H_5CH_2$	73°	111, 1303
C_6H_5	CH_3	CH_3	$C_6H_5CH(CH_3)$	95.2°	1303
C_6H_5	CH_3	CH_3	$2\text{-}HOC_6H_4CH_2$	196°	1303
C_6H_5	CH_3	CH_3	$C_6H_5CH_2CH_2$	84°	1303
C_6H_5	CH_3	CH_3	$C_6H_5CH_2CH_2CH_2$	—	1303
C_6H_5	CH_3	CH_3	$HOOCCH_2$	> 300°	524
C_6H_5	CH_3	CH_3	$NCCH_2$	112°	524
C_6H_5	CH_3	CH_3	H_2NOCCH_2	194°	524, 930
C_6H_5	CH_3	CH_3	$(CH_3)_2C(OH)CH(CONH_2)$	151°	1261
C_6H_5	CH_3	CH_3	HO_2SCH_2	—	1076
C_6H_5	CH_3	CH_3	HO_3SCH_2	231°(dec.)	164, 541
C_6H_5	CH_3	CH_3	$HO_3SCH(CH_3)$	124°	542
C_6H_5	CH_3	CH_3	$HO_3SCH(C_2H_5)$	124°	542
C_6H_5	CH_3	CH_3	$4\text{-}H_2NCSNHN{=}CHC_6H_4$	251°	1265
C_6H_5	CH_3	CH_3	$4\text{-}(C_6H_5NH)C_6H_4$	220.5°	417
C_6H_5	CH_3	CH_3	$2,4(H_2N)_2C_6H_3$	265°	417
C_6H_5	CH_3	CH_3	$2,4(NO_2)C_6H_3$	213°	417

C_6H_5	CH_3	CH_3	CH_3—C=C—CH_2; CH_3—N, C=O, N—C_6H_5	151°	111
C_6H_5	CH_3	CH_3	CH_3—C=C—N(C_6H_5)CO; CH_3N, C=O, N—C_6H_5	240° (dec.)	589
C_6H_5	CH_3	CH_3	CH_3—C=C—N(4-$CH_3C_6H_4$)CO; CH_3—N, C=O, N—C_6H_5	235°	589
C_6H_5	CH_3	CH_3	CH_3—C=C—N(4-$CH_3OC_6H_4$)CO; CH_3N, C=O, N—C_6H_5	200°	589

(*Table continued*)

TABLE XLIV (*continued*)

R^1	R^2	R^3	R^4	M.p.	Reference
C_6H_5	CH_3	CH_3	4-$C_2H_5OC_6H_4$–NCO– ; CH_3; CH_3N; =O; N–C_6H_5 (pyrazolone ring)	234°	589
C_6H_5	CH_3	CH_3	SO_3Na–CH– ; CH_3; CH_3N; =O; N–C_6H_5 (pyrazolone ring)	190° (dec.)	891
C_6H_5	CH_3	CH_3	2-C_6H_5-quinolin-4-yl (ring N; C_6H_5)	247°	717
C_6H_5	CH_3	CH_3	CH_3; =N; N; =O; N–C_6H_5 (pyrazolone ring)	200°	821

C_6H_5	CH_3	CH_3	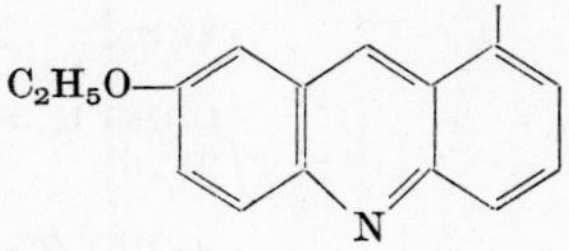 C_2H_5O– (acridinyl), N	257°	547
C_6H_5	CH_3	CH_3	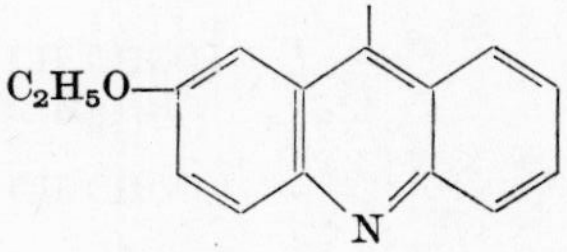 C_2H_5O– (acridinyl), N	—	951
C_6H_5	CH_3	CH_3	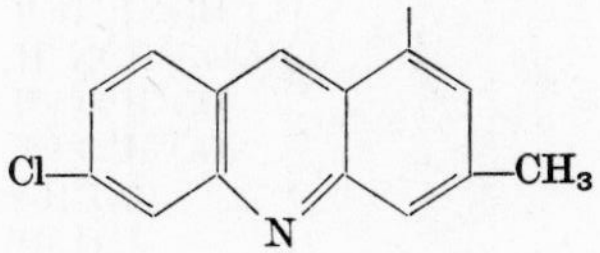 Cl–, –CH_3 (acridinyl), N	257°	69
C_6H_5	CH_3	CH_3	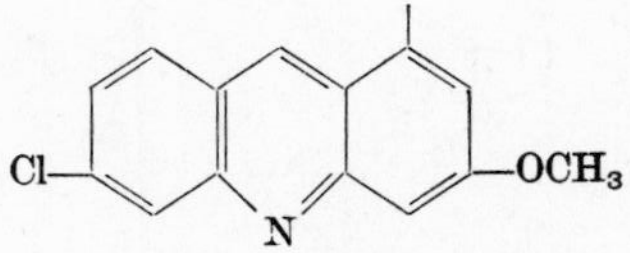 Cl–, –OCH_3 (acridinyl), N	248°	69
C_6H_5	CH_3	CH_3	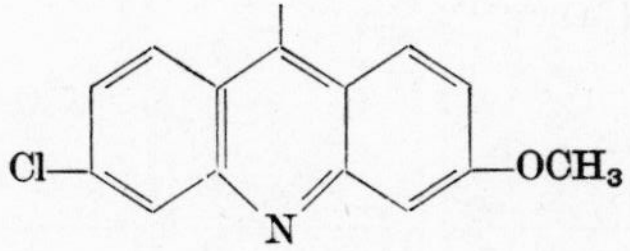 Cl–, –OCH_3 (acridinyl), N	250°	390

(Table continued)

TABLE XLIV (*continued*)

R^1	R^2	R^3	R^4	M.p.	Reference
C_6H_5	CH_3	CH_3	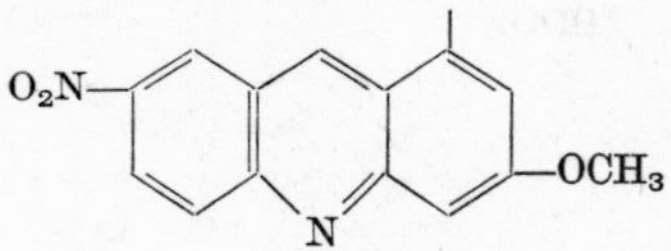 O_2N–, –OCH_3, N	278°	69
C_6H_5	CH_3	CH_3	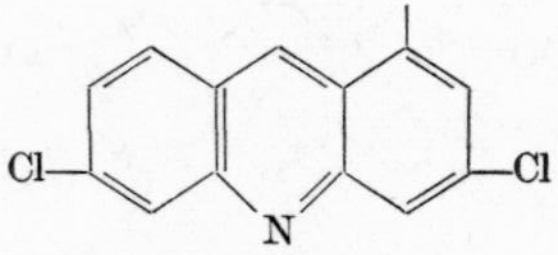 Cl–, –Cl, N	276°	69
C_6H_5	CH_3	CH_3	HCO	189°	618
C_6H_5	CH_3	CH_3	CH_3CO	198°	617, 618
C_6H_5	CH_3	CH_3	iso-C_3H_7CO	—	536
C_6H_5	CH_3	CH_3	iso-C_4H_9CO	—	58, 533
C_6H_5	CH_3	CH_3	$H_2NCH_2CO(HCl)$	260°	58, 731
C_6H_5	CH_3	CH_3	$(CH_3)_2NCH_2CO$	151°	1470, 1473
C_6H_5	CH_3	CH_3	$(C_2H_5)_2NCH_2CO$	111°	371, 1470, 1473
C_6H_5	CH_3	CH_3	CH_3CHCO (–$HNCH_3$)	175°	1471
C_6H_5	CH_3	CH_3	CH_3CHCO (–$N(CH_3)_2$)	181°	1470, 1471, 1473
C_6H_5	CH_3	CH_3	CH_3CHCO (–$N(C_2H_5)_2$)	79°	1470, 1473
C_6H_5	CH_3	CH_3	C_2H_5CHCO (–$N(CH_3)_2$)	168°	1470, 1473

C_6H_5	CH_3	CH_3	C_2H_5CHCO | $N(C_2H_5)_2$	119°	1470, 1473
C_6H_5	CH_3	CH_3	C_3H_7CHCO | $N(CH_3)_2$	130°	1470, 1473
C_6H_5	CH_3	CH_3	C_3H_7CHCO | $N(C_2H_5)_2$	80°	1470, 1473
C_6H_5	CH_3	CH_3	iso-C_3H_7CHCO | $N(CH_3)_2$	186°	1470, 1473
C_6H_5	CH_3	CH_3	iso-C_3H_7CHCO | $N(C_2H_5)_2$	177°	1470, 1473
C_6H_5	CH_3	CH_3	$ClCH_2CO$	187°, 198°	50, 1156, 1470, 1473
C_6H_5	CH_3	CH_3	CH_3CHCO | Cl	218°	1471
C_6H_5	CH_3	CH_3	CH_3CHCO | Br	206° (dec.)	1470, 1471, 1473
C_6H_5	CH_3	CH_3	C_2H_5CHCO | Br	208°	1470, 1473
C_6H_5	CH_3	CH_3	C_3H_7CHCO | Br	185°	1470, 1473
C_6H_5	CH_3	CH_3	iso-C_3H_7CHCO | Br	205°	533, 1470, 1473
C_6H_5	CH_3	CH_3	2-$CH_3COOC_6H_4CO$	219°	1346
C_6H_5	CH_3	CH_3	3,5-$Br_2C_6H_3CO$	252°	1414
C_6H_5	CH_3	CH_3	$COCH{=}NOH$	190°	731
C_6H_5	CH_3	CH_3	HOOC	—	549

(*Table continued*)

TABLE XLIV (*continued*)

R^1	R^2	R^3	R^4	M.p.	Reference
C_6H_5	CH_3	CH_3	C_2H_5OOC	206°	589
C_6H_5	CH_3	CH_3	ClCO	oil	589
C_6H_5	CH_3	CH_3	CH_3COOCO	—	371
C_6H_5	CH_3	CH_3	HCS	175°	472, 556, 1374
C_6H_5	CH_3	CH_3	$4\text{-}H_2NC_6H_4SO_2$	249°, 260°	70, 98, 356, 1105, 1197, 1504, 1633
C_6H_5	CH_3	CH_3	$(CH_3)_2NSO_2$	198°	489
C_6H_5	CH_3	CH_3	$(C_2H_5)_2NSO_2$	184°	489
C_6H_5	CH_3	CH_3	$4\text{-}(CH_3)_2NC_6H_4SO_2$	208°	98
C_6H_5	CH_3	CH_3	$4\text{-}CH_3CONHC_6H_4SO_2$	213°, 269°	98, 356, 1105, 1249, 1504
C_6H_5	CH_3	CH_3	(1-phenyl-2,3-dimethyl-5-oxo-pyrazolin-4-yl)SO_2: CH_3—C=C—SO_2; CH_3—N, N—C_6H_5, C=O	242°	745
C_6H_5	CH_3	CH_3	H_2NCO	—	929
C_6H_5	CH_3	CH_3	iso-$C_3H_7CH(Br)CONHCO$	70°	1300
C_6H_5	CH_3	CH_3	$4\text{-}C_2H_5OOCC_6H_4NHCO$	—	1367
C_6H_5	CH_3	CH_3	$3\text{-}HO\text{-}4\text{-}CH_3OOCC_6H_3NHCS$	200° (dec.)	49
C_6H_5	CH_3	CH_3	C_6H_5HNCO	236°	929
C_6H_5	CH_3	CH_3	H_2NHNCO	135°	929
C_6H_5	CH_3	CH_3	$C_2H_5CH{=}NNHCO$	209°	929
C_6H_5	CH_3	CH_3	$CH_3C(CH_2COOC_2H_5){=}NNHCO$	207°	929

C_6H_5	CH_3	CH_3	$C_6H_5CH{=}NNHCO$	225°	929
C_6H_5	CH_3	CH_3	$CH_3CONHCO$	214°	929
C_6H_5	CH_3	CH_3	$H_2NC(=NH)NHC(=NH)$	—	928
C_6H_5	CH_3	CH_3	$(CH_3O)_2OP$	186°	1496
C_6H_5	CH_3	CH_3	$(C_2H_5)_2OP$	—	1496
C_6H_5	CH_3	CH_3	$(C_3H_7O)_2OP$	102°	1496
C_6H_5	CH_3	CH_3	(iso-$C_3H_7O)_2OP$	156°	1496
C_6H_5	CH_3	CH_3	$(C_4H_9O)_2OP$	105°	1496
C_6H_5	CH_3	CH_3	(iso-$C_4H_9O)_2OP$	113°	1496
C_6H_5	CH_3	CH_3	(iso-$C_5H_{11}O)_2OP$	85°	1496
C_6H_5	CH_3	CH_3	$(ClCH_2CH_2O)_2OP$	—	1496
C_6H_5	CH_3	CH_3	$(C_6H_5CH_2O)_2OP$	—	1496
C_6H_5	CH_3	CH_3	$(C_6H_5O)_2OP$	176°	509
CH_3	CH_3	C_6H_5	H	109°	992
CH_3	CH_3	C_6H_5	HCO	209°	992
CH_3	CH_3	C_6H_5	CH_3CO	233°	992
CH_3	CH_3	C_6H_5	C_6H_5CO	234°	992
CH_3	CH_3	C_6H_5	C_2H_5OOC	190°	992
CH_3	CH_3	C_6H_5	$C_6H_5SO_2$	245°	992
CH_3	CH_3	C_6H_5	C_6H_5NHCS	210°	992
C_6H_5	C_2H_5	CH_3	H	117°	520
C_6H_5	C_2H_5	CH_3	$H_2NCH_2CO(HBr)$	150°	50
C_6H_5	C_2H_5	CH_3	$ClCH_2CO$	186°	50
C_6H_5	CH_3	$\rhd$—	H	125°	1477
2-$CH_3C_6H_4$	CH_3	CH_3	H	117°	521
2-$CH_3C_6H_4$	C_2H_5	CH_3	H	129°	521
4-$CH_3C_6H_4$	CH_3	CH_3	H	118°	521
4-$CH_3C_6H_4$	CH_3	CH_3	HO_3SCH_2	125° (dec.)	541
4-$CH_3C_6H_4$	C_2H_5	CH_3	H	—	145, 521

(*Table continued*)

TABLE XLIV (*continued*)

	R^2	R^3	R^4	M.p.	Reference
4-$CH_3C_6H_4$	C_2H_5	CH_3	HO_3SCH_2	—	145
4-$C_2H_5OC_6H_4$	CH_3	CH_3	H	132°	541
4-$C_2H_5OC_6H_4$	CH_3	CH_3	HO_3SCH_2	113°	541
4-$C_2H_5OC_6H_4$	C_2H_5	CH_3	H	—	145
4-$C_2H_5OC_6H_4$	C_2H_5	CH_3	HO_3SCH_2	—	145
4-$C_3H_7OC_6H_4$	CH_3	CH_3	H	99°	1149
3-$H_2NC_6H_4$	CH_3	CH_3	H	170°	978
CH_3	3-$H_2NC_6H_4$	CH_3	H	185°	1001
4-$H_2NC_6H_4$	CH_3	CH_3	H	239°	978
4-$H_2NC_6H_4$	CH_3	CH_3	$(CH_3)_2CHCH(Br)CONHCO$	74°	1300
4-$(CH_3)_2NC_6H_4$	CH_3	CH_3	$(CH_3)_2CHCH(Br)CONHCO$	94°	1300
4-$CH_3CONHC_6H_4$	CH_3	CH_3	CH_3CO	291°	978
4-$H_2O_3AsC_6H_4$	CH_3	CH_3	$CH_3CH{=}CHCO$	—	1363
C_6H_5	C_6H_5	CH_3	H	165°	647

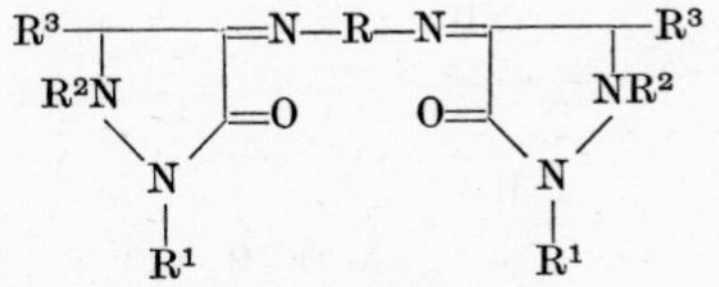

TABLE XLV. 4,4′-Bis(4-imino-3-pyrazolidinones)

R	R¹	R²	R³	M.p.	Reference
$(CH_3)(HOOC)C<$	H	C_6H_5	CH_3	299°	984
$(CH_3)(C_6H_5)C<$	H	C_6H_5	CH_3	296°	984
$(C_6H_5)_2C<$	H	C_6H_5	CH_3	301°	984
$—CH_2CH_2—$	C_6H_5	CH_3	CH_3	54°	927
$—CH_2CH_2—$	CH_3	CH_3	C_6H_5	132°	992
$—CH_2CH_2OCH_2CH_2—$	C_6H_5	CH_3	CH_3	—	460
C=S	H	4-BrC_6H_4	CH_3	289°	1001
C=O	C_6H_5	CH_3	CH_3	259°	589
C=S	H	C_6H_5	CH_3	265°	984
C=S	CH_3	CH_3	C_6H_5	225°	992
C=S	C_6H_5	CH_3	CH_3	248°	821

TABLE XLVI. Miscellaneous Bis(3,5-pyrazolidinediones), Bis(5-imino-3-pyrazolidinones), and Bis(4-imino-3-pyrazolidinones)

Compound	M.p.	Reference
O= =CH— =O HN NH =O O= N N C_6H_5 C_6H_5	310°(dec.)	1190
C_6H_5OCN= =$NCOC_6H_5$ HN NH =O O= N N C_6H_5 C_6H_5	290°	1538
4-ClC_6H_4CON= =$NCOC_6H_4$-4-Cl HN NH =O O= N N C_6H_5 C_6H_5	> 300°	1538
CH_3— =NCH_2SO_3H HSO_3CH_2N= —CH_3 CH_3N N—CH_3 =O O= N N As=As	—	1362
CH_3— =NCH_2SO_3H HN= —CH_3 CH_3—N N—CH_3 =O O= N N As=As	—	546
CH_3— =NH HN= —CH_3 CH_3—N N—CH_3 =O O= As=As	—	546

(Table continued)

TABLE XLVI (*continued*)

Compound	M.p.	Reference
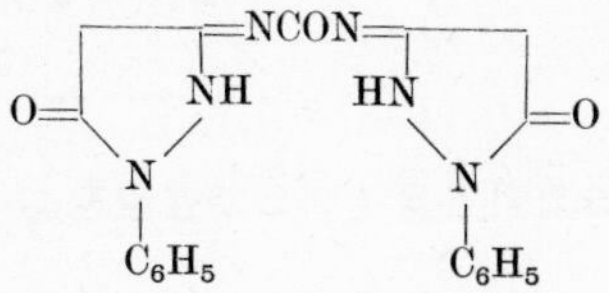 =NCON= NH HN O= =O N N C_6H_5 C_6H_5	260° (dec.)	797
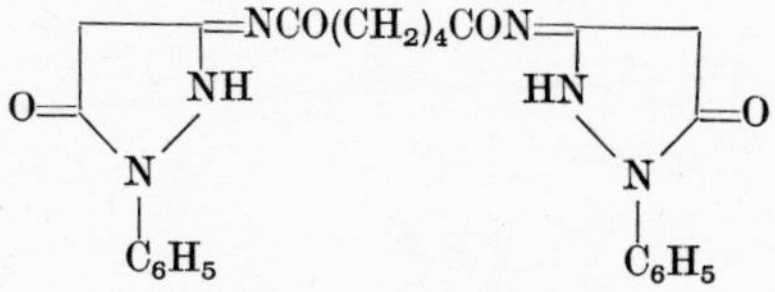 =NCO$(CH_2)_4$CON= NH HN O= =O N N C_6H_5 C_6H_5	281°	797
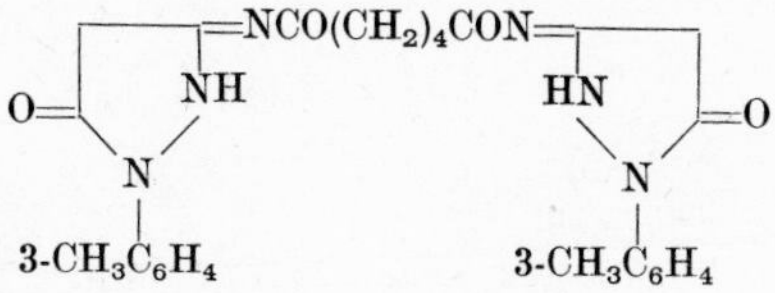 =NCO$(CH_2)_4$CON= NH HN O= =O N N 3-$CH_3C_6H_4$ 3-$CH_3C_6H_4$	—	797
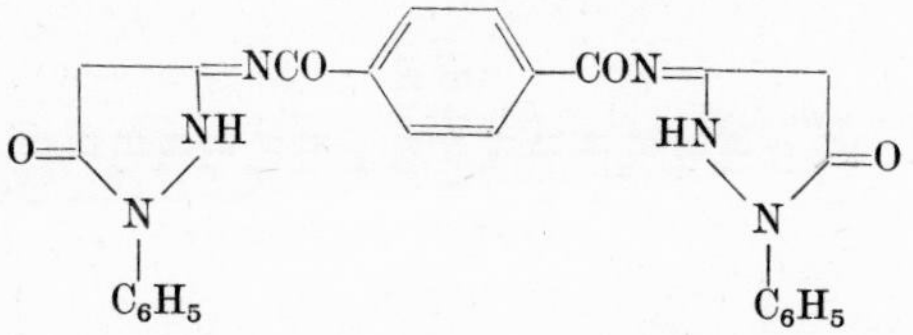 =NCO–C_6H_4–CON= NH HN O= =O N N C_6H_5 C_6H_5	—	797
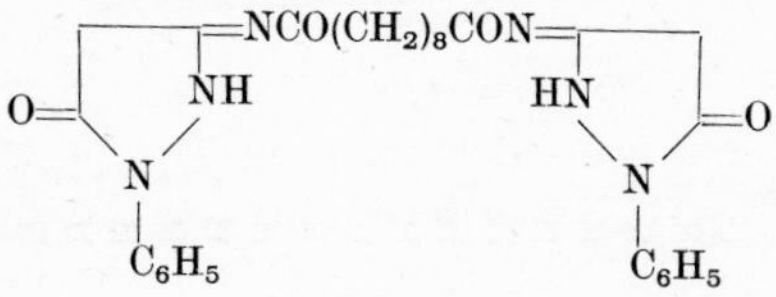 =NCO$(CH_2)_8$CON= NH HN O= =O N N C_6H_5 C_6H_5	251°	797
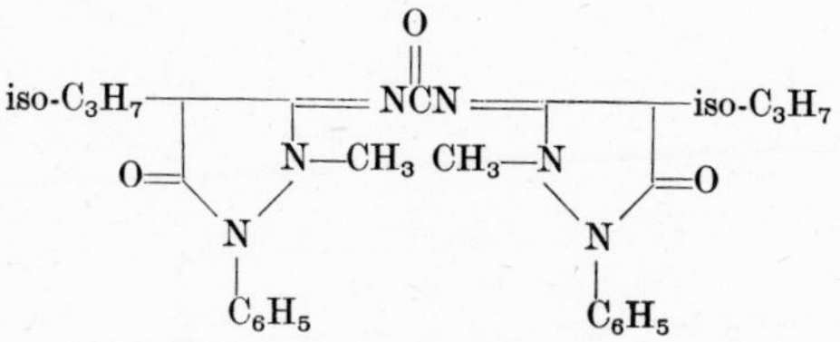 O ‖ iso-C_3H_7— =NCN= —iso-C_3H_7 N—CH_3 CH_3—N O= =O N N C_6H_5 C_6H_5	165°	1387

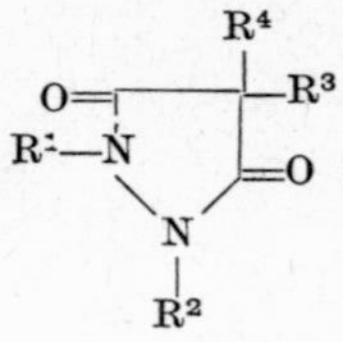

TABLE XLVII. 3,5-Pyrazolidinediones

Section A. Alkyl and Aralkyl Substituents

R^1	R^2	R^3	R^4	M.p.	Reference
CH_3	H	H	H	—	769
C_6H_{13}	H	H	H	250°	504
H	H	C_2H_5	C_2H_5	270°	248, 388, 1234
H	H	C_2H_5	C_3H_7	232°	1234
H	H	C_3H_7	C_3H_7	254°	388, 1234
H	H	C_3H_5	C_3H_5	280°	1234
H	H	C_3H_5	s-C_4H_9	186°	388
H	H	C_4H_9	C_4H_9	220°	248, 388
H	H	C_2H_5	iso-C_5H_{11}	228°	388
H	H	iso-C_5H_{11}	iso-C_5H_{11}	289°	388
H	H	$C_6H_5CH_2$	$C_6H_5CH_2$	301°	497
C_6H_{13}	H	CH_3	H	—	504
C_6H_{13}	H	C_2H_5	H	—	504
H	H	C_2H_5	C_2H_{13}	182°	388
C_6H_{13}	H	C_3H_7	H	83°	504
C_6H_{13}	H	C_4H_9	H	94°	504
C_6H_{13}	H	C_5H_{11}	H	93°	504
C_6H_{13}	H	C_6H_{13}	H	93°	504
C_6H_{13}	H	C_7H_{15}	H	81°	504

C_6H_{13}	H	$C_6H_5CH_2$	H	155°	504
$C_6H_5CH_2$	H	C_2H_5	C_2H_5	134°	248
$C_6H_5CH_2$	H	C_4H_9	C_4H_9	128°	248
$C_6H_5CH_2$	$C_6H_5CH_2$	C_2H_5	C_2H_5	74°	248, 734

TABLE XLVII (*continued*)

Section B. Alkyl, Aralkyl, Heterocyclicalkyl, Aryl and Acyl on Carbon Substituents

R^1	R^2	R^3	R^4	M.p.	Reference
C_6H_5	H	H	H	192°	248, 317, 496, 681, 976, 994, 997, 1512, 1596
2-ClC_6H_4	H	H	H	181°	504
3-ClC_6H_4	H	H	H	174°	504
4-ClC_6H_4	H	H	H	207°	504
4-BrC_6H_4	H	H	H	217°	997
4-$NO_2C_6H_4$	H	H	H	—	997
C_6H_5	CH_3	H	H	84°	1339
C_6H_5	H	CH_3	H	177°	496
C_6H_5	H	C_2H_5	H	108°	388, 496, 998
H	H	C_6H_5	C_2H_5	198°	381, 388, 1234

(Table continued)

TABLE XLVII, Section B (*continued*)

R¹	R²	R³	R⁴	M.p.	Reference
C_6H_5	H	C_3H_7	H	186°	496
C_6H_5	H	C_4H_9	H	99°, 149°	248, 496
C_6H_5	H	s-C_4H_9	H	94°	388
C_6H_5	H	C_5H_9	H	139°	496
C_6H_5	H	C_8H_{17}	H	154°	496
C_6H_5	H	$C_6H_5CH_2$	H	188°	496
H	H	C_6H_5	$C_6H_5CH_2CH_2$	—	612
C_6H_5	H	$C_6H_5CH{=}CH$	H	$b_{3.7}$ 372°	681
C_6H_5	H	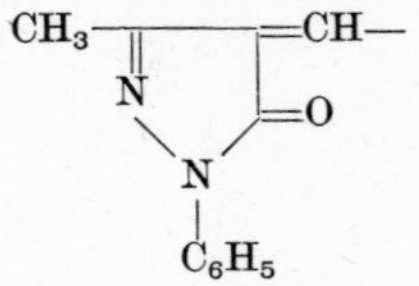 CH_3–C=N–N(C_6H_5)–C(=O)–C=CH— (ring)	H	262°	1190
C_6H_5	H	$(CH_3)_2C{=}$		164°	976
C_6H_5	H	$C_6H_5CH{=}$		—	681, 976
C_6H_5	H	2-$HOC_6H_4CH{=}$		—	681
C_6H_5	H	3,4-$(CH_3O)_2C_6H_3CH{=}$		—	681
C_6H_5	H	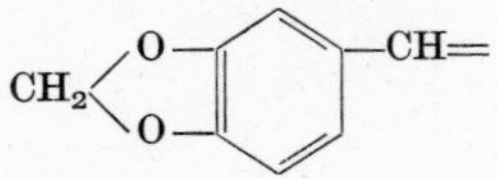 $CH_2\langle O_2\rangle C_6H_3$–CH= (ring)		—	681
C_6H_5	H	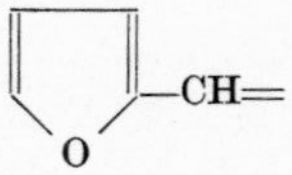 C_4H_3O–CH= (furan ring)		—	681
2-ClC_6H_4	H	CH_3	H	181°	504
2-ClC_6H_4	H	C_2H_5	H	160°	504
2-ClC_6H_4	H	C_3H_7	H	161°	504

2-ClC_6H_4	H	C_4H_9	H	169°	504
2-ClC_6H_4	H	C_5H_{11}	H	150°	504
2-ClC_6H_4	H	C_6H_{13}	H	154°	504
2-ClC_6H_4	H	C_7H_{15}	H	131°	504
2-ClC_6H_4	H	$C_6H_5CH_2$	H	197°	504
3-ClC_6H_4	H	CH_3	H	210°	504
3-ClC_6H_4	H	C_2H_5	H	196°	504
3-ClC_6H_4	H	C_3H_7	H	239°	504
3-ClC_6H_4	H	C_4H_9	H	155°	504
3-ClC_6H_4	H	C_5H_{11}	H	132°	504
3-ClC_6H_4	H	C_6H_{13}	H	110°	504
3-ClC_6H_4	H	C_7H_{15}	H	106°	504
3-ClC_6H_4	H	$C_6H_5CH_2$	H	187°	504
4-ClC_6H_4	H	CH_3	H	220°	504
4-ClC_6H_4	H	C_2H_5	H	202°	504
4-ClC_6H_4	H	C_3H_7	H	193°	504
4-ClC_6H_4	H	C_4H_9	H	193°	504
4-ClC_6H_4	H	C_5H_{11}	H	174°	504
4-ClC_6H_4	H	C_6H_{13}	H	147°	504
4-ClC_6H_4	H	C_7H_{15}	H	160°	504
4-ClC_6H_4	H	$C_6H_5CH_2$	H	181°	504
1-$C_{10}H_7$	H	C_8H_{17}	H	184°	506
1-$C_{10}H_7$	H	$C_6H_5CH_2$	H	169°	506
2-$C_{10}H_7$	H	C_4H_9	H	172°	506
2-$C_{10}H_7$	H	C_5H_{11}	H	157°	506
2-$C_{10}H_7$	H	C_6H_{13}	H	155°	506
2-$C_{10}H_7$	H	C_8H_{17}	H	147°	506
2-$C_{10}H_7$	H	$C_6H_5CH_2$	H	189°	506
C_6H_5	H	(benzoxazoline ring: O, N–C_6H_5)=CHCH=		313°	1330

(Table continued)

TABLE XLVII, Section B (*continued*)

R[1]	R[2]	R[3]	R[4]	M.p.	Reference
C_6H_5	C_6H_5	H	H	178°	248, 681, 766, 969, 1150, 1234, 1501
C_6H_5	H	C_6H_5	H	172°, 233°	222, 506, 612
C_6H_5	H	3,4-$(CH_3O)_2C_6H_3$	H	—	612
X-$CH_3C_6H_4$	X-$CH_3C_6H_4$	H	H	—	769
4-$CH_3OC_6H_4$	4-$CH_3OC_6H_4$	H	H	—	769
H	H	4-$H_2NC_6H_4$	4-$H_2NC_6H_4$	288° (dec.)	339
H	H	4-$(C_6H_5CH{=}N)C_6H_4$	4-$(4\text{-}C_6H_5CH{=}N)C_6H_4$	271°	339
4-ClC_6H_4	4-ClC_6H_4	H	H	177°	766
3-$NO_2C_6H_4$	3-$NO_2C_6H_4$	H	H	—	769
4-$(C_6H_5)C_6H_4$	4-$(C_6H_5)C_6H_4$	H	H	—	769
X—[quinoline ring]	X—[quinoline ring]	H	H	—	769
C_6H_5	H	CH_3	CH_3	176°	997
C_6H_5	H	C_2H_5	C_2H_5	113°	248, 388, 496
C_6H_5	CH_3	iso-C_3H_7	H	116°	1339
C_6H_5	H	C_3H_7	C_3H_7	105°	317, 496
C_6H_5	H	iso-C_3H_7	C_3H_5	$b_{0.1}$ 148°	248
C_6H_5	H	C_2H_5	iso-C_5H_{11}	$b_{0.3}$ 182°	248
C_6H_5	H	C_5H_{11}	C_5H_{11}	211°	496
C_6H_5	H	C_7H_{15}	C_7H_{15}	136°	496
C_6H_5	$C_6H_5CH_2$	C_4H_9	H	98°	248

C_6H_5	H	$C_6H_5CH_2$	C_4H_9	171°	248
C_6H_5	H	$C_6H_5CH_2$	$C_6H_5CH_2$	258°	496
2-$C_{10}H_7$	H	$C_6H_5CH_2$	$C_6H_5CH_2$	243°	506
C_6H_5	C_6H_5	CH_3	H	114°	1338
C_6H_5	H	C_6H_5	CH_3	168°	222, 612
C_6H_5	CH_3	C_6H_5	H	114°	222
6_6H_5	C_6H_5	C_2H_5	H	108°	1033, 1150, 1338
C_6H_5	H	C_6H_5	C_2H_5	172°	222, 612
C_6H_5	C_6H_5	C_3H_7	H	108°	188, 619, 1440
C_6H_5	C_6H_5	iso-C_3H_7	H	143°	188, 1338, 1437, 1439, 1440
C_6H_5	C_6H_5	C_3H_5	H	135°	619, 1338
C_6H_5	C_6H_5	C_4H_9	H	105°	63, 188, 612, 952, 1032, 1150, 1312, 1324, 1325, 1430, 1439
C_6H_5	H	C_6H_5	C_4H_9	168°	222
C_6H_5	C_6H_5	s-C_4H_9	H	118°	1338, 1440
C_6H_5	C_6H_5	iso-C_4H_9	H	127°	1338
C_6H_5	C_6H_5	2-C_4H_7	H	128°	1338
C_6H_5	C_6H_5	C_5H_{11}	H	104°	1338
C_6H_5	C_6H_5	iso-C_5H_{11}	H	137°	1338
C_6H_5	C_6H_5	$(CH_3)_2CHCH_2CH(CH_3)$	H	107°	1338

(Table continued)

TABLE XLVII, Section B (*continued*)

R^1	R^2	R^3	R^4	M.p.	Reference
C_6H_5	C_6H_5	C_7H_{15}	H	95°	1338
C_6H_5	C_6H_5	cyclopentyl	H	172°	188, 1338
C_6H_5	C_6H_5	cyclohexyl	H	177°	188, 619, 1338, 1430, 1440
C_6H_5	C_6H_5	$C_6H_5CH_2$	H	136°	188, 619, 1338, 1437, 1439, 1440
C_6H_5	H	C_6H_5	$C_6H_5CH_2$	176°	222, 612
C_6H_5	C_6H_5	$C_6H_5CH(CH_3)$	H	—	188
C_6H_5	C_6H_5	C_6H_5	H	184°	222
C_6H_5	C_6H_5	4-$CH_3C_6H_4CH_2$	H	—	188
C_6H_5	C_6H_5	3,4-methylenedioxybenzyl ($CH_2O_2C_6H_3CH_2$)	H	—	188
C_6H_5	C_6H_5	4-$ClC_6H_4CH_2$	H	—	188, 1338
C_6H_5	C_6H_5	$C_6H_5CH_2CH_2CH_2$	H	—	188
C_6H_5	C_6H_5	C_3H_7CO	H	77°	919
C_6H_5	C_6H_5	iso-C_3H_7CO	H	85°	919

C_6H_5	C_6H_5	CH_3COOCH_2CO	H	173°	919
C_6H_5	C_6H_5	$ClCH_2CO$	H	149°	919
C_6H_5	C_6H_5	CH_3SCH_2CO	H	154°	919
C_6H_5	C_6H_5	$C_4H_9SCH_2CO$	H	149°	919
C_6H_5	C_6H_5	3-HOC_4H_9	H	—	267
C_6H_5	C_6H_5	$C_2H_5OCH_2CH_2$	H	—	615
C_6H_5	C_6H_5	$C_3H_7OCH_2CH_2$	H	90°	615
C_6H_5	C_6H_5	iso-$C_3H_7OCH_2CH_2$	H	104°	615
C_6H_5	C_6H_5	$C_4H_9OCH_2CH_2$	H	93°	615
C_6H_5	C_6H_5	$C_3H_5OCH_2CH_2CH_2CH_2$	H	—	615
C_6H_5	C_6H_5	$C_6H_5OCH_2CH_2$	H	147°	615
C_6H_5	C_6H_5	$C_6H_5OCH_2CH_2CH_2CH_2$	H	—	615
C_6H_5	C_6H_5	$C_6H_5CH_2OCH_2CH_2CH_2CH_2$	H	—	615
C_6H_5	C_6H_5	NaO_2SCH_2	H	250°	919
C_6H_5	C_6H_5	$CH_3SCH_2CH_2$	H	120°	1454
C_6H_5	C_6H_5	$C_2H_5SCH_2CH_2$	H	92°	615
C_6H_5	C_6H_5	$C_3H_7SCH_2CH_2$	H	94°	615
C_6H_5	C_6H_5	iso-$C_3H_7SCH_2CH_2$	H	105°	615
C_6H_5	C_6H_5	$C_3H_5SCH_2CH_2CH_2$	H	—	615
C_6H_5	C_6H_5	$C_6H_5SCH_2CH_2$	H	—	233
C_6H_5	C_6H_5	4-$CH_3C_6H_4SCH_2CH_2$	H	101°	615
C_6H_5	C_6H_5	2,4-$(CH_3)_2C_6H_3SCH_2CH_2$	H	104°	615
C_6H_5	C_6H_5	4-$ClC_6H_4SCH_2CH_2$	H	117°	615
C_6H_5	C_6H_5	4-$BrC_6H_4SCH_2CH_2$	H	—	615
C_6H_5	C_6H_5	4-$CH_3OC_6H_4SCH_2CH_2$	H	—	615
C_6H_5	C_6H_5	$C_6H_5CH_2SCH_2CH_2$	H	—	615
C_6H_5	C_6H_5	$C_6H_5SCH_2CH_2CH_2$	H	112°	615
C_6H_5	C_6H_5	$C_6H_5SCH_2CH_2CH_2CH_2$	H	121°	615
C_6H_5	C_6H_5	$C_6H_5CH_2SCH_2CH_2CH_2CH_2$	H	—	615
C_6H_5	C_6H_5	$C_2H_5SOCH_2CH_2$	H	181°	615
C_6H_5	C_6H_5	$C_2H_5SO_2CH_2CH_2$	H	—	615
C_6H_5	C_6H_5	$C_6H_5SOCH_2CH_2$	H	—	615
C_6H_5	C_6H_5	$C_6H_5SO_2CH_2CH_2$	H	—	615
C_6H_5	C_6H_5	4-$CH_3OC_6H_4SO_2CH_2CH_2$	H	—	615

(Table continued)

TABLE XLVII, Section B (*continued*)

R^1	R^2	R^3	R^4	M.p.	Reference
C_6H_5	C_6H_5	$4\text{-}ClC_6H_4SOCH_2CH_2$	H	—	615
C_6H_5	C_6H_5	$4\text{-}ClC_6H_4SO_2CH_2CH_2$	H	—	615
C_6H_5	C_6H_5	$NCCH_2$	H	140°	919
C_6H_5	C_6H_5	CH_3NHCH_2	H	214°	919
C_6H_5	C_6H_5	$(CH_3)_2NCH_2$	H	208°	919
C_6H_5	C_6H_5	(piperidino ring)NCH_2	H	112°	919
C_6H_5	C_6H_5	$H_2NCH_2CH_2$	H	195°	919
C_6H_5	C_6H_5	$(CH_3)_2NCH_2CH_2$	H	—	614
C_6H_5	C_6H_5	$(C_2H_5)_2NCH_2CH_2$	H	228°	614
C_6H_5	C_6H_5	(piperidino ring)NCH_2CH_2	H	—	614
C_6H_5	C_6H_5	$(C_2H_5)_2NCH_2CH_2CH_2$	H	—	614
C_6H_5	C_6H_5	$C_3H_7CH(NH_2)$	H	195°	919
C_6H_5	C_6H_5	$CH_3CONHC(COOC_2H_5)_2CH_2$	H	133°	919
C_6H_5	C_6H_5	$HOOCCH(NH_2)CH_2$	H	290° (HCl)	919
C_6H_5	C_6H_5	$CH_3CH_2CH=$		260° (dec.)	681
C_6H_5	C_6H_5	$CH_3C(CH_3)=$		113°	681, 1501

C_6H_5	C_6H_5	$(CH_2)_4C{=}$	153°	188,1338
C_6H_5	C_6H_5	$(CH_2)_5C{=}$	173°	188, 1338, 1430
C_6H_5	C_6H_5	$C_6H_5CH{=}$	164°	188, 681, 1501
C_6H_5	C_6H_5	2-$HOC_6H_4CH{=}$	193°	681, 1502
C_6H_5	C_6H_5	3-$HOC_6H_4CH{=}$	194°	681, 1502
C_6H_5	C_6H_5	4-$HOC_6H_4CH{=}$	231°	681, 1502
C_6H_5	C_6H_5	4-$CH_3OC_6H_4CH{=}$	199°	681, 1502
C_6H_5	C_6H_5	4-$CH_3C_6H_4CH{=}$	175°	681, 1502
C_6H_5	C_6H_5	4-$(CH_3)_2NC_6H_4CH{=}$	256°	681, 1502
C_6H_5	C_6H_5	2-$NO_2C_6H_4CH{=}$	174°	1502
C_6H_5	C_6H_5	3-$NO_2C_6H_4CH{=}$	185°	1502
C_6H_5	C_6H_5	4-$NO_2C_6H_4CH{=}$	243°	681, 1502
C_6H_5	C_6H_5	3,4-$(HO)_2C_6H_3CH{=}$	255° (dec.)	681, 1502
C_6H_5	C_6H_5	3,4-$(CH_3O)_2C_6H_3CH{=}$	156°	681, 1502
C_6H_5	C_6H_5	3,4-$(O_2CH_2)C_6H_3CH{=}$	234°	681, 1502
C_6H_5	C_6H_5	$C_6H_5CH{=}CHCH{=}$	190°	188, 1501
C_6H_5	C_6H_5	$C_6H_5C(CH_3){=}$	148°	681, 1501
C_6H_5	C_6H_5	$C_6H_5C(C_6H_5){=}$	269°	1501

(*Table continued*)

TABLE XLVII, Section B (*continued*)

R^1	R^2	R^3	R^4	M.p.	Reference
C_6H_5	C_6H_5	$C_6H_5COC(C_6H_5)=$		—	1503
C_6H_5	C_6H_5	$C_6H_5CHOHC(C_6H_5)=$		—	1503
C_6H_5	C_6H_5	2-furyl–CH=		157°	681, 1501
C_6H_5	C_6H_5	6-CH_3-1-CH_3-pyridin-2-ylidene =CHCH=		295° (dec.)	1670
C_6H_5	C_6H_5	1-C_2H_5-quinolin-2-ylidene =CHCH=		296° (dec.)	1670
C_6H_5	C_6H_5	3-C_2H_5-benzothiazol-2-ylidene =CHCH=		291° (dec.)	1670

C_6H_5	C_6H_5	C_6H_5	H	184°	222, 619, 1031, 1032
C_6H_5	C_6H_5	$4\text{-}CH_3OC_6H_4$	H		188
C_6H_5	C_6H_5	$4\text{-}ClC_6H_4$	H	196°	1031, 1032
C_6H_5	$4\text{-}CH_3C_6H_4$	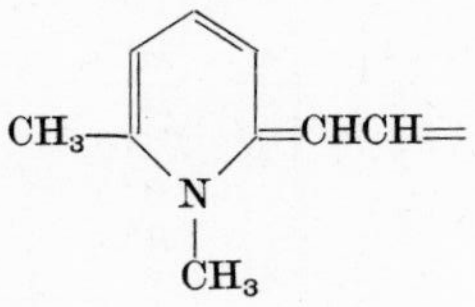 CH_3— N —CH_3 =CHCH=		225° (dec.)	1670
C_6H_5	$2\text{-}CH_3SC_6H_4$	C_4H_9	H	124°	613
$4\text{-}CH_3C_6H_4$	$4\text{-}CH_3C_6H_4$	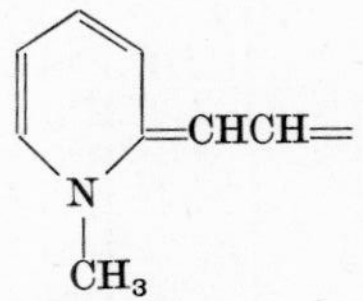 N —CH_3 =CHCH=		202°	1670
$4\text{-}CH_3C_6H_4$	$4\text{-}CH_3C_6H_4$	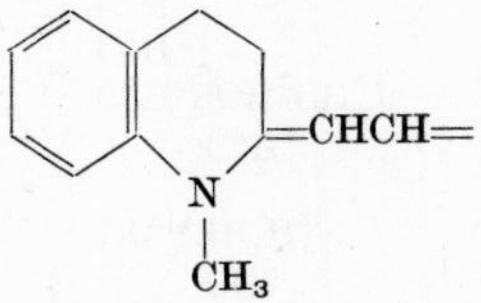 N —CH_3 =CHCH=		292° (dec.)	1670
$4\text{-}CH_3OC_6H_4$	$4\text{-}CH_3OC_6H_4$	$4\text{-}CH_3C_6H_4CH_2OCH_2$	H	—	615
$4\text{-}CH_3OC_6H_4$	$4\text{-}CH_3OC_6H_4$	$CH_3OCH_2CH_2$	H	—	615
$4\text{-}C_2H_5OC_6H_4$	$4\text{-}C_2H_5OC_6H_4$	$CH_3OCH_2CH_2$	H	—	615
$4\text{-}C_2H_5OC_6H_4$	$4\text{-}C_2H_5OC_6H_4$	$C_2H_5OCH_2CH_2$	H	—	615

(Table continued)

TABLE XLVII, Section B (*continued*)

R^1	R^2	R^3	R^4	M.p.	Reference
$2\text{-}CH_3SC_6H_4$	$2\text{-}CH_3SC_6H_4$	$iso\text{-}C_4H_9SCH_2CH_2$	H	—	615
$4\text{-}CH_3SC_6H_4$	$4\text{-}CH_3SC_6H_4$	$CH_3S\underset{CH_3}{\underset{\vert}{C}}HCH_2$	H	—	615
$4\text{-}CH_3SC_6H_4$	$4\text{-}CH_3SC_6H_4$	$CH_3\underset{OC_2H_5}{\underset{\vert}{C}}HCH_2$	H	—	615
$4\text{-}CH_3SC_6H_4$	$4\text{-}CH_3SC_6H_4$	$C_6H_5SCH_2CH_2$	H	—	615
$4\text{-}HO_2CC_6H_4$	$4\text{-}HO_2CC_6H_4$	C_2H_5	H	270° (dec.)	252
$4\text{-}HO_2CC_6H_4$	$4\text{-}HO_2CC_6H_4$	C_3H_7	H	228° (dec.)	252
$4\text{-}HO_2CC_6H_4$	$4\text{-}HO_2CC_6H_4$	$iso\text{-}C_3H_7$	H	275° (dec.)	252
$4\text{-}HO_2CC_6H_4$	$4\text{-}HO_2CC_6H_4$	C_4H_9	H	222° (dec.)	252
$4\text{-}HO_2CC_6H_4$	$4\text{-}HO_2CC_6H_4$	C_6H_{13}	H	245° (dec.)	252
$4\text{-}C_2H_5O_2CC_6H_4$	$4\text{-}C_2H_5O_2CC_6H_4$	C_2H_5	H	200°	252
$4\text{-}C_2H_5O_2CC_6H_4$	$4\text{-}C_2H_5O_2CC_6H_4$	C_3H_7	H	198°	252
$4\text{-}C_2H_5O_2CC_6H_4$	$4\text{-}C_2H_5O_2CC_6H_4$	$iso\text{-}C_3H_7$	H	180°	252
$(CH_2)_2N{-}C_6H_5$	$(CH_2)_2N{-}C_6H_5$	C_4H_9	H	—	1289
$4\text{-}C_2H_5O_2CC_6H_4$	$4\text{-}C_2H_5O_2CC_6H_4$	C_4H_9	H	158°	252
$4\text{-}C_2H_5O_2CC_6H_4$	$4\text{-}C_2H_5O_2CC_6H_4$	C_6H_{13}	H	132°	252
$3\text{-}HO\text{-}4\text{-}HO_2CC_6H_3$	$3\text{-}HO\text{-}4\text{-}HO_2CC_6H_3$	CH_3	H	272° (dec.)	252
$3\text{-}HO\text{-}4\text{-}HO_2CC_6H_3$	$3\text{-}HO\text{-}4\text{-}HO_2CC_6H_3$	C_2H_5	H	280° (dec.)	252
$3\text{-}HO\text{-}4\text{-}HO_2CC_6H_3$	$3\text{-}HO\text{-}4\text{-}HO_2CC_6H_3$	C_3H_7	H	256° (dec.)	252
$3\text{-}HO\text{-}4\text{-}HO_2CC_6H_3$	$3\text{-}HO\text{-}4\text{-}HO_2CC_6H_3$	$iso\text{-}C_3H_7$	H	270° (dec.)	252
$3\text{-}HO\text{-}4\text{-}HO_2CC_6H_3$	$3\text{-}HO\text{-}4\text{-}HO_2CC_6H_3$	C_4H_9	H	220° (dec.)	252
$3\text{-}HO\text{-}4\text{-}HO_2CC_6H_3$	$3\text{-}HO\text{-}4\text{-}HO_2CC_6H_3$	$iso\text{-}C_5H_{11}$	H	255° (dec.)	252
$3\text{-}HO\text{-}4\text{-}HO_2CC_6H_3$	$3\text{-}HO\text{-}4\text{-}HO_2CC_6H_3$	C_6H_{13}	H	225° (dec.)	252
$3\text{-}HO\text{-}4\text{-}CH_3O_2CC_6H_3$	$3\text{-}HO\text{-}4\text{-}CH_3O_2CC_6H_3$	CH_3	H	283°	252
$3\text{-}HO\text{-}4\text{-}CH_3O_2CC_6H_3$	$3\text{-}HO\text{-}4\text{-}CH_3O_2CC_6H_3$	C_2H_5	H	244°	252

3-HO-4-$CH_3O_2CC_6H_3$	3-HO-4-$CH_3O_2CC_6H_3$	C_3H_7	H	164°	252
3-HO-4-$CH_3O_2CC_6H_3$	3-HO-4-$CH_3O_2CC_6H_3$	iso-C_3H_7	H	186°	252
3-HO-4-$CH_3O_2CC_6H_3$	3-HO-4-$CH_3O_2CC_6H_3$	C_4H_9	H	154°	252
3-HO-4-$CH_3O_2CC_6H_3$	3-HO-4-$CH_3O_2CC_6H_3$	iso-C_5H_{11}	H	180°	252
3-HO-4-$CH_3O_2CC_6H_3$	3-HO-4-$CH_3O_2CC_6H_3$	C_6H_{13}	H	123°	252
3-CH_3CO_2-4-$CH_3O_2CC_6H_3$	3-CH_3CO_2-4-CH_3O_2-CC_6H_3	C_4H_9	H	143°	252
2-$C_{10}H_7$	H	$C_6H_5CH_2$	$C_6H_5CH_2$	243°	506
C_6H_5	CH_3	CH_3	CH_3	70°	248, 998
C_6H_5	CH_3	CH_3	C_2H_5	62°	998
C_6H_5	CH_3	C_2H_5	C_2H_5	94°	41, 248
C_6H_5	CH_3	C_2H_5	iso-C_5H_{11}	$b_{0.15}$ 123°	248
C_6H_5	CH_3	iso-C_3H_7	C_3H_5	$b_{0.03}$ 124°	248
C_6H_5	C_2H_5	C_2H_5	C_2H_5	57°	248
C_6H_5	C_3H_7	C_2H_5	C_2H_5	$b_{0.2}$ 130°	248
C_6H_5	iso-C_3H_7	C_2H_5	C_2H_5	$b_{0.02}$ 106°	248
C_6H_5	C_3H_5	C_2H_5	C_2H_5	42°	248, 734
C_6H_5	$C_6H_5CH_2$	C_2H_5	C_2H_5	93°	248
C_6H_5	$C_6H_5CH_2$	C_3H_5	iso-C_3H_7	$b_{0.06}$ 155°	248
C_6H_5	$C_6H_5CH_2$	C_2H_5	iso-C_5H_{11}	99°	248
C_6H_5	$C_6H_5CH_2$	$C_6H_5CH_2$	C_4H_9	$b_{0.01}$ 175°	248
C_6H_5	$(C_2H_5)_2NCH_2CH_2$	C_2H_5	C_2H_5	$b_{0.01}$ 144°	248
C_6H_5	$(CH_3)_2NCH_2CH_2$	$C_6H_5CH_2$	C_4H_9	$b_{0.05}$ 180°	248
C_6H_5	C_6H_5	C_4H_9	C_4H_9	121°	304
C_6H_5	$C_6H_5CH_2$	C_6H_5	CH_3	115°	222
C_6H_5	$C_6H_5CH_2$	C_6H_5	$C_6H_5CH_2$	110°	222
C_6H_5	C_6H_5	C_6H_5	CH_3	159°	222

TABLE XLVIII. 3,5-Pyrazolidinediones. Acyl on Nitrogen and Oxygen, Nitrogen, and Halogen Substituents

R^1	R^2	R^3	R^4	M.p.	Reference
C_6H_5	C_6H_5	C_4H_9	HO	132°	1312
C_6H_5	C_6H_5	$(CH_3)_2NCH_2CH_2O$	H	227°	1048
C_6H_5	H	H_2N	H	320° (dec.)	317
C_6H_5	CH_3	H_2N	H	180°	1339
C_6H_5	C_6H_5	H_2N	H	—	1048
C_6H_5	H	HON=		182°	976
C_6H_5	CH_3	HON=		193° (dec.)	981, 1339
C_6H_5	C_6H_5	HON=		163°	1501
C_6H_5	C_6H_5	$4\text{-}C_2H_5O_2CC_6H_4NH$	H	260°	1048
C_6H_5	H	$C_6H_5N{=}N$	H	232°	976
H	H	$C_6H_5N{=}N$	H	266°	257
C_6H_5	C_6H_5	$4\text{-}H_2NO_2SC_6H_4N{=}N$	H	268°	1048
C_6H_5	C_6H_5	4—(thiazol-2-yl—NHO_2S)$C_6H_4N{=}N$	H	261°	1048

4-$O_2NC_6H_4$	H	4-$O_2NC_6H_4N{=}N$	H	—	1340
C_6H_5	C_6H_5	Br	H	51°	1048
C_6H_5	C_6H_5	C_4H_9	Cl	106°	458
C_6H_5	C_6H_5	C_2H_5	Br	98°	1033
C_6H_5	C_6H_5	iso-C_3H_7	Br	100°	1033
C_6H_5	C_6H_5	C_4H_9	Br	116°	458, 1032, 1033
C_6H_5	C_6H_5	C_6H_5	Br	160°	1031, 1033
C_6H_5	C_6H_5	4-ClC_6H_4	Br	119°	1031
C_6H_5	C_6H_5NHCO	H	H	166°	976
C_6H_5	HCO	C_2H_5	C_2H_5	110°	734
C_6H_5	CH_3CO	C_2H_5	C_2H_5	96°	734
C_6H_5	C_6H_5CO	C_6H_5CO	H	111°	976
C_6H_5NHCO	H	C_6H_{13}	H	170° (dec.)	506
C_6H_5NHCO	H	C_7H_{15}	H	160° (dec.)	506
C_6H_5NHCO	H	C_8H_{17}	H	150°	506
C_6H_5NHCO	H	C_4H_9	C_4H_9	217°	506
C_6H_5NHCO	H	C_6H_{13}	C_6H_{13}	198°	506
C_6H_5NHCO	H	C_7H_{15}	C_7H_{15}	199°	506
C_6H_5NHCO	H	C_8H_{17}	C_8H_{17}	194°	506
C_6H_5NHCO	H	$C_6H_5CH_2$	$C_6H_5CH_2$	243°	506
C_6H_5 (3-Thiono)	CH_3	CH_3CO	H	81°	89, 109

$$R^5N{=}\underset{R^2-N}{C}\!-\!C(R^3)(R^4)\!-\!C{=}O,\ N\!-\!R^1$$

TABLE XLIX. 5-Imino-3-pyrazolidinones

Section A. Alkyl, Alicyclic, Aralkyl, Heterocyclicalkyl, Heterocyclic, and Aryl Substituents

R^1	R^2	R^3	R^4	R^5	M.p.	Reference
H	H	H	H	H	214°	594, 644, 1083
H	H	H	H	C_6H_5	255°	1597, 1649
H	H	H	H	2-$CH_3C_6H_4$	223° (dec.)	1651
H	H	H	H	3-$CH_3C_6H_4$	250° (dec.)	1651
H	H	H	H	4-$CH_3C_6H_4$	246° (dec.)	1649
H	H	H	H	2-$CH_3OC_6H_4$	200°	1651
H	H	H	H	3-$CH_3OC_6H_4$	212°	1651
H	H	H	H	4-$CH_3OC_6H_4$	205° (dec.)	1651
H	H	H	H	4-$C_2H_5OC_6H_4$	198° (dec.)	1651
H	H	H	H	3-BrC_6H_4	271° (dec.)	1651
H	H	H	H	4-BrC_6H_4	234°	1649
H	H	H	H	4-IC_6H_4	242° (dec.)	1651
H	H	H	H	2,4-$Br_2C_6H_3$	249° (dec.)	1651
H	H	H	H	1-$C_{10}H_7$	214°	1651
H	H	H	H	2-$C_{10}H_7$	239° (dec.)	1651
H	H	H	H	CH_3CO	227°	594
H	H	H	H	C_6H_5CO	227°	594
CH_3	H	H	H	H	192°	594
CH_3	H	H	H	C_6H_5	220°	1597
CH_3	H	H	H	C_6H_5CO	215°	594

H	CH_3	H		H	H	182°	594
H	CH_3	H		H	C_6H_5	208°	1597
H	CH_3	H		H	C_6H_5CO	243°	594
H	H	CH_3		H	H	242°	501
H	H	C_2H_5		H	H	247°	501
H	H	C_4H_9		H	H	128°	508
H	H	s-C_4H_9		H	H	145°	508
H	H	C_6H_{13}		H	H	133°	507
H	H	$(C_2H_5)_2CHCH_2$		H	H	190°	507
H	H	C_7H_{15}		H	H	136°	507
H	H	$C_4H_9CH(C_2H_5)CH_2$		H	H	131°	507
H	H	C_9H_{19}		H	H	222°	498
H	H	$C_{10}H_{21}$		H	H	234°	507
H	H	$C_{12}H_{25}$		H	H	152°	500
H	H	$C_{18}H_{37}$		H	H	200°	498
H	H	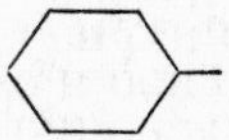 [structure]		H	H	239°	507
$C_5H_{11}CH(COOH)$	H	H		H	H	—	705
$C_5H_{11}CH(COOH)$	H	H		H	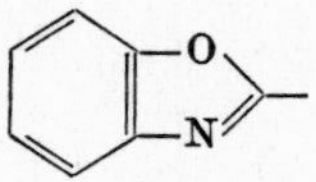 [structure]	—	705
H	H	$C_6H_5CH_2$		H	H	202°	497, 501
H	H	$C_6H_5CH(CH_3)$		H	H	80°	120
H	H		$C_6H_5CH=$		H	244°	644, 1085
H	H		$C_6H_5CH=$		HOOC	>280°	557

(Table continued)

TABLE XLIX, Section A (*continued*)

R^1	R^2	R^3	R^4	R^5	M.p.	Reference
H	H	$2\text{-}HOC_6H_4CH{=}$		H	199°	1083
H	H	$2\text{-}ClC_6H_4CH_2$	H	H	170°	500
H	H	$1\text{-}C_{10}H_7CH_2$	H	H	—	507
H	H	$H_2NHNOCCH_2$	H	H	212°	507
H	H	$C_6H_5N{=}CH$	H	H	—	1085
H	H	$C_6H_{11}CH_2CH_2$ (cyclohexyl–CH_2CH_2)	H	H	203°	498
H	H	$C_6H_5CH{=}CH$	H	H	198°	498
H	H	$CH_3SCH_2CH_2$	H	H	121°	508
H	H	$C_6H_5CH_2SCH_2CH_2$	H	H	109°	508
H	H	$C_6H_5OCH_2CH_2$	H	H	186°	501
H	H	$4\text{-}CH_3C_6H_4OCH_2CH_2$	H	H	184°	500
H	H	$4\text{-}C_2H_5C_6H_4OCH_2CH_2$	H	H	170°	500
H	H	$4\text{-}ClC_6H_4OCH_2CH_2$	H	H	203°	500
H	H	$3\text{-}C_2H_5C_6H_4OCH_2CH_2$	H	H	135°	120
H	H	$C_6H_5OCH_2CH_2CH_2$	H	H	110°	501
H	H	$4\text{-}CH_3C_6H_4OCH_2CH_2CH_2$	H	H	159°	500
H	H	$4\text{-}ClC_6H_4OCH_2CH_2CH_2$	H	H	203°	500
H	H	$2\text{-}BrC_6H_4OCH_2CH_2CH_2$	H	H	152°	120
H	H	$4\text{-}BrC_6H_4OCH_2CH_2CH_2$	H	H	214°	500
H	H	$2,4\text{-}Cl_2C_6H_3OCH_2CH_2CH_2$	H	H	183°	120
H	H	$3\text{-}C_2H_5C_6H_4OCH_2CH_2$	$3\text{-}C_2H_5C_6H_4OCH_2CH_2$	H	215°	120
H	H	$3\text{-}CH_3C_6H_4OCH_2CH_2CH_2$	$3\text{-}CH_3C_6H_4OCH_2CH_2CH_2$	H	215°	120
H	H	[structure: 5-hydroxybarbitur-5-yl ring — HN, O, OH, N–H, O]	H	H	—	1083

C_6H_5	H	H	H	H	219°	67, 317, 693, 870, 1141, 1595, 1601
C_6H_5	H	H	H	C_2H_5	153°	595, 596
C_6H_5	H	H	H	C_6H_5	219°	595, 1595
C_6H_5	H	H	H	2-$CH_3C_6H_4$	> 400°	595
C_6H_5	H	H	H	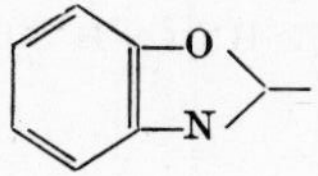 [structure: O, N]	227°	704
C_6H_5	H	H	H	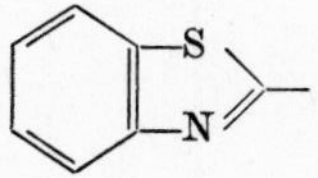 [structure: S, N]	257°	705
C_6H_5	H	H	H	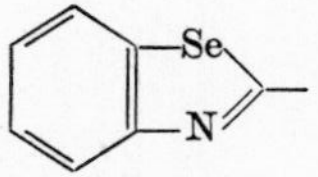 [structure: Se, N]	190°	704
C_6H_5	H	H	H	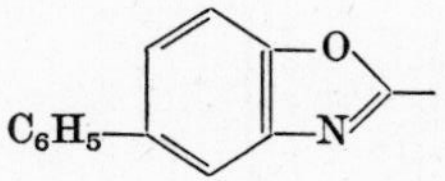 [structure: C_6H_5, O, N]	> 290°	704
C_6H_5	H	H	H	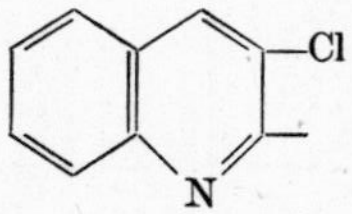 [structure: Cl, N]	224°	704

(Table continued)

TABLE XLIX, Section A (*continued*)

R^1	R^2	R^3	R^4	R^5	M.p.	Reference
C_6H_5	H	H	H	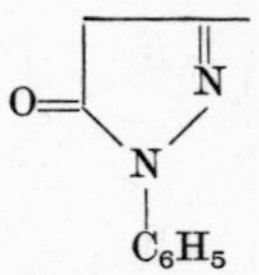 O=, N, N, C_6H_5	290°	595, 596
C_6H_5	H	H	H	CH_3CO	218°	693, 1139, 1595
C_6H_5	H	H	H	$HSCH_2CO$	—	1594
C_6H_5	H	H	H	$BrCH_2CO$	—	1602
C_6H_5	H	H	H	$CH_3CH_2CH(C_6H_5)CO$	170°	1255
C_6H_5	H	H	H	CH_3COSCH_2CO	195°	776
C_6H_5	H	H	H	$C_6H_5HNCH_2CO$	—	1602
C_6H_5	H	H	H	C_6H_5CO	220°	693, 1595
C_6H_5	H	H	H	3-$H_2NC_6H_4CO$	220°	67, 1139, 1247
C_6H_5	H	H	H	3-$O_2NC_6H_5CO$	215°	67, 1247
C_6H_5	H	H	H	2-$H_2NOCC_6H_4CO$	—	1139
C_6H_5	H	H	H	3-(3-$ClO_2SC_6H_4NH$)C_6H_4CO	188°	67
C_6H_5	H	H	H	3-{[4-(4-*t*-$C_5H_{11}C_6H_4O$)C_6H_4NHCO]$C_6H_4SO_2NH$}C_6H_4-CO	—	1602
C_6H_5	H	H	H	3-H_2N-4-$C_{18}H_{37}OC_6H_3CO$	138°	1246
C_6H_5	H	H	H	3-NO_2-4-$C_{18}H_{37}OC_6H_3CO$	155°	1246
C_6H_5	H	H	H	3-{2-[2,4-(*t*-C_5H_{11})$_2C_6H_3O$]-5-$H_2NC_6H_3CO$}C_6H_4CO	—	1087
C_6H_5	H	H	H	3-{2-[2,4-(*t*)C_5H_{11})$_2C_6H_3O$]-5-[2,5-(CH_3OOC)$_2$-$C_6H_3NHCOCONH$]C_6H_3CONH}C_6H_4CO	205°	1087
C_6H_5	H	H	H	3-(3-$ClO_2SC_6H_4CONH$)-4-$C_{18}H_{37}OC_6H_3CO$	152°	1246
C_6H_5	H	H	H	3-(3-$Cl_2O_2SC_6H_4CONH$)-4-$C_{12}H_{25}OC_6H_3CO$	—	1246

C_6H_5	H	H	H	3-[3,4-$(ClO_2S)_2C_6H_3CONH$]-4-$C_{12}H_{25}OC_6H_3CO$	—	1246
C_6H_5	H	H	H	3-[4-(4-*t*-C_5H_{11}-X-$ClO_2SC_6H_3O)C_6H_4CONH$]-4-$C_{12}H_{25}$-OC_6H_3CO	—	1246
C_6H_5	H	H	H	3-(2-$HO_3SC_6H_4CONH$)-4-$C_{12}H_{25}OC_6H_3CO$	—	1246
C_6H_5	H	H	H	3-(2-HOOC-X-$ClO_2SC_6H_3CONH$)-4-$C_{18}H_{37}OC_6H_3CO$	142°	1246
C_6H_5	H	H	H	3-(2-$HO_3SC_6H_4CONH$)-4-$C_{18}H_{37}OC_6H_3CO$	210°	1246
C_6H_5	H	H	H	3-[4-(4-*t*-C_5H_{11}-X-$ClO_2SC_6H_3CO)C_6H_4CONH$]-4-$C_{18}H_{37}OC_6H_3CO$	128°	1246
C_6H_5	H	H	H	3-[3,5-$(ClO_2S)_2C_6H_3CONH$]-4-$C_{18}H_{37}OC_6H_3CO$	148°	1246
C_6H_5	H	H	H	2,4-(*t*-$C_5H_{11})_2C_6H_3OCH_2CO$	204°	591
C_6H_5	H	H	H	3-{5-NO_2-2-[2,4-$(C_5H_{11})_2C_6H_3O]C_6H_3CONH\}C_6H_4CO$	—	1247
C_6H_5	H	H	H	3-{5-H_2N-2-[2,4-$(C_5H_{11})_2C_6H_3O]C_6H_3CONH\}C_6H_4CO$	—	1247
C_6H_5	H	H	H	3-{5-[2-$HO_3SC_6H_4CONH$]-2-[2,4-$(C_5H_{11})_2C_6H_3O$]-$C_6H_3CONH\}C_6H_4CO$	—	1247
C_6H_5	H	H	H	3-{5-$HO_3SCH_2CH_2CONH$-2-[2,4-$(C_5H_{11})_2C_6H_3O$]-$C_6H_3CONH\}C_6H_4CO$	—	1247
C_6H_5						
C_6H_5	H	H	H	3-(2-$HO_3SC_6H_4CONH)C_6H_4CO$	—	1247
C_6H_5	H	H	H	3-(2-$HO_3SC_6H_4CONH$)-4-$C_{12}H_{25}OC_6H_3CO$	—	1247
C_6H_5	H	H	H	3-(2-$HO_3SC_6H_4CONH$)-4-$C_{18}H_{37}OC_6H_3CO$	—	1247
C_6H_5	H	H	H	C_2H_5OOC	198°	1595
C_6H_5	H	H	H	C_6H_5NHCO	235°	1595
C_6H_5	H	H	H	C_6H_5NHCS	227°	705
H	C_6H_5	H	H	H	142°, 160°	1138, 1596, 1599
H	C_6H_5	H	H	C_6H_5	168°	1597
H	C_6H_5	H	H	CH_3CO	233°	1599
H	C_6H_5	H	H	C_6H_5CO	237°	1136, 1138, 1599
H	C_6H_5	H	H	C_6H_5NHCO	—	1138

(Table continued)

TABLE XLIX, Section A (*continued*)

R^1	R^2	R^3	R^4	R^5	M.p.	Reference
H	H	C_6H_5	H	H	246°	501
3-$CH_3C_6H_4$	H	H	H	H	182°	1600
4-$CH_3C_6H_4$	H	H	H	H	—	870
4-HOC_6H_4	H	H	H	H	300°	871
4-HOC_6H_4	H	H	H	$C_{15}H_{31}CO$	298° (dec.)	871
4-$CH_3OC_6H_4$	H	H	H	H	188°	1600
4-(4-t-$C_4H_9C_6H_4O)C_6H_4$	H	H	H	4-(t-$C_4H_9)C_6H_4OCH(CH_3)CO$	—	921
4-(4-t-$C_4H_9C_6H_4O)C_6H_4$	H	H	H	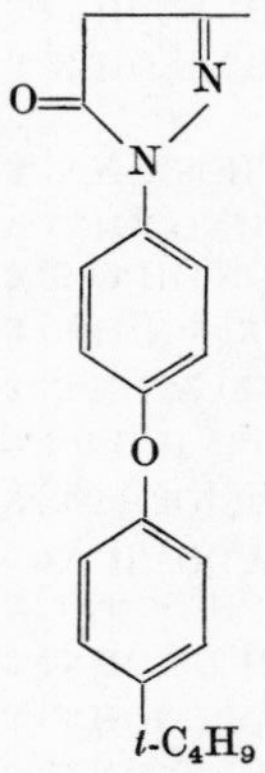 O= N N O t-C_4H_9	260°	595, 596
4-$H_2NC_6H_4$	H	H	H	$C_{11}H_{23}CO$	150°	592
4-$H_2NC_6H_4$	H	H	H	$C_{17}H_{35}CO$	148°	592
4-$H_2NC_6H_4$	H	H	H	2,4-$(C_5H_{11})_2C_6H_3OCH_2CO$	198°	592

$4\text{-}(3\text{-}ClO_2SC_6H_4CONH)C_6H_4$	H	H	H	$C_{11}H_{23}CO$	220° (dec.)	592
$4\text{-}(2\text{-}HO_3SC_6H_4CONH)C_6H_4$	H	H	H	$C_{17}H_{35}CO$	130°	592
$4\text{-}(3\text{-}HO_3SC_6H_4CONH)C_6H_4$	H	H	H	$C_{17}H_{35}CO$	—	592
$4\text{-}(2\text{-}HO_3SC_6H_4CONH)C_6H_4$	H	H	H	$4\text{-}(4\text{-}C_5H_{11}C_6H_4O)C_6H_4CO$	—	1247
$4\text{-}(2\text{-}HO_3SC_6H_4CONH)C_6H_4$	H	H	H	$4\text{-}[2,4\text{-}(C_5H_{11})_2C_6H_3O]C_6H_4CO$	—	1247
$4\text{-}(2\text{-}HO_3SC_6H_4CONH)C_6H_4$	H	H	H	$4\text{-}[2\text{-}(C_6H_5)C_6H_4]C_6H_4CO$	—	1247
$4\text{-}(2\text{-}HO_3SC_6H_4CONH)C_6H_4$	H	H	H	$2,4\text{-}(C_5H_{11})_2C_6H_3O(CH_2)_8CO$	—	1247
$4\text{-}(2\text{-}HO_3SC_6H_4CONH)C_6H_4$	H	H	H	$3\text{-}(4\text{-}C_5H_{11}C_6H_4O)C_6H_4CO$	—	592
$4\text{-}(2\text{-}HO_3SC_6H_4CONH)C_6H_4$	H	H	H	$2,4\text{-}(C_5H_{11})_2C_6H_3OCH_2CH_2CH_2CO$	—	592
$4\text{-}(2\text{-}HO_3SC_6H_4CONH)C_6H_4$	H	H	H	$2,4\text{-}(C_5H_{11})_2C_6H_3OCH_2CO$	—	592
$4\text{-}(2\text{-}HO_3SC_6H_4CONH)C_6H_4$	H	H	H	$4\text{-}[2\text{-}(C_6H_5)C_6H_4]C_6H_4CO$	—	592
$4\text{-}[3\text{-}(4\text{-}C_5H_{11}C_6H_4O)C_6H_4CONH]C_6H_4$	H	H	H	$3\text{-}(4\text{-}C_5H_{11}C_6H_4O)C_6H_4CO$	117°	592
$3\text{-}ClC_6H_4$	H	H	H	H	205°	870, 1600
$4\text{-}BrC_6H_4$	H	H	H	H	—	870
$4\text{-}NO_2C_6H_4$	H	H	H	H	248° (dec.)	1140, 1601
$4\text{-}NO_2C_6H_4$	H	H	H	$C_{11}H_{23}CO$	186°	592
$4\text{-}NO_2C_6H_4$	H	H	H	$C_{17}H_{35}CO$	—	592
$4\text{-}NO_2C_6H_4$	H	H	H	$2,4\text{-}(C_5H_{11})_2C_6H_3OCH_2CO$	195°	592
$3\text{-}HOOCC_6H_4$	H	H	H	H	273° (dec.)	871
$3\text{-}NCC_6H_4$	H	H	H	C_6H_5CO	—	1604
$4\text{-}NCC_6H_4$	H	H	H	H	224°	1601, 1604
$4\text{-}NCC_6H_4$	H	H	H	CH_3CO	—	1604
$4\text{-}NCC_6H_4$	H	H	H	$C_6H_5CH_2CO$	—	1604
$4\text{-}NCC_6H_4$	H	H	H	$3\text{-}NO_2C_6H_4CH_2CO$	—	1604
$4\text{-}NCC_6H_4$	H	H	H	$2,4\text{-}(C_5H_{11})_2C_6H_3OCH_2CO$	—	1604
$4\text{-}NCC_6H_4$	H	H	H	$4\text{-}[2,4\text{-}(t\text{-}C_5H_{11})_2C_6H_3OCH_2CONH]C_6H_4CH_2CO$	—	1604
$4\text{-}NCC_6H_4$	H	H	H	$3\text{-}[2,4(t\text{-}C_5H_{11})_2C_6H_3OCH_2CONH]C_6H_4CH_2CO$	—	1604
$4\text{-}NCC_6H_4$	H	H	H	$2,4\text{-}(C_5H_{11})_2C_6H_3OCH_2CH_2CO$	—	1604
$4\text{-}NCC_6H_4$	H	H	H	$4\text{-}[2,4\text{-}(t\text{-}C_5H_{11})_2C_6H_3O]C_6H_4CONHCH_2CH_2CH_2CO$	—	1604
$4\text{-}NCC_6H_4$	H	H	H	C_6H_5CO	254°	591, 1604
$4\text{-}NCC_6H_4$	H	H	H	$2\text{-}CH_3C_6H_4CO$	—	1604
$4\text{-}NCC_6H_4$	H	H	H	$4\text{-}CH_3C_6H_4CO$	—	1604
$4\text{-}NCC_6H_4$	H	H	H	$4\text{-}C_5H_{11}OC_6H_4CO$	—	1604
$4\text{-}NCC_6H_4$	H	H	H	$4\text{-}s\text{-}C_5H_{11}C_6H_4CO$	—	1604

(Table continued)

TABLE XLIX, Section A (*continued*)

R^1	R^2	R^3	R^4	R^5	M.p.	Reference
4-NCC_6H_4	H	H	H	2-$CH_3OC_6H_4CO$	—	1604
4-NCC_6H_4	H	H	H	3-$CH_3OC_6H_4CO$	—	1604
4-NCC_6H_4	H	H	H	4-$CH_3OC_6H_4CO$	—	1604
4-NCC_6H_4	H	H	H	3-$H_2NC_6H_4CO$	—	1604
4-NCC_6H_4	H	H	H	2-ClC_6H_4CO	—	1604
4-NCC_6H_4	H	H	H	3-ClC_6H_4CO	—	1604
4-NCC_6H_4	H	H	H	4-ClC_6H_4CO	—	1604
4-NCC_6H_4	H	H	H	2-$NO_2C_6H_4CO$	—	1604
4-NCC_6H_4	H	H	H	3-$NO_2C_6H_4CO$	254°	1604
4-NCC_6H_4	H	H	H	4-$NO_2C_6H_4CO$	—	1604
4-NCC_6H_4	H	H	H	4-NCC_6H_4CO	—	1604
4-NCC_6H_4	H	H	H	2,4-$Cl_2C_6H_3CO$	—	1604
4-NCC_6H_4	H	H	H	3,4-$Cl_2C_6H_3CO$	—	1604
4-NCC_6H_4	H	H	H	3-[4-(*t*-C_5H_{11})C_6H_4O]C_6H_4CO	—	1604
4-NCC_6H_4	H	H	H	3-[2,4-(*t*-C_5H_{11})$_2C_6H_3OCH_2CONH$]C_6H_5CO	—	1604
4-NCC_6H_4	H	H	H	3-{α-[2,4-(*t*-C_5H_{11})$_2C_6H_3O$]C_3H_6CONH}C_6H_4CO	—	1604
4-NCC_6H_4	H	H	H	4-[2,4-(*t*-C_5H_{11})$_2C_6H_3OCH_2CONH$]C_6H_4CO	—	1604
4-NCC_6H_4	H	H	H	2-[2,4-(*t*-C_5H_{11})$_2C_6H_3O$]-5-$H_2NC_6H_3CO$	—	1604
4-NCC_6H_4	H	H	H	2-[2,4-(*t*-C_5H_{11})$_2C_6H_3O$]-3-$NO_2C_6H_3CO$	—	1604
4-NCC_6H_4	H	H	H	2-[2,4-(*t*-C_5H_{11})$_2C_6H_3O$]-5-$NO_2C_6H_3CO$	—	1604
4-NCC_6H_4	H	H	H	4-[2,4-(*t*-C_5H_{11})$_2C_6H_3O$]-3-(4-$CH_3C_6H_4CO$)C_6H_3CO	—	1604
4-NCC_6H_4	H	H	H	4-[2,4-(*t*-C_5H_{11})$_2C_6H_3O$]-3-(4-ClC_6H_4CO)C_6H_3CO	—	1604
4-NCC_6H_4	H	H	H	2-[2,4-(*t*-C_5H_{11})$_2C_6H_3O$]-5-(4-s-$C_5H_{11}C_6H_4CO$)C_6H_3CO	—	1604
4-NCC_6H_4	H	H	H	4-[2,4-(*t*-C_5H_{11})$_2C_6H_3O$]-3-(4-s-$C_5H_{11}C_6H_4CO$)C_6H_3CO	—	1604
4-NCC_6H_4	H	H	H	3-{2-[2,4(*t*-C_5H_{11})$_2C_6H_3O$]-5-[3,5-(ClO_2S)$_2C_6H_3CO$]}-C_6H_4CO	—	1604
4-NCC_6H_4	H	H	H	3-{2-[2,4-(*t*-C_5H_{11})$_2C_6H_3O$]-5-[3-HOOC-4-$HOC_6H_3SO_2$-NH]C_6H_3CO}C_6H_4CO	—	1604

4-NCC_6H_4	H	H	H	4-[2-$(C_6H_5)C_6H_4]C_6H_4CO$	—	13, 1604
4-NCC_6H_4	H	H	H	[structure: furan ring (O) with –CO]		1604
4-NCC_6H_4	H	H	H	[structure: pyridine ring (N) with –CO]	—	1604
4-$HO_3SC_6H_4$	H	H	H	H	258° (dec.)	870, 871
4-$H_2NO_2SC_6H_4$	H	H	H	$C_{15}H_{31}CO$	199° (dec.)	695
4-$HO_3SC_6H_4$	H	H	H	C_6H_5CO	220°	871
4-$HO_3SC_6H_4$	H	H	H	C_6H_5CO	194°	695
4-$HO_3SC_6H_4$	H	H	H	[structure: pyrazolone ring, O=, N, N–C_6H_5]	—	705
4-$H_2NO_2SC_6H_4$	H	H	H	H	258°	1600
2,4-$Cl_2C_6H_3$	H	H	H	3-[2,4-(s-$C_4H_9)_2C_6H_3OCH_2CONH]C_6H_4CO$	133°	922
2,5-$Cl_2C_6H_3$	H	H	H	3-[2,4-(s-$C_4H_9)_2C_6H_3OCH_2CONH]C_6H_4CO$	—	922
2,5-$Cl_2C_6H_3$	H	H	H	3-[4-(t-$C_5H_{11})C_6H_4O]C_6H_4CO$	110°	922
4-C_6H_5O-3-$HO_3SC_6H_3$	H	H	H	H	>300°	871
4-C_6H_5O-3-$HO_3SC_6H_3$	H	H	H	$C_{15}H_{31}CO$	249° (dec.)	871
4-C_6H_5O-3-$HO_3SC_6H_3$	H	H	H	C_6H_5CO	>300°	871
4-C_6H_5O-X-$HO_3SC_6H_3$	H	H	H	H	>300°	871
4-C_6H_5O-X-$HO_3SC_6H_3$	H	H	H	$C_{17}H_{35}CO$	>300°	871
4-[3-(4-$C_5H_{11}C_6H_4O$)-X-ClO_2-$SC_6H_3O]C_6H_3$	H	H	H	2,4-$(C_5H_{11})_2C_6H_3OCH_2CO$	135°	592

(*Table continued*)

TABLE XLIX, Section A (*continued*)

R¹	R²	R³	R⁴	R⁵	M.p.	Reference
2,4,6-$Cl_3C_6H_2$	H	H	H	H	—	1254
2,4,6-$Cl_3C_6H_2$	H	H	H	$C_6H_5CH_2CO$	—	922
2,4,6-$Cl_3C_6H_2$	H	H	H	C_6H_5CO	—	922
2,4,6-$Cl_3C_6H_2$	H	H	H	3-$H_2NC_6H_4CO$	—	1254
2,4,6-$Cl_3C_6H_2$	H	H	H	3-$NO_2C_6H_4CO$	—	1254
2,4,6-$Cl_3C_6H_2$	H	H	H	3-[2,4-(s-$C_4H_9)_2C_6H_3OCH_2CONH]C_6H_4CO$	—	922
2,4,6-$Cl_3C_6H_2$	H	H	H	3-[2,4-(*t*-$C_5H_{11})_2C_6H_3OCH_2CONH]C_6H_4CO$	138°, 220°	922, 1603
2,4,6-$Br_3C_6H_2$	H	H	H	H	—	922
2,4,6-$Br_3C_6H_2$	H	H	H	$C_6H_5CH_2CO$	—	922
2,4,6-$Br_3C_6H_2$	H	H	H	C_6H_5CO	274°	922
2,4,6-$Br_3C_6H_2$	H	H	H	3-(4-*t*-$C_5H_{11}C_6H_4O)C_6H_4CO$	270°	922
2,4,6-$Br_3C_6H_2$	H	H	H	3-[2,4-(s-$C_4H_9)_2C_6H_3OCH_2CONH]C_6H_4CO$	—	922
2,4,6-$Br_3C_6H_2$	H	H	H	3-[2,4(*t*-$C_5H_{11})_2C_6H_3OCH_2CONH]C_6H_4CO$	225°	922
2,6-Cl_2-4-NCC_6H_2	H	H	H	2,4-(*t*-$C_5H_{11})_2C_6H_3OCH_2CH_2CO$	—	1604
2,6-Cl_2-4-NCC_6H_2	H	H	H	C_6H_5CO	—	1604
2,6-Cl_2-4-NCC_6H_2	H	H	H	3-[2,4-(*t*-$C_5H_{11})_2C_6H_3OCH_2CO]C_6H_4CO$	—	1604
4-[2-$(C_6H_5)C_6H_4]C_6H_4$	H	H	H	H	223°	13, 14
4-[2-$(C_6H_5)C_6H_4]C_6H_4$	H	H	H	C_6H_5CO	234°	13, 14
[structure: 2-pyridyl]	H	H	H	H	277°	1142, 1601
H	[structure: 2-pyridyl]	H	H	H	188°	1600

H	2-pyridyl	H	H	C_6H_5	201°	1601
3-pyridyl	H	H	H	H	216° (dec.)	1142, 1600, 1601
4-pyridyl	H	H	H	H	239° (dec.)	1142, 1600, 1601
2-benzoxazolyl	H	H	H	H	220° (dec.)	1142, 1601
2-benzothiazolyl	H	H	H	H	254°	1601
2-benzothiazolyl	H	H	H	C_6H_5CO	225°	1601
H	2-benzothiazolyl	H	H	H	234° (dec.)	1600

(Table continued)

TABLE XLIX, Section A (*continued*)

R^1	R^2	R^3	R^4	R^5	M.p.	Reference
H	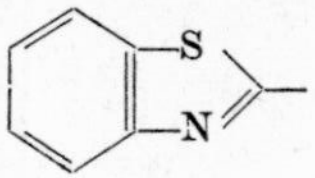	H	H	CH_3CO	252°	1600
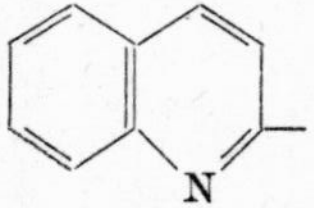	H	H	H	H	196°	1601
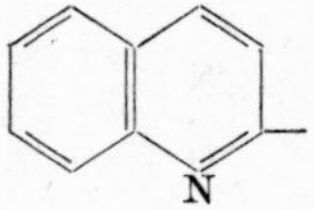	H	H	H	C_6H_5CO	187°	1142, 1601
H	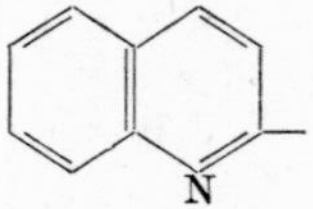	H	H	H	218° (dec.)	1600
CH_3	H	CH_3	H	H	140°	499
CH_3	H	CH_3	H	C_2H_5OOC	250°	499
H	CH_3	CH_3	H	H	223°	499
H	H	CH_3	CH_3	H	249°	507
CH_3	CH_3	H	H	CH_3OOC	200°	167
H	H	CH_3	C_4H_9	H	196°	391
H	CH_3	C_5H_{11}	H	H	85°	499
H	CH_3	C_6H_{13}	H	H	101°	499
H	CH_3	C_7H_{15}	H	H	79°	499
H	CH_3	C_8H_{17}	H	H	86°	499

H	H	C_2H_5	C_2H_5	H	208°	391
H	H	C_2H_5	C_4H_9	H	192°	391
H	H	C_3H_7	C_3H_7	H	175°, 236°	391, 507
H	H	C_4H_9	C_4H_9	H	223°	507
H	H	C_5H_{11}	C_5H_{11}	H	200°	507
H	H	$C_6H_5CH_2$	$C_6H_5CH_2$	H	242°	501
C_6H_5	CH_3	H	H	H	230°	167, 697, 1339, 1387
C_6H_5	CH_3	H	H	$C_6H_5CH_2$	69°	1052
C_6H_5	CH_3	H	H	CH_3CO	257°	1339
C_6H_5	CH_3	H	H	C_6H_5CO	233°	1339
C_6H_5	CH_3	H	H	C_2H_5OOC	222°	167, 1387
C_6H_5	CH_3	H	H	C_4H_9OOC	194°	167
C_6H_5	CH_3	H	H	$HOCH_2CH_2OOC$	212°	167
C_6H_5	H	CH_3	H	H	137°	499
C_6H_5	H	CH_3	H	C_2H_5OOC	242°	499
H	C_6H_5	CH_3	H	H	227°	501
C_6H_5	C_2H_5	H	H	H	145°, 226°	167, 499, 1395
C_6H_5	C_2H_5	H	H	C_2H_5OOC	213°	167, 499, 1395
C_6H_5	C_2H_5	H	H	iso-C_3H_7OOC	211°	167
H	C_6H_5	C_2H_5	H	H	213°	501
H	H	C_2H_5	C_6H_5	H	215°	391
H	C_6H_5	C_9H_{19}	H	H	167°	498
H	C_6H_5	$C_6H_{11}CH_2CH_2$	H	H	154°	498
C_6H_5	H	$C_6H_5CH_2$	H	H	206°	498
C_6H_5	H	$C_6H_5CH_2$	H	C_2H_5OOC	178°	498
C_6H_5	H	$C_6H_5CH_2$	H	C_6H_5CO	225°	498

(Table continued)

TABLE XLIX, Section A (*continued*)

R¹	R²	R³	R⁴	R⁵	M.p.	Reference
H	C_6H_5	$C_6H_5CH_2$	H	H	160°	498, 501
H	C_6H_5	$C_6H_5CH_2$	H	C_6H_5CO	197°	498
C_6H_5	H	4-$CH_3OC_6H_4CH$=		$CH_3CH_2CH(C_6H_5)CO$	162°	1255
H	C_6H_5	$C_6H_5OCH_2CH_2$	H	H	136°	501
H	C_6H_5	$C_6H_5OCH_2CH_2CH_2$	H	H	108°	501
H	H			H	238°	501
C_6H_5	H	O, N–C_2H_5 =CHCH=		H	206° (dec.)	1330
C_6H_5	H	C_2H_5, N, O, O=, =CH, N, C_2H_5, O	H	H	165°	776
C_6H_5	H	C_2H_5, N, O, S=, =CHCH=CHCH=CH, N, C_2H_5, O	H	CH_3COSCH_2CO	219°	776

C_6H_5	H	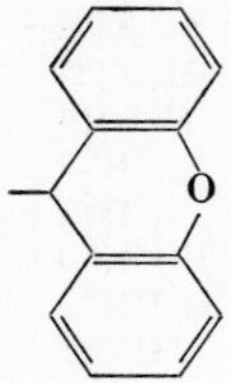 [structure: O]	H	C_2H_5CHCO (with C_6H_5 on CH)	220°	1253
C_6H_5	H	C_6H_5	H	H	153°	506
C_6H_5	H	C_6H_5	H	C_6H_5OOC	193°	506
H	C_6H_5	C_6H_5	H	H	234°	506
H	H	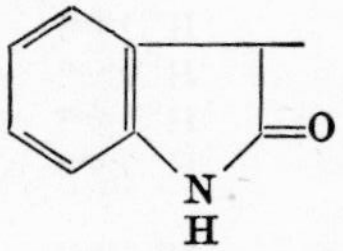 [structure: O, N, H]	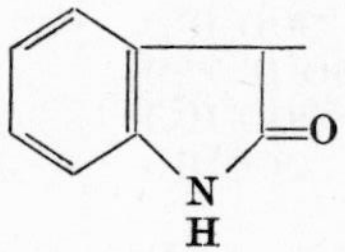 [structure: O, N, H]	H	—	1083
2,4,6-$Cl_3C_6H_2$	H	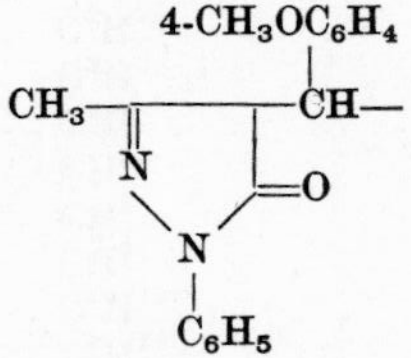 [structure: 4-$CH_3OC_6H_4$, CH_3, CH—, N, O, N, C_6H_5]	H	3-[2,4-(t-C_5H_{11})$_2$-$C_6H_3OCH_2$-CONH]C_6H_4CO	152°	1254
2,4,6-$Cl_3C_6H_2$	H	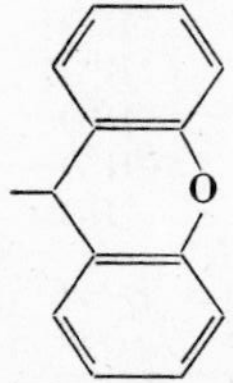 [structure: O]	H	3-[2,4-(t-C_5H_{11})$_2$-$C_6H_3OCH_2CO$-NH]C_6H_4CO	120°	1253

(Table continued)

TABLE XLIX, Section A (*continued*)

R^1	R^2	R^3	R^4	R^5	M.p.	Reference
CH_3	H	CH_3	C_4H_9	H	140°	391
CH_3	H	C_2H_5	C_2H_5	H	190°	391
CH_3	H	C_2H_5	C_2H_5	CH_3CO	206°	391
CH_3	H	C_2H_5	C_2H_5	C_6H_5CO	178°	391
H	CH_3	C_4H_9	C_4H_9	H	141°	499
H	CH_3	C_6H_{13}	C_6H_{13}	H	188°	499
H	CH_3	C_7H_{15}	C_7H_{15}	H	135°	499
C_6H_5	CH_3	CH_3	H	H	196°	167
C_6H_5	CH_3	CH_3	H	CH_3OOC	188°	167
C_6H_5	CH_3	CH_3	H	iso-C_3H_7OOC	157°	167
C_6H_5	CH_3	C_2H_5	H	H	157°	167
C_6H_5	CH_3	C_2H_5	H	CH_3OOC	144°	167
CH_3	H	C_2H_5	C_6H_5	H	141°	391
C_6H_5	CH_3	iso-C_3H_7	H	H	204°	167, 1395, 1400
C_6H_5	CH_3	iso-C_3H_7	H	CH_3OOC	126°	167
C_6H_5	CH_3	iso-C_3H_7	H	C_2H_5OOC	141°	167
C_6H_5	CH_3	iso-C_3H_7	H	iso-C_3H_7OOC	139°	167
C_6H_5	CH_3	iso-C_3H_7	H	C_3H_5OOC	102°	167
C_6H_5	CH_3	iso-C_3H_7	H	$ClCH_2CH_2OOC$	135°	167
C_6H_5	CH_3	iso-C_3H_7	H	$HOCH_2CH_2OOC$	136°	167
C_6H_5	CH_3	iso-C_3H_7	H	H_2NOC	165°	167
C_6H_5	CH_3	s-C_4H_9	H	H	204°	167
C_6H_5	CH_3	s-C_4H_9	H	CH_3OOC	109°	167
C_6H_5	CH_3	$C_6H_5CH_2$	H	H	137°	167
C_6H_5	CH_3	$C_6H_5CH_2$	H	CH_3OOC	158°	167
H	C_2H_5	C_2H_5	C_6H_5	H	138°	391
H	C_3H_7	C_2H_5	C_6H_5	H	105°	391
C_6H_5	C_2H_5	iso-C_3H_7	H	H	204°, 230°	1395, 1400
C_6H_5	C_2H_5	iso-C_3H_7	H	CH_3OOC	126°	1395
C_6H_5	C_2H_5	iso-C_3H_7	H	C_2H_5OOC	141°	1395

C_6H_5	C_2H_5	s-C_4H_9	H	H	204°	1395
C_6H_5	C_2H_5	s-C_4H_9	H	CH_3OOC	126°	1395
H	C_6H_5	C_3H_7	C_3H_7	H	211°	317
H	C_6H_5	$C_6H_5CH_2$	$C_6H_5CH_2$	H	259°	501
C_6H_5	CH_3	C_6H_5	H	H	241°	167
C_6H_5	CH_3	C_6H_5	H	CH_3OOC	124°	167
4-$CH_3C_6H_4$	CH_3	iso-C_3H_7	H	H	205°	167
4-$CH_3C_6H_5$	CH_3	iso-C_3H_7	H	CH_3OOC	191°	167
CH_3	CH_3	C_2H_5	C_2H_5	H	76°	391
CH_3	CH_3	C_2H_5	C_2H_5	C_2H_5OOC	b_{13} 173°	391
CH_3	CH_3	C_2H_5	C_6H_5	H	$b_{0.1}$ 155°	391

TABLE XLIX (*continued*)

Section B. Acyl, Carboxyl, and Carboxyl Derivatives

R[1]	R[2]	R[3]	R[4]	R[5]	M.p.	Reference
H	C_6H_5	CH_3CO	H	H	233°	498, 1599
H	H	HOOC	H	H	> 300°	557
H	H	C_2H_5OOC	H	H	—	1083
H	H	C_2H_5OOC	H	C_6H_5	194°	1650
H	H	C_2H_5OOC	H	2-$CH_3C_6H_4$	215°	1650
H	H	C_2H_5OOC	H	4-$CH_3C_6H_4$	200°	1650
H	H	C_2H_5OOC	H	HOOC	187°	557
C_6H_5	H	$CH_3C(=NNHC_6H_5)$	H	H	185° (dec.)	557
C_6H_5	H	2,4(t-C_5H_{11})$_2C_6H_3OCH_2CO$	H	2,4-(t-C_5H_{11})$_2C_6H_3OCH_2CO$	140°	591

(*Table continued*)

TABLE XLIX, Section B (*continued*)

R[1]	R[2]	R[3]	R[4]	R[5]	M.p.	Reference
CH_3CO	H	H	H	C_6H_5	207° (dec.)	1598
H	CH_3CO	H	H	C_6H_5	203°	1598
CH_3CO	H	H	H	CH_3CO	195°	594
C_6H_5CO	H	H	H	C_6H_5	198°	1598
C_6H_5CO	H	H	H	C_6H_5CO	171°	594
C_6H_5CO	H	$C_6H_5CH_2$	H	C_2H_5OOC	160°	497
H	C_6H_5CO	C_3H_7	H	H	234°	497
H	C_6H_5CO	C_4H_9	H	H	232°	497
H	C_6H_5CO	C_5H_{11}	H	H	233°	497
H	C_6H_5CO	C_6H_{13}	H	H	235°	497
H	C_6H_5CO	C_7H_{15}	H	H	234°	497
H	C_6H_5CO	C_8H_{17}	H	H	236°	497
H	C_6H_5CO	$C_6H_5CH_2$	H	H	236°	497
H	C_6H_5CO	C_3H_7	C_3H_7	H	236°	497
H	C_6H_5CO	C_4H_9	C_4H_9	H	235°	497
H	C_6H_5CO	C_5H_{11}	C_5H_{11}	H	236°	497
H	C_6H_5CO	C_6H_{13}	C_6H_{13}	H	236°	497
H	C_6H_5CO	C_7H_{15}	C_7H_{15}	H	237°	497
H	C_6H_5CO	$C_6H_5CH_2$	$C_6H_5CH_2$	H	238°	497
H	H_2NOC	C_3H_7	C_3H_7	H	304°	498
H	H_2NOC	C_4H_9	C_4H_9	H	278°	498
H	H_2NOC	$C_3H_7CH(CH_3)$	$C_3H_7CH(CH_3)$	H	300°	498
H	H_2NOC	C_5H_{11}	C_5H_{11}	H	273°	498
H	H_2NOC	C_6H_{13}	C_6H_{13}	H	261°	498
H	H_2NOC	C_7H_{15}	C_7H_{15}	H	270°	498
H	H_2NOC	C_8H_{17}	C_8H_{17}	H	266°	498
H	H_2NOC	C_9H_{19}	C_9H_{19}	H	259°	498
H	C_6H_5NHOC	C_4H_9	H	H	117°	506

H	C_6H_5NHOC	C_5H_{11}	H	H	115°	506
H	C_6H_5NHOC	C_6H_{13}	H	H	113°	506
H	C_6H_5NHOC	C_7H_{15}	H	H	110°	506
H	C_6H_5NHOC	C_8H_{17}	H	H	264°	506
H	C_6H_5NHOC	$C_6H_5CH_2$	H	H	240°	506
H	C_6H_5NHOC	C_4H_9	C_4H_9	H	234°	506
H	C_6H_5NHOC	C_5H_{11}	C_5H_{11}	H	95°	506
H	C_6H_5NHOC	C_6H_{13}	C_6H_{13}	H	100°	506
H	C_6H_5NHOC	C_8H_{17}	C_8H_{17}	H	167°	506

TABLE XLIX *(continued)*

Section C. Halogen, Nitroso, Amino, Imino, Azo, and Amido Substituents

R[1]	R[2]	R[3]	R[4]	R[5]	M.p.	Reference
H	C_6H_5	HON=		H	223°	317
C_6H_5	CH_3	Br	H	CH_3OOC	102°	167
C_6H_5	CH_3	Br	H	$C_6H_5CH_2OOC$	212° (dec.)	697
H	H	H_2N	H	H	—	644
H	H	$HOCH_2NH$	H	H	—	644
C_6H_5	CH_3	H_2N	H	H	180°	1339
C_6H_5	H	4-$(C_2H_5)_2NC_6H_4N$=		H	78°	519
C_6H_5	H	4-$(C_2H_5)_2NC_6H_4N$=		CH_3CO	125°	519
C_6H_5	H	4-$(HOCH_2CH_2N)C_6H_4N$= (N–C_2H_5)		H	180°	519
C_6H_5	H	2-CH_3-4-$(C_2H_5)_2NC_6H_3N$=		H	148°, 169°	244, 519
C_6H_5	H	2-CH_3-4-$(C_2H_5)_2NC_6H_3N$=		C_6H_5	173°	244

(Table continued)

TABLE XLIX, Section C (*continued*)

R^1	R^2	R^3	R^4	R^5	M.p.	Reference
C_6H_5	H	2-CH_3-4-$(C_2H_5)_2NC_6H_3N{=}$		$CH_3CH_2CH(C_6H_5)CO$	168°	1255, 1539
C_6H_5	H	2-CH_3-4-$(C_2H_5)_2NC_6H_3N{=}$		C_6H_5CO	207°	1538
C_6H_5	H	2-CH_3-4-$(C_2H_5)_2NC_6H_3N{=}$		4-ClC_6H_4CO	215°	1538
H	H	NO	H	H	>300°	644
H	H	NO	H	CH_3OOC	218° (dec.)	337
H	H	NO	H	C_2H_5OOC	174° (dec.)	337
H	H	NO	H	C_6H_5	—	1649
C_6H_5	CH_3	NO	H	H	193° (dec.)	1339
H	H	$C_6H_5N{=}N$	H	C_6H_5	211° (dec.)	1649
H	H	4-$H_2NO_2SC_6H_4N{=}N$	H	H	274°	356
H	H	2-HO-4-HO_3S-1-$C_{10}H_5N{=}N$	H	H	—	920
H	H	2-HO-4-HO_3S-1-$C_{10}H_5N{=}N$	H	C_6H_5	—	920
H	H	2-HO-4-HO_3S-1-$C_{10}H_5N{=}N$	H	CH_3CO	—	920
CH_3	H	4-$CH_3OC_6H_4N{=}N$	H	H	172°	594
CH_3	H	4-$CH_3OC_6H_4N{=}N$	H	C_2H_5OOC	181°	594
H	CH_3	4-$CH_3OC_6H_4N{=}N$	H	H	240°	594
C_6H_5	H	$C_6H_5N{=}N$	H	2,4-(5-$C_5H_{11})_2C_6H_3OCH_2CO$	175°	591
C_6H_5	H	4-$CH_3OC_6H_4N{=}N$	H	$CH_3CH_2CH(C_6H_5)CO$	192°	1255, 1539
C_6H_5	H	2-HOOC-5-$HO_3SC_6H_3N{=}N$	H	H	—	920
C_6H_5	H	2-HOOC-4-$HO_3SC_6H_3N{=}N$	H	H	—	920
C_6H_5	H	2-HOOC-4-$HO_3SC_6H_3N{=}N$	H	CH_3CO	—	920
C_6H_5	H	2-HO-3-NO_2-5-$HO_3SC_6H_2N{=}N$	H	H	—	920
C_6H_5	H	2,5-$(CH_3OOC)_2C_6H_3N{=}N$	H	3-{2-[2,4(*t*-$C_5H_{11})_2C_6H_3O$]-5-(2-HO_3-$SC_6H_4CONH)C_6H_3CONH$}C_6H_4CO	—	1247
C_6H_5	H	4-$HOOCCH_2OC_6H_4N{=}N$	H	3-{2-[2,4-(*t*-$C_5H_{11})_2C_6H_3O$]-5-[3,5-$(CH_3OOC)_2$-$C_6H_3NHCOCONH]C_6H_3CONH$}$C_6H_4CO$	205°	1087

4-$NO_2C_6H_4$	H	4-$CH_3OC_6H_4N{=}N$	H	$CH_3CH_2CH(C_6H_5)CO$	250°	1539
4-NCC_6H_4	H	$C_6H_5N{=}N$	H	C_6H_5CO	258°	591
C_6H_5	CH_3	$C_6H_5N{=}N$	H	H	224°	1339
H	H	H_2NCONH	H	H	—	644
H	H	$C_6H_5NHSCNH$	H	C_5H_5NHSC	—	644

TABLE L. 4,4′-Bis(5-imino-3-pyrazolidinones)

R = Single Bond $R^1 = R^4$	$R^2 = R^3$	M.p.	Reference
H	C_6H_5	—	72
C_6H_5	4-$CH_3OC_6H_4$	—	72
C_6H_5	1-$C_{10}H_7CH_2CO$	—	72
	C_6H_5	—	72

(Table continued)

TABLE L (*continued*)

R	R^1	R^2	R^3	R^4	M.p.	Reference
$4\text{-}CH_3OC_6H_4CH$	C_6H_5	CH_3CH_2CHCO (with C_6H_5 on CH)	CH_3CH_2CHCO (with C_6H_5 on CH)	C_6H_5	142°	1255
$4\text{-}CH_3OC_6H_4CH$	S N	$3\text{-}[3\text{-}(t\text{-}C_5H_{11})C_6H_4]C_6H_4CO$	H	C_6H_5	145°	1254
$4\text{-}CH_3OC_6H_4$	C_6H_5	CH_3CH_2CHCO (with C_6H_5 on CH)	$4\text{-}[4\text{-}(t\text{-}C_4H_9)C_6H_4O]C_6H_4$	$4\text{-}[4\text{-}(C_4H_9)\text{-}C_6H_4O]C_6H_4CO$	120°	1254
$4\text{-}CH_3O_6HC_4$	S N	$4\text{-}\{4\text{-}[3\text{-}(t\text{-}C_5H_{11})C_6H_4O]C_6\text{-}H_4CONH\}C_6H_4(CH_2)_4CO$	CH_3CH_2CHCO (with C_6H_5 on CH)	C_6H_5	150°	1254

TABLE L (*continued*)

R	$R^1 = R^4$	$R^2 = R^3$	M.p.	Reference
C_6H_5CH	$2,4,6\text{-}Cl_3C_6H_2$	$3\text{-}[2,4\text{-}(t\text{-}C_6H_{11})_2C_6H_3OCH_2CONH]C_6H_4CO$	170°	1603
$4\text{-}HOC_6H_5CH$	$2,4,6\text{-}Cl_3C_6H_2$	$3\text{-}[2,4\text{-}(t\text{-}C_5H_{11})_2C_6H_3OCH_2CONH]C_6H_4CO$	173°	1603
$4\text{-}CH_3OC_6H_4CH$	$2,4,6\text{-}Cl_3C_6H_2$	$3\text{-}[2,4\text{-}(t\text{-}C_5H_{11})_2C_6H_3OCH_2CONH]C_6H_4CO$	215°	1603
$2\text{-}ClC_6H_4CH$	$2,4,6\text{-}Cl_3C_6H_2$	$3\text{-}[2,4\text{-}(t\text{-}C_5H_{11})_2C_6H_3OCH_2CONH]C_6H_4CO$	218°	1603
$4\text{-}ClC_6H_4CH$	$2,4,6\text{-}Cl_3C_6H_2$	$3\text{-}[2,4\text{-}(t\text{-}C_5H_{11})_2C_6H_3OCH_2CONH]C_6H_4CO$	203°	1603
$4\text{-}NO_2C_6H_4CH$	$2,4,6\text{-}Cl_3C_6H_2$	$3\text{-}[2,4\text{-}(t\text{-}C_5H_{11})_2C_6H_3OCH_2CONH]C_6H_4CO$	192°	1603
$3\text{-}CH_3O\text{-}4\text{-}HOC_6H_3CH$	$2,4,6\text{-}Cl_3C_6H_2$	$3\text{-}[2,4\text{-}(t\text{-}C_5H_{11})_2C_6H_3OCH_2CONH]C_6H_4CO$	195°	1603
$3,5\text{-}(CH_3O)_2\text{-}4\text{-}HOC_6H_2CH$	$2,4,6\text{-}Cl_3C_6H_2$	$3\text{-}[2,4\text{-}(t\text{-}C_5H_{11})_2C_6H_3OCH_2CONH]C_6H_4CO$	170°	1603

	2,4,6-$Cl_3C_6H_2$	3-[2,4-(t-C_5H_{11})$_2$$C_6H_3OCH_2CONH$]$C_6H_4CO$	190°	1253
	4-(4-t-$C_4H_9C_6H_4O$)C_6H_4	CH_3CHCO O t-C_4H_9	164°	1253
	4-(4-t-$C_4H_9C_6H_4O$)C_6H_4	3-(3-t-$C_5H_{11}C_6H_4O$)C_6H_4CO	225°	1253
S	4-[4-(t-C_4H_9)C_6H_4O]C_6H_4	4-(t-C_4H_9)C_6H_4OCHCO CH_3	134°	921
S	C_6H_5	H	> 300° (2 HCl)	693
S	C_6H_5	CH_3CO	> 300°	693
S—S	C_6H_5	H	> 300° (2 HCl)	693
S—S	C_6H_5	C_6H_5CO	> 300°	693

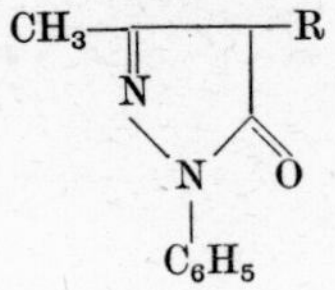

CH_3 — R; N; N; O; C_6H_5

TABLE LI. 3-Methyl-1-phenyl-2-pyrazolin-5-ones. Dyes

R	M.p.	Reference
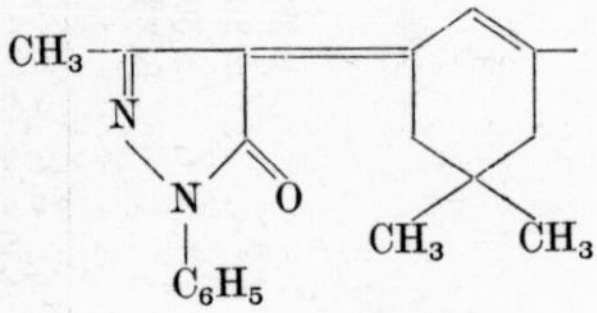 CH_3, N, N, O, C_6H_5; CH_3, CH_3	257° (dec.)	754
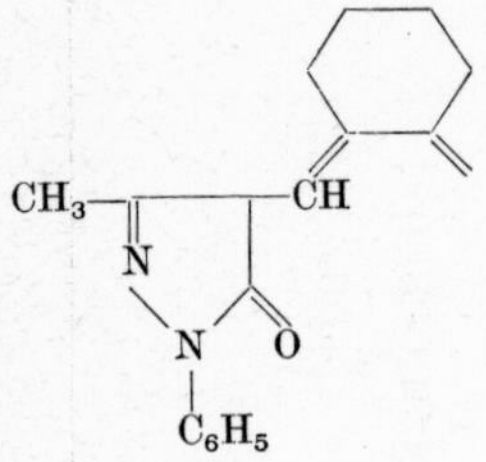 CH; CH_3, N, N, O, C_6H_5	—	703
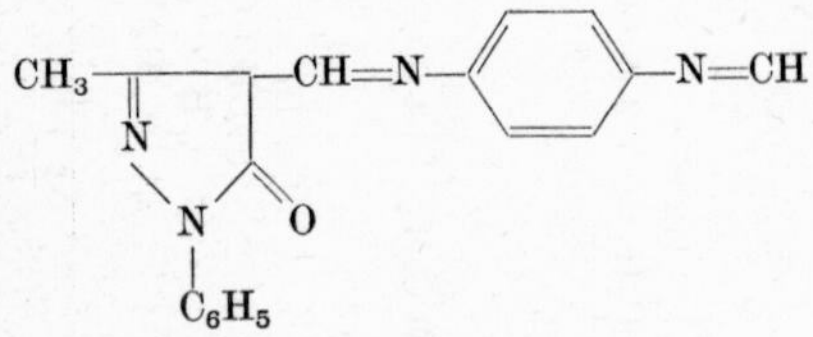 CH_3 —CH=N— —N=CH; N, N, O, C_6H_5	—	33
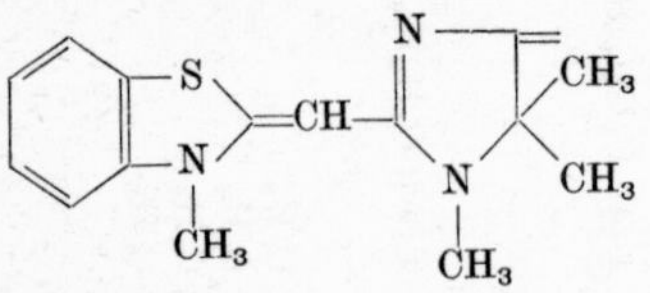 S, N, CH_3, =CH—, N, CH_3, CH_3, N, CH_3	290°	761
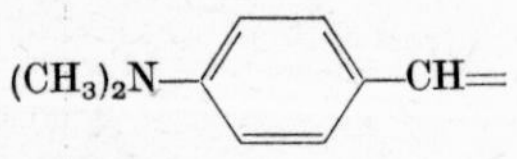 $(CH_3)_2N$— —CH=	—	237
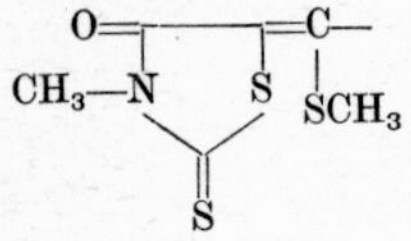 O=, CH_3—N, S, =C—, SCH_3, S	285°	411

(Table continued)

TABLE LI (*continued*)

R	M.p.	Reference
C_2H_5, N, O, O=, =CH—, N, H, O	234°	776
4-$C_2H_5OC_6H_4$, N, O, O=, =CH—, N, O, 4-$C_2H_5OC_6H_4$	255°	776
C_2H_5, N, O, S=, =CH—, N, O, C_2H_5	188°	776
S, N, CH_3	—	1516
S, =CHCH=, S, N, CH_3, O, N, C_2H_5	287°	488
S, =CHCH=, N	238°	235

(*Table continued*)

TABLE L1 (*continued*)

R	M.p.	Reference
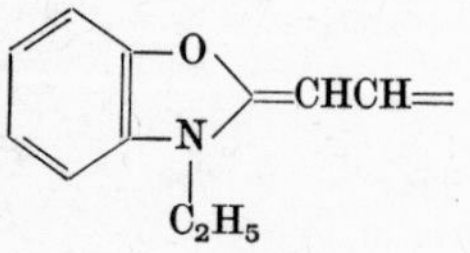 O; N; =CHCH=; C_2H_5	210°	236, 1667
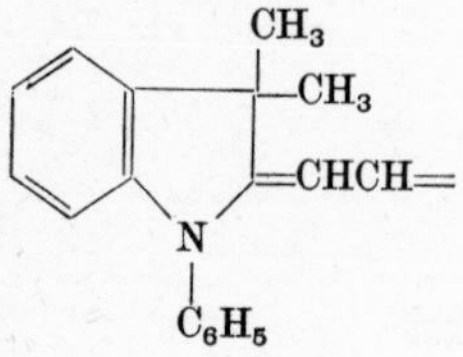 CH_3; CH_3; =CHCH=; N; C_6H_5	218	237
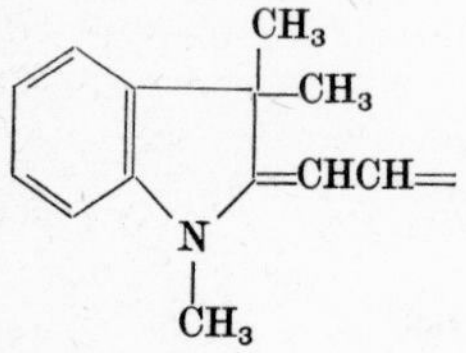 CH_3; CH_3; =CHCH=; N; CH_3	184°, 212°	237, 747, 772, 773
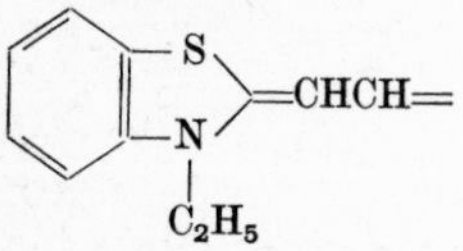 S; N; =CHCH=; C_2H_5	216° (dec.)	620, 772, 1668
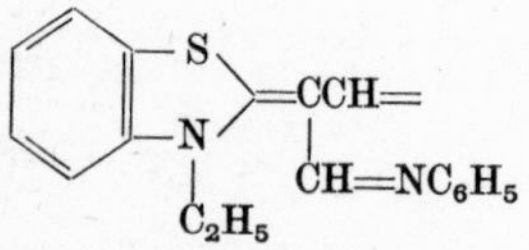 S; N; =CCH=; $CH{=}NC_6H_5$; C_2H_5	205°	620
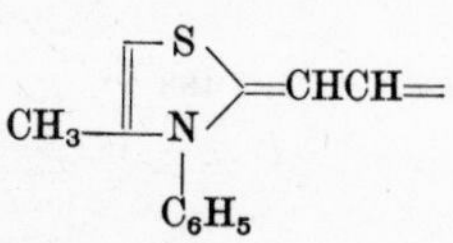 S; CH_3—N; =CHCH=; C_6H_5	—	706
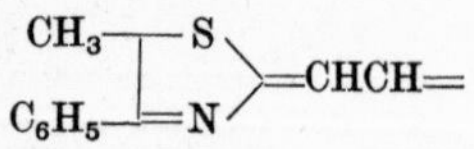 CH_3—S; C_6H_5—=N; =CHCH=	—	707
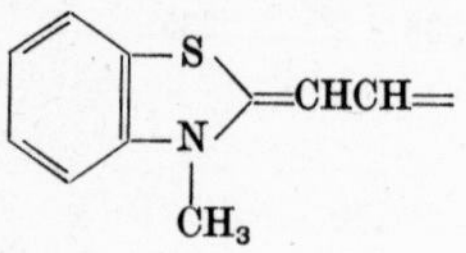 S; N; =CHCH=; CH_3	257°	747

(*Table continued*)

TABLE LI *(continued)*

R	M.p.	Reference
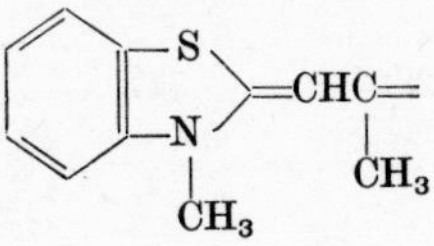 S; N; $=CHC=$; CH_3; CH_3	248°, 261°	747, 764, 772
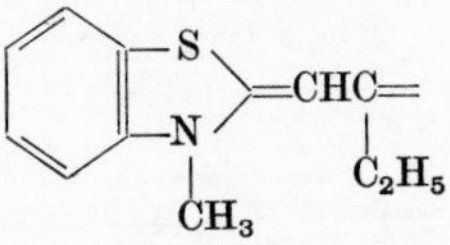 S; N; $=CHC=$; C_2H_5; CH_3	254°	747, 764, 765
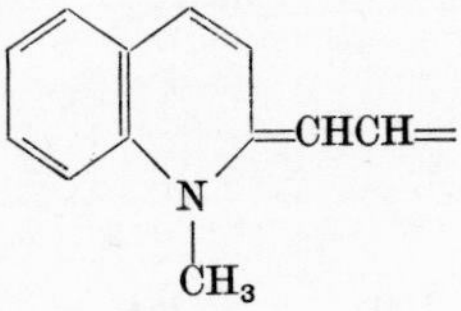 $=CHCH=$; N; CH_3	130° (dec.)	747
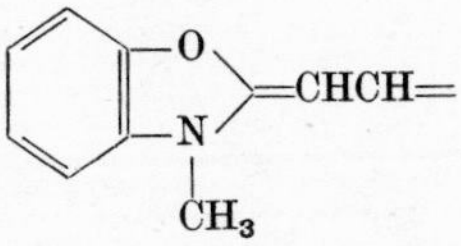 O; N; $=CHCH=$; CH_3	183°	747, 772
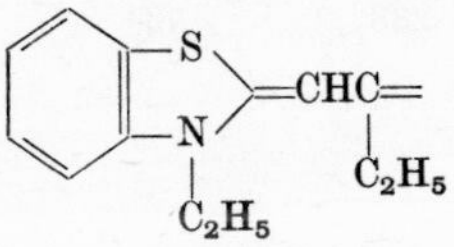 S; N; $=CHC=$; C_2H_5; C_2H_5	100°	747
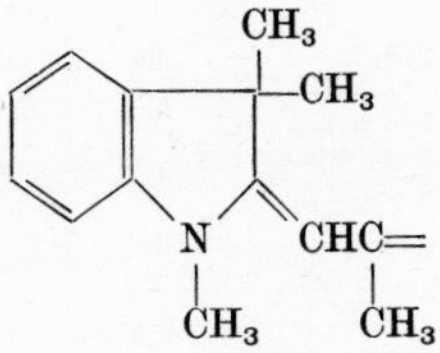 CH_3; CH_3; N; $CHC=$; CH_3; CH_3	197°	747
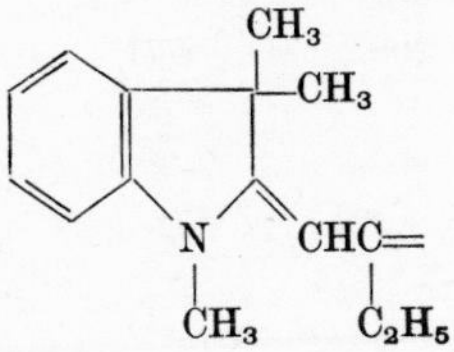 CH_3; CH_3; N; $CHC=$; CH_3; C_2H_5	209°	747
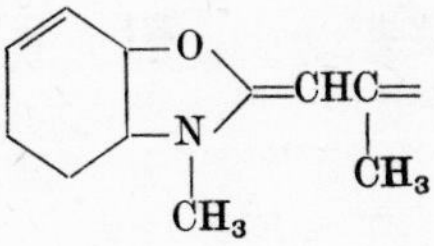 O; N; $=CHC=$; CH_3; CH_3	180°	747, 764

(Table continued)

TABLE LI (*continued*)

R	M.p.	Reference
Se, N, C_2H_5, =CHCH=	222°	747
CHCH=, N, CH_3	251°	747
O, N, CH_3, =CHC=, C_2H_5	100°	764
S, N, CH_3, =CHC=, C_6H_5	238°	764
S, N, CH_3, =NC=, CH_3	260°	764
S, N, CH_3, =CHC=, OC_2H_5	208°	771
CH_3O, CH_3O, S, N, C_2H_5, =CHC=, OC_2H_5	226°	771

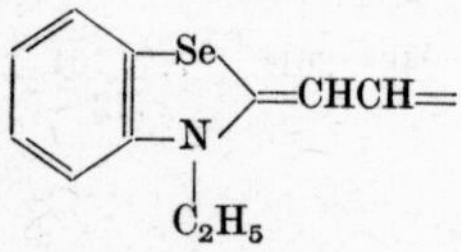

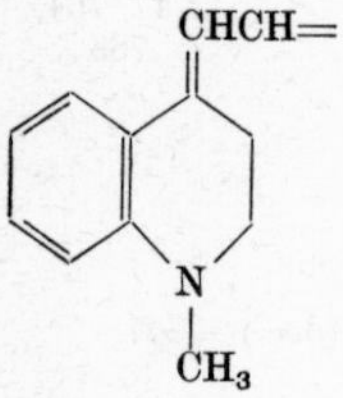

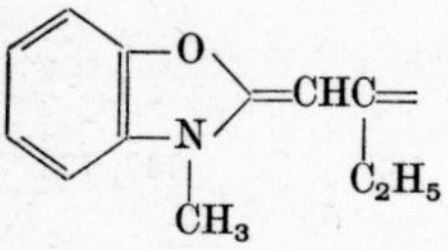

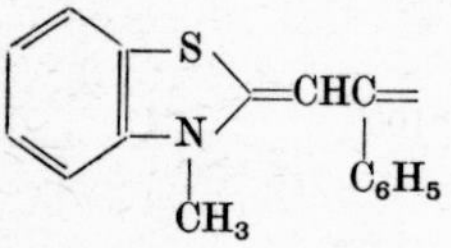

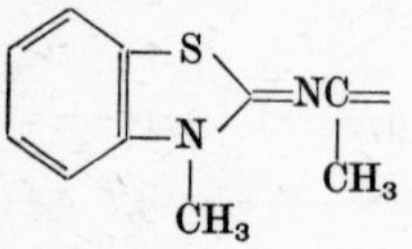

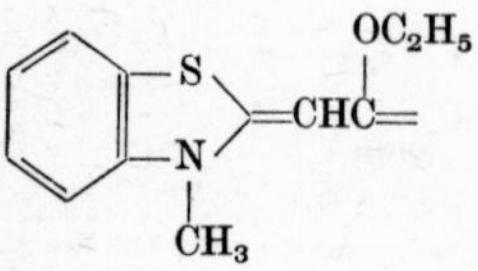

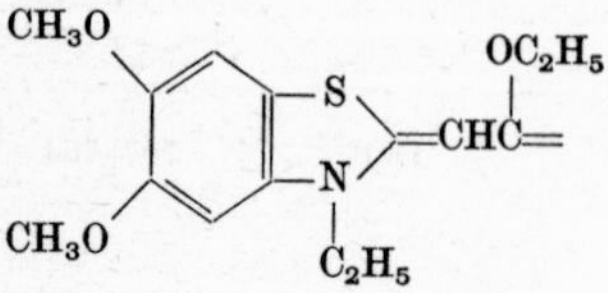

(*Table continued*)

TABLE LI *(continued)*

R	M.p.	Reference
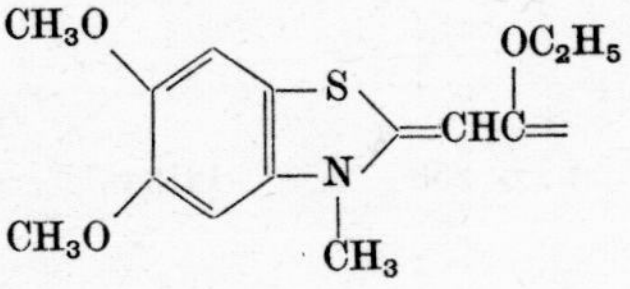 CH_3O, CH_3O, S, N, CH_3, OC_2H_5, $=CH\overset{\vert}{C}=$	233°	771
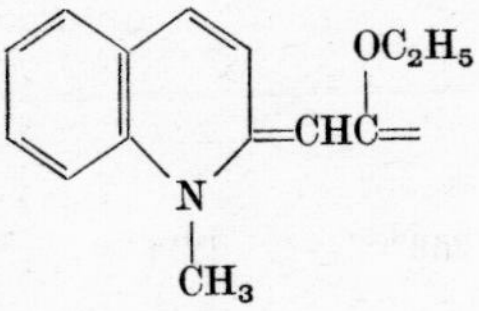 N, CH_3, OC_2H_5, $=CH\overset{\vert}{C}=$	145° (dec.)	771
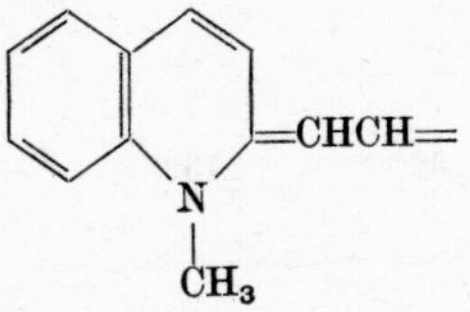 N, CH_3, $=CHCH=$	90°, 171° (dec.)	772, 1668
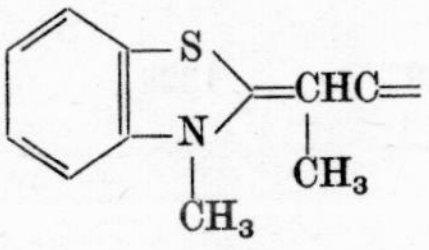 S, N, CH_3, $=CHC=$, CH_3	171°	772
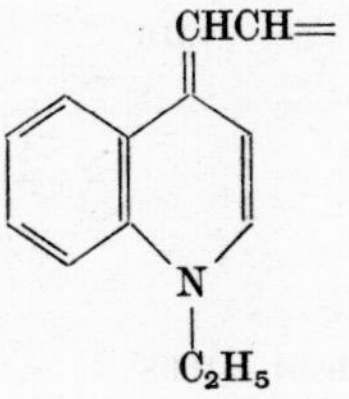 $CHCH=$, N, C_2H_5	162°	1069
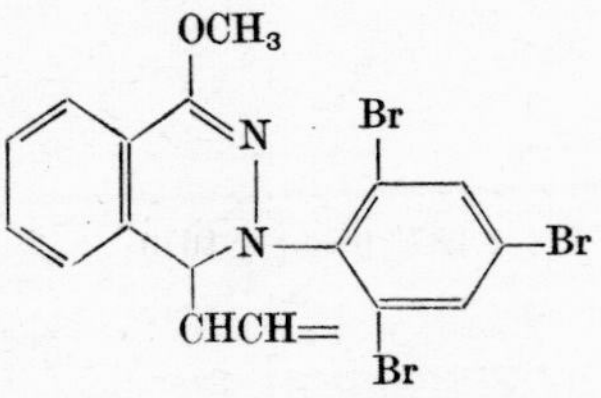 OCH_3, N, N, Br, Br, Br, $CHCH=$	224°	1110

(Table continued)

TABLE LI (*continued*)

R	M.p.	Reference
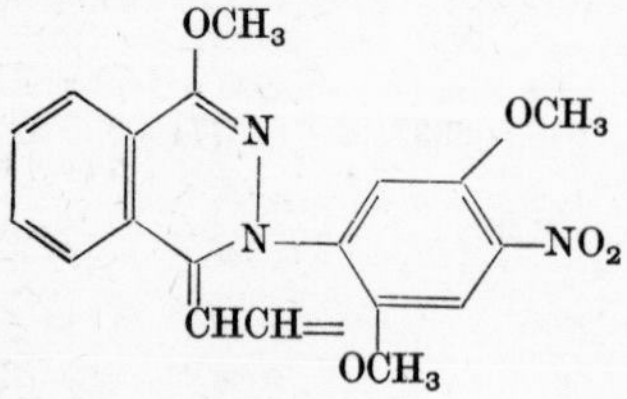 OCH_3, N, N, OCH_3, NO_2, CHCH=, OCH_3	258°	1213
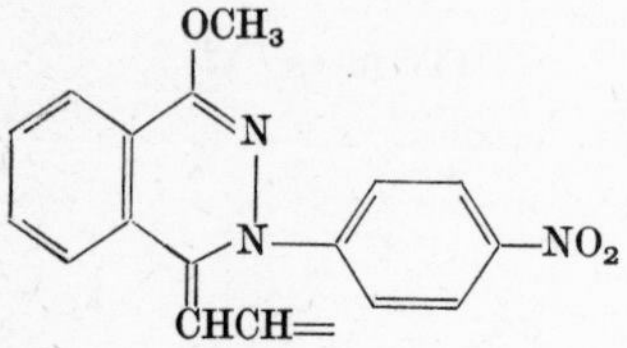 OCH_3, N, N, NO_2, CHCH=	258°	1214
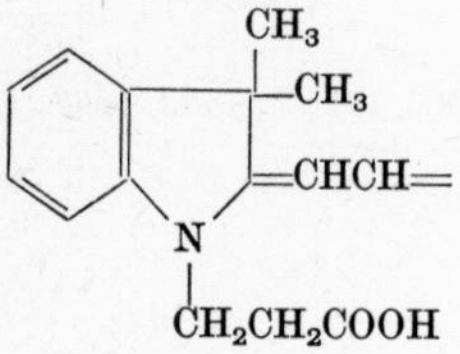 CH_3, CH_3, =CHCH=, N, CH_2CH_2COOH	156°	1328
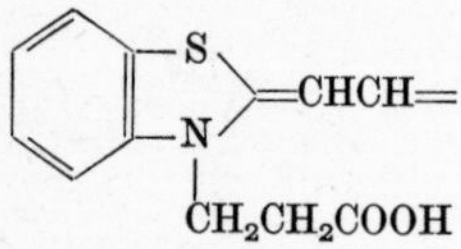 S, =CHCH=, N, CH_2CH_2COOH	239°	1328
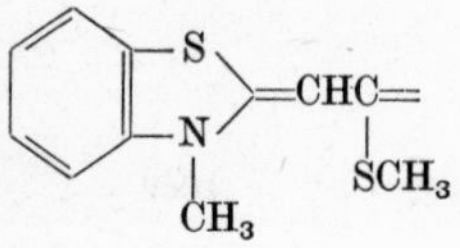 S, =CHC=, N, SCH_3, CH_3	—	1516
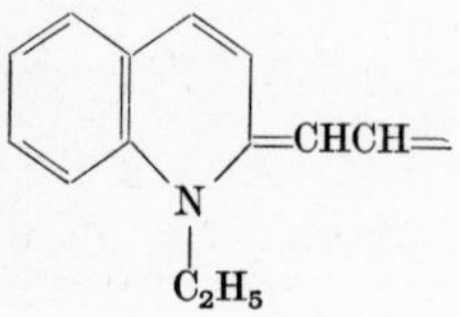 =CHCH=, N, C_2H_5	178° (dec.)	1668
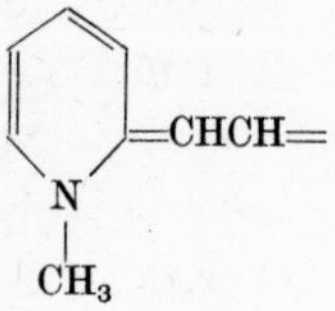 =CHCH=, N, CH_3	287° (dec.)	1670

(*Table continued*)

TABLE LI (*continued*)

R	M.p.	Reference
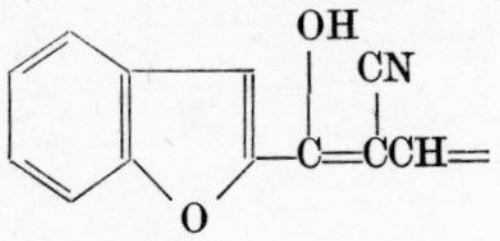 OH, CN, O, C=CCH=	141°	775
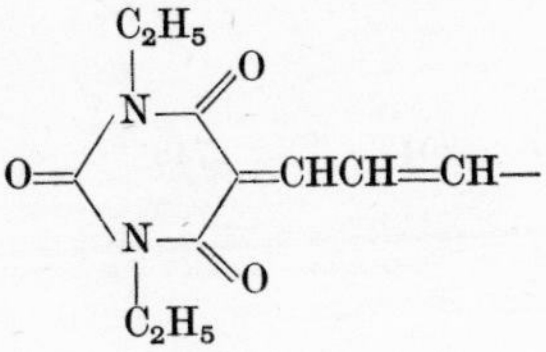 C_2H_5, O, N, O=, =CHCH=CH—, N, O, C_2H_5	248°	776
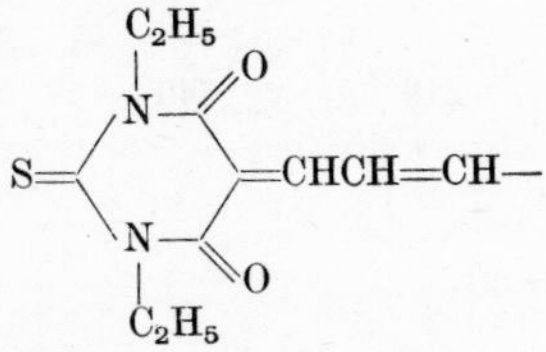 C_2H_5, O, N, S=, =CHCH=CH—, N, O, C_2H_5	165°	78
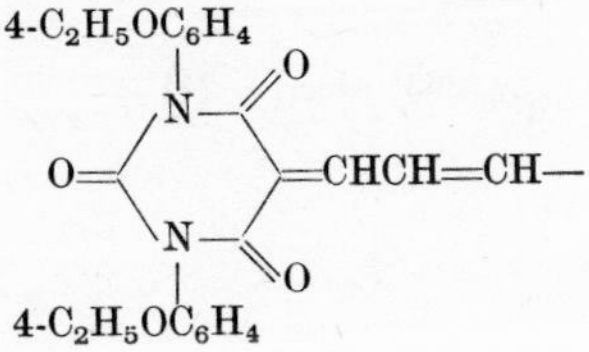 4-$C_2H_5OC_6H_4$, O, N, O=, =CHCH=CH—, N, O, 4-$C_2H_5OC_6H_4$	194°	776
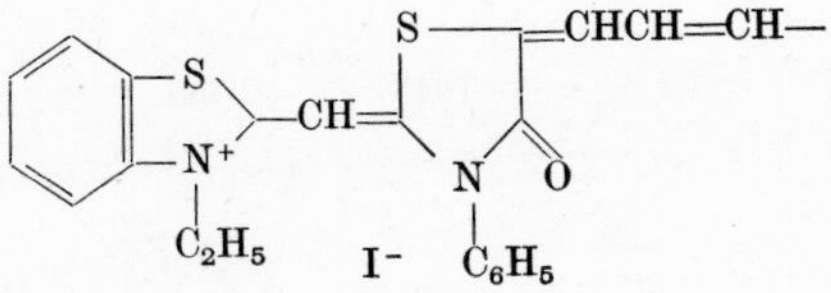 S, =CHCH=CH—, S, CH=, N^+, N, O, C_2H_5, I^-, C_6H_5	—	1488
$C_6H_5NCH=CHCH=$, $COCH_3$	—	30
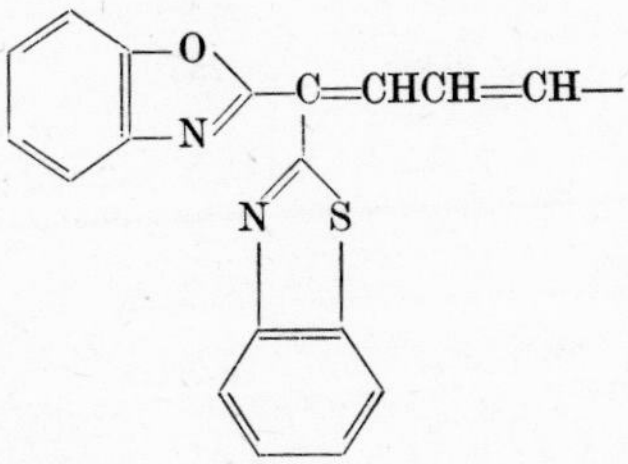 O, C=CHCH=CH—, N, N, S	—	29, 30, 31

(*Table continued*)

TABLE LI (*continued*)

R	M.p.	Reference
3-($CH_2CH_2OC_6H_5$)-benzothiazolin-2-ylidene=CHCH=CHCH=	—	32
3-(CH_3)-benzothiazolin-2-ylidene=CHCH=CHCH=	204°	748
3-(CH_3)-benzothiazolin-2-ylidene=CHCH=CHC(CH_3)=	219°	749
(3-(CH_3)-benzothiazolin-2-ylidene=CH)$_2$C=	293° (dec.)	241
3-(C_2H_5)-benzothiazolin-2-ylidene=CHCH=C(3-C_2H_5-benzothiazolium-2-yl, N^+)—CH= I^-	194°	755
CH_3-3-(C_2H_5)-benzothiazolin-2-ylidene=CHCH=C(CH_3-3-C_2H_5-benzothiazolium-2-yl, N^+)—CH= I^-	258°	755

(Table continued)

TABLE LI (*continued*)

R	M.p.	Reference
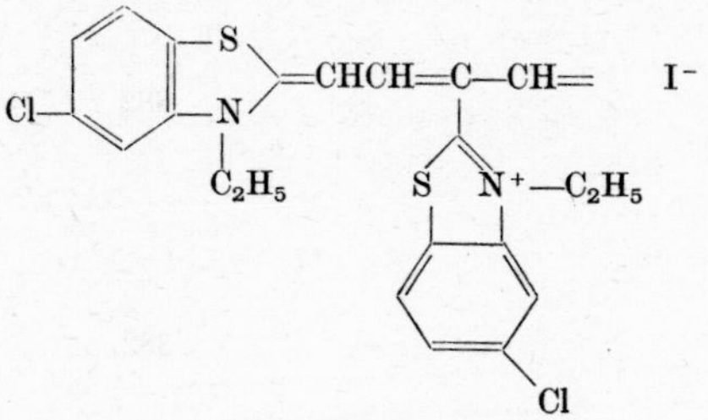 S; =CHCH=C—CH=; I^-; Cl—; N; C_2H_5; S; $N^+—C_2H_5$; Cl	236°	755
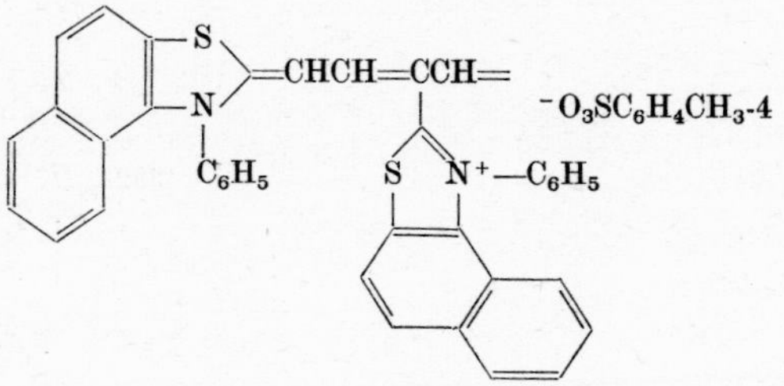 S; =CHCH=CCH=; $^-O_3SC_6H_4CH_3$-4; N; C_6H_5; S; $N^+—C_6H_5$	212°	755
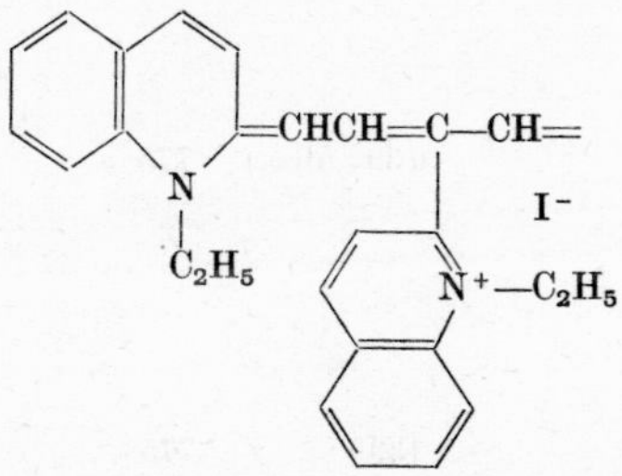 =CHCH=C—CH=; N; C_2H_5; I^-; $N^+—C_2H_5$	260°	755
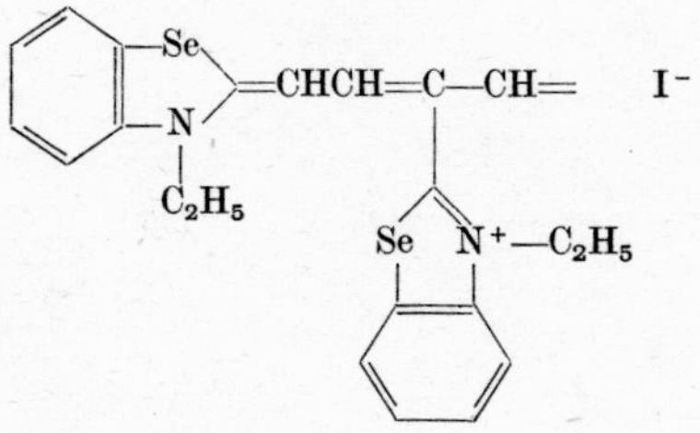 Se; =CHCH=C—CH=; I^-; N; C_2H_5; Se; $N^+—C_2H_5$	193°	755
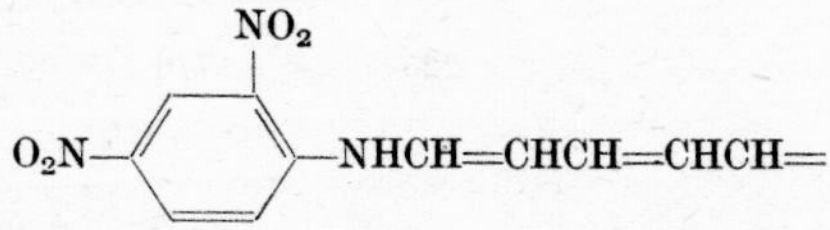 NO_2; O_2N—; —NHCH=CHCH=CHCH=	257°	382

(*Table continued*)

TABLE LI (*continued*)

R	M.p.	Reference
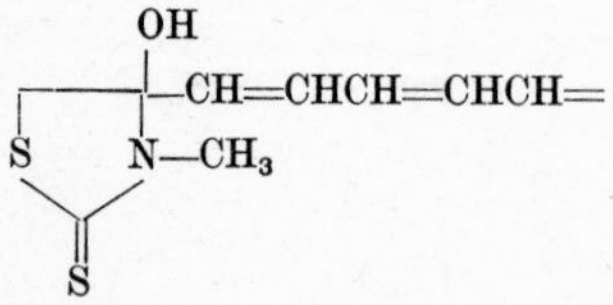 OH —CH=CHCH=CHCH= S N—CH_3 S	—	382
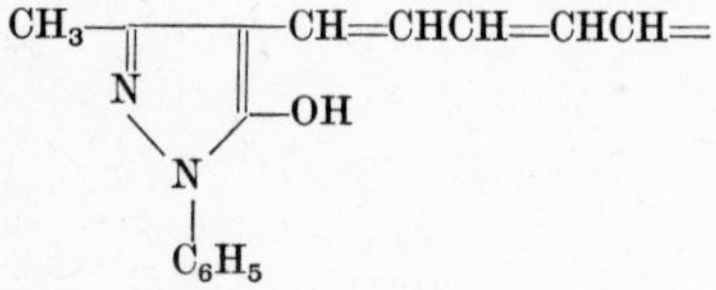 CH_3— —CH=CHCH=CHCH= N —OH N C_6H_5	—	382
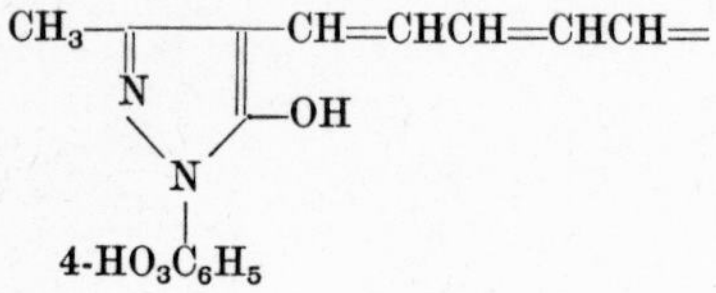 CH_3— —CH=CHCH=CHCH= N —OH N 4-$HO_3C_6H_5$	—	382
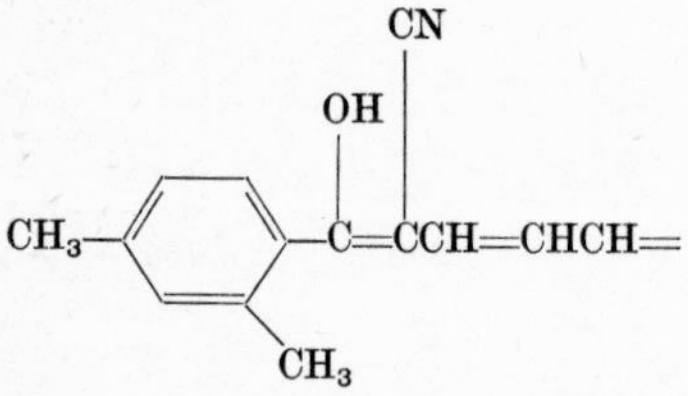 CN OH CH_3— —C=CCH=CHCH= CH_3	139° (dec.)	775
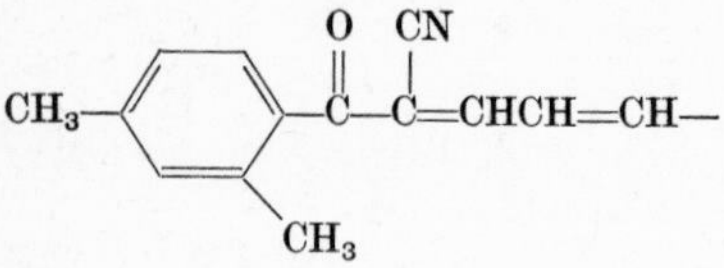 O CN CH_3— —C—C=CHCH=CH— CH_3	139°	775
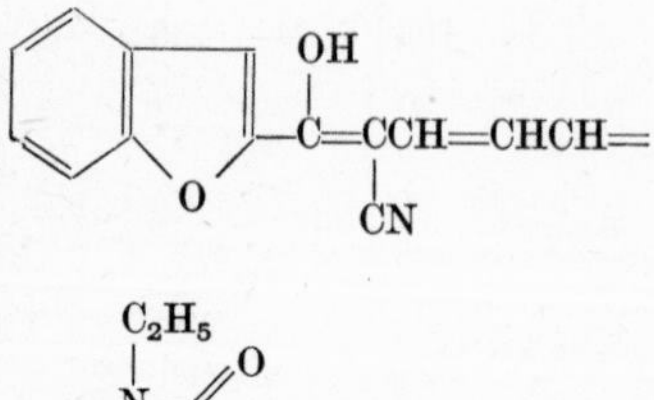 OH —C=CCH=CHCH= O CN	242°	775
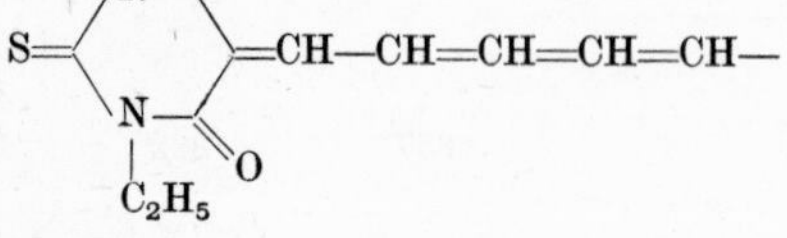 C_2H_5 N— O S= =CH—CH=CH=CH=CH— N— O C_2H_5	225°	776

(*Table continued*)

TABLE LI *(continued)*

R	M.p.	Reference
1,3-dioxoindan-2-ylidene=CHCH=CHCH=CH	169°	776
$C_6H_5N(COCH_3)CH{=}CHCH{=}CHCH{=}$	—	776
$C_6H_5NHCH{=}CHCH{=}CHCH{=}$	185°	1519
HO–(3-methyl-2-thioxothiazoline-5-yl)–CH=CHCH=CHCH=	230° (dec.)	1519
(2,4,6-trioxohexahydropyrimidin-5-ylidene)=CHCH=CHCH=CH—	242°	1472
(4,6-dioxo-2-thioxohexahydropyrimidin-5-yl)–CH=CHCH=CHCH=	240° (dec.)	1519
(benzothiazol-2-ylidene)=CH(CH=CH)$_2$CH—	—	382
(1-methyl-2(1H)-quinolylidene)=CH(CH=CH)$_2$C(CH$_3$)=	215°	763
p-Cl–C$_6$H$_4$–CH=CHC(CH$_3$)=	154°	1129

(Table continued)

TABLE LI (*continued*)

R	M.p.	Reference
$4\text{-}(CH_3)_2NC_6H_4CH{=}CHC(CH_3){=}$	178°	1129
$4\text{-}O_2NC_6H_4CH{=}CHC(CH_3){=}$	171°	1129
$2\text{-}NO_2C_6H_4CH{=}CHC(CH_3){=}$	—	1129
$3\text{-}NO_2C_6H_4CH{=}CHC(CH{=}CH\text{-}C_6H_4\text{-}4\text{-}N(CH_3)_2){=}$	150°	1129
$3\text{-}HOC_6H_4CH{=}CHC(C_6H_5){=}$	77°	1129
$4\text{-}(CH_3)_2NC_6H_4CH{=}CHC(C_6H_5){=}$	210°	1129
$4\text{-}(C_2H_5)_2NC_6H_4CH{=}CHC(C_6H_5){=}$	167°	1129
$4\text{-}ClC_6H_4CH{=}CHC(C_6H_5){=}$	146°	1129
$2\text{-}NO_2C_6H_4CH{=}CHC(C_6H_5){=}$	194°	1129
$4\text{-}NO_2C_6H_4CH{=}CHC(C_6H_5){=}$	218°	1129
$2,4\text{-}Cl_2C_6H_3CH{=}CHC(C_6H_5){=}$	155°	1129
$4\text{-}HO\text{-}3\text{-}CH_3OC_6H_3CH{=}CHC(C_6H_5){=}$	220°	1129

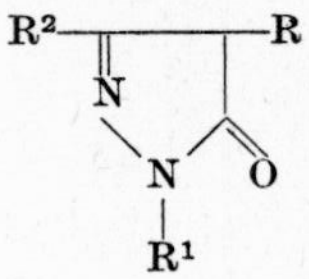

TABLE LII. 2-Pyrazolin-5-ones. Dyes

R^2 N N–R^1 O R

R	R^1	R^2	M.p.	Reference
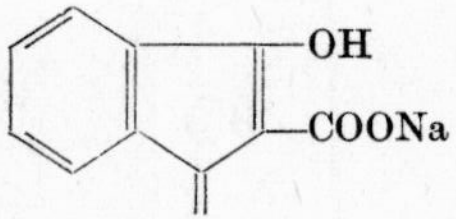 (indene structure: OH, COONa, =)	4-$NaO_3SC_6H_4$	CH_3	—	703
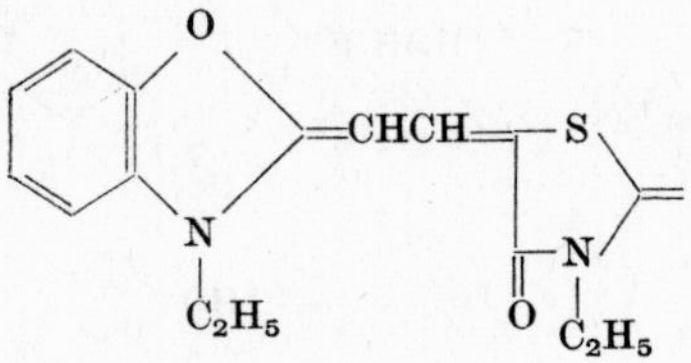 (benzoxazole structure: O, N–C_2H_5, =CHCH=; thiazolidinone ring: S, N–C_2H_5, O, =)	4-$HO_3SC_6H_4$	CH_3	311°	238, 242
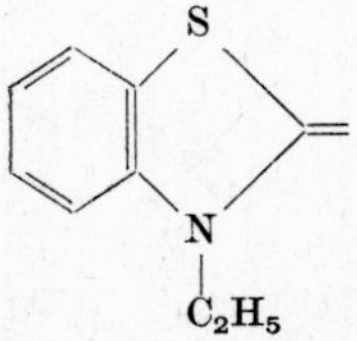 (benzothiazole structure: S, N–C_2H_5, =)	4-$HO_3SC_6H_4$	CH_3	325°	242

(Table continued)

TABLE LII (*continued*)

R	R^1	R^2	M.p.	Reference
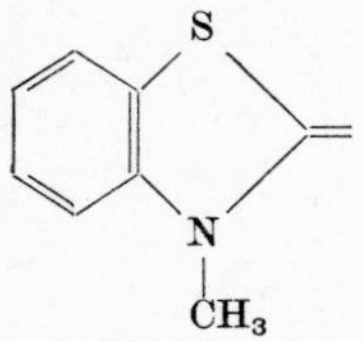 S, N–CH_3 (ring structure)	4-$HO_3SC_6H_4$	CH_3	—	881
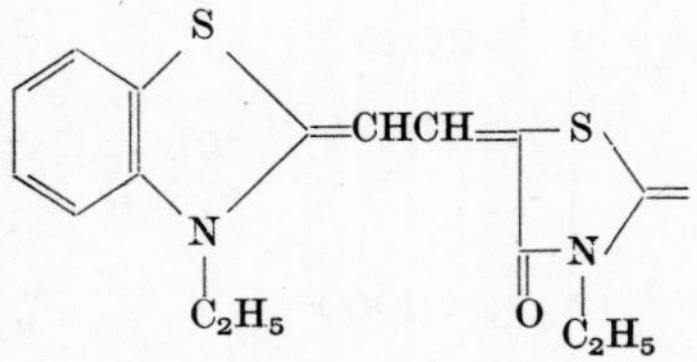 S, N–C_2H_5 (ring structure) =CHCH= S, O, N–C_2H_5 (ring structure)	4-$HO_3SC_6H_4$	CH_3	287°	238, 242
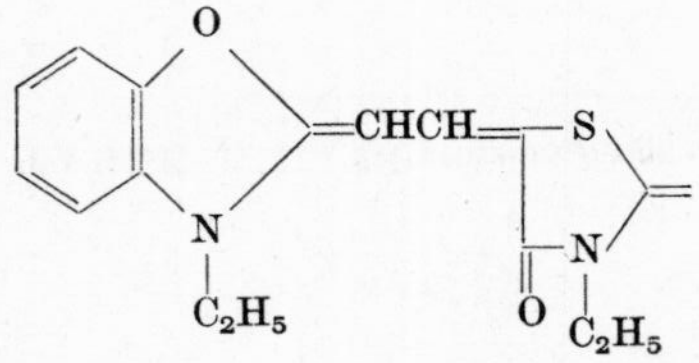 O, N–C_2H_5 (ring structure) =CHCH= S, O, N–C_2H_5 (ring structure)	4-$HOOCC_6H_4$	CH_3	—	238
4-$(CH_3)_2NC_6H_4CH$=	C_6H_5	H	216°	237

CH_3, CH_3, $=CHCH=$, N, CH_3	H	CH_3	240°	772
CH_3, CH_3, $=CHCH=$, N, CH_3	C_6H_5	H	244°	237
CH_3, CH_3, $=CHCH=$, N, C_6H_5	C_6H_5	H	234°	237
O, $-C=CCH=$, OH, CN	$4\text{-}CH_3C_6H_4$	CH_3	243°	775

(*Table continued*)

TABLE LII (*continued*)

R	R[1]	R[2]	M.p.	Reference
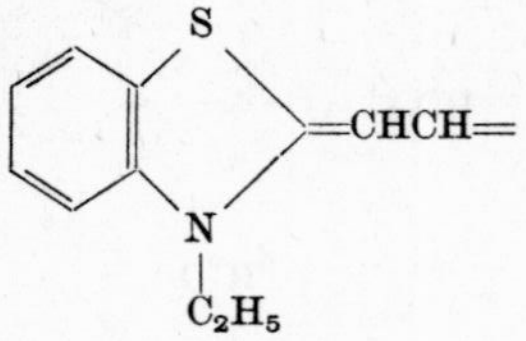 S; N–C_2H_5; =CHCH=	4-$HO_3SC_6H_4$	CH_3	> 325°	236, 620
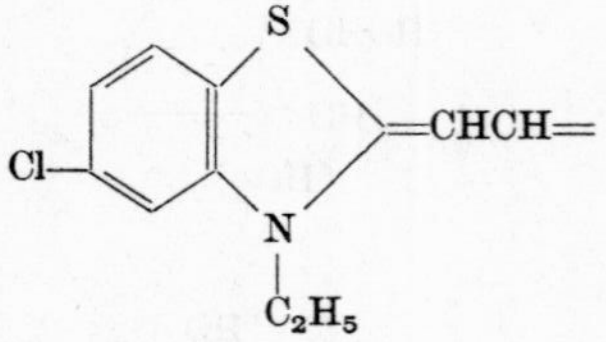 Cl–; S; N–C_2H_5; =CHCH=	4-$HO_3SC_6H_4$	CH_3	315°	238, 242
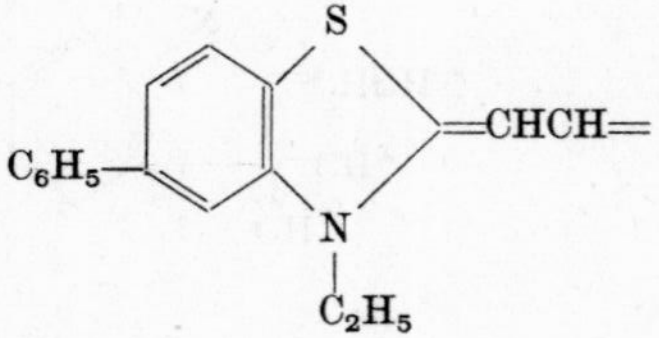 C_6H_5–; S; N–C_2H_5; =CHCH=	4-$HO_3SC_6H_4$	CH_3	> 325°	238, 242
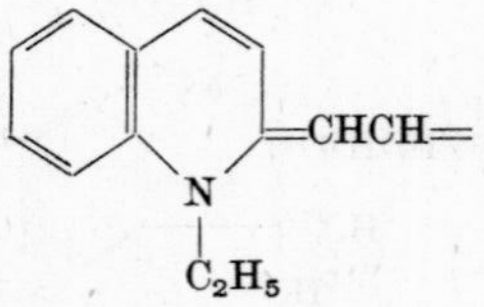 N–C_2H_5; =CHCH=	4-$HO_3SC_6H_4$	CH_3	> 315°	238, 242

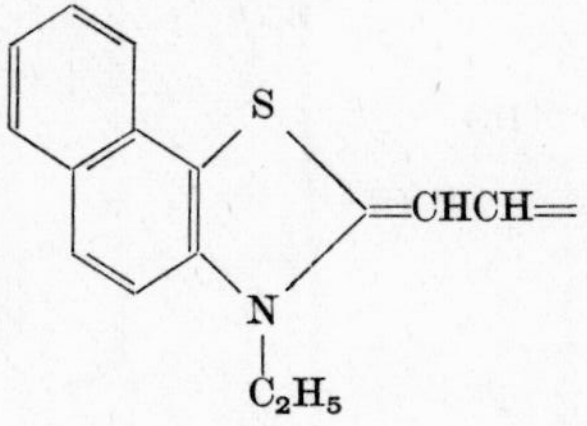 S; =CHCH=; N–C_2H_5	4-$HO_3SC_6H_4$	CH_3	315°	238, 242
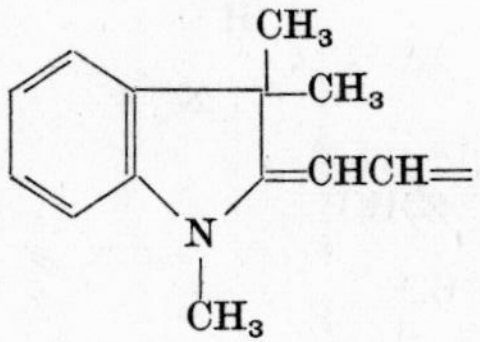 CH_3; CH_3; =CHCH=; N–CH_3	4-$HO_3SC_6H_4$	CH_3	> 325°	238, 242
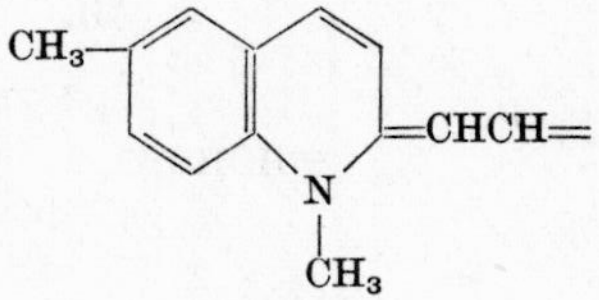 CH_3–; =CHCH=; N–CH_3	4-$HO_3SC_6H_4$	CH_3	> 310°	238, 242
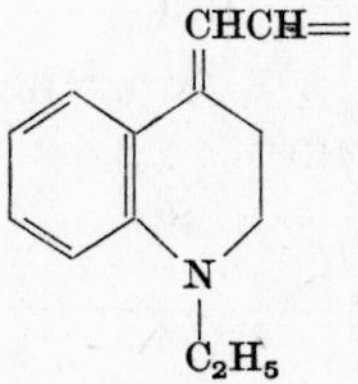 CHCH=; N–C_2H_5	4-$HO_3SC_6H_4$	CH_3	> 315°	238, 242

(Table continued)

16+c.h.c. 20

TABLE LII (*continued*)

R	R^1	R^2	M.p.	Reference
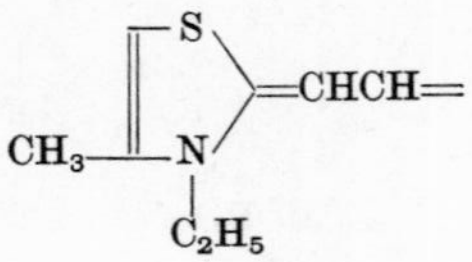 S, $=CHCH=$, CH_3, N, C_2H_5	$4\text{-}HO_3SC_6H_4$	CH_3	> 315°	238, 242
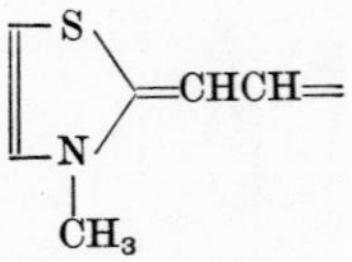 S, $=CHCH=$, N, CH_3	$4\text{-}HO_3SC_6H_4$	CH_3	> 315°	238, 242
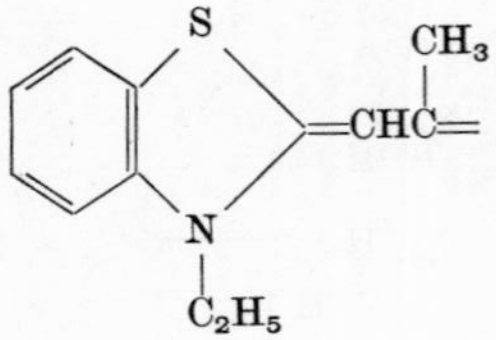 S, CH_3, $=CHC=$, N, C_2H_5	$4\text{-}HO_3SC_6H_4$	CH_3	> 315°	238, 242
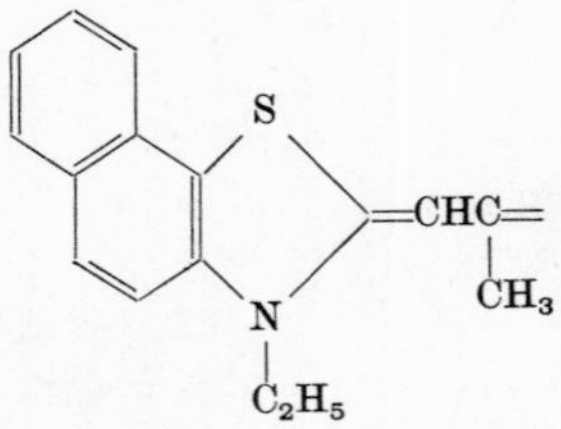 S, $=CHC=$, CH_3, N, C_2H_5	$4\text{-}HO_3SC_6H_4$	CH_3	> 300°	238, 242

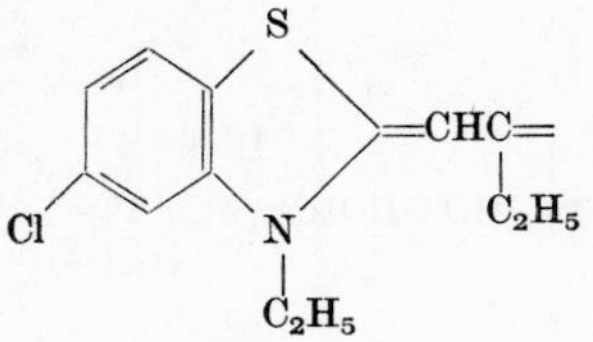 S; Cl; N; C_2H_5; =CHC=; C_2H_5	4-$HO_3SC_6H_4$	CH_3	294°	238, 242
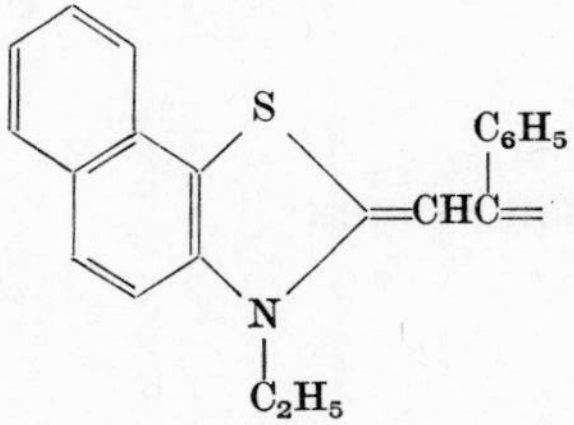 S; N; C_2H_5; C_6H_5; =CHC=	4-$HO_3SC_6H_4$	CH_3	285°	238, 242
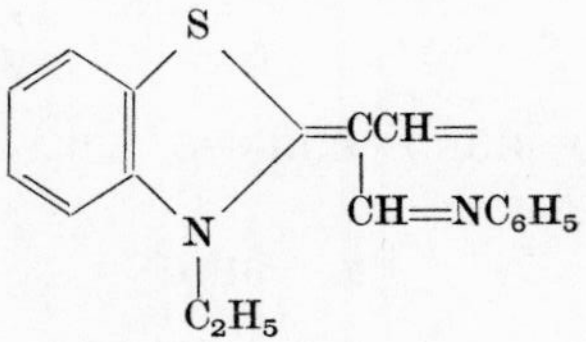 S; N; C_2H_5; =CCH=; CH=NC_6H_5	4-$HO_3SC_6H_5$	CH_3	240°	620
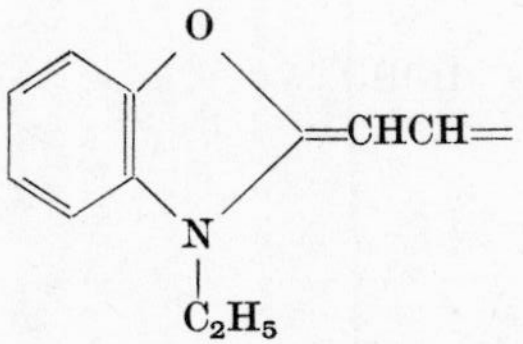 O; N; C_2H_5; =CHCH=	4-$HO_3SC_6H_4$	CH_3	—	1301

(Table continued)

TABLE LII (*continued*)

R	R^1	R^2	M.p.	Reference
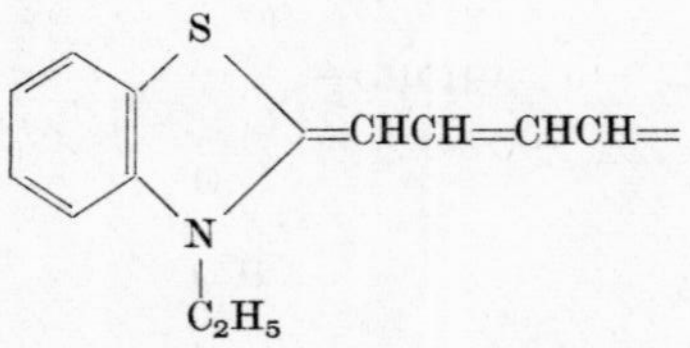 S; N; C_2H_5; =CHCH=CHCH=	4-$HO_3SC_6H_4$	CH_3	279°	238, 242
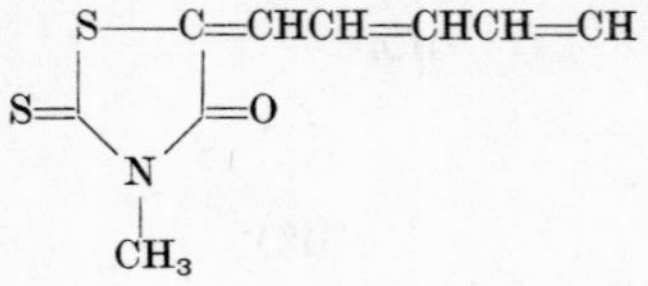 S—C=CHCH=CHCH=CH; S=; =O; N; CH_3	4-$HO_3SC_6H_4$	CH_3	—	1519
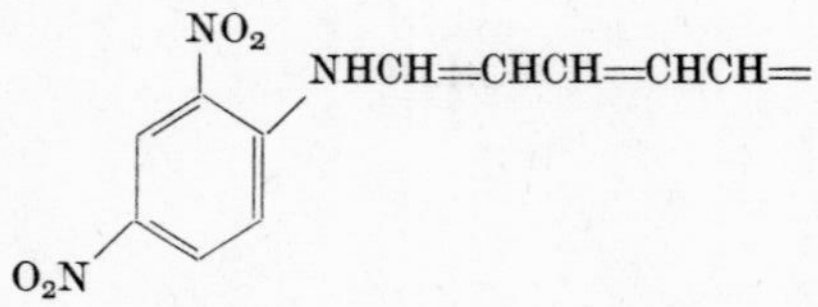 NO_2; NHCH=CHCH=CHCH=; O_2N	4-$HO_3SC_6H_4$	CH_3	200°	382
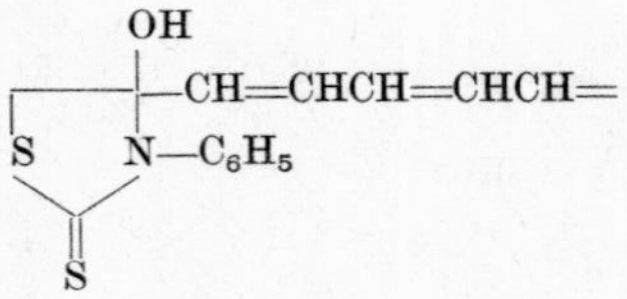 OH; CH=CHCH=CHCH=; S; N—C_6H_5; S	4-$KO_3SC_6H_4$	CH_3	—	382

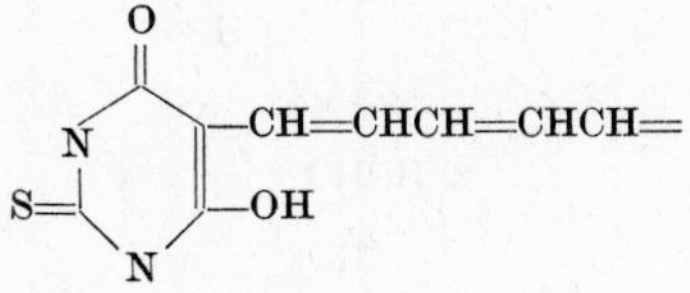 O, N, S=, N, —OH; —CH=CHCH=CHCH=	4-$KO_3SC_6H_4$	CH_3	—	382
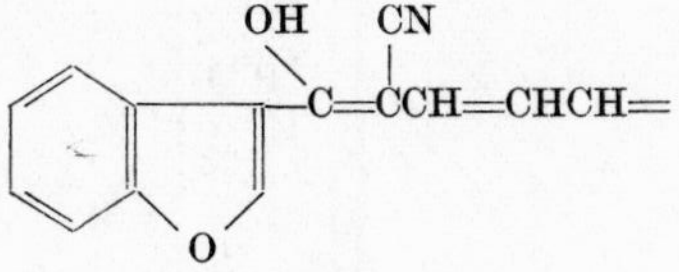 OH, CN, O; —C=CCH=CHCH=	4-$HO_3SC_6H_4$	CH_3	240°	775
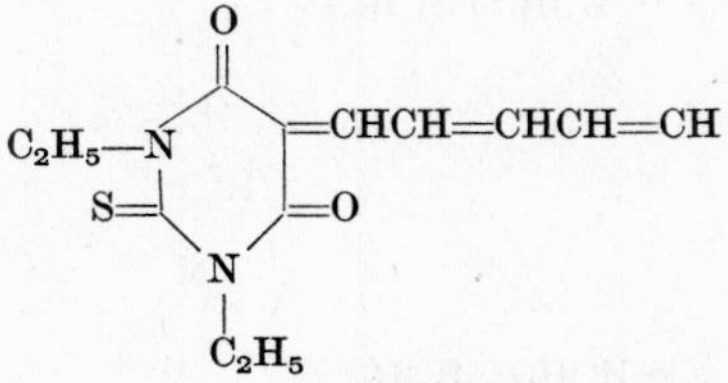 O, C_2H_5—N, S=, =O, N, C_2H_5; =CHCH=CHCH=CH	4-$HO_3SC_6H_4$	CH_3	196°	776
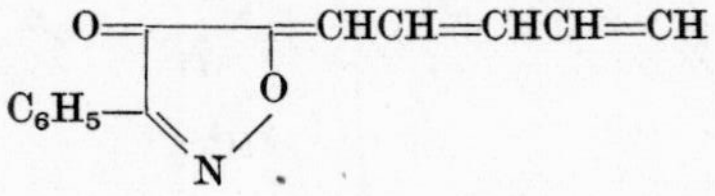 O=, C_6H_5—, O, N; =CHCH=CHCH=CH	4-$HO_3SC_6H_4$	CH_3	188°	776
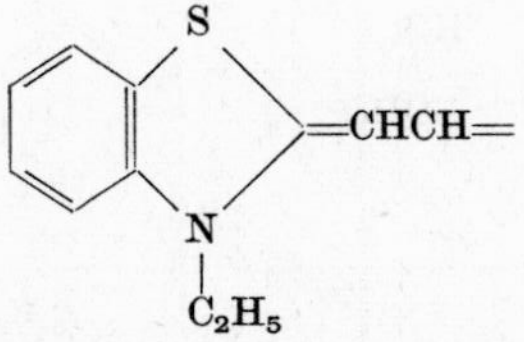 S, N, C_2H_5; =CHCH=	4-$HOOCC_6H_4$	CH_3	> 315°	238, 242

(Table continued)

TABLE LII (*continued*)

R	R¹	R²	M.p.	Reference
S, N–C_2H_5, =CHC(–CH_3)=	4-$HOOCC_6H_4$	CH_3	289°	238, 242
O, N–C_2H_5, =CHCH=CHCH=	4-$HOOCC_6H_4$	CH_3	232°	238
O, C_2H_5–N, S=, =O, N–C_2H_5, =CHCH=CHCH=CH	4-$HOOCC_6H_4$	$C_{15}H_{31}$	184°	776
CH_3, –CH_3, =CHCH=, N–CH_3	2-$C_{10}H_7$	CH_3	245°	747

O; N–C_2H_5; $=CHCH=$	$4\text{-}HO_3S\text{-}1\text{-}C_{10}H_6$	CH_3	—	1301
S; N–C_2H_5; $=CHCH=$	$4\text{-}KO_3S\text{-}1\text{-}C_{10}H_6$	CH_3	> 310°	238, 242
S; N–C_2H_5; $=CHC(OC_2H_5)=$	C_6H_5	C_6H_5	135°	771
S; N–C_2H_5; $=CHC(CH_3)=$	C_6H_5		250°	764

(Table continued)

TABLE LII (*continued*)

R	R^1	R^2	M.p.	Reference
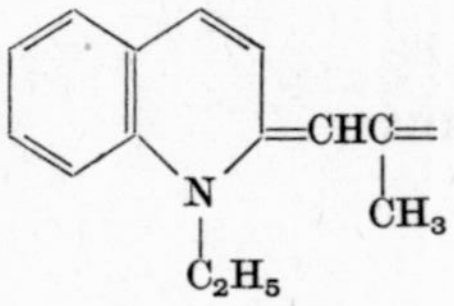 N–C_2H_5, $=CHC(CH_3)=$	C_6H_5	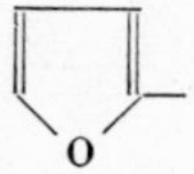 O	> 185°	764
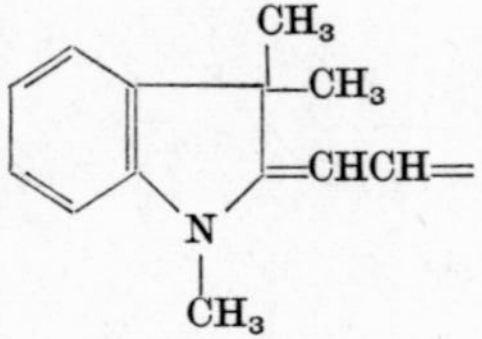 CH_3, CH_3, $=CHCH=$, N–CH_3	C_6H_5	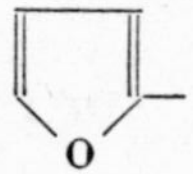 O	180°	747
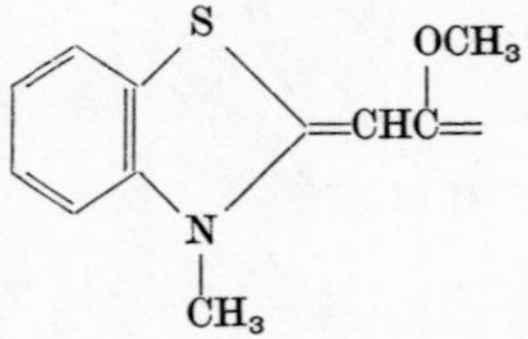 S, N–CH_3, $=CHC(OCH_3)=$	C_6H_5	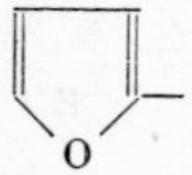 O	185°	771
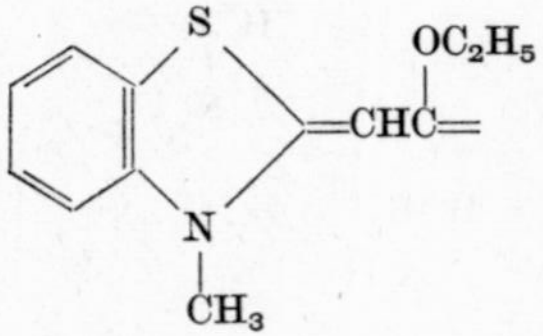 S, N–CH_3, $=CHC(OC_2H_5)=$	C_6H_5	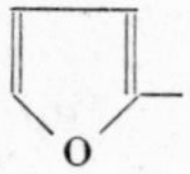 O	190°	771

CH_3, CH_3, O, N, CH_3, OC_2H_5, $=CHC=$	C_6H_5		175°	771
CH_3, CH_3, N, CH_3, $=CHCH=$	$2\text{-}C_{10}H_7$		212°	747
O, OH, CN, $-C=CCH=CHCH=CHCH=$	C_6H_5	$HOOCCH_2$	153°	775
CH_3, CH_3, N, CH_3, $=CHCH=$	C_6H_5	C_2H_5OOC	190°	772
$C_6H_5NCH=CHCH=CHCH=$ (N–$COCH_3$)	$4\text{-}HOOCC_6H_4$	$C_{15}H_{31}$	—	1329

(Table continued)

TABLE LII (*continued*)

R	R¹	R²	M.p.	Reference
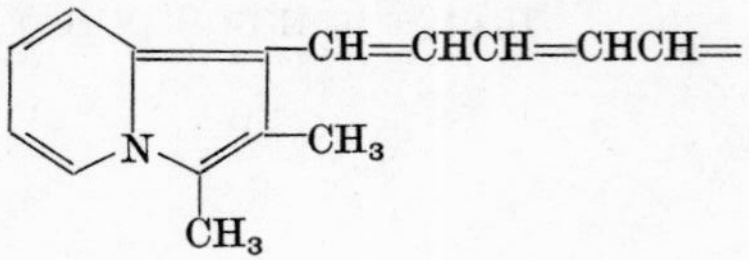 N; —CH=CHCH=CHCH=; —CH₃; CH₃	4-$HOOCC_6H_4$	$C_{15}H_{31}$	—	1329
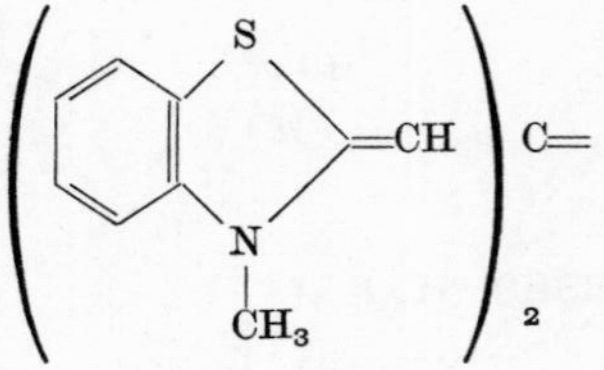 (S; =CH; N; CH_3)₂ C=	C_6H_5	H	175°	241
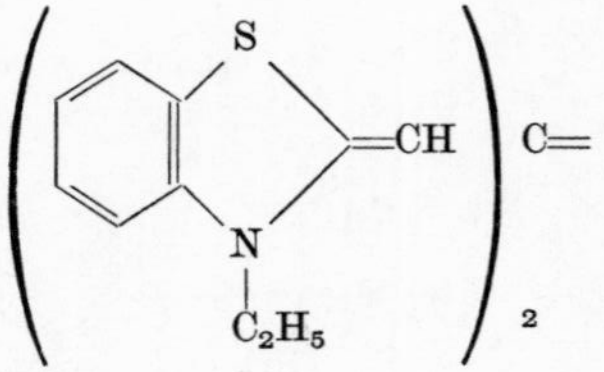 (S; =CH; N; C_2H_5)₂ C=	C_6H_5	H	249°	241
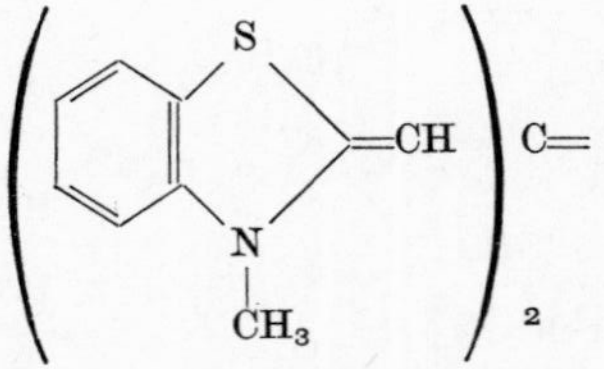 (S; =CH; N; CH_3)₂ C=	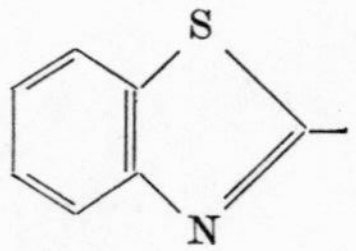 S; N; —	CH_3	333°	241

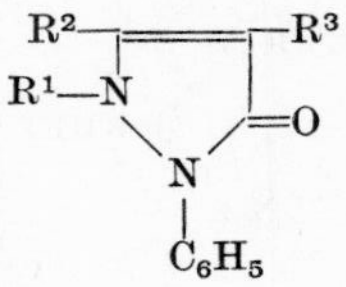

TABLE LIII. 3-Pyrazolin-5-ones. Dyes

R^2 R^3 R^1—N =O N C_6H_5

R^1	R^2	R^3	M.p.	Reference
CH_3	H	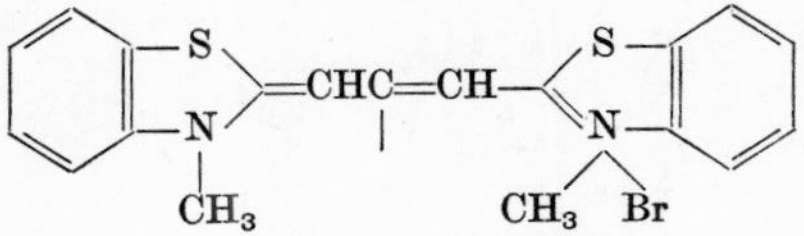 S, =CHC=CH—, S, N, N, CH_3, CH_3 Br	247° (dec.)	765
CH_3	H	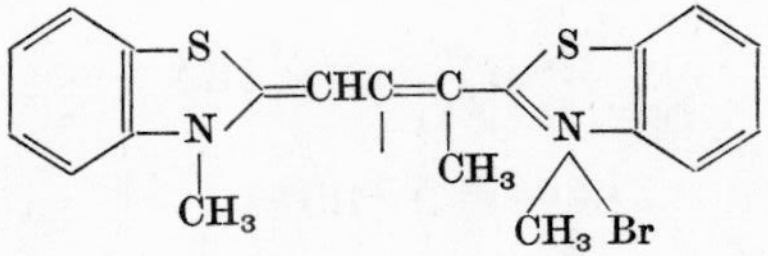 S, =CHC=C—, S, N, CH_3, N, CH_3, CH_3 Br	—	765
CH_3	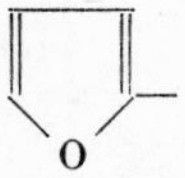 O	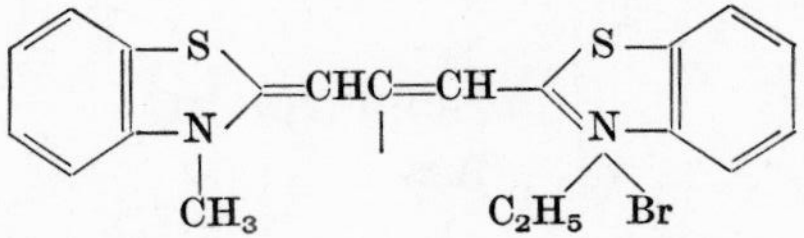 S, =CHC=CH—, S, N, N, CH_3, C_2H_5 Br	224° (dec.)	765
CH_3	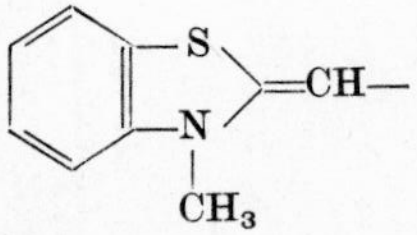 S, =CH—, N, CH_3	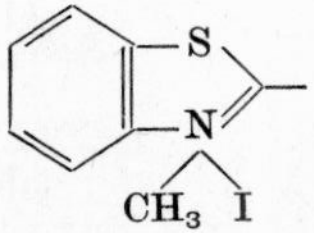 S, N, CH_3 I	208°	1516

(*Table continued*)

TABLE LIII (*continued*)

R^1	R^2	R^3	M.p.	Reference
CH_3	CH_3	Benzothiazolium (S, N⁺–CH_3) –CH=C(SCH₃)– ; CH_3 $SO_3C_6H_4CH_3$-4	—	1517
CH_3	CH_3	3-Methylbenzothiazolin-2-ylidene =CH–C= (S, O, O, N–C_2H_5 ring)	259°	1517
CH_3	CH_3	3-Methylbenzothiazolin-2-ylidene =CH–C= (O, N, N–C_6H_5, –CH_3 ring)	208°	1517
CH_3	CH_3	3-Methylbenzothiazolin-2-ylidene =CHC=C(CN)(COOC₂H₅)	140°	1517

CH_3	CH_3	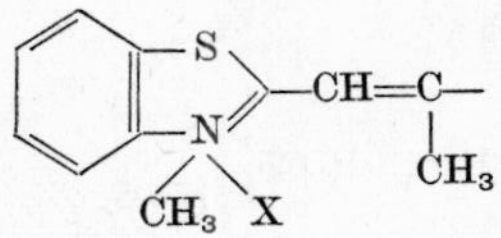 S, N; $-CH{=}C-$; CH_3; CH_3 X	—	1516
CH_3	CH_3	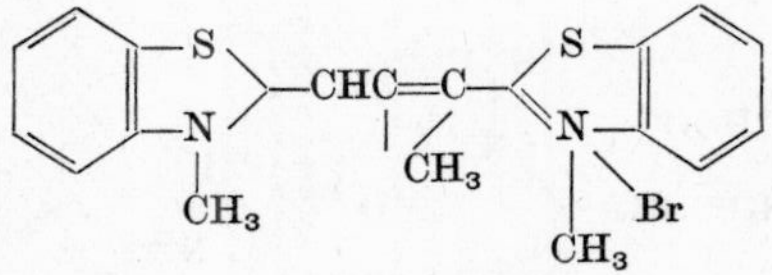 S, N, CH_3; $-CHC{=}C-$; CH_3; S, N, CH_3 Br	230° (dec.)	765
CH_3	CH_3	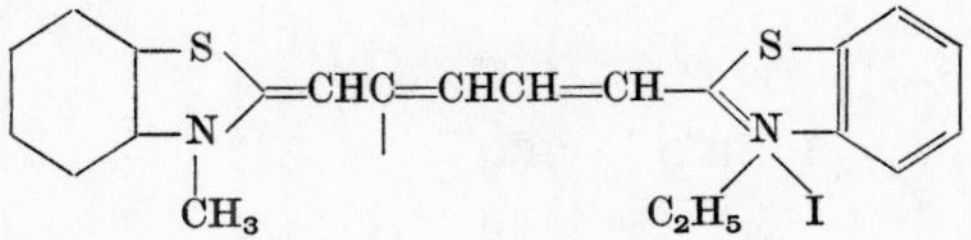 S, N, CH_3; ${=}CHC{=}CHCH{=}CH-$; S, N, C_2H_5 I	194° (dec.)	765
CH_3	CH_3	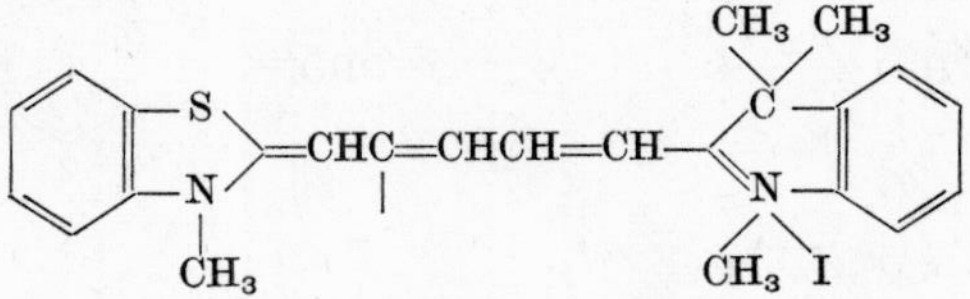 S, N, CH_3; ${=}CHC{=}CHCH{=}CH-$; CH_3 CH_3 C, N, CH_3 I	248° (dec.)	765
CH_3	CH_3	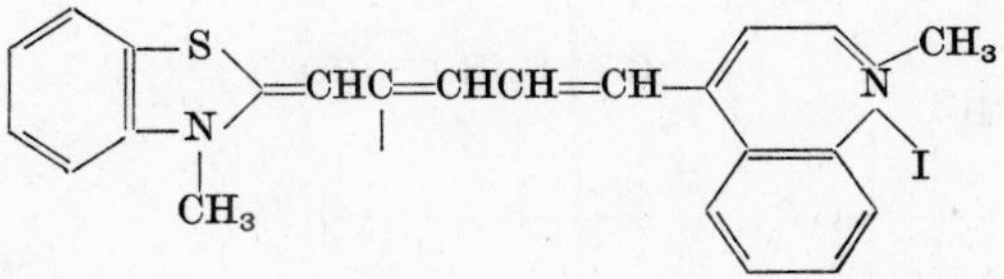 S, N, CH_3; ${=}CHC{=}CHCH{=}CH-$; N, CH_3, I	205°	765

(*Table continued*)

TABLE LIII (*continued*)

R^1	R^2	R^3	M.p.	Reference
CH_3	CH_3	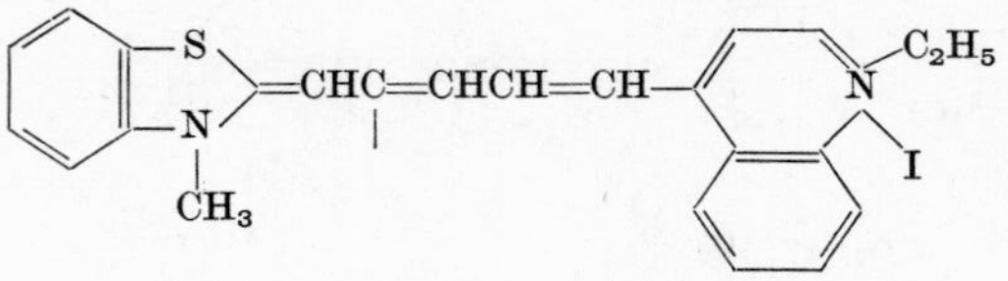 S, N, CH_3 =CHC=CHCH=CH– N C_2H_5 I	186° (dec.)	765
CH_3	CH_3	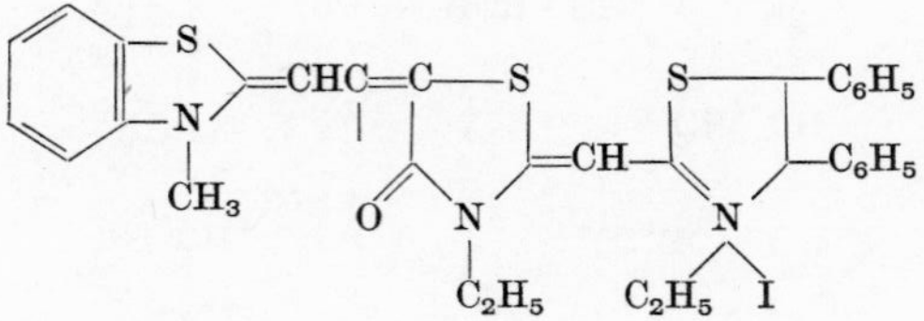 S, N, CH_3 =CHC=C—S, O, N, C_2H_5 =CH– S, N, C_6H_5, C_6H_5, C_2H_5 I	286°	1517
CH_3	CH_3	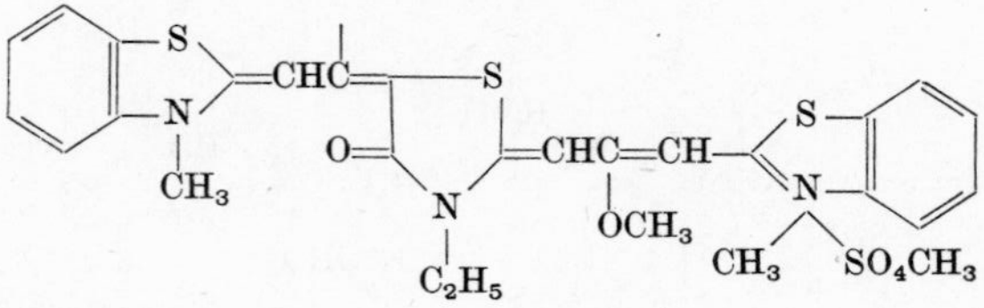 S, N, CH_3 =CHC= S, O=, N, C_2H_5 =CHC=CH– OCH_3 S, N, CH_3 SO_4CH_3	260°	1517
CH_3	CH_3	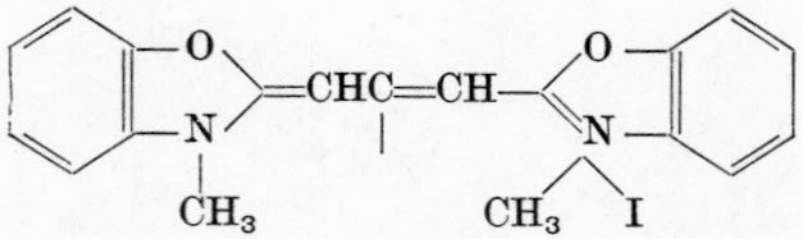 O, N, CH_3 =CHC=CH– O, N, CH_3 I	270° (dec.)	765

CH_3	CH_3	(benzothiazoline, S, N–CH_3)=C(CH_3)C=CH–(benzothiazolium, S, N(CH_3) I)	—	765
C_2H_5	CH_3	(benzothiazoline, S, N–C_2H_5)=CHC=CH–(benzothiazolium, S, N(C_2H_5) X)	250°	1516
C_2H_5	CH_3	(benzothiazoline, S, N–CH_3)=CHCH(CH_3)–	—	1516
C_2H_5	CH_3	(benzothiazoline, S, N–CH_3)=CHC=CH–(benzothiazolium, S, N(C_2H_5) Br)	280° (dec.)	765
C_2H_5	CH_3	(benzothiazoline, S, N–C_2H_5)=CHC=CH–(quinolinium, N(C_2H_5) I)	197° (dec.)	765

(Table continued)

TABLE LIII (*continued*)

R^1	R^2	R^3	M.p.	Reference
C_2H_5	CH_3		198°	765
C_2H_5	CH_3		281° (dec.)	765
C_2H_5	CH_3		248° (dec.)	765
C_2H_5	CH_3		285° (dec.)	765

C_2H_5	CH_3	5-Cl-benzothiazoline (S, N–C_2H_5)=CHC(–)=CH–benzothiazolium (S, N–C_2H_5) I	233°	765
C_2H_5	CH_3	naphthothiazoline (S, N–C_2H_5)=CHC(–)=CH–naphthothiazolium (S, N–C_2H_5) Br	> 300°	765
C_2H_5	CH_3	benzoxazoline (O, N–C_2H_5)=CHC(–)=CH–benzoxazolium (O, N–C_2H_5) ClO_4	285° (dec.)	765

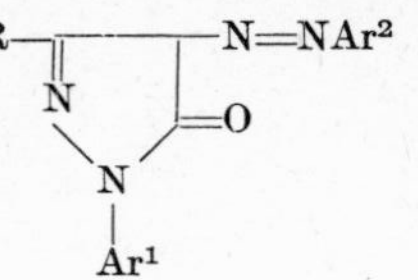

TABLE LIV. 4-Arylazo-3-pyrazolin-5-ones. Dyes

Name	R	Ar^1	Ar^2
Tartrazine	NaOOC	$4\text{-}NaO_3SC_6H_4$	$4\text{-}NaO_3SC_6H_4$
Kiton Yellow S	HOOC	$4\text{-}HO_3SC_6H_4$	C_6H_5
Wool Silk Yellow G	H_5C_2OOC	$4\text{-}NaO_3SC_6H_4$	$2\text{-}ClC_6H_4$
Fast Light Yellow G	CH_3	$4\text{-}NaO_3SC_6H_4$	C_6H_5
Saturn Yellow GG	H_5C_2OOC	$2\text{-}Cl\text{-}4\text{-}NaO_3S\text{-}6\text{-}CH_3C_6H_2$	$2\text{-}CH_3\text{-}3\text{-}ClC_6H_3$
Wool Fast Yellow 3GL	CH_3	$2\text{-}Cl\text{-}5\text{-}NaO_3SC_6H_3$	C_6H_5
Xylene Light Yellow	CH_3	$2,5\text{-}Cl_2\text{-}4\text{-}NaO_3SC_6H_2$	$4\text{-}NaO_3SC_6H_4$
Normal Yellow 3GL	HOOC	$4\text{-}HO_3SC_6H_4$	$2,4\text{-}(CH_3)_2\text{-}5\text{-}HO_3SC_6H_2$
Pyrazole Orange	NaOOC	$4\text{-}NaO_3SC_6H_4$	$4\text{-}[4\text{-}(2\text{-}NaOOC\text{-}4\text{-}HOC_6H_3N{=}N)C_6H_4]C_6H_4$
Acid Alizarin Bordeaux B	H_2NOC	C_6H_5	$2\text{-}HO\text{-}3\text{-}NaO_3S\text{-}5\text{-}ClC_6H_2$
Anthralan Yellow G	CH_3	$2\text{-}CH_3\text{-}4\text{-}NaO_3S\text{-}6\text{-}ClC_6H_2$	$4\text{-}NaO_3SC_6H_4$
Eriochrome Red B	CH_3	CH_3	$2\text{-}HO\text{-}4\text{-}NaO_3S\text{-}1\text{-}C_{10}H_5$
Supramine Yellow 3G	CH_3	$2\text{-}Cl\text{-}4\text{-}NaO_3SC_6H_3$	$2\text{-}CH_3\text{-}5\text{-}(CH_3CON(C_2H_5))C_6H_3$
Polar Yellow 5G	CH_3	$3\text{-}NaO_3S\text{-}4\text{-}ClC_6H_3$	$4\text{-}(4\text{-}CH_3C_6H_4SO_2O)C_6H_4$
Diamond Red G	CH_3	$4,8\text{-}(NaO_3S)_2\text{-}2\text{-}C_{10}H_5$	$2\text{-}HO\text{-}4\text{-}NO_2C_6H_4$
Acid Alizarin Flavin GF	CH_3	$2\text{-}HO\text{-}3\text{-}NaOOC\text{-}5\text{-}NaO_3SC_6H_2$	$2\text{-}NaOOCC_6H_4$
Metachrome Red 5G	CH_3	C_6H_5	$2\text{-}HO\text{-}3\text{-}HO_3S\text{-}5\text{-}ClC_6H_2$
Pigment Fast Yellow G	CH_3	C_6H_5	$2\text{-}HOOC\text{-}5\text{-}HO_3SC_6H_3$

References

1. Adams and Fawthrop, U.S. Pat., 2,584,314 (1952).
2. Adickes, *J. prakt. Chem.*, **161**, 271 (1943).
3. Adickes and Meister, *Ber.*, **68**, 2191 (1935).
4. Adler and Adler, Fr. Pat., 697,881 (1930).
5. Adler and Adler, U.S. Pat., 1,954,909 (1934).
6. Aggarwal and Ray, *J. Chem. Soc.*, **1930**, 492.
7. Ahuja and Dutt, *J. Indian Chem. Soc.*, **28**, 12 (1951).
8. Airan and Wagle, *J. Univ. Bombay*, **23**, Pt. 3, *Sci. No.*, Sect. A, No. 36, 29 (1954); through *Chem. Abstracts*, **49**, 10272 (1955).
9. Ajello, *Gazz. chim. ital.*, **70**, 401 (1940).
10. Albanese, *Gazz. chim. ital.*, **60**, 21 (1930).
11. Albertson, Tullar, King, Fishburn and Archer, *J. Am. Chem. Soc.*, **70**, 1150 (1948).
12. Allan and Můzik, *Chem. Listy*, **47**, 380 (1953); through *Chem. Abstracts*, **49**, 207 (1955).
13. Allen, U.S. Pat., 2,550,661 (1951).
14. Allen, Burness, Edens, Kibler and Salminen, *J. Org. Chem.*, **14**, 169 (1949).
15. Allen and Byers, U.S. Pat., 2,772,282 (1956).
16. Allen and Laakso, U.S. Pat., 2,646,421 (1953).
17. Amâl, *Rev. faculté sci. univ. Istanbul*, Ser. A, **5**, 237 (1940); through *Chem. Abstracts*, **37**, 3091 (1943).
18. Amâl, *Rev. faculté sci. univ. Istanbul*, **14**, 44 (1949); through *Chem. Abstracts*, **45**, 611 (1951).
19. Amâl, *Rev. faculté sci. univ. Istanbul*, **14**, 90 (1949); through *Chem. Abstracts*, **44**, 6414 (1950).
20. Amâl, *Rev. faculté sci. univ. Istanbul*, **14**, 311 (1949); through *Chem. Abstracts*, **45**, 611 (1951).
21. Amâl, *Rev. faculté sci. univ. Istanbul*, **14**, 317 (1949); through *Chem. Abstracts*, **44**, 6853 (1950).
22. Amâl and Kapuano, *Pharm. Acta Helv.*, **26**, 379 (1951); through *Chem. Abstracts* **47**, 5933 (1953).
23. Amâl and Kapuano, *Pharm. Acta Helv.*, **28**, 87 (1953); through *Chem. Abstracts*, **48**, 5181 (1954).
24. Amâl and Özger, *Rev. faculté sci. univ. Istanbul*, **16**, 71 (1951); through *Chem. Abstracts*, **46**, 4534 (1952).
25. Amorosa, *Ann. chim. farm.* (Suppl. to *Farm. ital.*), May **1940**, 54; through *Chem. Abstracts*, **34**, 7910 (1940).
26. Anderson, U.S. Pat., 2,107,321 (1938).

27. Angelini and Martani, *Ann. Chim. (Rome)*, **45**, 64 (1955); through *Chem. Abstracts*, **50**, 1649 (1956).
28. Angelini and Martani, *Ann. Chim. (Rome)*, **45**, 156 (1955); through *Chem. Abstracts*, **50**, 3416 (1956).
29. Anish, U.S. Pat., 2,450,390 (1948).
30. Anish, Brit. Pat., 620,482 (1949).
31. Anish, U.S. Pat., 2,496,843 (1950).
32. Anish, U.S. Pat., 2,504,615 (1950).
33. Anish and Hensley, U.S. Pat., 2,500,111 (1950).
34. Anker and Cook, *J. Chem. Soc.*, **1944**, 489.
35. Anschutz, *Ann.*, **306**, 1 (1899).
36. Arbuzov, *Zhur. Priklad. Khim.*, **23**, 866 (1950); through *Chem. Abstracts*, **45**, 10105 (1951).
37. Arens and Tiang, *Indonesia J. Nat. Sci.*, **109**, 215 (1953); through *Chem. Abstracts*, **49**, 8305 (1955).
38. Armatys, U.S. Pat., 2,454,766 (1948).
39. Armento, U.S. Pat., 2,607,769 (1952).
40. Armento, U.S. Pat., 2,746,955 (1956).
41. Arndt, Loewe and Ergener, *Rev. faculté sci. univ. Istanbul*, **13**, 103 (1948); through *Chem. Abstracts*, **43**, 579 (1949).
42. Asahina, Yanagita and Sakurai, *Ber.*, **70**, 227 (1937).
43. Asano, Arata and Ban, *J. Pharm. Soc. Japan*, **61**, 220 (1941); through *Chem. Abstracts*, **45**, 1518 (1951).
44. Astin and Riley, *J. Chem. Soc.*, **1934**, 844.
45. Astre and Aubouy, *Bull. soc. chim. France*, [3], **35**, 856 (1906).
46. Astre and Vidal, *Bull. soc. chim. France*, [4], **9**, 309 (1911).
47. Astre and Vidal, *Bull. soc. chim. France*, [4], **9**, 836 (1911).
48. Auboy, *Bull. soc. chim. France*, [4], **3**, 388 (1908).
49. Aumüller, Horner, Kimmig, Meyer-Rohn, Junghahns and Pohl, *Chem. Ber.*, **85**, 760 (1952).
50. Austrian Pat., 86,136; through *Chem. Abstracts*, **17**, 1305 (1923).
51. Auwers and Bähr, *J. prakt. Chem.*, **116**, 65 (1927).
52. Auwers, Dannehl and Boennecke, *Ann.*, **378**, 210 (1911).
53. Auwers and Dersch, *Ann.*, **462**, 104 (1928).
54. Auwers, Niemeyer, Mauss and Daniel, *J. prakt. Chem.*, **110**, 153 (1925).
55. Awe and Stog, *Naturwissenschaften*, **37**, 452 (1950).
56. Axford, *Brit. J. Phot.*, **103**, 88 (1956).
57. Axford and Kendall, *Science and Inds. phot.*, **24**, 467 (1953); through *Chem. Abstracts*, **48**, 484 (1954).
58. Bachem, *Therap. Monatsh.*, **23**, 588 (1909).
59. Bachmann and Cronyn, *Chem. of Penicillin*, **1949**, 849.
60. Backman and Heisey, *J. Am. Chem. Soc.*, **71**, 1985 (1949).
61. Backer and Meyer, *Rec. trav. chim.*, **45**, 82 (1926).
62. Backer and Meyer, *Rec. trav. chim.*, **45**, 428 (1926).
63. Badia, Span. Pat., 219,066 (1955).
64. Bahner, U.S. Pat., 2,425,270 (1947).
65. Baker, *J. Chem. Soc.*, **1950**, 1302.
66. Barnes, U.S. Pat., 2,753,371 (1956).
67. Barr, Salminen and Weissberger, *J. Am. Chem. Soc.*, **73**, 4131 (1951).
68. Basel and Kaufler, Ger. Pat., 524,638 (1926).

69. Basu and Das Gupta, *J. Indian Chem. Soc.*, **15,** 160 (1938).
70. Basu and Das Gupta, *J. Indian Chem. Soc.*, **18,** 167 (1941).
71. Battegay and Wolff, *Bull. soc. chim. France*, [4], **33,** 1481 (1923).
72. Bavely, U.S. Pat., 2,411,915 (1946).
73. Bavely, U.S. Pat., 2,435,550 (1948).
74. Bayer, Heidieckerhoff and Schindhelm, Ger. Pat. 614,327 (1935).
75. Bayer, Heidieckerhoff and Schindhelm, U.S. Pat., 2,073,600 (1937).
76. Bayley, U.S. Pat., 2,425,503 (1947).
77. Beech and Mendoza, Brit. Pat., 560,892 (1944).
78. Beech and Mendoza, Brit. Pat., 587,334 (1947).
79. Beech and Mendoza, U.S. Pat., 2,429,600 (1947).
80. Beech and Mendoza, Brit. Pat., 594,925 (1947).
81. Beech and Mendoza, Brit. Pat., 624,247 (1947).
82. Beersmans, Brit. Pat., 626,470 (1949).
83. Belg. Pat., 447,815 (1942).
84. Belg. Pat., 445,959 (1942).
85. Belg. Pat., 450,727 (1943).
86. Bell, *J. Chem. Soc.*, **1941,** 285.
87. Bell and Lindwall, *J. Org. Chem.*, **13,** 547 (1948).
88. Benary, *Ber.*, **66,** 924 (1933).
89. Benary and Schmidt, *Ber.*, **57,** 517 (1924).
90. Benary and Schwoch, *Ber.*, **57,** 332 (1924).
91. Bernstein, Stearns, Shaw and Lott, *J. Am. Chem. Soc.*, **69,** 1151 (1947).
92. Bertho and Nüssel, *Ann.*, **457,** 278 (1927).
93. Betti and Mundici, *Gazz. chim. ital.*, **36,** I, 178 (1906).
94. Beyer and Stehwein, *Arch. Pharm.*, **286,** 13 (1953).
95. Biquard and Grammaticakis, *Bull. soc. chim. France*, [5], **8,** 246 (1941).
96. Birkhofer and Storch, *Chem. Ber.*, **86,** 32 (1953).
97. Blaise and Cornillot, *Compt. rend.*, **178,** 1186 (1924).
98. Blanc, *Ann. pharm. franc.*, **10,** 40 (1952).
99. Bockmühl, *Med. u. Chem. Abhandl. med-chem. Forschungsstätten I. G. Farbenind.*, **3,** 294 (1936); through *Chem. Abstracts*, **31,** 5796 (1937).
100. Bockmühl and Ebert, U.S. Pat., 1,056,881 (1913).
101. Bockmühl and Krohs, Ger. Pat., 611,003 (1935).
102. Bockmühl and Krohs, U.S. Pat., 2,068,790 (1937).
103. Bockmühl and Krohs, Can. Pat., 374,822 (1938).
104. Bockmühl, Krohs, Racke and Windisch, U.S. Pat., 2,193,788 (1940).
105. Bockmühl and Stein, Ger. Pat., 617,237 (1935).
106. Bockmühl and Stein, Ger. Pat., 644,647 (1937).
107. Bodendorf, Mildner and Lehman, *Ann.*, **563,** 1 (1949).
108. Bodendorf and Popelak, *Ann.*, **566,** 84 (1950).
109. Bodendorf and Popelak, *Arch. Pharm.*, **285,** 310 (1952).
110. Bodendorf and Raaf, *Ann.*, **592,** 26 (1955).
111. Bodendorf and Raaf, *Arzneimittel-Forsch.*, **5,** 695 (1955).
112. Bodendorf and Ziegler, *Arch. Pharm.*, **288,** 500 (1955).
113. Bodendorf and Ziegler, *Ber.*, **88,** 1197 (1955).
114. Boese, U.S. Pat., 2,165,445 (1939).
115. Boese, *Ind. Eng. Chem.*, **32,** 16 (1940).
116. Boeseken and Roos, *Rec. trav. chim.*, **58,** 58 (1939).
117. Böhme and Mundlos, *Chem. Ber.*, **86,** 1414 (1953).

118. Böhme, Freimuth and Mundlos, *Chem. Ber.*, **87**, 1661 (1954).
119. Boie and Wulzinger, U.S. Pat., 2,323,193 (1944).
120. Boivin, Gagnon, Renaud and Bridgeo, *Can. J. Chem.*, **30**, 994 (1952).
121. Bonfils, Hardouin and Delbaue, *Compt. rend. soc. biol.*, **148**, 881 (1954).
122. Bonhote and Schmid, U.S. Pat., 1,991,312 (1935).
123. Böniger, Brit. Pat., 266,533 (1926).
124. Borsche and Lewinsohn, *Ber.*, **66**, 1792 (1933).
125. Borsche and Manteuffel, *Ann.*, **505**, 177 (1933).
126. Borsche and Manteuffel, *Ann.*, **512**, 97 (1934).
127. Borsche and Manteuffel, *Ann.*, **526**, 22 (1936).
128. Bossard and Reding, U.S. Pat., 2,545,872 (1951).
129. Böttcher and Bauer, *Ann.*, **568**, 227 (1950).
130. Böttcher and Stoltz, Ger. Pat., 489,363 (1925).
131. Bougealt, Cattelain and Chabrier, *Compt. rend.*, **225**, 876 (1947).
132. Bouvealt, *Bull. soc. chim. France*, [3], **4**, 647 (1890).
133. Bouvier, U.S. Pat., 2,499,265 (1950).
134. Bouvier, U.S. Pat., 2,525,518 (1950).
135. Bowman, *J. Chem. Soc.*, **1950**, 322.
136. Bowman and Fordham, *J. Chem. Soc.*, **1952**, 3945.
137. Boyd and Walter, U.S. Pat., 2,631,991 (1953).
138. Bradshaw, Stephen and Weizmann, *J. Chem. Soc.*, **107**, 803 (1915).
139. Brady and Porter, *J. Chem. Soc.*, **1933**, 840.
140. Brandstätter, *Z. physik. Chem.*, **192**, 260 (1943).
141. Braun, Anton, Haensel, Irmische, Michaelis and Teuffert, *Ann.*, **507**, 14 (1933).
142. Breig, Glietenberg and Nüssler, Ger. Pat., 927,705 (1955).
143. Breusch and Keskin, *Rev. faculté sci. univ. Istanbul*, **11**, 24 (1946); through *Chem. Abstracts*, **40**, 5400 (1946).
144. Brit. Pat., 13,383 (1907).
145. Brit. Pat., 15,759 (1912).
146. Brit. Pat., 27,485 (1907).
147. Brit. Pat., 28,583 (1910).
148. Brit. Pat., 118,448 (1917).
149. Brit. Pat., 146,870 (1920).
150. Brit. Pat., 198,615 (1922).
151. Brit. Pat., 210,669 (1923).
152. Brit. Pat., 219,653 (1923).
153. Brit. Pat., 243,758 (1924).
154. Brit. Pat., 245,107 (1924).
155. Brit. Pat., 255,434 (1925).
156. Brit. Pat., 389,310 (1933).
157. Brit. Pat., 414,684 (1934).
158. Brit. Pat., 433,053 (1935).
159. Brit. Pat., 452,868 (1936).
160. Brit. Pat., 458,417 (1936).
161. Brit. Pat., 468,375 (1937).
162. Brit. Pat., 468,946 (1937).
163. Brit. Pat., 486,747 (1938).
164. Brit. Pat., 500,224 (1939).
165. Brit. Pat., 502,664 (1939).

166. Brit. Pat., 556,266 (1943).
167. Brit. Pat., 563,279 (1944).
168. Brit. Pat., 578,014 (1946).
169. Brit. Pat., 578,964 (1946).
170. Brit. Pat., 584,255 (1947).
171. Brit. Pat., 592,614 (1947).
172. Brit. Pat., 595,703 (1947).
173. Brit. Pat., 597,131 (1948).
174. Brit. Pat., 597,414 (1948).
175. Brit. Pat., 600,739 (1948).
176. Brit. Pat., 602,170 (1948).
177. Brit. Pat., 604,921 (1948).
178. Brit. Pat., 611,320 (1948).
179. Brit. Pat., 619,373 (1949).
180. Brit. Pat., 621,642 (1949).
181. Brit. Pat., 632,832 (1949).
182. Brit. Pat., 632,944 (1949).
183. Brit. Pat., 633,790 (1949).
184. Brit. Pat., 633,824 (1949).
185. Brit. Pat., 636,681 (1950).
186. Brit. Pat., 637,404 (1950).
187. Brit. Pat., 646,123 (1950).
188. Brit. Pat., 646,597 (1950).
189. Brit. Pat., 648,364 (1951).
190. Brit. Pat., 648,715 (1951).
191. Brit. Pat., 649,656 (1951).
192. Brit. Pat., 649,674 (1951).
193. Brit. Pat., 654,495 (1951).
194. Brit. Pat., 665,627 (1952).
195. Brit. Pat., 666,258 (1952).
196. Brit. Pat., 666,578 (1952).
197. Brit. Pat., 673,623 (1952).
198. Brit. Pat., 676,270 (1952).
199. Brit. Pat., 678,492 (1952).
200. Brit. Pat., 681,376 (1952).
201. Brit. Pat., 686,614 (1953).
202. Brit. Pat., 688,225 (1953).
203. Brit. Pat., 688,850 (1953).
204. Brit. Pat., 694,204 (1953).
205. Brit. Pat., 695,534 (1953).
206. Brit. Pat., 697,056 (1953).
207. Brit. Pat., 699,976 (1953).
208. Brit. Pat., 701,140 (1953).
209. Brit. Pat., 701,241 (1953).
210. Brit. Pat., 702,016 (1954).
211. Brit. Pat., 706,370 (1954).
212. Brit. Pat., 707,337 (1954).
213. Brit. Pat., 708,681 (1954).
214. Brit. Pat., 709,495 (1954).
215. Brit. Pat., 717,000 (1954).

216. Brit. Pat., 723,719 (1955).
217. Brit. Pat., 727,199 (1955).
218. Brit. Pat., 727,528 (1955).
219. Brit. Pat., 730,036 (1955).
220. Brit. Pat., 730,384 (1955).
221. Brit. Pat., 730,547 (1955).
222. Brit. Pat., 732,820 (1955).
223. Brit. Pat., 737,619 (1955).
224. Brit. Pat., 741,602 (1955).
225. Brit. Pat., 743,907 (1956).
226. Brit. Pat., 744,441 (1956).
227. Brit. Pat., 744,829 (1956).
228. Brit. Pat., 746,944 (1956).
229. Broadbent and Chu, *J. Am. Chem. Soc.*, **75**, 226 (1953).
230. Brodie and Axelrod, *J. Pharmacol. and Exptl. Therap.*, **99**, 171 (1950).
231. Brodie, Axelrod, Shore and Udenfried, *J. Biol. Chem.*, **208**, 741 (1954).
232. Brodie, Lowman, Burns, Lee, Chenkin, Goldman, Weiner and Steele, *Am. J. Med.*, **16**, 181 (1954).
233. Brodie, Yü, Burns, Chenkin, Paton, Steele and Gutman, *Proc. Soc. Exptl. Biol. Med.*, **86**, 884 (1954).
234. Bromberg and Vilenskiĭ, *Zhur. Priklad. Khim.*, **22**, 128 (1949); through *Chem. Abstracts*, **44**, 465 (1950).
235. Brooker and Cressman, U.S. Pat., 2,398,999 (1946).
236. Brooker, Keyes, Sprague, Van Dyke, Van Lare, Van Zandt and White, *J. Am. Chem. Soc.*, **73**, 5326 (1951).
237. Brooker, Keyes, Sprague, Van Dyke, Van Lare, Van Zandt, White, Cressman and Dent, *J. Am. Chem. Soc.*, **73**, 5332 (1951).
238. Brooker and White, U.S. Pat., 2,493,747 (1950).
239. Brooker and White, U.S. Pat., 2,526,632 (1950).
240. Brooker and White, U.S. Pat., 2,646,409 (1953).
241. Brooker and White, U.S. Pat., 2,739,964 (1956).
242. Brooker, White and Keyes, Brit. Pat., 606,141 (1948).
243. Brown, *Chemistry of Penicillin*, **1949**, 473.
244. Brown, Graham, Vittum and Weissberger, *J. Am. Chem. Soc.*, **73**, 919 (1951).
245. Brown, Hukins, Le Fevre, Northcott and Wilson, *J. Chem. Soc.*, **1949**, 2812.
246. Brown and Partridge, *J. Am. Chem. Soc.*, **67**, 1423 (1945).
247. Bruner and Moser, *Monatsh.*, **53** and **54**, 682 (1929).
248. Büchi, Ammon, Lieberherr and Eichenberger, *Helv. Chim. Acta*, **36**, 75 (1953).
249. Büchi, Meyer, Hirt, Hunziker, Eichenberger and Lieberherr, *Helv. Chim. Acta*, **38**, 1670 (1955).
250. Büchi, Ursprung and Lauener, *Helv. Chim. Acta*, **32**, 984 (1949).
251. Buck, Fearnley, Meanock and Patley, *Lancet*, **266**, 225 (1954).
252. Budziarek, Drain, Macrae, McLean, Newbold, Seymour, Spring and Stansfield, *J. Chem. Soc.*, **1955**, 3158.
253. Buehler and Moser, Brit. Pat., 709,401 (1954).
254. Buehler and Zickendraht, U.S. Pat., 2,727,032 (1955).
255. Bülow, *Ber.*, **40**, 3787 (1907).
256. Bülow, *Ber.*, **42**, 4429 (1909).
257. Bülow and Bozenhardt, *Ber.*, **43**, 234 (1910).

258. Bülow and Bozenhardt, *Ber.*, **43**, 551 (1910).
259. Bülow and Busse, *Ber.*, **39**, 3861 (1906).
260. Bülow and Engler, *Ber.*, **51**, 1246 (1918).
261. Bülow and Dick, *Ber.*, **57**, 1281 (1924).
262. Bülow and Haas, *Ber.*, **43**, 2647 (1910).
263. Bülow and Hecking, *Ber.*, **44**, 467 (1911).
264. Bülow and Schauf, *Ber.*, **41**, 2355 (1908).
265. Burger, "Medicinal Chemistry", New York, Interscience Publishers Inc., 1951, Vol. 1, p. 191.
266. Burkat, *Zhur. Obshcheĭ, Khim.*, **26**, 1379 (1956); through *Chem. Abstracts*, **50**, 14432 (1956).
267. Burns, Rose, Goodwin, Reichental, Hornung and Brodie, *J. Pharmacol. Exptl. Therap.*, **113**, 481 (1955).
268. Burr and Rowe, *J. Soc. Dyers and Colourists*, **44**, 205 (1928).
269. Burrus and Powell, *J. Am. Chem. Soc.*, **67**, 1468 (1945).
270. Calderon and Perez, *Anales asoc. quim. Argentina*, **28**, 5 (1940); through *Chem. Abstracts*, **34**, 5430 (1940).
271. Callsen, Can. Pat., 269,837 (1927).
272. Calzolari, *Boll. chim. farm.*, **50**, 763 (1911); through *Chem. Abstracts*, **6**, 1809 (1912).
273. Canals and Peyrot, *Compt. rend.*, **206**, 1179 (1958).
274. Cannon and Whidden, *J. Org. Chem.*, **17**, 685 (1952).
275. Carrière, *Ann. chim.*, **17**, 38 (1921); through *Chem. Abstracts*, **16**, 2478 (1922).
276. Carson, U.S. Pat., 2,443,226 (1948).
277. Cason, Rinehart and Thornton, *J. Org. Chem.*, **18**, 1594 (1953).
278. Casoni, *Boll. sci. facoltà chim. ind. Bologna*, **9**, 4 (1951); through *Chem. Abstracts*, **45**, 7353 (1951).
279. Casoni, *Boll. sci. facoltà chim. ind. Bologna*, **9**, 9 (1951); through *Chem. Abstracts*, **45**, 7355 (1951).
280. Casoni, *Boll. sci. facoltà chim. ind. Bologna*, **9**, 13 (1951); through *Chem. Abstracts*, **45**, 7355 (1951).
281. Casoni, *Gazz. chim. ital.*, **85**, 404 (1955).
282. Cavallini, Massarani, Mazzucchi and Ravenna, *Farm. sci. e. tec.*, **7**, 397 (1952); through *Chem. Abstracts*, **47**, 8015 (1953).
283. Chargaff and Magasanik, *J. Am. Chem. Soc.*, **69**, 1459 (1947).
284. Charonnat and Delaby, *Compt. rend.*, **189**, 850 (1929).
285. Chattaway and Adair, *J. Chem. Soc.*, **1932**, 1022.
286. Chattaway and Ashworth, *J. Chem. Soc.*, **1933**, 475.
287. Chattaway and Ashworth, *J. Chem. Soc.*, **1933**, 1389.
288. Chattaway and Ashworth, *J. Chem. Soc.*, **1933**, 1624.
289. Chattaway and Ashworth, *J. Chem. Soc.*, **1934**, 1985.
290. Chattaway, Ashworth and Grimwade, *J. Chem. Soc.*, **1935**, 117.
291. Chattaway and Humphrey, *J. Chem. Soc.*, **1927**, 1323.
292. Chattaway and Humphrey, *J. Chem. Soc.*, **1927**, 2133.
293. Chattaway and Humphrey, *J. Chem. Soc.*, **1927**, 2793.
294. Chattaway and Lye, *Proc. Roy. Soc. (London)*, **A135**, 282 (1932).
295. Chattaway and Parkes, *J. Chem. Soc.*, **1935**, 1005.
296. Chattaway and Strouts, *J. Chem. Soc.*, **125**, 2423 (1924).
297. Chatterjee and Das, *J. Am. Chem. Soc.*, **41**, 707 (1919).

298. Chatterjee and Ghosh, *Proc. Asiatic Soc. Bengal*, 15, CXXXII (1919); through *Chem. Abstracts*, **14**, 1674 (1920).
299. Checchi, Papini and Ridi, *Gazz. chim. ital.*, **85**, 1160 (1955).
300. Checchi, Ridi and Papini, *Ann. chim.* (*Rome*), **44**, 522 (1954); through *Chem. Abstracts*, **49**, 14774 (1955).
301. Checchi, Ridi and Papini, *Gazz. chim. ital.*, **85**, 1558 (1955).
302. Cherchi, *Gazz. chim. ital.*, **50**, 120 (1920).
303. Chi and Yang, *J. Am. Chem. Soc.*, **58**, 1152 (1936).
304. Chrzczonowicz, Zwierzak and Achmatowicz, *Zeszyty Nauk. Politech. Łódz.*, No. **2**, *Chem.*, No. **1**, 97 (1954); through *Chem. Abstracts*, **49**, 14742 (1955).
305. Ciusa, *Atti e relazioni accad. pugliese sci.*, **6**, 3 pp. (1948); through *Chem. Abstracts*, **43**, 2316 (1949).
306. Claisen and Haase, *Ber.*, **28**, 35 (1895).
307. Clemo and Holmes, *J. Chem. Soc.*, **1934**, 1739.
308. Clemo, Holmes and Leitch, *J. Chem. Soc.*, **1938**, 753.
309. Clemo and Welch, *J. Chem. Soc.*, **1928**, 2621.
310. Coan and Becker, *J. Am. Chem. Soc.*, **76**, 501 (1954).
311. Cocker and Turner, *J. Chem. Soc.*, **1940**, 57.
312. Coffey and Everatt, Brit. Pat., 405,003 (1934).
313. Cohn and Kolthoff, *J. Biol. Chem.*, **148**, 711 (1943).
314. Coles and Hamilton, *J. Am. Chem. Soc.*, **68**, 2588 (1946).
315. Collins, Robinson and Fry, Brit. Pat., 674,356 (1952).
316. Combes, Hebbelynck and Ledrut, *Bull. soc. chim. France*, **1953**, 315.
317. Conrad and Zart, *Ber.*, **39**, 2282 (1906).
318. Cook and Heilbron, *Chemistry of Penicillin*, **1949**, 921.
319. Cornforth, *Chemistry of Penicillin*, **1949**, 688.
320. Cornforth and Cornforth, *J. Chem. Soc.*, **1953**, 93.
321. Cousin, *Bull. soc. chim. France*, [4], **5**, 121 (1909).
322. Crippa and Caracci, *Gazz. chim. ital.*, **70**, 389 (1940).
323. Crippa and Caracci, *Gazz. chim. ital.*, **71**, 574 (1941).
324. Crippa and Guarneri, *Il Farmaco* (*Pavia*), *Ed. Sci.*, **10**, 691 (1955); through *Chem. Abstracts*, **50**, 8605 (1956).
325. Crippa and Guarneri, *Gazz. chim. ital.*, **85**, 199 (1955).
326. Crippa and Long, *Gazz. chim. ital.*, **61**, 99 (1931).
327. Crippa, Long and Perroncito, *Gazz. chim. ital.*, **62**, 944 (1932).
328. Crippa and Maffei, *Gazz. chim. ital.*, **72**, 97 (1942).
329. Crippa and Perroncito, *Gazz. chim. ital.*, **66**, 649 (1936).
330. Cudkowicz and Jacobs, *Lancet*, **264**, 223 (1953).
331. Curatolo, *Giorn. med. militare*, **101**, 283 (1951); through *Chem. Abstracts*, **47**, 2169 (1953).
332. Currie, *Lancet*, **263**, 15 (1952).
333. Curtius, *J. prakt. Chem.*, **85**, 37 (1912).
334. Curtius, *J. prakt. Chem.*, **85**, 137, 393 (1912).
335. Curtius and Bleicher, *J. prakt. Chem.*, **107**, 86 (1924).
336. Curtius and Bourcart, *J. prakt. Chem.*, **91**, 39 (1915).
337. Curtius and Gockel, *J. prakt. Chem.*, **83**, 279 (1911).
338. Curtius and Jay, *J. prakt. Chem.*, **39**, 43 (1889).
339. Curtius and Mühlhäusser, *J. prakt. Chem.*, **125**, 211 (1930).
340. Cusmano, *Gazz. chim. ital.*, **69**, 594 (1939).
341. Cusmano, *Gazz. chim. ital.*, **70**, 86 (1940).

342. Cusmano, *Gazz. chim. ital.*, **81**, 380 (1951).
343. Cusmano and Sprio, *Gazz. chim. ital.*, **82**, 191 (1952).
344. Cusmano and Sprio, *Gazz. chim. ital.*, **82**, 373 (1952).
345. Cusmano and Tiberio, *Gazz. chim. ital.*, **78**, 896 (1948).
346. Cusmano and Tiberio, *Gazz. chim. ital.*, **80**, 229 (1950).
347. Dahlen and Friedrich, U.S. Pat., 2,153,615 (1939).
348. Dains and Brown, *J. Am. Chem. Soc.*, **31**, 1148 (1909).
349. Dains and Daily, *Univ. of Kansas Sci. Bulletin*, **19**, 215 (1930); through *Chem. Abstracts*, **26**, 427 (1932).
350. Dains, Malleis and Meyers, *J. Am. Chem. Soc.*, **35**, 970 (1913).
351. Dains, O'Brien and Johnson, *J. Am. Chem. Soc.*, **38**, 1510 (1916).
352. Dakin, *Biochem. J.*, **11**, 79 (1917).
353. Darapsky, Berger and Neuhaus, *J. prakt. Chem.*, **147**, 145 (1936).
354. Dayton, *Comp. rend.*, **237**, 185 (1953).
355. De, *Quart. J. Indian Chem. Soc.*, **3**, 30 (1926).
356. De and Datta, *Science and Culture*, **11**, 150 (1945); through *Chem. Abstracts*, **40**, 1804 (1946).
357. De and Dutt, *J. Indian Chem. Soc.*, **5**, 459 (1928).
358. De and Dutt, *J. Indian Chem. Soc.*, **7**, 473 (1930).
359. De and Rakshit, *J. Indian Chem. Soc.*, **13**, 509 (1936).
360. Decombe, *Ann. chim.*, **18**, 81 (1932); through *Chem. Abstracts*, **27**, 2135 (1933).
361. Deeving, Gray, Platt and Stephenson, *J. Chem. Soc.*, **1942**, 239.
362. DeGraef, Ledrut and Combes, *Bull. soc. chim. Belges*, **61**, 331 (1952); through *Chem. Abstracts*, **47**, 12363 (1953).
363. Delaby and Charonnat, *Compt. rend.*, **190**, 59 (1930).
364. Demers and Lynn, *J. Am. Pharm. Assoc.*, **30**, 327 (1941).
365. Dent and Brooker, U.S. Pat., 2,533,206 (1950).
366. Desai, *J. Chem. Soc.*, **1932**, 1088.
366a. DeStevens, Halamandaris, Wenk and Dorfman, *J. Am. Chem. Soc.*, **81**, 8292 (1959).
367. Devoto, *Atti accad. Lincei*, **21**, 819 (1935); through *Chem. Abstracts*, **30**, 3290 (1936).
368. Dewar and King, *J. Chem. Soc.*, **1945**, 114.
369. Dickey, Byers and McNally, U.S. Pat., 2,439,798 (1948).
370. Diels and Reese, *Ann.*, **511**, 168 (1934).
371. Dihlmann, *Naturwissenschaften*, **40**, 510 (1953).
372. Dimroth and Schweizer, *Ber.*, **56**, 1375 (1923).
373. Dinets, *Sovet. Med.*, **1940**, No. 18, 26; through *Chem. Abstracts*, **38**, 5967 (1944).
374. Dittmar and Pütter, Ger. Pat., 929,567 (1956).
375. Dittmar, Pütter and Suckfull, U.S. Pat., 2,734,052 (1956).
376. Dmowska and Weil, *Roczniki Chem.*, **18**, 170 (1938); through *Chem. Abstracts*, **33**, 592 (1939).
377. Dohrn and Diedrich, U.S. Pat., 2,345,385 (1944).
378. Dohrn and Hamann, Ger. Pat., 697,801 (1940).
379. Dohrn, Hamann and Hillemann, Ger. Pat., 703,678 (1941).
380. Domenjoz, *Intern. Record of Med.*, **165**, 467 (1952).
381. Donatelli, Scarinci and Di Carlo, *Arch. sci. biol. (Italy)*, **39**, 257 (1955); through *Chem. Abstracts*, **50**, 14971 (1956).

382. Dormael and Ghys, Brit. Pat., 628,837 (1949).
383. Dornow and Boberg, *Ann.*, **578**, 94 (1952).
384. Dornow and Theis, *Ann.*, **581**, 219 (1953).
385. Dorough and McQueen, U.S. Pat., 2,310,943 (1943).
386. Douglas, Parkinson and Wakefield, Brit. Pat., 603,753 (1948).
387. Douris, *Compt. rend.*, **218**, 514 (1944).
388. Dox, *J. Am. Chem. Soc.*, **54**, 3674 (1932).
389. Dreyfuss and Gaspar, U.S. Pat., 2,677,683 (1954).
390. Drozdov and Cherntzov, *J. Gen. Chem.* (*U.S.S.R.*), **5**, 1736 (1935); through *Chem. Abstracts*, **30**, 3432 (1936).
391. Druey and Schmidt, *Helv. Chim. Acta*, **37**, 1828 (1954).
392. Drummond and Atlas, *S. African Med. J.*, **27**, 997 (1953).
393. Dubský, Winter and Mareth, *Pub. faculté sci. univ. Masaryk*, **271**, 1 (1939); through *Chem. Abstracts*, **33**, 7230 (1939).
394. Dubský and Wintrova, *Collection Czech. Chem. Commun.*, **11**, 526 (1939).
395. Ducommun and Ducommun-Lehmann, *Rev. Can. biol.*, **11**, 298 (1952).
396. Duffin and Kendall, *J. Chem. Soc.*, **1954**, 408.
397. Duffin and Kendall, *J. Chem. Soc.*, **1955**, 3969.
398. Duffin and Kendall, Brit. Pat., 743,505 (1956).
399. Duquénois, *J. pharm. chim.*, **26**, 353 (1937).
400. Duquénois, *Rev. faculté sci. univ. Istanbul*, **6**, 116 (1941); through *Chem. Abstracts*, **37**, 3560 (1943).
401. Duquénois, *Bull. soc. chim. France*, **1946**, 425.
402. Duquénois and Amal, *Bull. soc. chim. France*, [5], **9**, 718 (1942).
403. Dutch Pat., 71,532 (1953).
404. Dutt, *Proc. Leeds Phil. Lit. Soc., Sci. Sect.*, **1**, 113 (1926); through *Chem. Abstracts*, **21**, 1118 (1927).
405. Dutt, *J. Indian Chem. Soc.*, **28**, 533 (1951).
406. Dutt and Dharam, *Proc. Indian Acad. Sci.*, **10A**, 55 (1939); through *Chem. Abstracts*, **34**, 425 (1940).
407. Dutt and Goswami, *J. Indian Chem. Soc.*, **30**, 275 (1953).
408. Dutt and Mukherjee, *J. Indian Chem. Soc.*, **30**, 272 (1953).
409. Eccles, *J. Am. Chem. Soc.*, **24**, 1050 (1902).
410. Eckmann, U.S. Pat., 1,347,083 (1920).
411. Edwards and Kendall, U.S. Pat., 2,531,973 (1950).
412. Efimovsky and Rumpf, *Bull. soc. chim. France*, **1954**, 1401.
413. Efros and Davidenkov, *Zhur. Obshcheĭ Khim.*, **21**, 2046 (1951); through *Chem. Abstracts*, **46**, 8100 (1952).
414. Eichwede and Fischer, U.S. Pat., 1,766,813 (1930).
415. Eisenberg and Keenan, *J. Assoc. Official Agr. Chem.*, **27**, 177 (1944).
416. Eisenberg and Keenan, *J. Assoc. Official Agr. Chem.*, **27**, 458 (1944).
417. Eisenstaedt, *J. Org. Chem.*, **3**, 153 (1958).
418. Eisner, Elvidge and Linstead, *J. Chem. Soc.*, **1950**, 2223.
419. Eisner, Elvidge and Linstead, *J. Chem. Soc.*, **1951**, 1501.
420. Eistert, *Chem. Ber.*, **80**, 47 (1947).
421. Ekstrand, *Acta Chem. Scand.*, **2**, 294 (1948).
422. Emerson, U.S. Pat., 2,194,201 (1940).
423. Emerson, Beacham and Beegle, *J. Org. Chem.*, **8**, 417 (1943).
424. Emerson and Beegle, *J. Org. Chem.*, **8**, 429 (1943).
425. Emerson and Beegle, *J. Org. Chem.*, **8**, 433 (1943).

426. Emerson and Kelly, *J. Org. Chem.*, **13**, 532 (1948).
427. Emerson, Kelly, Beacham and Beagle, *J. Org. Chem.*, **9**, 226 (1944).
428. Emery, *J. Am. Pharm. Assoc.*, **16**, 932 (1927).
429. Emery and Palkin, *J. Am. Chem. Soc.*, **38**, 2166 (1916).
430. Erdös and Sürü, *Magyar Gyógyszéraztud. Tarsaság Értesitöje*, **10**, 424 (1934); through *Chem. Abstracts*, **29**, 1816 (1935).
431. Erlenbach and Sieglitz, Brit. Pat., 693,249 (1953).
432. Ershov, Lyashenko and Grachev, *Anilinokrasochnaya Prom.*, **4**, 306 (1934); through *Chem. Abstracts*, **28**, 7538 (1934).
433. Eury, *Bull. sci. pharmacology*, **15**, 384 (1908); through *Chem. Abstracts*, **3**, 1862 (1909).
434. Fabre, *Bull. soc. chim. France*, [4], **33**, 791 (1923).
435. Fabre and Mach, *Schweiz. Med. Wochschr.*, **81**, 473 (1951); through *Chem. Abstracts*, **45**, 9731 (1951).
436. Falkof, Witten and Gehauf, U.S. Pat., 2,678,260 (1954).
437. Fand and Spoerri, *J. Am. Chem. Soc.*, **74**, 853 (1952).
438. Fargher and Furness, *J. Chem. Soc.*, **107**, 688 (1915).
439. Felix and Heckendorn, U.S. Pat., 2,495,243 (1950).
440. Felix, Heckendorn, Reich and Oesterlein, U.S. Pat., 2,496,386 (1950).
441. Felix, Heckendorn and Widmer, U.S. Pat., 2,478,185 (1949).
442. Felix, Heckendorn and Widmer, U.S. Pat., 2,570,052 (1951).
443. Fenton and Jones, *J. Chem. Soc.*, **79**, 91 (1901).
444. Feofilaktov, *Bull. acad. sci. U.R.S.S., Classe sci. chim.*, **1941**, 521; through *Chem. Abstracts*, **37**, 2348 (1943).
445. Feofilaktov and Ivanova, *Zhur. Obshcheĭ Khim.*, **25**, 125 (1955); through *Chem. Abstracts*, **50**, 1781 (1956).
446. Fichter, *J. prakt. Chem.*, **74**, 297 (1906).
447. Fichter and de Montmillon, *Helv. Chim. Acta*, **5**, 256 (1922).
448. Fichter, Jetzer and Leepin, *Ann.*, **395**, 1 (1913).
449. Fierke and Barclay, U.S. Pat., 2,503,717 (1950).
450. Fischer and Knoevenagel, *Ann.*, **239**, 194 (1887).
451. Fischer and Niemann, *Z. physiol. Chem.*, **146**, 196 (1925).
452. Fischer and Reinecke, *Z. physiol. Chem.*, **258**, 243 (1939).
453. Fleischauer, Müller and Schultis, U.S. Pat., 2,384,419 (1945).
454. Flett, U.S. Pat., 2,469,378 (1949).
455. Forrest, Fuller and Walker, *J. Chem. Soc.*, **1948**, 1501.
456. Forster and Müller, *J. Chem. Soc.*, **95**, 2072 (1909).
457. Fosse, Hieulle and Bass, *Compt. rend.*, **178**, 811 (1924).
458. Franchi, *Il Farmaco* (*Pavia*), *Ed. Sci.*, **10**, 628, 1955; through *Chem. Abstracts*, **50**, 8611 (1956).
459. Franzen, *J. prakt. Chem.*, **76**, 205 (1907).
460. Freedman, U.S. Pat., 2,076,714 (1937).
461. Freedman and Sherndal, U.S. Pat., 1,877,166 (1932).
462. Fr. Pat., 44,843 (1935).
463. Fr. Pat., 362,465 (1906).
464. Fr. Pat., 377,130 (1907).
465. Fr. Pat., 378,486 (1907).
466. Fr. Pat., 403,919 (1908).
467. Fr. Pat., 661,224 (1928).
468. Fr. Pat., 734,776 (1932).

469. Fr. Pat., 769,572 (1934).
470. Fr. Pat., 771,486 (1934).
471. Fr. Pat., 820,328 (1937).
472. Fr. Pat., 822,533 (1937).
473. Fr. Pat., 830,124 (1938).
474. Fr. Pat., 848,896 (1939).
475. Fr. Pat., 966,764 (1950).
476. Fr. Pat., 983,719 (1951).
477. Fr. Pat., 988,579 (1951).
478. Freri, *Atti Accad. Lincei*, **22**, 264 (1935); through *Chem. Abstracts*, **30**, 6375 (1936).
479. Freri, *Atti V Congr. Nazl. chim. pura applicata, Rome*, **1935**, Pt. I, 361 (1936); through *Chem. Abstracts*, **31**, 3914 (1937).
480. Freri, *Gazz. chim. ital.*, **66**, 23 (1936).
481. Fresenius, *Arzneimittel-Forsch.*, **1**, 128 (1951).
482. Fricke, *Z. anorg. Chem.*, **253**, 173 (1947).
483. Fröhlich and Schneider, U.S. Pat., 2,307,399 (1943).
484. Fröhlich and Schneider, U.S. Pat., 2,357,393 (1944).
485. Fröhlich, Schneider and Zeh, U.S. Pat., 2,348,463 (1944).
486. Froning, U.S. Pat., 2,362,477 (1944).
487. Froning, Brit. Pat., 581,305 (1946).
488. Fry and Kendall, U.S. Pat., 2,388,963 (1945).
489. Fuhrmann and Degering, *J. Am. Chem. Soc.*, **67**, 1245 (1945).
490. Fujimara, *Bull. Inst. Chem. Research, Kyoto Univ.*, **30**, 53 (1952); through *Chem. Abstracts*, **47**, 9561 (1953).
491. Fujinaga, Jap. Pat., 8048 (1954).
492. Fujisawa *et al.*, Jap. Pat., 3086 (1953).
493. Furuya, Mujazawa and Komuro, *J. Soc. Sci. Phot. Japan*, **12**, No. 1, 8 (1949); through *Chem. Abstracts*, **46**, 2936 (1952).
494. Furuya and Ueno, *J. Soc. Sci. Phot. Japan*, **13**, No. 4, 27 (1951); through *Chem. Abstracts*, **46**, 7447 (1952).
495. Gaglio, *Reumatisamo*, **6**, *Suppl.* No. 2, 32 (1954); through *Chem. Abstracts*, **49**, 1973 (1955).
496. Gagnon, Boivin and Boivin, *Can. J. Research*, **28B**, 720 (1956).
497. Gagnon, Boivin, Boivin and Craig, *Can. J. Chem.*, **30**, 52 (1952).
498. Gagnon, Boivin, Boivin and Jones, *Can. J. Chem.*, **29**, 182 (1951).
499. Gagnon, Boivin and Chisholm, *Can. J. Chem.*, **30**, 904 (1952).
500. Gagnon, Boivin and Giguère, *Can. J. Chem.*, **29**, 328 (1951).
501. Gagnon, Boivin and Jones, *Can. J. Research*, **27B**, 190 (1949).
502. Gagnon, Boivin and Jones, *Can. J. Research*, **28B**, 34 (1950).
503. Gagnon, Boivin and Laflamme, *Can. J. Chem.*, **34**, 530 (1956).
504. Gagnon, Boivin, MacDonald and Yoffe, *Can. J. Chem.*, **32**, 823 (1954).
505. Gagnon, Boivin and Paquin, *Can. J. Chem.*, **31**, 1025 (1953).
506. Gagnon, Boivin and Tremblay, *Can. J. Chem.*, **31**, 673 (1953).
507. Gagnon, Nolin and Jones, *Can. J. Chem.*, **29**, 843 (1951).
508. Gagnon, Savard, Gaudry and Richardson, *Can. J. Research*, **25B**, 28 (1947).
509. Gailliot and Debarre, U.S. Pat., 2,744,912 (1956).
510. Gardner, Smith, Wenis and Lee, *J. Org. Chem.*, **16**, 1121 (1951).
511. Gasper, U.S. Pat., 2,470,769 (1949).
512. Gault and Thirode, *Compt. rend.*, **150**, 1123 (1910).

513. Gault and Wendling, *Compt. rend.*, **199**, 1052 (1934).
514. Gault and Wendling, *Bull. soc. chim. France*, [5], **3**, 53 (1936).
515. Gault and Wendling, *Bull. soc. chim. France*, [5], **3**, 369 (1936).
516. Gautier, *Compt. rend. soc. biol.*, **80**, 672 (1917).
517. Gebauer, Ger. Pat., 590,174 (1933).
518. Geller, U.S. Pat., 856,413 (1932).
519. Gerbaux, *Bull. soc. chim. Belges*, **58**, 498 (1949).
520. Ger. Pat., 91,504; through *Beil.* I, **24**, 277.
521. Ger. Pat., 92,009; through *Beil.* I, **24**, 277, 278.
522. Ger. Pat., 131,537; through *J. Chem. Soc.*, **82**, 730 (1902).
523. Ger. Pat., 176,954; through *J. Chem. Soc.*, **92**, 363 (1907).
524. Ger. Pat., 184,850 (1906).
525. Ger. Pat., 189,842 (1907).
526. Ger. Pat., 193,632 (1907).
527. Ger. Pat., 203,753 (1907).
528. Ger. Pat., 206,637 (1907).
529. Ger. Pat., 208,593 (1908).
530. Ger. Pat., 214,716 (1908).
531. Ger. Pat., 217,557 (1909); through *J. Chem. Soc.*, **98**, 340 (1910).
532. Ger. Pat., 217,558 (1909); through *J. Chem. Soc.*, **98**, 340 (1910).
533. Ger. Pat., 227,013 (1908).
534. Ger. Pat., 233,068 (1910).
535. Ger. Pat., 238,256 (1910).
536. Ger. Pat., 238,373 (1910).
537. Ger. Pat., 243,197 (1910).
538. Ger. Pat., 248,887 (1911).
539. Ger. Pat., 249,626 (1911).
540. Ger. Pat., 254,487 (1911).
541. Ger. Pat., 254,711; through *J. Chem. Soc.*, **104**, 401 (1913).
542. Ger. Pat., 259,577 (1911).
543. Ger. Pat., 261,081 (1911) and 261,082 (1912).
544. Ger. Pat., 264,287; through *J. Chem. Soc.*, **106**, 93 (1914).
545. Ger. Pat., 299,510 (1917).
546. Ger. Pat., 313,320.
547. Ger. Pats., 360,421; 364,034; 364,032; 367,084.
548. Ger. Pat., 360,423.
549. Ger. Pat., 360,424.
550. Ger. Pat., 469,285 (1923).
551. Ger. Pat., 479,348 (1927).
552. Ger. Pat., 484,763 (1927).
553. Ger. Pat., 496,647 (1928).
554. Ger. Pat., 499,823 (1923).
555. Ger. Pat., 582,806 (1933).
556. Ger. Pat., 675,881 (1939).
557. Ghosh, *J. Indian Chem. Soc.*, **13**, 86 (1936).
558. Ghosh, *J. Indian Chem. Soc.*, **15**, 89 (1938).
559. Ghosh and Das Gupta, *J. Indian Chem. Soc.*, **16**, 63 (1939).
560. Giacalone, *Gazz. chim. ital.*, **67**, 460 (1937).
561. Giacalone and Di Maggio, *Gazz. chim. ital.*, **69**, 122 (1939).

562. Gialdroni and Grassi, *Boll. soc. ital. biol. sper.*, **28,** 1580 (1952); through *Chem. Abstracts*, **47,** 4487 (1953).
563. Gidvani, Kon and Wright, *J. Chem. Soc.*, **1932,** 1027.
564. Gilman, Tolman, Yeoman, Woods, Shirley and Avakian, *J. Am. Chem. Soc.*, **68,** 426 (1946).
565. Ginzburg, *Zhur. Obshcheĭ Khim.*, **23,** 1504 (1953); through *Chem. Abstracts*, **48,** 1776 (1954).
566. Ginzburg, *Zhur. Obshcheĭ Khim.*, **23,** 1677 (1953); through *Chem. Abstracts*, **48,** 13685 (1954).
567. Ginzburg, *Zhur. Obshcheĭ Khim.*, **23,** 1890 (1953); through *Chem. Abstracts*, **49,** 1049 (1955).
568. Ginzburg and Ioffe, *Zhur. Obshcheĭ Khim.*, **25,** 1739 (1955); through *Chem. Abstracts*, **50,** 5645 (1956).
569. Ginzburg, Ioffe and Mel'nikova, *Zhur. Obshcheĭ Khim.*, **25,** 358 (1955) through *Chem. Abstracts*, **50,** 2552 (1956).
570. Ginzburg and Terushkin, *Zhur. Obshcheĭ Khim.*, **23,** 1049 (1953); through *Chem. Abstracts*, **48,** 8221 (1954).
571. Girard, U.S. Pat., 2,256,261 (1941).
572. Giua, *Gazz. chim. ital.*, **46,** II, 61 (1916).
573. Giua, *Gazz. chim. ital.*, **54,** 204 (1924).
574. Giuliano and Stein, *Il Farmaco (Pavia), Ed. sci.*, **11,** 3 (1956); through *Chem. Abstracts*, **50,** 12986 (1956).
575. Glass, Vittum and Weissberger, U.S. Pat., 2,455,170 (1948).
576. Glassman, U.S. Pat., 2,514,236 (1950).
577. Glassman and Sarfas, Brit. Pat., 633,218 (1949).
578. Glauert and Mann, *J. Chem. Soc.*, **1952,** 2401.
579. Gluck, Brit. Pat., 566,520 (1945).
580. Gluck, U.S. Pat., 2,387,115 (1945).
581. Godtfredsen and Vangedal, *Acta Chem. Scand.*, **9,** 1498 (1955).
582. Gold and Piepenbrink, Ger. Pat., 842,978 (1952).
583. Gol'mov, *Zhur. Obshcheĭ Khim.*, **20,** 1881 (1950); through *Chem. Abstracts*, **45,** 2411 (1951).
584. Gomez, *Rev. acad. cienc. Madrid*, **31,** 563 (1934); through *Chem. Abstracts*, **29,** 5422 (1935).
585. Goodings and Rogers, U.S. Pat., 2,410,604 (1946).
586. Goodings and Rogers, U.S. Pat., 2,437,465 (1948).
587. Goodman and Gilman, "The Pharmacological Basis of Therapeutics", New York, The Macmillan Company, 1955, 2nd Edn., pp. 318, 322.
588. Goryainova and Gurevich, *Farmatsiya i Farmakol.*, **1937,** No. 11, 60; through *Chem. Abstracts*, **34,** 6192 (1940).
589. Göttler, *Ber.*, **48,** 1765 (1915).
590. Grachev, *Zavodskaya Lab.*, **11,** 154 (1945); through *Chem. Abstracts*, **40,** 1106 (1946).
591. Graham, U.S. Pat., 2,694,703 (1954).
592. Graham, U.S. Pat., 2,710,871 (1955).
593. Graham, U.S. Pat., 2,725,291 (1955).
594. Graham, Porter and Weissberger, *J. Am. Chem. Soc.*, **71,** 983 (1949).
595. Graham, Reckhow and Weissberger, *J. Am. Chem. Soc.*, **76,** 3993 (1954).
596. Graham and Weissberger, U.S. Pat., 2,691,659 (1954).
597. Green and Williams, *Lancet*, **264,** 575 (1953).

598. Gregory, U.S. Pat., 2.472,581 (1949).
599. Gresham, Jansen, Shaver, Bankert and Kiedorp, *J. Am. Chem. Soc.*, **73**, 3168 (1951).
600. Grothaus and Dains, *J. Am. Chem. Soc.*, **58**, **1334** (1936).
601. Grotowsky, Ger. Pat., 514,421 (1926).
602. Guha and Roy-Choudhury, *J. Indian Chem. Soc.*, **5**, **149** (1928).
603. Gulinov, Gurarii and Pashchenka, Russ. Pat., 46,924 (1936).
604. Gundermann, *Ann.*, **578**, 48 (1952).
605. Gunn, *Quart. J. Pharm. and Pharmacol.*, **6**, **643** (1933).
606. Gunst, U.S. Pat., 2,686,178 (1954).
607. Gurevich, *Farmatsiya*, **1940**, No. 2–3, 5; through *Chem. Abstracts*, **34**, 6192 (1940).
608. Gusev and Beĭles, *Zhur. Obshcheĭ Khim.*, **21**, 1971 (1951); through *Chem. Abstracts*, **46**, 3442 (1952).
609. Gusev and Beĭles, *Zhur. Anal. Khim.*, **7**, 219 (1952); through *Chem. Abstracts*, **47**, 1532 (1953).
610. Gutsche and Hillman, *J. Am. Chem. Soc.*, **76**, 2236 (1954).
611. Gysling and Schwarzenbach, *Helv. Chim. Acta*, **32**, 1484 (1949).
612. Haas and Kraft, *Arzneimittel-Forsch.*, **4**, 249 (1954).
613. Häfliger, U.S. Pat., 2,674,600 (1954).
614. Häfliger, U.S. Pat., 2,700,670 (1955).
615. Häfliger, U.S. Pat., 2,700,671 (1955).
616. Hagenbach and Gysin, *Experientia*, **8**, 184 (1952).
617. Halberkann and Fretwurst, *Arquivos. inst. biol.* (*Sao Paulo*), **11**, 149 (1940); through *Chem. Abstracts*, **36**, 101 (1942).
618. Halberkann and Fretwurst, *Z. physiol. Chem.*, **285**, 97 (1950).
619. Hallman, Ringhardtz and Fischer, *Chem. Ber.*, **90**, 537 (1957).
620. Hamer, *J. Chem. Soc.*, **1951**, 294.
621. Hanford, U.S. Pat., 2,495,000 (1950).
622. Hanhart, U.S. Pat., 2,709,166 (1955).
623. Harradence and Lions, *J. Proc. Roy. Soc. N.S. Wales*, **72**, 233 (1939); through *Chem. Abstracts*, **33**, 5856 (1939).
624. Harrington, U.S. Pat., 2,366,616 (1945).
625. Harrison and Twitchell, Brit. Pat., 691,475 (1953).
626. Hartmann, Kaegi and Isler, U.S. Pat., 1,886,481 (1932).
627. Hasselquist, *Arkiv Kemi*, **7**, 121 (1954); through *Chem. Abstracts*, **49**, 6260 (1955).
628. Hauser and Lindsay, *J. Org. Chem.*, **22**, 482 (1957).
629. Hauser, Shivers and Skell, *J. Am. Chem. Soc.*, **67**, 409 (1945).
630. Hayashi, Oshima, Tsuruoka and Seo, *Rept. Japan Assoc. Adv. Sci.*, **17**, 50 (1942); through *Chem. Abstracts*, **44**, 3258 (1950).
631. Hazelton, Tusing and Holland, *J. Pharmacol. and Exptl. Therap.*, **109**, 387 (1953).
632. Heiduschka and Rothacker, *J. prakt. Chem.*, **80**, 289 (1909).
633. Heiduschka and Rothacker, *J. prakt. Chem.*, **84**, 533 (1911).
634. Heimbach, U.S. Pat., 2,584,349 (1952).
635. Hein and Pierce, *J. Am. Chem. Soc.*, **77**, 4107 (1955).
636. Helferich and Koster, *Ber.*, **56**, 2088 (1923).
637. Hellmann and Opitz, *Chem. Ber.*, **89**, 81 (1956).
638. Hellmann and Schumacher, *Chem. Ber.*, **89**, 95 (1956).

639. Hemming and Kuzell, *Antibiotics and Chemotherapy*, **3**, 634 (1953).
640. Henn and King, *Phot. Sci. and Tech.* (II), **1**, 126 (1954).
641. Henn and Reynolds, U.S. Pat., 2,691,589 (1954).
642. Henne, *Klin. Wochschr.*, **31**, 522 (1953).
643. Henry and Dehn, *J. Am. Chem. Soc.*, **71**, 2297 (1949).
644. Hepner and Fajersztejn, *Bull. soc. chim.* [5], **4**, 854 (1937).
645. Hermann, Streitwolf and Fehrle, Ger. Pat., 505,799 (1928).
646. Heseltine and Brooker, U.S. Pat., 2,719,151 (1955).
647. Heymons and Rohland, *Ber.*, **66**, 1654 (1933).
648. Heyna and Hensel, Ger. Pat., 938,143 (1956).
649. Heyna and Hensel, Ger. Pat., 938,145 (1956).
650. Heyna, Hensel and Schumacher, Ger. Pat., 940,482 (1956).
651. Heyna, Hensel and Schnorrenberg, Ger. Pat., 925,121 (1955).
652. Heyna and Schumacher, U.S. Pat., 2,657,205 (1953).
653. Hill and Black, *Am. Chem. J.*, **33**, 292 (1905).
654. Hiller and Strauss, *Die Medizinische*, **1954**, 613; through *Chem. Abstracts*, **48**, 8406 (1954).
655. Himmelbauer, *J. prakt. Chem.* [2], **51**, 532 (1895).
656. Hindermann, U.S. Pat., 2,472,109 (1949).
657. Hindermann, U.S. Pat., 2,505,244 (1950).
658. Hindermann, U.S. Pat., 2,517,312 (1950).
659. Hindermann, U.S. Pat., 2,544,087 (1951).
660. Hirst, MacBeth and Traill, *Proc. Roy. Irish Acad.*, **37B**, 47 (1925); through *Chem. Abstracts*, **19**, 2931 (1925).
661. Hoffmann, U.S. Pat., 1,531,286 (1925).
662. Homeyer, U.S. Pat., 2,630,437 (1953).
663. Hörlin, Linke and Messmer, *Deut. Arch. klin. Med.*, **201**, 690 (1955).
664. Hovorka and Sýkora, *Collection Czech. Chem. Commun.*, **11**, 70 (1939).
665. Hovorka and Sýkora, *Collection Czech. Chem. Commun.*, **11**, 124 (1939).
666. Hovorka and Sýkora, *Chem. listy*, **35**, 89 (1941); through *Chem. Abstracts*, **37**, 3023 (1943).
667. Howland, U.S. Pat., 2,458,780 (1949).
668. Hrynakowski and Smoczkiewiczowa, *Roczniki Chem.*, **17**, 165 (1937); through *Chem. Abstracts*, **31**, 6096 (1937).
669. Hrynakowski and Szmyt, *Z. physik. Chem.*, **A181**, 113 (1937).
670. Huebner and Link, *J. Am. Chem. Soc.*, **67**, 102 (1945).
671. Huebner and Link, *J. Am. Chem. Soc.*, **72**, 4812 (1950).
672. Hugounenq, Florence and Couture, *Bull. soc. chim. biol.*, **7**, 58 (1925).
673. Humphlett, Weiss and Hauser, *J. Am. Chem. Soc.*, **70**, 4020 (1948).
674. Hung. Pat., 135,432 (1949).
675. Hünig, *Ann.*, **574**, 106, 112 (1951).
676. Hunter and Sundholm, U.S. Pat., 2,510,696 (1950).
677. Huntress and Olsen, *J. Am. Chem. Soc.*, **70**, 2856 (1948).
678. Hurwitz and Thompson, *Arch. Ophthalmol.*, **43**, 712 (1950); *Am. J. Ophthalmol.*, **34**, 130 (1951).
679. Huston, Sell and Brigham, *J. Am. Chem. Soc.*, **55**, 3407 (1933).
680. Hüttel, Büchele and Jochum, *Chem. Ber.*, **88**, 1577 (1955).
681. Imanishi, *J. Chem. Phys.*, **18**, 1307 (1950).
682. Ingraffia, *Gazz. chim. ital.*, **64**, 778 (1934).

683. Ioffe and Khavin, *Zhur. Obshcheĭ Khim.*, **14,** 882 (1944); through *Chem. Abstracts*, **40,** 2847 (1946).
684. Ioffe and Khavin, *Zhur. Obshcheĭ Khim.*, **17,** 522 (1947); through *Chem. Abstracts*, **42,** 903 (1948).
685. Ioffe and Khavin, *Zhur. Obshcheĭ Khim.*, **17,** 528 (1947); through *Chem. Abstracts*, **42,** 1933 (1948).
686. Ionescu, *Bul. soc. stünte Cluj*, **3,** 381 (1927); through *Chem. Abstracts*, **22** 1353 (1928).
687. Ionescu and Georgescu, *Bull. soc. chim. France*, [4], **41,** 881 (1927).
688. Ionescu and Georgescu, *Bull. soc. chim. France*, [4], **41,** 1514 (1927).
689. Ionescu and Popescu, *Bull. soc. chim. France*, [4], **51,** 1215 (1932).
690. Iseki, Sugiura, Yasunaga and Nakasina, *Ber.*, **74,** 1420 (1941).
691. Ishihara and Ito, Jap. Pat., 2668 (1950).
692. Ishikawa, Kano and Katayama, *J. Pharm. Soc. Japan*, **74,** 138 (1954); through *Chem. Abstracts*, **49,** 1707 (1955).
693. Itano, *J. Pharm. Soc. Japan*, **71,** 540 (1951); through *Chem. Abstracts*, **46,** 4532 (1952).
694. Itano, *J. Pharm. Soc. Japan*, **71,** 1456 (1951); through *Chem. Abstracts*, **46,** 7095 (1952).
695. Itano, *J. Pharm. Soc. Japan*, **75,** 441 (1955); through *Chem. Abstracts*, **50,** 2552 (1956).
696. Ito, *J. Pharm. Soc. Japan*, **76,** 167 (1956); through *Chem. Abstracts*, **50,** 13939 (1956).
697. Ito, *J. Pharm. Soc. Japan*, **76,** 820 (1956); through *Chem. Abstracts*, **51,** 1148 (1957).
698. Ito, *J. Pharm. Soc. Japan*, **76,** 822 (1956); through *Chem. Abstracts*, **51,** 1149 (1957).
699. Jacobs, "Heterocyclic Compounds", New York, John Wiley and Sons, Inc., 1957, Vol. 5, p. 153.
700. Jacobsen and Jost, *Ann.*, **400,** 195 (1913).
701. James and Vanselow, *P S A Journal, Sect. B, Phot. Sci. Tech.*, Ser. II, I, 77 (1954); through *Chem. Abstracts*, **48,** 11228 (1954).
702. Jamicka, Hiszpanska and Weil, *Roczniki Chem.*, **18,** 158 (1938); through *Chem. Abstracts* **33,** 592 (1939).
703. Jennen, U.S. Pat., 2,611,698 (1952).
704. Jennen, U.S. Pat., 2,619,419 (1952).
705. Jennen, U.S. Pat., 2,672,417 (1954).
706. Jennen and Michaelis, U.S. Pat., 2,495,260 (1950).
707. Jennen and Michaelis, U.S. Pat., 2,544,322 (1951).
708. Jennings, U.S. Pat., 2,397,865 (1946).
709. Jennings, U.S. Pat., 2,397,867 (1946).
710. Jennings, U.S. Pat., 2,422,680 (1947).
711. Jennings and Middleton, U.S. Pat., 2,200,924 (1940).
712. Jennings, Murray and White, U.S. Pat., 2,397,864 (1946).
713. Jensen, *Acta Chem. Scand.*, **9,** 1498 (1955).
714. Jensen, *Dansk Tids. Farm.*, **15,** 299 (1941); through *Chem. Abstracts*, **36,** 5793 (1942).
715. Jensen and Friediger, *Kgl. Danske Widenskab. Selskab, Math-fys. Medd.*, **20,** No. 20, 1 (1943); through *Chem. Abstracts*, **39,** 2068 (1945).
716. Jensen and Hansen, *Acta Chem. Scand.*, **6,** 195 (1952).

717. John, Swiss Pat., 183,197 (1936).
718. John and Ottawa, *J. prakt. Chem.*, **131**, 346 (1931).
719. John and Schmit, *J. prakt. Chem.*, **132**, 15 (1931).
720. John and Schmit, *J. prakt. Chem.*, **133**, 177 (1932).
721. Johnson, *J. Chem. Soc.*, **1947**, 1626.
722. Johnson, *J. Soc. Chem. Ind.*, **40**, 176 (1921).
723. Johnston, U.S. Pat., 2,017,815 (1935).
724. Jolles, Wardleworth and Wood, Brit. Pat., 650,850 (1951).
725. Jones, *J. Am. Chem. Soc.*, **78**, 159 (1956).
726. Justoni and Fusco, *Gazz. chim. ital.*, **68**, 59 (1938).
727. Kaiser, U.S. Pat., 2,490,967 (1949).
728. Kanao, Jap. Pat., 5682 (1953).
729. Kano, *J. Pharm. Soc. Japan*, **73**, 383 (1953); through *Chem. Abstracts*, **48**, 3342 (1954).
730. Kano and Makisumi, *Pharm. Bull.* (*Japan*), **3**, 270 (1955); through *Chem. Abstracts*, **50**, 12061 (1956).
731. Karrer, Dieckmann and Haebler, *Helv. Chim. Acta*, **7**, 1031 (1924).
732. Karrer and Hershberger, *Helv. Chim. Acta*, **17**, 1014 (1934).
733. Kartaschoff and Merian, U.S. Pat., 2,555,973 (1951).
734. Kaufmann, *Z. Angew. Chem.*, **40**, 69 (1927).
735. Kaufmann, U.S. Pat., 2,109,445 (1938).
736. Kaufmann, Ger. Pat., 660,620 (1938).
737. Kaufmann, Ger. Pat., 668,387 (1938).
738. Kaufmann, U.S. Pat., 2,234,866 (1941).
739. Kaufmann, Ger. Pat., 735,266 (1943).
740. Kaufmann, Huang and Bückmann, *Ber.*, **75**, 1236 (1942).
741. Kaufmann, Huang, Schnitz, Hultenschmidt and Bückmann, *Ber.*, **75**, 1214 (1942).
742. Kaufmann and Liepe, *Ber.*, **56**, 2514 (1923).
743. Kaufmann and Ritter, *Arch. Pharm.*, **267**, 212 (1929).
744. Kaufmann, Seher and Pankoke, *Arch. Pharm.*, **284**, 330 (1951).
745. Kaufmann and Steinhoff, *Arch. Pharm.*, **278**, 437 (1940).
746. Keller and Zweidler, U.S. Pat., 2,462,405 (1949).
747. Kendall, Brit. Pat., 519,895 (1940).
748. Kendall, Brit. Pat., 555,936 (1943).
749. Kendall, U.S. Pat., 2,397,013 (1946).
750. Kendall, Brit. Pat., 650,911 (1951).
751. Kendall, *Brit. J. Phot.*, **100**, 56 (1953); through *Chem. Abstracts*, **47**, 3157 (1953).
752. Kendall and Collins, U.S. Pat., 2,213,986 (1940).
753. Kendall and Doyle, Brit. Pat., 595,785 (1947).
754. Kendall and Doyle, Brit. Pat., 604,217 (1948).
755. Kendall and Doyle, U.S. Pat., 2,518,476 (1950).
756. Kendall and Duffin, Brit. Pat., 679,677 (1952).
757. Kendall and Duffin, Brit. Pat., 679,678 (1952).
758. Kendall and Duffin, U.S. Pat., 2,704,762 (1955).
759. Kendall and Duffin, Brit. Pat., 730,489 (1955).
760. Kendall and Duffin, U.S. Pat., 2,726,248 (1955).
761. Kendall and Duffin, Brit. Pat., 749,192 (1956).
762. Kendall, Duffin and Axford, U.S. Pat., 2,688,024 (1954).

763. Kendall and Edwards, U.S. Pat., 2,412,816 (1946).
764. Kendall and Frye, Brit. Pat., 544,647 (1942).
765. Kendall and Fry, U.S. Pat., 2,385,815 (1945).
766. Kendall and Fry, Brit. Pat., 577,260 (1946).
767. Kendall and Fry, Brit. Pat., 585,780 (1947).
768. Kendall and Fry, Brit. Pat., 585,781 (1947).
769. Kendall and Fry, U.S. Pat., 2,427,911 (1947).
770. Kendall and Fry, U.S. Pat., 2,457,823 (1949).
771. Kendall, Fry and Morgan, Brit. Pat., 672,291 (1952).
772. Kendall and Majer, U.S. Pat., 2,369,355 (1945).
773. Kendall and Majer, *J. Chem. Soc.*, **1948**, 687.
774. Kersley and Mandel, *Lancet*, **263**, 1046 (1952).
775. Keyes and Brooker, U.S. Pat., 2,533,472 (1950).
776. Keyes and Brooker, U.S. Pat., 2,611,696 (1952).
777. Khromov-Bousov, *Zhur. Obshcheĭ Khim.*, **25**, 136 (1955); through *Chem. Abstracts*, **49**, 8257 (1955).
778. Kidd, Robins and Walker, *J. Chem. Soc.*, **1953**, 3244.
779. Kiely and Stickney, *Proc. Staff Meetings Mayo Clinic*, **28**, 341 (1953).
780. Kirby, U.S. Pat., 2,396,275 (1946).
781. Klebanskii and Lemke, *J. Applied Chem.* (*U.S.S.R.*), **8**, 269 (1935); through *Chem. Abstracts*, **29**, 6891 (1935).
782. Kleene, U.S. Pat., 2,512,251 (1950).
783. Konek and Szasz, *Wein. Chem.-Ztg.*, **46**, 266 (1944); through *Chem. Abstracts*, **40**, 6063 (1946).
784. Kitamura and Ishiwatari, *J. Pharm. Soc. Japan*, **57**, 1011 (1937); through *Chem. Abstracts*, **32**, 2534 (1938).
785. Kitamura, *J. Pharm. Soc. Japan*, **58**, 447 (1938); through *Chem. Abstracts*, **32**, 6648 (1938).
786. Kitamura, *J. Pharm. Soc. Japan*, **58**, 613, 676 (1938); through *Chem. Abstracts*, **32**, 8416 (1938).
787. Kitamura, *J. Pharm. Soc. Japan*, **59**, 84 (1939); through *Chem. Abstracts*, **33**, 3791 (1939).
788. Kitamura, *J. Pharm. Soc. Japan*, **60**, 45 (1940); through *Chem. Abstracts*, **34**, 3737 (1940).
789. Kitamura, *J. Pharm. Soc. Japan*, **61**, 19 (1941); through *Chem. Abstracts*, **35**, 4770 (1941).
790. Kitamura, *J. Pharm. Soc. Japan*, **61**, 33 (1941); through *Chem. Abstracts*, **35**, 3633 (1941).
791. Kitamura, *J. Pharm. Soc. Japan*, **61**, 94 (1941); through *Chem. Abstracts*, **36**, 473 (1942).
792. Kitamura, *Rept. Japan. Assoc. Advancement Sci.*, **16**, 541 (1942); through *Chem. Abstracts*, **44**, 3489 (1950).
793. Kitamura and Sunagawa, *J. Pharm. Soc. Japan*, **60**, 60 (1940).
794. Kitamura and Sunagawa, *J. Pharm. Soc. Japan*, **60**, 65 (1940).
795. Kitamura and Sunagawa, *J. Pharm. Soc. Japan*, **61**, 26 (1941); through *Chem. Abstracts*, **35**, 4770 (1941).
796. Kitamura, *Bull. Inst. Phys. Chem. Research* (*Tokyo*), **20**, 848 (1941); through *Chem. Abstracts*, **43**, 8386 (1949).
797. Kleiger and Hugos, U.S. Pat., 2,671,021 (1954).
798. Klosa, *Arch. Pharm.*, **286**, 391 (1953).

799. Klosa, *Arch. Pharm.*, **288**, 217 (1955).
800. Klosa, *Arch. Pharm.*, **288**, 545 (1955).
801. Knevel and Miller, *Proc. N. Dakota Acad. Sci.*, **7**, 39 (1953); through *Chem. Abstracts*, **48**, 13685 (1954).
802. Knight, U.S. Pat., 2,384,749 (1945).
803. Knight, Brit. Pat., 706,427 (1954).
804. Knight, Brit. Pat., 706,857 (1954).
805. Knorr, *Ber.*, **16**, 2597 (1883).
806. Knorr, *Ber.*, **17**, 546 (1884).
807. Knorr, *Ber.*, **17**, 2032 (1884).
808. Knorr, *Ber.*, **20**, 1107 (1887).
809. Knorr, *Ann.*, **238**, 137 (1887).
810. Knorr, *Ber.*, **28**, 701 (1895).
811. Knorr, *Ber.*, **28**, 706 (1895).
812. Knorr, *Ber.*, **28**, 714 (1895).
813. Knorr, *Ber.*, **29**, 249 (1896).
814. Knorr and Blank, *Ber.*, **17**, 2049 (1884).
815. Knorr and Bülow, *Ber.*, **17**, 2057 (1884).
816. Knorr and Duden, *Ber.*, **25**, 759 (1892).
817. Knorr and Geuther, *Ann.*, **293**, 55 (1896).
818. Knorr and Klotz, *Ber.*, **20**, 2545 (1887).
819. Knorr, Pemsel and Morentz, *Ber.*, **37**, 3520 (1904).
820. Knorr and Pschorr, *Ann.*, **293**, 49 (1896).
821. Knorr and Stolz, *Ann.*, **293**, 58 (1896).
822. Knorr and Taufkirch, *Ber.*, **25**, 768 (1892).
823. Knott, Brit. Pat., 614,471 (1948).
824. Knott, U.S. Pat., 2,515,878 (1950).
825. Knott, *J. Chem. Soc.*, **1951**, 3033.
826. Kocwa, *Bull. intern. acad. polon. sci., Classe sci. math. nat.*, **1936A**, 766; through *Chem. Abstracts*, **31**, 1803 (1937).
827. Kocwa, *Bull. intern. acad. polon. sci., Classe sci. math. nat.*, **1936A**, 382, 390; through *Chem. Abstracts*, **31**, 1804 (1937).
828. Kocwa, *Bull. intern. acad. polon. sci., Classe sci. math. nat.*, **1937A**, 571; through *Chem. Abstracts*, **32**, 4986 (1938).
829. Kocwa, *Polska Akad. Umiejętności, Prace Kom. Nauk Farmaceut., Dissertationes Pharm.*, **1**, 55 (1949); through *Chem. Abstracts*, **44**, 1490 (1950).
830. Kocwa, *Polska Akad. Umiejętności, Prace Kom. Nauk Farmaceut., Dissertationes Pharm.*, **1**, 143 (1949); through *Chem. Abstracts*, **44**, 1491 (1950).
831. Kocwa, *Polska Akad. Umiejętności, Prace Kom. Nauk Farmaceut., Dissertationes Pharm.*, **2**, 21 (1950); through *Chem. Abstracts*, **45**, 9534 (1951).
832. Koelsch, *J. Am. Chem. Soc.*, **67**, 569 (1945).
833. Koenigs, Weiss and Zscharn, *Ber.*, **59**, 316 (1926).
834. Kohlbach, *Arkiv. Hem. Farm.*, **11**, 99 (1937); through *Chem. Abstracts*, **33**, 2897 (1939).
835. Kohler and Baltzly, *J. Am. Chem. Soc.*, **54**, 4015 (1932).
836. Kohlstadt, *Helv. Chem. Acta*, **27**, 685 (1944).
837. Koike, Iida and Kashioka, *J. Chem. Soc. Japan, Ind. Chem. Sect.*, **57**, 123 (1954); through *Chem. Abstracts*, **49**, 11629 (1955).
838. Koike, Iida, Okawa and Kashioka, *J. Chem. Soc. Japan, Ind. Chem. Sect.*, **57**, 56 (1954); through *Chem. Abstracts*, **49**, 11629 (1955).

839. Koike, Suzuki, Tanakadate and Iida, *Repts. Gov. Chem. Ind. Research Inst. Tokyo*, **49**, 158 (1954); through *Chem. Abstracts*, **48**, 11079 (1954).
840. Koike, Suzuki, Tanakadate, Iida and Okiwa, *Repts. Gov. Chem. Ind. Research Inst. Tokyo*, **49**, 153 (1954); through *Chem. Abstracts*, **48**, 11079 (1954).
841. Kolb, *Z. anorg. Chem.*, **83**, 143 (1913).
842. Koll and Fleischmann, *Arch. exptl. Path. Pharmakol.*, **198**, 390 (1941); through *Chem. Abstracts*, **39**, 3355 (1945).
843. Kolthoff, *Rec. trav. chim.*, **41**, 135 (1922).
844. Komada, *J. Chem. Soc. Japan*, **58**, 1091, 1096, 1193, 1295, 1305, 1315 (1937); through *Chem. Abstracts*, **32**, 9082 (1938).
845. Komada, *J. Chem. Soc. Japan*, **59**, 412, 477, 485 (1938); through *Chem. Abstracts*, **32**, 9083 (1938).
846. Komada, *J. Chem. Soc. Japan*, **59**, 490 (1938); through *Chem. Abstracts*, **32**, 9081 (1938).
847. Kondo, *J. Pharm. Soc. Japan*, **57**, 832 (1937); through *Chem. Abstracts*, **32**, 1239 (1938).
848. Konek, *Ber.*, **53**, 1666 (1920).
849. Konek and Mitterhauser, *Ber.*, **51**, 865 (1918).
850. Konek and Schleifer, *Ber.*, **51**, 842 (1918).
851. Kopp and Gangneux, U.S. Pat., 2,477,487 (1949).
852. Korns, Schriebers and Dirscherl, *Arzneimittel-Forsch.*, **6**, 596 (1956).
853. Korolev and Rostovtseva, *Org. Chem. Ind.* (*U.S.S.R.*), **4**, 609 (1937); through *Chem. Abstracts*, **32**, 6245 (1938).
854. Kosakada, Jap. Pat., 130 (1954).
855. Kosuge, Okeda, Aburatani, Ito and Kosaka, *J. Pharm. Soc. Japan*, **74**, 1086 (1954); through *Chem. Abstracts*, **49**, 11628 (1955).
856. Kracker, U.S. Pat., 2,688,613 (1954).
857. Kracker and Schmid, Ger. Pat., 622,113 (1935).
858. Krauth and Pfleger, Ger. Pat., 71,253.
859. Krohs, *Med. u. Chem. Abhandl. med.-chem. Forschungsstätten I.G. Farbenind.*, **3**, 310 (1936); through *Chem. Abstracts*, **31**, 5795 (1937).
860. Krohs, *Chem. Ber.*, **88**, 866 (1955).
861. Kropp, U.S. Pat., 1,151,885 (1915).
862. Kropp and Taub, U.S. Pat., 1,508,401 (1924).
863. Krzikalla, Eistert, Schmitt and Kracker, Ger. Pat., 597,589 (1934).
864. Krzikalla and Toepel, Ger. Pat., 821,977 (1951).
865. Krzikalla and Trofimov, Ger. Pat., 917,632 (1954).
866. Kufferath, *J. prakt. Chem.*, **64**, 334 (1901).
867. Kuga, *J. Biochem.* (*Japan*), **35**, 293 (1942); through *Chem. Abstracts*, **45**, 7960 (1951).
868. Kumov, *Zhur. Obshcheĭ Khim.*, **21**, 1765 (1951); through *Chem. Abstracts*, **47**, 2622 (1953).
869. Kumov, *Zhur. Anal. Khim.*, **7**, 301 (1952); through *Chem. Abstracts*, **47**, 2629 (1953).
870. Kunimine, *J. Soc. Sci. Phot.* (*Japan*), **14**, 37 (1951); through *Chem. Abstracts*, **47**, 3155 (1953).
871. Kunimine and Itano, *J. Pharm. Soc. Japan*, **74**, 726 (1954); through *Chem. Abstracts*, **49**, 11627 (1955).
872. Küster, *Z. physiol. Chem.*, **145**, 53 (1925).
873. Küster, U.S. Pat., 2,633,463 (1953).

874. Küster, U.S. Pat., 2,659,720 (1953).
875. Labes and Bergstermann, *Arch. exptl. Path. Pharmakol.*, **187**, 389 (1937); through *Chem. Abstracts*, **33**, 4594 (1939).
876. La Du, Gaudette, Trousof and Brodie, *J. Biol. Chem.*, **214**, 741 (1955).
877. Langbein, Ger. Pat., 888,733 (1953).
878. Langbein, Ger. Pat., 906,063 (1954).
879. Lantz and Mingasson, U.S. Pat., 2,647,113 (1953).
880. La Parola, *Gazz. chim. ital.*, **67**, 645 (1937).
881. Larivé and Collet, U.S. Pat., 2,708,669 (1955).
882. Lauer and Brodoway, *J. Am. Chem. Soc.*, **75**, 5406 (1953).
883. Lauer and Kilburn, *J. Am. Chem. Soc.*, **59**, 2586 (1937).
884. Lecher, Parker and Conn, U.S. Pat., 2,227,654 (1941).
885. Lecher, Parker and Conn, *J. Am. Chem. Soc.*, **66**, 1959 (1944).
886. Lecher, Parker and Denton, U.S. Pat., 2,385,088 (1945).
887. Lechleitner and Ritzer, Austrian Pat., 178,164 (1954).
888. Lederer, *J. prakt. Chem.* [2], **45**, 83 (1892).
889. Ledrut, U.S. Pat., 2,622,086 (1952).
890. Ledrut, U.S. Pat., 2,628,233 (1953).
891. Ledrut, U.S. Pat., 2,650,219 (1953).
892. Ledrut, U.S. Pat., 2,651,638 (1953).
893. Ledrut, Can. Pat., 506,562 (1954).
894. Ledrut, Can. Pat., 510,619 (1955).
895. Ledrut and Combes, *Bull. soc. chim. France*, **1948**, 674.
896. Ledrut and Combes, *Bull. soc. chim. France*, **1950**, 127.
897. Ledrut and Combes, *Bull. soc. chim. France*, **1950**, 228.
898. Ledrut and Combes, *Bull. soc. chim. France*, **1950**, 786.
899. Ledrut and Combes, *Compt. rend.*, **231**, 1513 (1950).
900. Ledrut and Combes, *Bull. soc. chim. France*, **1952**, 189.
901. Ledrut, Combes and Swierkot, *Bull. soc. chim. France*, **1952**, 185.
902. Ledrut, Combes and Swierkot, *Bull. soc. chim. France*, **1950**, 232.
903. Ledrut and Swierkot, *Bull. soc. chim. Belges*, **59**, 238 (1950); through *Chem. Abstracts*, **45**, 2486 (1951).
904. Legg, Brit. Pat., 738,999 (1955).
905. Lehr, Terranova and Boyd, *Urol. and Cutaneous Rev.*, **47**, 661 (1943); through *Chem. Abstracts*, **38**, 5584 (1944).
906. Leonard, *Brit. Med. J.*, **1953**, I, 1311.
907. Leulier, *J. pharm. chim.*, **29**, 447 (1924).
908. Leulier and Cohen, *J. pharm. chim.*, **29**, 245 (1939).
909. Levine and Hauser, *J. Am. Chem. Soc.*, **66**, 1768 (1944).
910. Lieberman and Wagner, *J. Org. Chem.*, **14**, 1001 (1949).
911. Lieser and Kemmer, *Chem. Ber.*, **84**, 4 (1951).
912. Linares, Bayes and Cardona, *Pubs. inst. quim. "Alonso Barba"*, **4**, 310 (1950); through *Chem. Abstracts*, **46**, 8082 (1952).
913. Locke, U.S. Pat., 2,418,416 (1947).
914. Locke, U.S. Pat., 2,478,768 (1949).
915. Lockemann, Brit. Pat., 214,261 (1923).
916. Lockemann, Brit. Pat., 223,182 (1923).
917. Locquin, *Bull. soc. chim. France*, [3], **35**, 962 (1906).
918. Logemann, Almirante and Caprio, *Chem. Ber.*, **87**, 1175 (1954).
919. Logemann, Lauria and Zamboni, *Chem. Ber.*, **88**, 1353 (1955).

920. Long and Lewis, U.S. Pat., 2,437,645 (1948).
921. Loria, Vittum and Weissberger, U.S. Pat., 2,592,303 (1952).
922. Loria, Weissberger and Vittum, U.S. Pat., 2,600,788 (1952).
923. Losco, *Gazz. chim. ital.*, **67**, 553 (1937).
924. Losco, *Gazz. chim. ital.*, **68**, 474 (1938).
925. Losco, *Gazz. chim. ital.*, **69**, 639 (1939).
926. Losco, *Gazz. chim. ital.*, **70**, 284 (1940).
927. Luft, *Ber.*, **38**, 4044 (1905).
928. Lumière, Lumière and Perrin, *Bull. soc. chim. France*, [3], **33**, 205 (1905).
929. Lumière, Lumière and Barbier, *Bull. soc. chim. France*, [3], **33**, 503 (1905).
930. Lumière and Perrin, *Bull. soc. chim. France*, [3], **30**, 966 (1903).
931. Lund, *J. Chem. Soc.*, **1933**, 686.
932. Lund, *J. Chem. Soc.*, **1935**, 418.
933. Lundsgaard, Brit. Pat., 163,946 (1920).
934. Luttringhaus and Grohman, *Z. Naturforsch.*, **10b**, 365 (1955).
935. MacKenzie and Nestler, U.S. Pat., 2,434,173 (1948).
936. Mackie and Cutler, *Rec. trav. chim.*, **71**, 1198 (1952).
937. Madaus, *Arzneimittel-Forsch.*, **1**, 375 (1951).
938. Maeda, Jap. Pat., 153,365 (1942).
939. Magidson, *Zhur. Obshcheĭ Khim.*, **26**, 1137 (1956); through *Chem. Abstracts*, **50**, 16764 (1956).
940. Magidson and Gorbovitskii, Russ. Pat., 53,677 (1938).
941. Magidson and Gorbovitskii, Russ. Pat., 52,991 (1940).
942. Mangini and Dal Monte, *Chimie et industrie*, **63**, No. 3 bis, 463 (1950); through *Chem. Abstracts*, **47**, 868 (1953).
943. Mann and Haworth, *J. Chem. Soc.*, **1944**, 670.
944. Mannich and Heilner, *Ber.*, **55**, 365 (1922).
945. Mannich and Katler, *Arch. Pharm.*, **257**, 18 (1919).
946. Mannich and Krösche, *Arch. Pharm.*, **250**, 647 (1913).
947. Mansberg and Shaw, *J. Chem. Soc.*, **1953**, 3467.
948. Marschall and Williams, U.S. Pat., 2,739,963 (1956).
949. Martin, U.S. Pat., 2,476,986 (1949).
950. Martini, *Anales asoc. quim. Argentina*, **31**, 69 (1943); through *Chem. Abstracts*, **38**, 531 (1944).
951. Marx, U.S. Pat., 2,718,487 (1955).
952. Massot, Span. Pat., 225,801 (1956).
953. Matsumoto, *Tech. Bull. Kagawa Agr. Coll.* (*Japan*), **5**, 103 (1953–54); through *Chem. Abstracts*, **49**, 7493 (1955).
954. Mattu, *Gazz. chim. ital.*, **81**, 891 (1951).
955. Mauthner, *Ber.*, **41**, 2530 (1908).
956. Mauthner, *Ann.*, **395**, 273 (1913).
957. Mauthner, *J. prakt. Chem.*, **116**, 321 (1927).
958. Mayer and Widmer, U.S. Pat., 2,476,259 (1949).
959. Mayer and Widmer, U.S. Pat., 2,476,261 (1949).
960. Mayhew, U.S. Pat., 2,476,991 (1949).
961. McCormick, *GP*, **14**, 95 (1956).
962. McMillan and King, *J. Am. Chem. Soc.*, **77**, 3376 (1955).
963. McNally and Dickey, U.S. Pat., 2,391,180 (1945).
964. McQueen, U.S. Pat., 2,367,036 (1945).
965. McQueen, U.S. Pat., 2,428,108 (1947).

966. McQueen, U.S. Pat., 2,477,462 (1949).
967. Mendoza, Brit. Pat., 300,321 (1927).
968. Mendoza, U.S. Pat., 1,841,621 (1932).
969. Mester, Span. Pat., 212,764 (1954).
970. Metais and Duquenois, *Bull. soc. chim. France*, **1949**, 415.
971. Meyer and Bouchet, *Compt. rend.*, **227**, 345 (1948).
972. Michaelis, *Ber.*, **38**, 154 (1905).
973. Michaelis and Bender, *Ber.*, **36**, 523 (1903).
974. Michaelis and Bressel, *Ann.*, **407**, 274 (1915).
975. Michaelis, Brust, Preuner, Blume, Hepner and Danzfuss, *Ann.*, **339**, 117 (1905).
976. Michaelis and Burmeister, *Ber.*, **25**, 1502 (1892).
977. Michaelis and Engelhardt, *Ber.*, **41**, 2668 (1908).
978. Michaelis, Graff, Gesing and Boie, *Ann.*, **378**, 293 (1911).
979. Michaelis and Hepner, *Ber.*, **36**, 3271 (1903).
980. Michaelis and Horn, *Ann.*, **373**, 213 (1910).
981. Michaelis and Kirstein, *Ber.*, **46**, 3603 (1913).
982. Michaelis and Klopstock, *Ann.*, **354**, 102 (1907).
983. Michaelis and Kobert, *Ber.*, **42**, 2765 (1909).
984. Michaelis, Kotelmann and Drews, *Ann.*, **350**, 288 (1906).
985. Michaelis and Lachwitz, *Ber.*, **43**, 2106 (1910).
986. Michaelis, Lagenkamp and Duntze, *Ann.*, **404**, 21 (1914).
987. Michaelis, Leonhardt and Wohle, *Ann.*, **338**, 215 (1905).
988. Michaelis, Mayer, Behrens and Hahn, *Ann.*, **338**, 267 (1905).
989. Michaelis and Mielecke, *Ber.*, **40**, 4482 (1907).
990. Michaelis, Pander, Lehmann and Dulk, *Ann.*, **361**, 251 (1908).
991. Michaelis, Rademacher and Schmiedenkampf, *Ann.*, **354**, 55 (1907).
992. Michaelis, Rassman, von der Hagen, Dorn and Wrede, *Ann.*, **352**, 152 (1907).
993. Michaelis and Renny, *Ber.*, **40**, 1020 (1907).
994. Michaelis and Röhmer, *Ber.*, **31**, 3003 (1898).
995. Michaelis and Schäfer, *Ann.*, **407**, 229 (1915).
996. Michaelis, Schäfer, Klappert and Titius, *Ann.*, **397**, 119 (1913).
997. Michaelis and Schenk, *Ber.*, **40**, 3568 (1907).
998. Michaelis and Schenk, *Ber.*, **41**, 3865 (1908).
999. Michaelis and Schlecht, *Ber.*, **39**, 1955 (1906).
1000. Michaelis and Stau, *Ber.*, **46**, 3612 (1913).
1001. Michaelis, Stiegler and Willert, *Ann.*, **358**, 127 (1907).
1002. Michaelis, Walter, Wurl, Doepmann, Thomas, Isert and Mentzel, *Ann.*, **385**, 1 (1911).
1003. Michaelis and Willert, *Ann.*, **358**, 171 (1907).
1004. Michaelis, Ziesel, Krug, Leo and Käding, *Ann.*, **373**, 129 (1910).
1005. Minsk, U.S. Pat., 2,759,816 (1956).
1006. Mitra, *J. Indian Chem. Soc.*, **8**, 471 (1931).
1007. Mitra, *J. Indian Chem. Soc.*, **10**, 491 (1933).
1008. Mitra, *J. Indian Chem. Soc.*, **15**, 31 (1938).
1009. Möhlau, Viertel and Reiner, *Ber.*, **45**, 2233, 3596 (1912).
1010. Mohr, *J. prakt. Chem.*, **79**, 1 (1909).
1011. Mohr, *J. prakt. Chem.*, **90**, 223 (1914).
1012. Montague, *Bull. soc. chim. France*, **1946**, 63.
1013. Montague and Roch, *Bull. soc. chim. France*, [5], **10**, 193 (1943).

1014. Monti, *Gazz. chim. ital.*, **60,** 39 (1930).
1015. Morgan and Ackerman, *J. Chem. Soc.*, **123,** 1308 (1923).
1016. Morgan and Reilly, *Proc. Chem. Soc.*, **28,** 334 (1913).
1017. Morgan and Reilly, *J. Chem. Soc.*, **103,** 808 (1913).
1018. Morgan and Reilly, *J. Chem. Soc.*, **103,** 1494 (1913).
1019. Morgan and Reilly, *J. Chem. Soc.*, **105,** 435 (1915).
1020. Moser, U.S. Pat., 2,399,447 (1946).
1021. Mossini and Guerci, *Boll. chim. farm.*, **80,** 343 (1941); through *Chem. Abstracts*, **37,** 3756 (1943).
1022. Moureu, Choivin and Petit, *Compt. rend.*, **241,** 1954 (1955).
1023. Moureu and Lazennec, *Compt. rend.*, **142,** 1534 (1906).
1024. Moureu and Lazennec, *Bull. soc. chim. France*, [3], **35,** 843 (1906).
1025. Moureu and Lazennec, *Compt. rend.*, **143,** 1239 (1906).
1026. Moureu and Lazennec, *Bull. soc. chim. France*, [4], **1,** 1071 (1907).
1027. Mozingo and Folkers, *Chemistry of Penicillin*, **1949,** 535.
1028. Muckermann, *Ber.*, **42,** 3449 (1909).
1029. Muckermann, *J. prakt. Chem.*, **84,** 278 (1911).
1030. Mueller, U.S. Pat., 2,615,917 (1952).
1031. Mukherjee, Indian Pats., 49,798 and 50,925 (1955).
1032. Mukherjee, Gupta, Laskar and Raymahassay, *J. Indian Chem. Soc.*, **30,** 841 (1953).
1033. Mukherjee, Gupta, Laskar and Raymahassay, *J. Indian Chem. Soc.*, **31,** 835 (1954).
1034. Muller and Scheidegger, U.S. Pat., 2,424,493 (1947).
1035. *Münch. med. Wochschr.*, **59,** 469; through *Chem. Abstracts*, **6,** 1180 (1912).
1036. Mundici, *Gazz. chim. ital.*, **39,** II, 123 (1909).
1037. Munro and Wilson, *J. Chem. Soc.*, **1928,** 1257.
1038. Mur, *Zhur. Obshcheĭ Khim.*, **24,** 572 (1954); through *Chem. Abstracts*, **49,** 6198 (1955).
1039. Mur, *Zhur. Obshcheĭ Khim.*, **25,** 374 (1955); through *Chem. Abstracts*, **50,** 2460 (1956).
1040. Mur, *Zhur. Obshcheĭ Khim.*, **26,** 384 (1956); through *Chem. Abstracts*, **50,** 13881 (1956).
1041. Murray, U.S. Pat., 2,463,794 (1949).
1042. Musante, *Gazz. chim. ital.*, **67,** 682 (1937).
1043. Musante, *Gazz. chim. ital.*, **72,** 537 (1942).
1044. Musante, *Gazz. chim. ital.*, **73,** 355 (1943).
1045. Musante, *Gazz. chim. ital.*, **75,** 109 (1945).
1046. Musante, *Gazz. chim. ital.*, **78,** 178 (1948).
1047. Musante and Fabbrini, *Il Farmico* (*Pavia*), *Ed. Sci.*, **8,** 264 (1953); through *Chem. Abstracts*, **48,** 4536 (1954).
1048. Musante and Fabbrini, *Gazz. chim. ital.*, **84**. 595 (1954).
1049. Musante and Mugnaini, *Gazz. chim. ital.*, **77,** 182 (1947).
1050. Musante and Parrini, *Gazz. chim. ital.*, **84,** 209 (1954).
1051. Naito, Taki, Shioda, Fujikawa, Nakajima, Fujii, Tokuoka, Okarmoto and Hitosa, *J. Pharm. Soc. Japan*, **71,** 811 (1951); through *Chem. Abstracts*, **46,** 1615 (1952).
1052. Naito, Yoshida and Sano, *J. Pharm. Soc. Japan*, **72,** 346 (1952); through *Chem. Abstracts*, **47,** 6408 (1953).
1053. Nandi, *J. Indian Chem. Soc.*, **17,** 449 (1940).

1130. Poraĭ-Koshits and Dinaburg, *Zhur. Obshcheĭ Khim.*, **24**, 2208 (1954); through *Chem. Abstracts*, **50**, 310 (1956).
1131. Poraĭ-Koshits and Dinaburg, *Zhur. Obshcheĭ Khim.*, **25**, 151 (1955); through *Chem. Abstracts*, **50**, 1780 (1956).
1132. Poraĭ-Koshits, Ginzburg and Poraĭ-Koshits, *Zhur. Obshcheĭ Khim.*, **17**, 1752 (1947); through *Chem. Abstracts*, **42**, 6357 (1958).
1133. Poraĭ-Koshits, Poraĭ-Koshits and Ginzburg, *Compt. rend. acad. sci. U.R.S.S.*, **47**, 407 (1945); through *Chem. Abstracts*, **40**, 4217 (1946).
1134. Poraĭ-Koshits, Poraĭ-Koshits and Lipina, *Zhur. Obshcheĭ Khim.*, **25**, 1604 (1955); through *Chem. Abstracts*, **50**, 4917 (1956).
1135. Poraĭ-Koshits, Poraĭ-Koshits and Lipina, *Zhur. Obshcheĭ Khim.*, **26**, 842 (1956); through *Chem. Abstracts*, **50**, 14720 (1956).
1136. Porter and Weissberger, U.S. Pat., 2,343,702 (1944).
1137. Porter and Weissberger, U.S. Pat., 2,343,703 (1944).
1138. Porter and Weissberger, U.S. Pat., 2,367,523 (1945).
1139. Porter and Weissberger, U.S. Pat., 2,369,489 (1945).
1140. Porter and Weissberger, U.S. Pat., 2,376,380 (1945).
1141. Porter and Weissberger, *Org. Syn.*, **28**, 87 (1948).
1142. Porter and Weissberger, Brit. Pat., 599,919 (1948).
1143. Porter, Weissberger and Gregory, U.S. Pat, 2,439,098 (1948).
1144. Poskočil and Allan, *Chem. listy*, **47**, 1801 (1953); through *Chem. Abstracts*, **48**, 4221 (1954).
1145. Posner and Schreiber, *Ber.*, **57**, 1127 (1924).
1146. Prelog and Kohlbach, *Collection Czech. Chem. Commun.*, **8**, 377 (1936).
1147. Priewe and Poljak, *Chem. Ber.*, **88**, 1932 (1955).
1148. Profft and Buchmann, *Chem. Tech. (Berlin)*, **7**, 138 (1955); through *Chem. Abstracts*, **50**, 7070 (1956).
1149. Profft, Runge and Blanke, *J. prakt. chem.* [4], **1**, 110 (1954).
1150. Quintilla, Span. Pat., 211,285 (1955).
1151. Quiroga and Magnin, *Actas Dermobibliog. (Madrid)*, **44**, 397 (1953); *Excerpta Med., Sect.* XIII, **8**, 135 (1954); through *Chem. Abstracts*, **49**, 13593 (1955).
1152. Qvist, *Acta Acad. Aboensis Math. phys.*, **4**, No. 3, 25 pp.; through *Chem. Abstracts*, **22**, 4485 (1928).
1153. Qvist, *Acta Acad. Aboensis Math. phys.*, **5**, No. 2, 16 pp.; through *Chem. Abstracts*, **24**, 3788 (1930).
1154. Rahe and Elze, *Ann.*, **323**, 83 (1902).
1155. Ragno, *Gazz. chim. ital.*, **68**, 741 (1938).
1156. Raiziss and Clemence, *J. Am. Chem. Soc.*, **52**, 2019 (1930).
1157. Raiziss, Clemence and Freifelder, *J. Am. Chem. Soc.*, **63**, 2739 (1941).
1158. Răscanu, *Ann. sci. univ. Jassy*, **18**, 72 (1933); through *Chem. Abstracts*, **28**, 4677 (1934).
1159. Rath and Binz, Ger. Pat., 516,534 (1924).
1160. Rath and Gebauer, Ger. Pat., 589,146 (1933).
1161. Rechenberg, *Klin. Wochschr.*, **29**, 726 (1951).
1162. Reed, Brit. Pat., 644,897 (1950).
1163. Reeves, *J. Chem. Soc.*, **127**, 911 (1925).
1164. Regenbogen, *Pharm. Weekblad*, **55**, 1126 (1918); through *Chem. Abstracts*, **12**, 2408 (1918).

1165. Reilly and MacSweeney, *Proc. Roy. Irish Acad.*, **39B**, 497 (1930); through *Chem. Abstracts*, **25**, 1523 (1931).
1166. Reilly and Madden, *J. Chem. Soc.*, **127**, 2936 (1925).
1167. Reitz, *Z. physik. Chem.*, **B46**, 165 (1940).
1168. Remy and Kümmell, *Z. Elektrochem.*, **15**, 254 (1909).
1169. Renard, *Bull. classe sci., Acad. roy. Belg.*, **29**, No. 7/9, 536 (1943); through *Chem. Abstracts*, **40**, 6422 (1946).
1170. Renkin, *Am. J. Physiol.*, **173**, 125 (1953).
1171. Reppe *et al.*, *Ann.*, **596**, 158 (1955).
1172. Reppe *et al.*, *Ann.*, **596**, 38 (1955).
1173. Reuter, U.S. Pat., 2,005,505 (1935).
1174. Reuter, U.S. Pat., 2,005,506 (1935).
1175. Reuter, Ger. Pat., 617,360 (1935).
1176. Reynolds, U.S. Pat., 2,688,548 (1954).
1177. Reynolds and Tinker, U.S. Pat., 2,743,279 (1956).
1178. Riat and Mayer, U.S. Pat., 2,536,957 (1951).
1179. Rice, *J. Am. Chem. Soc.*, **45**, 222 (1923).
1180. Ridi, *Ann. chim. applicata*, **30**, 495 (1940); through *Chem. Abstracts*, **35**, 2890 (1941).
1181. Ridi, *Gazz. chim. ital.*, **71**, 95 (1941).
1182. Ridi, *Gazz. chim. ital.*, **71**, 100 (1941).
1183. Ridi, *Gazz. chim. ital.*, **71**, 106 (1941).
1184. Ridi, *Gazz. chim. ital.*, **71**, 462 (1941).
1185. Ridi, *Gazz. chim. ital.*, **71**, 542 (1941).
1186. Ridi, *Gazz. chim. ital.*, **77**, 3 (1947).
1187. Ridi, *Gazz. chim. ital.*, **80**, 533 (1950).
1188. Ridi, *Gazz. chim. ital.*, **82**, 746 (1952).
1189. Ridi and Checchi, *Gazz. chim. ital.*, **83**, 36 (1953).
1190. Ridi and Checchi, *Ann. chim.* (*Rome*), **43**, 816 (1953); through *Chem. Abstracts*, **49**, 6234 (1955).
1191. Ridi and Feroci, *Gazz. chim. ital.*, **79**, 175 (1948).
1192. Ridi and Papini, *Gazz. chim. ital.*, **77**, 99 (1947).
1193. Ridi and Papini, *Gazz. chim. ital.*, **78**, 3 (1948).
1194. Ridi, Papini, Checchi and Conti, *Gazz. chim. ital.*, **84**, 781 (1954).
1195. Riester, Ger. Pat., 821,524 (1951).
1196. Robins, *J. Am. Chem. Soc.*, **78**, 784 (1956).
1197. Roblin, Williams, Winnek and English, *J. Am. Chem. Soc.*, **62**, 2002 (1940).
1198. Rodionov, *Bull. soc. chim. France*, [4], **39**, 305 (1926).
1199. Rodionov and Fedorova, *Izvest. Akad. Nauk S.S.S.R., Otdel. Khim. Nauk*, **1952**, 1049; through *Chem. Abstracts*, **48**, 671 (1954).
1200. Rodionov and Suvorov, *Zhur. Obshcheĭ Khim.*, **20**, 1273 (1950); through *Chem. Abstracts*, **45**, 1543 (1951).
1201. Roedig, Becker, Fugmann and Schoedel, *Ann.*, **597**, 214 (1955).
1202. Rohde, *J. prakt. Chem.*, **143**, 325 (1935).
1203. Rohde and Hartwick, Ger. Pat., 638,533 (1936).
1204. Rohde and Tenzer, *J. prakt. Chem.*, **87**, 541 (1913).
1205. Rojahn, *Ber.*, **55**, 2959 (1922).
1206. Rojahn and Fahr, *Ann.*, **434**, 252 (1923).
1207. Rojahn and Fegeler, *Ber.*, **63**, 2510 (1930).
1208. Romain, *Bull. soc. chim. France*, **1957**, 1417.

1209. Rondestvedt and Chang, *J. Am. Chem. Soc.*, **77**, 6532 (1955).
1210. Rose, *J. Chem. Soc.*, **1952**, 3448.
1211. Rosenthaler, *Rev. faculté sci. univ. Istanbul*, **9A**, 132 (1944); through *Chem. Abstracts*, **40**, 1755 (1946).
1212. Roura, *Rev. Asoc. bioquim. Argentina*, **19**, 225 (1954); through *Chem. Abstracts*, **49**, 6022 (1955).
1213. Rowe, Desai and Peters, *J. Chem. Soc.*, **1948**, 2811.
1214. Rowe and Twitchett, *J. Chem. Soc.*, **1936**, 1704.
1215. Royals, Hoppe, Jordan and Robinson, *J. Am. Chem. Soc.*, **73**, 5857 (1951).
1216. Rozovskaya and Shterenson, *Farmakol. i Toksikol.*, **8**, No. 2, 46 (1945); through *Chem. Abstracts*, **40**, 5845 (1946).
1217. Rubtsov, *Zhur. Obshcheĭ Khim.*, **16**, 221 (1946); through *Chem. Abstracts*, **41**, 431 (1947).
1218. Ruckstuhl, Senn and Wehrli, U.S. Pat., 2,572,394 (1951).
1219. Ruggli and Disler, *Helv. Chim. Acta*, **10**, 938 (1927).
1220. Ruggli and Hartmann, *Helv. Chim. Acta*, **3**, 493 (1920).
1221. Ruggli and Maeder, *Helv. Chim. Acta*, **25**, 936 (1942).
1222. Ruggli and Maeder, *Helv. Chim. Acta*, **26**, 1476 (1943).
1223. Ruggli and Maeder, *Helv. Chim. Acta*, **27**, 436 (1944).
1224. Ruggli and Schetty, *Helv. Chim. Acta*, **23**, 718 (1940).
1225. Ruggli and Staub, *Helv. Chim. Acta*, **19**, 962 (1936).
1226. Ruggli and Theilheimer, *Helv. Chim. Acta*, **24**, 899 (1941).
1227. Ruggli, Weis and Rupe, *Helv. Chim. Acta*, **29**, 1788 (1946).
1228. Ruhemann, *Ber.*, **27**, 1658 (1894).
1229. Ruhemann, *J. Chem. Soc.*, **69**, 1394 (1896).
1230. Ruhemann and Morrell, *J. Chem. Soc.*, **61**, 791 (1892).
1231. Ruhemann and Morrell, *Ber.*, **27**, 2743 (1894).
1232. Ruhemann and Morrell, *Ber.*, **28**, 987 (1895).
1233. Ruhemann and Orton, *J. Chem. Soc.*, **67**, 1002 (1895).
1234. Ruhkopf, *Ber.*, **73**, 820 (1940).
1235. Ruhnau, *Deut. tierärtzl. Wochschr.*, **59**, 38 (1952); through *Chem. Abstracts*, **47**, 781 (1953).
1236. Rupe and Heckendorn, *Helv. Chim. Acta*, **9**, 980 (1926).
1237. Rupe and Zickendraht, *Helv. Chim. Acta*, **29**, 1529 (1946).
1238. Ryabchikov and Terent'eva, *Compt. rend. acad. sci. U.S.S.R.*, **51**, 291 (1946); through *Chem. Abstracts*, **40**, 6362 (1946).
1239. Rydon, *J. Chem. Soc.*, **1939**, 1544.
1240. Rydon and Siddappa, *J. Chem. Soc.*, **1951**, 2462.
1241. Sachs and Appenzellen, *Ber.*, **41**, 91 (1908).
1242. Sachs and Barschall, *Ber.*, **35**, 1437 (1902).
1243. Sachs and Becherescu, *Ber.*, **36**, 1132 (1903).
1244. Sachs and Kraft, *Ber.*, **36**, 757 (1903).
1245. Sah, *Rec. trav. chim.*, **69**, 1407 (1950).
1246. Salminen and Weissberger, U.S. Pat., 2,694,635 (1954).
1247. Salminen and Weissberger, U.S. Pat., 2,694, 718 (1954).
1248. Sanna, *Rend. seminar. fac. sci. univ. Cagliari*, **10**, 54 (1940); through *Chem. Abstracts*, **37**, 2356 (1943).
1249. Sanna and Sollai, *Gazz. chim. ital.*, **72**, 313 (1942).
1250. Sastry, *J. Chem. Soc.*, **109**, 270 (1916).
1251. Saunders, *J. Chem. Soc.*, **117**, 1264 (1920).

1252. Sawa, *J. Pharm. Soc. Japan*, **57**, 953 (1937); through *Chem. Abstracts*, **32**, 2533 (1938).
1253. Sawdey, U.S. Pat., 2,632,702 (1953).
1254. Sawdey, U.S. Pat., 2,706,683 (1955).
1255. Sawdey, Ruoff and Vittum, *J. Am. Chem. Soc.*, **72**, 4947 (1950).
1256. Scheitlin, Ger. Pat., 199,844 (1907).
1257. Scheitlin, Brit. Pat., 12,889 (1907).
1258. Scheitlin, Brit. Pat., 462,949 (1937).
1259. Schetty, *J. Soc. Dyers and Colourists*, **71**, 705 (1955).
1260. Schickh, Ger. Pat., 588,045 (1933).
1261. Schickh, *Ber.*, **69**, 967 (1936).
1262. Schiedt, *J. prakt. Chem.*, **157**, 203 (1941).
1263. Schiemann and Winkelmüller, *Ber.*, **66**, 727 (1933).
1264. Schmid, U.S. Pat., 2,211,293 (1940).
1265. Schmidt, Behnisch and Mietzsch, U.S. Pat., 2,664,425 (1953).
1266. Schmidt and Druey, *Helv. Chim. Acta*, **39**, 986 (1956).
1267. Schmid and Moser, U.S. Pat., 2,399,066 (1946).
1268. Schmid and Schetty, U.S. Pat., 2,494,969 (1950).
1269. Schneider, U.S. Pat., 2,186,734 (1940).
1270. Schneider and Fröhlich, U.S. Pat., 2,200,306 (1940).
1271. Schneider and Fröhlich, U.S. Pat., 2,437,063 (1948).
1272. Schneider, Fröhlich and Zeh, Ger. Pat., 736,867 (1943).
1273. Schneider and Hagedorn, U.S. Pat., 2,178,612 (1939).
1274. Schöberl and Eck, *Ann.*, **522**, 97 (1936).
1275. Schrauth and Bauerschmidt, *Ber.*, **47**, 2736 (1914).
1276. Schreiber, *Ann. chim.* [12], **2**, 84 (1947); through *Chem. Abstracts*, **41**, 6204 (1947).
1277. Schroeter, Kesseler, Liesche and Müller, *Ber.*, **49**, 2697 (1916).
1278. Schultz and Mayer, *Deut. Apoth.-Ztg.*, **92**, 358 (1952); through *Chem. Abstracts*, **46**, 11580 (1952).
1279. Schultz and Rohde, *J. prakt. Chem.*, **87**, 119 (1913).
1280. Schuster and Krzikalla, U.S. Pat., 2,132,193 (1938).
1281. Schwartz and Dehn, *J. Am. Chem. Soc.*, **39**, 2444 (1917).
1282. Schwarz and Dossmann, Ger. Pat., 701,135 (1946).
1283. Schweitzer and Bayer, Ger. Pat., 859,185 (1952).
1284. Scott, O'Sullivan and Reilly, *J. Am. Chem. Soc.*, **75**, 5309 (1953).
1285. Searles and Kash, *J. Org. Chem.*, **19**, 928 (1954).
1286. Seibert, *Chem. Ber.*, **80**, 494 (1947).
1287. Seidel, *J. prakt. Chem.* [2], **58**, 129 (1898).
1288. Seidel, Thier, Uber and Dittmer, *Ber.*, **68**, 1913 (1935).
1289. Selmiciu, Lupu and Cirstescu, *Rev. chim.* (*Bucharest*), **6**, 578 (1955); through *Chem. Abstracts*, **50**, 16958 (1956).
1290. Seppi, *Bull. soc. ital. biol. sper.*, **16**, 280 (1941); through *Chem. Abstracts*, **40**, 6060 (1946).
1291. Seruto, U.S. Pats., 2,709,697 and 2,709,698 (1955).
1292. Sharp and Hamilton, *J. Am. Chem. Soc.*, **68**, 588 (1946).
1293. Sharvin, Arbuzov and Varshavaskie, *J. Chem. Ind.* (*Moscow*), **6**, 1407 (1929); through *Chem. Abstracts*, **25**, 502 (1931).
1294. Shavel, Leonard, McMillan and King, *J. Am. Pharm. Assoc.*, **42**, 402 (1953).
1295. Shaw, *J. Chem. Soc.*, **1952**, 3428.

1296. Shestakov and Kazakov, *J. Russ. Phys. Chem. Soc.*, **44**, 1312; through *Chem. Abstracts*, **7**, 1984 (1913).
1297. Shimidzu, *J. Pharm. Soc. Japan*, No. 5, **27**, 12 (1926); through *Chem. Abstracts*, **20**, 2857 (1926).
1298. Shinoda, Jap. Pat., 2779 (1952).
1299. Shirai and Yashiro, *Bull. Nagoya City Univ. Pharm. School*, No. **3**, 30 (1955); through *Chem. Abstracts*, **50**, 16754 (1956).
1300. Siegfried, Swiss Pat., 136, 848–50 (1928).
1301. Silberstein and Carroll, U.S. Pat., 2,527,583 (1950).
1302. Siminov, *Zhur. Obshcheĭ Khim.*, **10**, 1220 (1940); through *Chem. Abstracts*, **35**, 2868 (1941).
1303. Skita, Keil, Stühmer, Jaeschke, Ziegler, Kampmann, Arendts and Gerlach, *Ber.*, **75**, 1696 (1942).
1304. Slifkin, U.S. Pat., 2,536,398 (1951).
1305. Slifkin and Trojnar, U.S. Pat., 2,537,098 (1951).
1306. Sluzewska and Mazur, *Roczniki Państwowego Zakładu Hig.*, **5**, 171 (1954); through *Chem. Abstracts*, **49**, 8032 (1955).
1307. Smith, *Kgl. Fysiograf. Sällskap. Lund., Förh.*, **18**, No. 1, 3 (1948); through *Chem. Abstracts*, **44**, 1490 (1950).
1308. Smith and Carlin, *J. Am. Chem. Soc.*, **64**, 433 (1942).
1309. Smith, Merits and Norlöv, *Kgl. Fysiograf. Sällskap. Lund., Förh.*, **23**, 51 (1953); through *Chem. Abstracts*, **49**, 15863 (1955).
1310. Smith and Thorpe, *J. Chem. Soc.*, **91**, 1899 (1907).
1311. Smyth and Clark, *J. Chronic Diseases*, **5**, 734 (1957).
1312. Sokolova and Magidson, *Zhur. Obshcheĭ Khim.*, **26**, 604 (1956); through *Chem. Abstracts*, **50**, 13879 (1956).
1313. Soliman and Youssef, *J. Chem. Soc.*, **1954**, 4655.
1314. Sommelet, *Bull. soc. chim. France*, [4], **9**, 33 (1911).
1315. Sommelet, *Compt. rend.*, **154**, 706 (1912).
1316. Sommelet, *Bull. soc. chim.*, **29**, 553 (1921).
1317. Sommer and Pioch, *J. Am. Chem. Soc.*, **76**, 1606 (1954).
1318. Somogyi and Hofstetter, Swiss Pat., 275,620 (1951).
1319. Somogyi and Hofstetter, Swiss Pat., 285,030 (1952).
1320. Sonn and Litten, *Ber.*, **66**, 1512 (1933).
1321. Sonn and Litten, *Ber.*, **66**, 1582 (1933).
1322. Souchay, *Bull. soc. chim. France*, [5], **7**, 797 (1940).
1323. Span. Pat., 208,830 (1954).
1324. Span. Pat., 211,291 (1954).
1325. Span. Pat., 216,773 (1954).
1326. Sparkes, Libby and Trepagnier, U.S. Pat., 2,448,158 (1948).
1327. Spasov and Kurtev, *Annuaire univ. Sofia, Faculté phys.-math.*, **43**, Livre 2, 37 (1946–7); through *Chem. Abstracts*, **44**, 1491 (1950).
1328. Sprague, U.S. Pat., 2,519,001 (1950).
1329. Sprague, U.S. Pat., 2,706,193 (1955).
1330. Sprague, Brooker and Dent, U.S. Pat., 2,639,282 (1953).
1331. Sprung, U.S. Pat., 2,687,957 (1954).
1332. Stallman and Langerak, U.S. Pat., 2,643,250 (1953).
1333. Staněk, *Collection Czech. Chem. Commun.*, **13**, 37 (1948).
1334. Staněk and Holub, *Chem. listy*, **47**, 404 (1953); through *Chem. Abstracts*, **49**, 232 (1955).

1335. Stanfield, Brodie and Yeoman, *Proc. Soc. Exptl. Biol. Med.*, **83**, 254 (1953).
1336. Stenzl, Ger. Pat., 565,799 (1931).
1337. Stenzl, U.S. Pat., 1,972,036 (1934).
1338. Stenzl, U.S. Pat., 2,562,830 (1951).
1339. Stenzl, Staub, Simon and Baumann, *Helv. Chim. Acta*, **33**, 1183 (1950).
1340. Stepanov and Kuzin, *Ber.*, **65**, 1239 (1932).
1341. Stevens and Beutel, *J. Am. Chem. Soc.*, **65**, 449 (1943).
1342. Stodola, *J. Org. Chem.*, **13**, 757 (1948).
1343. Stoermer and Johannsen, *Ber.*, **40**, 3701 (1907).
1344. Stoermer and Martinsen, *Ann.*, **352**, 322 (1907).
1345. Stoermer, Schenk and Bushmann, *Ber.*, **61**, 2312 (1928).
1346. Stoll, Morg. and Peyer, U.S. Pat., 2,401,522 (1946).
1347. Stollé, *Ber.*, **38**, 3023 (1905).
1348. Stolyarova and Chel'tsov, *Doklady Akad. Nauk S.S.S.R.*, **87**, 1025 (1952); through *Chem. Abstracts*, **49**, 5068 (1955).
1349. Stolyarova and Chel'tsov, *Zhur. Fiz. Khim.*, **27**, 640 (1953); through *Chem. Abstracts*, **48**, 2441 (1954).
1350. Stolz, *Ber.*, **27**, 407 (1894).
1351. Stolz, *Ber.*, **28**, 623 (1895).
1352. Stolz, *Ber.*, **36**, 3279 (1903).
1353. Stolz, *Ber.*, **41**, 3849 (1908).
1354. Stolz, U.S. Pat., 1,053,240 (1913).
1355. Stolz and Korndörfer, U.S. Pat., 990,310 (1911).
1356. Stolz and Kross, Ger. Pat., 500,521 (1929).
1357. Strain and Dickey, U.S. Pat., 2,430,484 (1947).
1358. Straub and Brassel, U.S. Pat., 2,404,198 (1946).
1359. Straub, Brassel and Pieth, U.S. Pat., 2,439,153 (1948).
1360. Straub, Brassel and Pieth, U.S. Pat., 2,557,057 (1951).
1361. Straub, Hanhart and Mannhart, U.S. Pat., 2,494,416 (1950).
1362. Streitwolf, Fehrle and Hallensleben, Ger. Pat., 540,700 (1928).
1363. Streitwolf, Fehrle and Herrmann, Ger. Pat., 581,329 (1933).
1364. Streitwolf, Fehrle and Herrmann, U.S. Pat., 2,161,538 (1939).
1365. Streitwolf, Fehrle, Hermann and Fritsche, Ger. Pat., 520,225 (1928).
1366. Stüsser and Petersen, Ger. Pat., 762,445 (1952).
1367. St. Weil and Zyngier, *Roczniki Chem.*, **8**, 177 (1928); through *Chem. Abstracts*, **22**, 4506 (1928).
1368. Sudborough and Beard, *J. Chem. Soc.*, **97**, 773 (1910).
1369. Sudo, *J. Chem. Soc. Japan, Pure Chem. Sect.*, **74**, 658 (1953); through *Chem. Abstracts*, **48**, 2510 (1954).
1370. Sugasawa and Mizukami, *Pharm. Bull.* (*Japan*), **3**, 393 (1955); through *Chem. Abstracts*, **50**, 15534 (1956).
1371. Sumio and Miyahara, Jap. Pat., 3082 (1953).
1372. Sumpter and Wilken, *J. Am. Chem. Soc.*, **70**, 1980 (1948).
1373. Swiss Pats., 167,709–13 (1934).
1374. Swiss Pat., 199,648 (1938).
1375. Swiss Pat., 214,905 (1941).
1376. Swiss Pat., 216,108 (1941).
1377. Swiss Pat., 220,106 (1942).
1378. Swiss Pats., 220,411–15, 220,750–51 (1942).
1379. Swiss Pat., 220,748 (1942).

1380. Swiss Pats., 222,139–48 (1942).
1381. Swiss Pats., 223,703–04 (1943).
1382. Swiss Pat., 224,118 (1943).
1383. Swiss Pat., 224,352 (1942).
1384. Swiss Pat., 224,647 (1943).
1385. Swiss Pat., 229,184 (1944).
1386. Swiss Pat., 230,906 (1944).
1387. Swiss Pat., 232,460 (1944).
1388. Swiss Pats., 232,270–71 (1944).
1389. Swiss Pat., 233,084 (1944).
1390. Swiss Pat., 233,085 (1944).
1391. Swiss Pat., 233,186 (1944).
1392. Swiss Pats., 233,353–54 (1944).
1393. Swiss Pat., 233,570 (1944).
1394. Swiss Pat., 234,937 (1945).
1395. Swiss Pats., 235,509–12 (1945).
1396. Swiss Pat., 236,764 (1945).
1397. Swiss Pats., 238,461–62 (1945).
1398. Swiss Pats., 238,463–66 (1945).
1399. Swiss Pats., 238,334–41 (1946).
1400. Swiss Pat., 239,883 (1946).
1401. Swiss Pats., 240,122–24 (1946).
1402. Swiss Pat., 240,994 (1946).
1403. Swiss Pat., 241,415 (1946).
1404. Swiss Pats., 244,510–15 (1947).
1405. Swiss Pat., 246,476 (1947).
1406. Swiss Pat., 248,694 (1948).
1407. Swiss Pat., 248,698 (1948).
1408. Swiss Pats., 248,805–6 (1948).
1409. Swiss Pats., 249,027–30 (1948).
1410. Swiss Pat., 249,551 (1948).
1411. Swiss Pat., 251,797 (1948).
1412. Swiss Pats., 252,949–51 (1948).
1413. Swiss Pats., 253,398–406 (1948).
1414. Swiss Pat., 253,641 (1948).
1415. Swiss Pats., 253,877–78 (1948).
1416. Swiss Pats., 253,879–83 (1948).
1417. Swiss Pat., 261,361 (1949).
1418. Swiss Pat., 255,314 (1949).
1419. Swiss Pats., 257,026–30 (1949).
1420. Swiss Pats., 259,723–27 (1950).
1421. Swiss Pats., 259,822 and 263,845 (1949).
1422. Swiss Pats., 261,056–57 (1949).
1423. Swiss Pat., 261,364 (1949).
1424. Swiss Pat., 263,284 (1949).
1425. Swiss Pats., 259,822 and 263,841 (1949).
1426. Swiss Pat., 265,105 (1950).
1427. Swiss Pat., 265,418 (1950).
1428. Swiss Pat., 265,720 (1950).
1429. Swiss Pat., 266,100 (1950).

1430. Swiss Pats., 266,236–37 (1950).
1431. Swiss Pat., 266,368 (1950).
1432. Swiss Pat., 267,269 (1950).
1433. Swiss Pats., 267,305–12 (1950).
1434. Swiss Pat., 268,422 (1950).
1435. Swiss Pat., 268,512 (1950).
1436. Swiss Pat., 269,045 (1950).
1437. Swiss Pat., 269,087 (1950).
1438. Swiss Pat., 269,509 (1950).
1439. Swiss Pats., 269,980–82 (1950).
1440. Swiss Pats., 269,983–87 (1950).
1441. Swiss Pats., 270,539; 272,495–500 (1951).
1442. Swiss Pat., 270,833 (1950).
1443. Swiss Pat., 273,078 (1951).
1444. Swiss Pat., 278,449 (1952).
1445. Swiss Pat., 281,647 (1952).
1446. Swiss Pat., 287,117 (1953).
1447. Swiss Pat., 287,198 (1953).
1448. Swiss Pat., 291,812 (1953).
1449. Swiss Pat., 292,087 (1953).
1450. Swiss Pats., 293,699; 293,901–04 (1953).
1451. Swiss Pats., 293,861–66; 293,868; 293,870 (1954).
1452. Swiss Pats., 294,228–29 (1954).
1453. Swiss Pat., 298,511 (1954).
1454. Swiss Pat., 299,099 (1954).
1455. Swiss Pat., 299,598 (1954).
1456. Swiss Pats., 300,457–65 (1954).
1457. Swiss Pat., 300,593 (1954).
1458. Swiss Pat., 301,439 (1954).
1459. Swiss Pat., 302,154 (1954).
1460. Swiss Pats., 302,544; 306,246–50 (1955).
1461. Swiss Pats., 303,280; 306,251; 306,261–62; 306,266–67 (1955).
1462. Swiss Pats., 303,885–93 (1955).
1463. Swiss Pats., 304,613–14 (1955).
1464. Swiss Pats., 305,714 (1955).
1465. Swiss Pats., 305,715 and 305,717 (1955).
1466. Sato and Sogabe, *Sci. Papers Inst. Phys. Chem. Research* (*Tokyo*), **38**, 231 (1941); through *Chem. Abstracts*, **35**, 4666 (1941).
1467. Taboury, *Compt. rend.*, **214**, 764 (1942).
1468. Taboury and Boureau, *Bull. soc. chim. France*, [5], **12**, 598 (1945).
1469. Taboury and Gray, *Bull. soc. chim. France*, [5], **11**, 435 (1944).
1470. Takahashi and Ogyu, Jap. Pat., 3663 (1954).
1471. Takahashi, Okada and Hori, *J. Pharm. Soc. Japan*, **75**, 1431 (1955); through *Chem. Abstracts*, **50**, 10086 (1956).
1472. Takahashi and Satake, *J. Pharm. Soc. Japan*, **75**, 14 (1955); through *Chem. Abstracts*, **50**, 1005 (1956).
1473. Takahashi and Senda, *J. Pharm. Soc. Japan*, **72**, 614 (1952); through *Chem. Abstracts*, **47**, 6406 (1953).
1474. Takahashi and Yoshii, *Pharm. Bull.* (*Japan*), **2**, 382 (1954); through *Chem. Abstracts*, **50**, 13032 (1956).

1475. Takeda, Jap. Pat., 1717 (1951).
1476. Takeda, Kurizuka, Okano and Majima, *Yokohama Med. Bull.*, **3**, 291 (1952); through *Chem. Abstracts*, **48**, 3352 (1954).
1477. Taube, U.S. Pat., 2,731,473 (1956).
1478. Taylor and Hartke, *J. Am. Chem. Soc.*, **81**, 2452, 2456 (1959).
1479. Ten Cate and Knoppers, *Arch. néerland. physiol.*, **26**, 329 (1942); through *Chem. Abstracts*, **38**, 5587 (1944).
1480. Teramura, Itagaki and Oda, *Bull. Inst. Chem. Research, Kyoto Univ.*, **31**, 223 (1953); through *Chem. Abstracts*, **48**, 7551 (1954).
1481. Teramura, Itagaki and Oda, *J. Chem. Soc. Japan, Ind. Chem. Sect.*, **57**, 126 (1954); through *Chem. Abstracts*, **49**, 11625 (1955).
1482. Thesing, Uhrig and Müller, *Angew. Chem.*, **67**, 31 (1955).
1483. Thesing, Zeig and Mayer, *Chem. Ber.*, **88**, 1978 (1955).
1484. Thiele, U.S. Pat., 1,582,802 (1926).
1485. Thielepape and Spreklesen, *Ber.*, **55**, 2929 (1922).
1486. Thiess, Ger. Pat., 831,716 (1952).
1487. Thiess, Ger. Pat., 832,178 (1952).
1488. Thompson, U.S. Pat., 2,518,730 (1950).
1489. Thompson, Swanson and Norman, *Botan. Gazz.*, **107**, 476 (1946).
1490. Thoms and Ritsert, *Ber. Pharm. Ges.*, **31**, 65 (1921); through *Chem. Abstracts*, **15**, 2852 (1921).
1491. Thoms and Schnupp, *Ann.*, **434**, 296 (1923).
1492. Thurston, U.S. Pat., 2,309,679 (1943).
1493. Thurston, U.S. Pat., 2,444,013 (1948).
1494. Tomasik, *Roczniki Chem.*, **8**, 345 (1928); through *Chem. Abstracts*, **23**, 2176 (1929).
1495. Tomek, *Arzneimittel-Forsch.*, **5**, 53 (1955).
1496. Tonutti, Schoeller and Jonas, Brit. Pat., 691,800 (1953).
1497. Torrey and Rabsky, *J. Am. Chem. Soc.*, **32**, 1489 (1910).
1498. Torrey and Zanetti, *J. Am. Chem. Soc.*, **30**, 1241 (1908).
1499. Torrey and Zanetti, *Am. Chem. J.*, **44**, 391 (1910).
1500. Tripodo and Capaldo, *Riv. biol. (Perugia)*, **46**, 501 (1954); through *Chem. Abstracts*, **49**, 8501 (1955).
1501. Tsumaki, *Bull. Chem. Soc. Japan*, **6**, 1 (1931); through *Chem. Abstracts*, **25**, 2145 (1931).
1502. Tsumaki, *Bull. Chem. Soc. Japan*, **7**, 45 (1932); through *Chem. Abstracts*, **26**, 2977 (1932).
1503. Tsumaki and Hattori, *J. Chem. Soc. Japan*, **62**, 1022 (1941); through *Chem. Abstracts*, **41**, 3095 (1947).
1504. Terpeinen and Kallio, *Suomen Kemistilehti*, **14B**, 8 (1941); through *Chem. Abstracts*, **36**, 426 (1942).
1505. Twomey, *Proc. Roy. Irish Acad.*, **57B**, 39 (1954); through *Chem. Abstracts*, **50**, 340 (1956).
1506. U.S. Pat., 936,380 (1909).
1507. Vaĭsman and Kogan, *Aptechnoe Delo*, **1952**, No. 3, 17; through *Chem. Abstracts*, **47**, 1006 (1953).
1508. Valyashko and Bliznyukov, *Ukrainskii Khem. Zhur., Sci. Pt.*, **5**, 47 (1930); through *Chem. Abstracts*, **24**, 5751 (1930).
1509. Valyashko and Bliznyukov, *J. Gen. Chem. (U.S.S.R.)*, **10**, 1343 (1940); through *Chem. Abstracts*, **35**, 3633 (1941).

1510. Valyashko and Bliznyukov, *J. Gen. Chem.* (*U.S.S.R.*), **11**, 23 (1941); through *Chem. Abstracts*, **35**, 5496 (1941).
1511. Valyashko and Bliznyukov, *J. Gen. Chem.* (*U.S.S.R.*), **11**, 559 (1941); through *Chem. Abstracts*, **35**, 7961 (1941).
1512. van Alphen, *Rec. trav. chim.*, **43**, 823 (1924).
1513. van Alphen, *Rec. trav. chim.*, **64**, 109 (1945).
1514. van Alphen, *Rec. trav. chim.*, **64**, 305 (1945).
1515. van de Straete and Schouwenaars, U.S. Pat., 2,557,806 (1951).
1516. van Dormael, *Chimie et industrie*, **63**, No. 3 bis, 478 (1950); through *Chem. Abstracts*, **47**, 6285 (1953).
1517. van Dormael and Nys, *Bull. soc. chim. Belges*, **62**, 199 (1953); through *Chem. Abstracts*, **48**, 6295 (1954).
1518. van Dormael and van der Aurwa, U.S. Pat., 2,566,814 (1951).
1519. van Dormael and van der Auwers, U.S. Pat., 2,621,125 (1952).
1520. Veibel and Arnfred, *Acta Chem. Scand.*, **2**, 914 (1948).
1521. Veibel, Eggersen and Linholt, *Acta Chem. Scand.*, **6**, 1066 (1952).
1522. Veibel, Eggersen and Linholt, *Acta Chem. Scand.*, **8**, 768 (1954).
1523. Veibel and Kjaer, *Proc. XIth Inter. Congr. Pure and Applied Chem.* (*London*), **2**, 329 (1947); through *Chem. Abstracts*, **45**, 6128 (1951).
1524. Veibel, Kjaer and Plejl, *Acta Chem. Scand.*, **5**, 1283 (1951).
1525. Veibel and Linholt, *Acta Chem. Scand.*, **8**, 1007 (1954).
1526. Veibel and Linholt, *Acta Chem. Scand.*, **8**, 1383 (1954).
1527. Veibel and Linholt, *Acta Chem. Scand.*, **9**, 963,970 (1955).
1528. Veibel and Westöö, *Acta Chem. Scand.*, **7**, 119 (1953).
1529. Veldstra and Wiardi, *Rec. trav. chim.*, **61**, 627 (1942).
1530. Venus-Danilova and Fabritsy, *Zhur. Obshcheĭ Khim.*, **26**, 884 (1956); through *Chem. Abstracts*, **50**, 14721 (1956).
1531. Verkade and Dhont, *Rec. trav. chim.*, **64**, 165 (1945).
1532. Vila, *Ion*, **7**, 150 (1947); through *Chem. Abstracts*, **42**, 2933 (1948).
1533. Vila and Carreras, *Anales fis. y quim.* (*Madrid*), **41**, 807 (1945); through *Chem. Abstracts*, **41**, 6549 (1947).
1534. Vila and Carreras, *Anales fis. y quim.* (*Madrid*), **43**, 51 (1947); through *Chem. Abstracts*, **41**, 4469 (1947).
1535. Vila and Massó, *Anales real soc. españ. fis. y quim.*, **48B**, 155 (1952); through *Chem. Abstracts*, **47**, 6871 (1953).
1536. Vila and Pulido, *Anales fis. y quim.* (*Madrid*), **43**, 389 (1947); through *Chem. Abstracts*, **42**, 129 (1948).
1537. Viscontini, Bally and Meier, *Helv. Chim. Acta*, **35**, 451 (1952).
1538. Vittum and Duennebier, *J. Am. Chem. Soc.*, **72**, 1536 (1950).
1539. Vittum, Sawdey, Herdle and Scholl, *J. Am. Chem. Soc.*, **72**, 1533 (1950).
1539a. Vittum and Weissberger, *J. Phot. Sci.*, **6**, 157 (1958).
1540. Vittum, Weissberger and Porter, U.S. Pat. Appl., 668,778, *Official Gaz.*, **631**, 283 (1950).
1541. Voelkel, *Arch. intern. pharmacodynamie*, **102**, 194 (1955); through *Chem. Abstracts*, **49**, 15046 (1955).
1542. von Meyer, *J. prakt. Chem.*, **90**, 1 (1914).
1543. von Meyer and Spreckels, *J. prakt. Chem.*, **92**, 174 (1915).
1544. von Rothenburg, *Ber.*, **25**, 3441 (1892).
1545. von Rothenburg, *Ber.*, **26**, 415 (1893).
1546. von Rothenburg, *Ber.*, **26**, 868 (1893).

1547. von Rothenburg, *Ber.*, **26**, 1719 (1893).
1548. von Rothenburg, *Ber.*, **26**, 1722 (1893).
1549. von Rothenburg, *Ber.*, **26**, 2053 (1893).
1550. von Rothenburg, *Ber.*, **26**, 2972 (1893).
1551. von Rothenburg, *Ber.*, **27**, 782 (1894).
1552. von Rothenburg, *Ber.*, **27**, 783 (1894).
1553. von Rothenburg, *Ber.*, **27**, 790 (1894).
1554. von Rothenburg, *Ber.*, **27**, 946 (1894).
1555. von Rothenburg, *Ber.*, **27**, 1098 (1894).
1556. von Rothenburg, *Ber.*, **27**, 1099 (1894).
1557. von Rothenburg, *J. prakt. Chem.* [2], **50**, 227 (1894).
1558. von Rothenburg, *J. prakt. Chem.* [2], **51**, 157 (1895).
1559. von Rothenburg, *J. prakt. Chem.* [2], **51**, 522 (1895).
1560. von Rothenburg, *J. prakt. Chem.* [2], **52**, 23 (1895).
1561. von Rothenburg, *J. prakt. Chem.* [2], **52**, 45 (1895).
1562. von Walther, *J. prakt. Chem.*, **83**, 171 (1911).
1563. von Walther and Hirschberg, *J. prakt. Chem.* [2], **67**, 377 (1903).
1564. von Walther and Rothacker, *J. prakt. Chem.* [2], **74**, 207 (1906).
1565. Vorbrodt, *Bull. intern. acad. polon. sci., Classe sci. math. et nat.*, **103**, I, 177 (1951); through *Chem. Abstracts*, **46**, 8727 (1952).
1566. Votocek and Valentin, *Collection Czechoslov. Chem. Commun.*, **5**, 84 (1933).
1567. Votocek and Wichterle, *Collection Czechoslov. Chem. Commun.*, **7**, 388 (1935).
1568. Vystrčil and Prokěs, *Chem. listy*, **46**, 670 (1952); through *Chem. Abstracts*, **48**, 165 (1954).
1569. Vystrčil and Stejskal, *Časopis Českého Lékárnictva*, **63**, 75 (1950); through *Chem. Abstracts*, **46**, 7566 (1952).
1570. Vystrčil and Vidlička, *Chem. listy*, **45**, 407 (1951); through *Chem. Abstracts*, **46**, 7567 (1952).
1571. Wachsmuth, *J. Pharm. Chim.* [9], **1**, 383 (1941).
1572. Wagner, *Arch. Pharm.*, **289**, 121 (1956).
1573. Wahl, *Bull. soc. chim. France*, [4], **1**, 726 (1907).
1574. Wahl, *Bull. soc. chim. France*, [4], **1**, 729 (1907).
1575. Wahl, *Compt. rend.*, **206**, 521 (1938).
1576. Wahl and Doll, *Bull. soc. chim. France*, [4], **13**, 468 (1913).
1577. Wahl, Goedkoop and Heberlein, *Compt. rend.*, **206**, 191 (1938).
1578. Wahl and Meyer, *Compt. rend.*, **145**, 192 (1907).
1579. Wahl and Meyer, *Bull. soc. chim. France*, [4], **3**, 957 (1908).
1580. Wahl and Rolland, *Ann. Chim.* [10], **10**, 5 (1928); through *Chem. Abstracts*, **23**, 3218 (1929).
1581. Wahl and Silberzweig, *Bull. soc. chim. France*, [4], **11**, 61 (1912).
1582. Wahlberg, *Ber.*, **44**, 2071 (1911).
1583. Wales and Nelson, *J. Am. Chem. Soc.*, **45**, 1657 (1923).
1584. Walker, *Am. Chem. J.*, **16**, 430 (1894).
1585. Walker, *J. Chem. Soc.*, **1942**, 347.
1586. Wallenfels, *Ber.*, **74**, 1598 (1941).
1587. Wallenfels and Sund, *Arch. exptl. Pathol. Pharmakol.*, **232**, 338 (1957).
1588. Wallingford and Homeyer, U.S. Pat., 2,367,362 (1945).
1589. Wallingford and Homeyer, U.S. Pat., 2,407,942 (1946).
1590. Wallingford, Homeyer and Jones, *J. Am. Chem. Soc.*, **63**, 2252 (1941).

1591. Wang and Yuen, *J. Chinese Chem. Soc.*, **15**, 215 (1948); through *Chem. Abstracts*, **42**, 7266 (1948).
1592. Waser, *Helv. Chim. Acta*, **8**, 117 (1925).
1593. Weissberger and Edens, U.S. Pat., 2,589,004 (1952).
1594. Weissberger, Kibler and Young, U.S. Pat., 2,412,700 (1946).
1595. Weissberger and Porter, *J. Am. Chem. Soc.*, **64**, 2133 (1942).
1596. Weissberger and Porter, *J. Am. Chem. Soc.*, **65**, 52 (1943).
1597. Weissberger and Porter, *J. Am. Chem. Soc.*, **65**, 732 (1943).
1598. Weissberger and Porter, *J. Am. Chem. Soc.*, **65**, 1495 (1943).
1599. Weissberger and Porter, *J. Am. Chem. Soc.*, **65**, 2180 (1943).
1600. Weissberger and Porter, *J. Am. Chem. Soc.*, **66**, 1849 (1944).
1601. Weissberger, Porter and Gregory, *J. Am. Chem. Soc.*, **66**, 1851 (1944).
1602. Weissberger and Salminen, U.S. Pat., 2,484,477 (1949).
1603. Weissberger and Vittum, U.S. Pat., 2,618,641 (1952).
1604. Weissberger, Vittum and Eden, U.S. Pat., 2,511,231 (1950).
1605. Westöö, *Acta Chem. Scand.*, **6**, 1499 (1952).
1606. Westöö, *Acta Chem. Scand.*, **7**, 352 (1953).
1607. Westöö, *Acta Chem. Scand.*, **7**, 355 (1953).
1608. Westöö, *Acta Chem. Scand.*, **7**, 360 (1953).
1609. Westöö, *Acta Chem. Scand.*, **7**, 449 (1953).
1610. Westöö, *Acta Chem. Scand.*, **7**, 453 (1953).
1611. Westöö, *Acta Chem. Scand.*, **7**, 456 (1953).
1612. Westöö, *Acta Chem. Scand.*, **9**, 797 (1955).
1613. Westöö, *Acta Chem. Scand.*, **10**, 9 (1956).
1614. Westöö, *Acta Chem. Scand.*, **10**, 587 (1956).
1615. Weygand, Grisebach, Kirchner and Haselhorst, *Chem. Ber.*, **88**, 487 (1955).
1616. Widmer and Buehler, U.S. Pat., 2,570,085 (1951).
1617. Widmer, Fasciati and Reich, U.S. Pat., 2,606,185 (1952).
1618. Widmer and Heckendorn, U.S. Pat., 2,599,331 (1951).
1619. Widmer, Kaiser, Buehler and Zickendraht, U.S. Pat., 2,538,568 (1951).
1620. Widmer and Ruegg, U.S. Pat., 2,538,610 (1951).
1621. Widmer and Zickendraht, U.S. Pat., 2,565,898 (1951).
1622. Wiley, Hart, Davies and Smith, *J. Am. Chem. Soc.*, **76**, 4931 (1954).
1623. Wilhelmi, *Schweiz. med. wochschr.*, **80**, 936 (1950); through *Chem. Abstracts*, **45**, 4823 (1951).
1624. Wilhelmi and Currie, *Schweiz. med. wochschr.*, **84**, 1315 (1954); through *Chem. Abstracts*, **49**, 4868 (1955).
1625. Wilhelmi and Domenjoz, *Arch. intern. pharmacodynamie*, **85**, 129 (1951); through *Chem. Abstracts*, **45**, 3941 (1951).
1626. Wilkinson and Brown, *Am. J. Med. Sci.*, **225**, 153 (1953).
1627. Williams, U.S. Pat., 2,243,324 (1941).
1628. Willstaedt, *Svensk Kim. Tid.*, **55**, 214 (1943); through *Chem. Abstracts*, **39**, 2059 (1945).
1629. Willstaedt, Borggard and Myrbäck, *Arkiv Kemi*, **1**, 331 (1949); through *Chem. Abstracts*, **44**, 3955 (1950).
1630. Wilson, U.S. Pat., 2,685,515 (1954).
1631. Wilson, U.S. Pat., 2,685,516 (1954).
1632. Wilson, Baird, Burns, Munro and Stephen, *J. Roy. Tech. Coll.* (*Glasgow*), **2**, No. 1, 56 (1929); through *Chem. Abstracts*, **23**, 5164 (1929).
1633. Winnek, U.S. Pat., 2,281,014 (1942).

1634. Winternitz, Ledrut and Combes, *Bull. soc. chim. France*, **1952**, 398.
1635. Wislicenus, *Ber.*, **19**, 3225 (1886).
1636. Wislicenus, *Ber.*, **20**, 2930 (1887).
1637. Wislicenus, *Ber.*, **24**, 1261 (1891).
1638. Wislicenus and Bilfinger, *Ber.*, **46**, 3948 (1913).
1639. Wislicenus and Eble, *Ber.*, **50**, 250 (1917).
1640. Wislicenus, Eichert, Marquardt and Riethmuller, *Ann.*, **436**, 82, 88 (1924).
1641. Wislicenus, Elvert and Kurtz, *Ber.*, **46**, 3395 (1913).
1642. Wislicenus and Göz, *Ber.*, **44**, 3491 (1911).
1643. Wislicenus and Schrötter, *Ann.*, **424**, 215 (1921).
1644. Wolff, Luttringhaus and Fertig, *Ann.*, **313**, 1 (1900).
1645. Wolff and Thielepape, *Ann.*, **420**, 275 (1920).
1646. Wollers and Behrend, *Ann.*, **323**, 279 (1902).
1647. Woodward, U.S. Pat., 2,415,381 (1947).
1648. Woodward, U.S. Pat., 2,415,382 (1947).
1649. Worrall, *J. Am. Chem. Soc.*, **44**, 1551 (1922).
1650. Worrall, *J. Am. Chem. Soc.*, **45**, 3092 (1923).
1651. Worrall, *J. Am. Chem. Soc.*, **46**, 2832 (1924).
1652. Worrall, *J. Am. Chem. Soc.*, **59**, 933 (1937).
1653. Worrall, *J. Am. Chem. Soc.*, **59**, 1486 (1937).
1654. Worrall, *J. Am. Chem. Soc.*, **60**, 1198 (1938).
1655. Worrall and Lavin, *J. Am. Chem. Soc.*, **61**, 104 (1939).
1656. Worrall, Lerner and Washnock, *J. Am. Chem. Soc.*, **61**, 105 (1939).
1657. Wyngaarden, *J. Clin. Invest.*, **34**, 256 (1955).
1658. Yagupol'skiĭ and Kiprianov, *Zhur. Obshcheĭ Khim.*, **22**, 2216 (1952); through *Chem. Abstracts*, **47**, 4771 (1953).
1659. Yale, Losee, Martins, Holsing, Perry and Bernstein, *J. Am. Chem. Soc.*, **75**, 1933 (1953).
1660. Yano, *Folio Pharmacol. Japan*, **23**, 211 (1937); through *Chem. Abstracts*, **31**, 2354 (1937).
1661. Yasuda, *Repts. Sci. Research Inst.* (*Japan*), **30**, 340 (1954); through *Chem. Abstracts*, **49**, 12836 (1955).
1662. Yosida, Jap. Pat., 132,943 (1959).
1663. Yü, Burns, Paton, Gutman and Brodie, *J. Pharm. Exptl. Therapeutics*, **123**, 63 (1958).
1664. Yü, Sirota and Gutman, *J. Clin. Invest.*, **32**, 1121 (1953).
1665. Zeller, *Verhandl. Ver. Schweiz. Physiol.*, **21**, 43 (1942); through *Chem. Abstracts*, **38**, 5509 (1944).
1666. Zeller and Bisseger, *Helv. Chim. Acta*, **26**, 1619 (1943).
1667. Zenno, *J. Soc. Sci. Phot. Japan*, **15**, 37 (1952); through *Chem. Abstracts*, **49**, 300 (1955).
1668. Zenno, *J. Pharm. Soc. Japan*, **73**, 589 (1953); through *Chem. Abstracts*, **48**, 5858 (1954).
1669. Zenno, *J. Pharm. Soc. Japan*, **73**, 1063 (1953); through *Chem. Abstracts*, **48**, 8543 (1954).
1670. Zenno, *J. Soc. Sci. Phot. Japan*, **15**, 99 (1953); through *Chem. Abstracts*, **48**, 11063 (1954).
1671. Zervas, Ger. Pat., 745,625 (1943).
1672. Zervas, U.S. Pat., 2,315,836 (1943).
1673. Zervas, U.S. Pat., 2,322,907 (1944).

1674. Zervas, U.S. Pat., 2,337,845 (1943).
1675. Zerweck and Fleischharrer, Ger. Pat., 818,221 (1951).
1676. Zeuner, *Zentr. Bakt. Parasitenk.*, I *Orig.*, **150**, 116 (1943); through *Chem. Abstracts*, **38**, 414 (1944).
1677. Zhadek, *Zhur. Priklad. Khim.*, **25**, 109 (1952); through *Chem. Abstracts*, **47**, 867 (1953).
1678. Zhivopistsev, *Doklady Akad. Nauk S.S.S.R.*, **73**, 1193 (1950); through *Chem. Abstracts*, **45**, 492 (1951).
1679. Zhivopistsev, *Zhur. Priklad. Khim.*, **26**, 335 (1953); through *Chem. Abstracts*, **47**, 12113 (1953).
1680. Zickendraht and Buehler, U.S. Pat., 2,673,201 (1954).
1681. Zickendraht and Buehler, U.S. Pat., 2,727,031 (1955).
1681a. Ziegler and Locher, *Ber.*, **20**, 834 (1887).
1682. Ziegler and Sauermilch, *Ber.*, **63**, 1851 (1930).
1683. Zimmerman and Cuthbertson, *Z. physiol. Chem.*, **205**, 38 (1932).
1684. Zischler, U.S. Pat., 2,265,221 (1941).
1685. Zorn and Schmidt, *Hoppe-Zeyler's Z. physiol. Chem.*, **298**, 140 (1954).
1686. Zoss and Hennion, *J. Am. Chem. Soc.*, **63**, 1151 (1941).
1687. Zwart and Wibaut, *Rec. trav. chim.*, **74**, 1062 (1955).

Index